Digital Computer Design Fundamentals

Digital Computer

McGraw-Hill Book Company, Inc.

New York   San Francisco   Toronto   London

Design Fundamentals

Yaohan Chu

Lecturer, University of Maryland
Manager, Information Electronics
Research Division, Melpar Inc.

Digital Computer Design Fundamentals

10800

To My Wife, Elizabeth

Preface

This book is an outgrowth of a course on electronic digital computers which the author has been teaching since 1953. It has been written for seniors and graduate students in engineering and science who are interested in the logic and circuit aspects of the electronic digital computer. No previous acquaintance with the subject is needed; but knowledge is required of college mathematics, plus a general understanding of electronics.

One major task of the electronic digital computer is to perform arithmetic operations (Chapters 1 and 2) which are realized by "logic" operations (Chapters 3 and 4). Logic circuits (Chapters 5 to 9) implement logic operations. Thus, the study of computer elements (Chapter 10) and arithmetic and control unts (Chapters 11 and 12) requires knowledge of the fundamental topics of digital arithmetic, Boolean algebra, and logic circuits. For this reason these fundamental topics are presented, not only comprehensively, but also in an integrated manner. For example, the discussion of Boolean matrices and switching matrices (Chapter 9) shows their correspondence and thus integrates logic concept and logic circuitry.

The symbolic method for logic design of the digital computer is introduced in Chapter 10 and is exemplified in Chapters 11 and 12. In this method, the operations of the computer are first expressed in symbolic statements and then in logic equations; the latter (in turn) prescribe the interconnection of logic circuits. Although the symbolic method is a variation of the newer Boolean-equation approach, the older block-diagram approach is also included because one complements the other.

Of the book's twelve chapters, the first four are primarily mathematical. It is a major objective in the first two chapters (on digital arithmetic) to develop arithmetic algorithms for digital operation. Although arithmetic is a grade-school subject, it is not always easy for newcomers. Consequently, quite a number of examples are given in these two chapters. Boolean algebra in Chapter 3 is treated in a comprehensive manner, including the topics on symmetrical Boolean functions, linear sequential functions, and flipflop equations. Minimization of Boolean functions in Chapter 4 receives a relatively less comprehensive treatment because of practical limitations in applying these minimization methods. The general subject of sequential switching circuits is not treated, because the author feels that the symbolic method is more useful to the logic designer in handling sequential circuits. The concept of computer state is introduced, however, by state equations in Chapter 3 and state diagrams in Chapters 10 and 11.

Chapters 5 to 9 cover various types of logic circuits. The dual nature of a logic circuit (positive and negative logic) and the resulting complementary circuits are pointed out early in Chapter 5; positive and negative logic designation is emphasized as logic circuits are introduced. Circuit design is omitted, generally, because of space limitations; a few special cases appeared to justify some discussion—such as flipflop circuit design. Chapters 5 to 8 concern mainly the implementation of a single logic equation, while Chapter 9 shows implementation of a set of logic equations which describe a multiple-output circuit. Since most logic circuits in a digital computer are multiple-output circuits, representation of a switching matrix in Chapter 9 provides a new look that may become useful in building a microelectronic digital computer.

Chapters 10 to 12 deal with computer logic. The important concept of information transfer and the logic equations of basic computer elements (such as the counter, shift register, and accumulator) are presented in Chapter 10. The simple digital computer discussed in Chapter 11 was originated by Reed and Jeffery of the MIT Lincoln Laboratory. For simplicity in explaining computer logic, this parallel computer was chosen (instead of a serial computer) as a detailed example of logic design. More sophisticated arithmetic units and control units are described in Chapter 12, which includes basic arithmetic circuits (such as adders, subtractors, and complementers), the floating-point arithmetic unit, and microprogrammed control units. Some versions of the microprogrammed control unit may become more popular in the future as faster but smaller digital memories (such as magnetic thin-film and tunnel-diode memories) become available.

References at the end of each chapter provide additional sources of information. Accompanying most chapters, a number of problems will aid the reader in familiarizing himself with the subject matter.

The original manuscript of this book included chapters on digital memories, input and output devices, and computer organization. To keep the size of this book within reasonable limits, these chapters were deleted, and some chapters now in the book were shortened. In its present form, the book can be used as a two-term digital computer design course. A single-term course on digital computer design may include Chapters 1, 3, 4, 9, 10, and 11. For a single-term course on logic circuitry, Chapters 3, 5, 6, 7, 8, and 9 may be used. In any of these single-term courses the instructor may, of course, omit some portions of these chapters, augmenting them by using portions of other chapters.

Much of the information for this book was taken from the large amount of available literature on digital computers. The author wishes to acknowledge the work by these writers. The bracketed number appearing throughout the book indicates, in many cases, the source of the information and thus credits the worker. The author also wishes to acknowledge Dr. Stanley Frankel's suggestion of using the term *logic design* instead of *logical design*. The author is indebted to Professor George F. Corcoran, Chairman of the Electrical Engineering Department, University of Maryland, whose inspiration and help made this book possible; and to Professor Howard Hess, Chairman of the Electrical Engineering Department, Wayne State University, where the author first taught the digital computer course.

The author wishes to make further acknowledgment to Mr. Kenneth Mack, Electronic Division of Westinghouse Electric Corporation, and to Mr. Robert E. Miller and Dr. Paul E. Ritt of Melpar, Inc., for their encouragement and assistance in providing clerical help; and to Robert J. Winter, now at IBM Federal Systems Division, for his assistance in editing the manuscript.

Yaohan Chu

Contents

Preface   vii

1. *Digital Arithmetic—I*   **1**

1-1 Number Systems   1
1-2 Number Base Conversion   5
1-3 Single-digit Binary Arithmetic   9
1-4 Signed Binary Numbers   10
1-5 Binary Addition and Subtraction—I   15
1-6 Binary Addition and Subtraction—II   18
1-7 Binary Addition and Subtraction—III   22
1-8 Binary Multiplication   24
1-9 Binary Division   35
1-10 Binary Square Root   43
1-11 Round-off and Overflow   48
Problems   50
References   52

2. *Digital Arithmetic—II*   **53**

2-1 Binary-coded Decimal Number Systems   53
2-2 Signed Decimal Numbers   56
2-3 Decimal Addition and Subtraction   57
2-4 Decimal Multiplication   61
2-5 Decimal Division   65
2-6 Floating-point Arithmetic   70
2-7 Residue Number Arithmetic   73
2-8 Error-checking Codes   78
Problems   87
References   87

3. Boolean Algebra   **89**

3-1 Postulates   89
3-2 Fundamental Theorems   93
3-3 Use of Fundamental Theorems   96
3-4 Boolean Functions and Truth Table   99
3-5 Canonical Forms of Boolean Functions   101
3-6 Theorems on Boolean Functions   104
3-7 Boolean Functions of Two Variables   108
3-8 Elementary Terms and Elementary Forms   110
3-9 Other Basic Logic Operations   112
3-10 Symmetric Boolean Functions   116
3-11 Canonical Symmetric Functions   118
3-12 Simple Symmetric Functions   120
3-13 Delay and Sequential Functions   122
3-14 Linear Sequential Functions   125
3-15 Flipflops and State Equations   127
3-16 Majority and Minority Logic Operations   130
     Problems   132
     References   134

4. Minimization of the Boolean Function   **136**

4-1 Veitch-diagram Method   136
4-2 Harvard-chart Method   147
4-3 Minimization by Quine-McCluskey Method   153
4-4 Machine Minimization   155
4-5 Limitations of Minimization Methods   156
     Problems   157
     References   158

5. Logic Circuits—I   **160**

5-1 Logic Circuits   160
5-2 Relay Logic Circuits   163
5-3 Vacuum-tube Logic Circuits   165
5-4 Diode Logic Circuits   168
5-5 Switching Properties of Junction Transistors   174
5-6 Resistance-coupled Transistor Logic (RCTL) Circuits   179
5-7 Transistor Flipflops   185
5-8 Transistor-Diode Logic (TDL) Circuits   194
5-9 Transistor-Resistor Logic (TRL) Circuits   196
5-10 Direct-coupled Transistor Logic (DCTL) Circuits   198
5-11 Transistor-current-switch Logic (TCSL) Circuits   205
5-12 Clocking Configuration   209
5-13 Other Digital Circuits   209
     Problems   214
     References   215

6. *Logic Circuits—II*   218

6-1   Switching Characteristics of Cryotrons   218
6-2   Cryotron Logic Circuits   223
6-3   Thin-film Cryotrons   229
6-4   Tunnel-diode Logic Circuits   232
6-5   Parametric-phase-locked-oscillator (PLO) Logic Circuits   240
6-6   Microwave Logic Circuits   242
6-7   Electroluminescent-Photoconductor Logic Circuits   244
       References   248

7. *Magnetic-core Logic Circuits*   251

7-1   Magnetic-core Characteristics   251
7-2   Logic Operations on a Single Core   257
7-3   Single-diode Transfer-loop Circuits   261
7-4   Single-shift-line Transfer-loop Circuits   263
7-5   Other Transfer Loops   269
7-6   Magnetic-core–Transistor Logic Circuits   273
7-7   Ferractor Magnetic-amplifier Logic Circuits   275
7-8   Mirror Symbol   277
7-9   Synthesis of Magnetic-core Logic Circuits   280
7-10   Magnetic-rod Logic Circuits   285
7-11   Parametron Logic Circuits   286
       Problems   290
       References   290

8. *Magnetic Multiaperture-core Logic Circuits*   293

8-1   Flux-summation-core Logic Circuits   293
8-2   Laddic Logic Circuits   296
8-3   Biax Logic Circuits   298
8-4   Transfluxor Logic Circuits   300
8-5   MAD Logic Circuits   303
       References   307

9. *Switching Matrices*   309

9-1   Multiple-output Switching Circuits   309
9-2   Switching Matrices   312
9-3   Applications of Switching Matrices   317
9-4   Diode Switching Matrices   318
9-5   Synthesis of Diode Switching Matrices   322
9-6   Binary Sequence Generators   328
9-7   Simplification of Boolean Matrix Function   333
9-8   Magnetic-core Switching Matrices   337
9-9   Synthesis of Magnetic-core Switching Matrices   344
9-10   Magnetic-core Current-steering Matrices   348
9-11   Transistor Switching Matrices   350

9-12 Other Switching Matrices   353
       Problems   360
       References   361

10. Digital Computer Elements   363

10-1 Binary Adders and Subtractors   363
10-2 Binary Complementers   365
10-3 Shift Registers   368
10-4 Counters   371
10-5 Information Transfer   378
10-6 Binary Accumulators   382
10-7 Propagation of Carry or Borrow   386
10-8 Generation of Control Signals   392
       Problems   393
       References   394

11. Logic Design of a Simple Digital Computer   396

11-1 Computer Design   396
11-2 System Design   397
11-3 Functional-design Phase   399
11-4 Symbolic-design Phase   402
11-5 A Tabular Study of Sequential Operations   411
11-6 Detail-design Phase   415
11-7 Complete Computer   423
       Problems   428
       References   429

12. Arithmetic and Control Units   430

12-1 A Parallel Binary Arithmetic Unit   430
12-2 A Serial Binary Arithmetic Unit   437
12-3 Binary Multipliers   444
12-4 A Serial Binary Floating-point Arithmetic Unit   448
12-5 Instruction Formats and Repertoire   451
12-6 Control Units   456
12-7 Microprogrammed Control Unit   461
12-8 Other Microprogrammed Control Units   465
       Problems   470
       References   470

    Index   473

1

Digital Arithmetic—I

Digital arithmetic refers to the algorithms† which implement the arithmetic operations of a digital machine. These algorithms have been developed to take into account many factors, such as binary circuit operation, method of representing a negative number, the finite range of numbers representable in the computer, the limited (and usually fixed) number of digits in a computer word, and location of the digit point (such as the binary point of a binary number). Ordinary arithmetic algorithms prove generally unsuitable for digital computers. New sets of rules have had to be devised, and the name *digital arithmetic* thus distinguishes the new from the more conventional rules of calculation.

The material on digital arithmetic is divided into two chapters. This chapter deals mostly with binary arithmetic, while the next chapter is concerned mostly with decimal arithmetic.

1-1 Number Systems

Number Representation. A number N can be represented by any one of the following three forms,

$$N = d_{n-1}d_{n-2} \cdots d_1 d_0 \cdot d_{-1} \cdots d_{-m} \tag{1-1}$$

$$N = d_{n-1} \times r^{n-1} + \cdots + d_0 \times r^0 + d_{-1} \times r^{-1} + \cdots + d_{-m} \times r^{-m} \tag{1-2}$$

$$N = \sum_{i=-m}^{n-1} d_i r^i \qquad 0 \le d_i \le (r-1) \tag{1-3}$$

where d represents the digit, r the radix, or base, n the number of integral digits, and m the number of fractional digits. As an example, the decimal number 123.45 and the binary number 101.01 mean the following sums:

$$123.45 = 1 \times 10^2 + 2 \times 10^1 + 3 \times 10^0 + 4 \times 10^{-1} + 5 \times 10^{-2}$$
$$101.01 = 1 \times 2^2 + 0 \times 2^1 + 1 \times 2^0 + 0 \times 2^{-1} + 1 \times 2^{-2}$$

Thus, a *digit* of a number system is a symbol which represents an integral quan-

---

† According to Webster, algorithm (or algorism) means "the art of calculating with any species of notation; as, the algorithms of fractions, surds, etc." It means here a set of rules for an arithmetic calculation.

tity.   The number of permissible digit symbols in a number system is called the *radix*, or *base*.   A number is a quantity represented by a series of digits.   Digit d_{n-1} in expression (1-1) is the *most significant digit* (m.s.d.) of the number and digit d_{-m} the *least significant digit* (l.s.d.).   The term binary digit occurs so often that a shortened word, *bit*, is used.   For instance, the binary number 10101 has 5 bits, or 5 binary digits.

In the representations (1-1) to (1-3), if m is zero, the number is an *integer*.   If n is zero instead, the number is a fraction.   If both m and n are nonzero integers, it is a *mixed number*.   The digit point which is indicated between the digits d_0 and d_{-1} does not exist physically in the computer.   However, the logic circuits of the computer are so implemented that the computation gives the results which correspond to the existence of a chosen location of the digit point.

In the binary number system, the two digit symbols are 0 and 1.   In the decimal number system, the ten digit symbols are 0, 1, 2, 3, 4, 5, 6, 7, 8, and 9.   In the octal number system, the eight digit symbols are 0 to 7.   In order to distinguish a number as to its radix, a radix subscript, written at the end of a number, is commonly used.   For example, 12345_{10}, 10101_2, and 12345_8 represent, respectively, the decimal number 12345, the binary number 10101, and the octal number 12345.   For convenience, we shall use no subscript at all if the number is decimal, and the subscript for a binary number may be dropped if its absence does not impair clarity.   Several number systems with their radices are shown below:

Radix	Number system
2	Binary
3	Ternary
4	Quaternary
5	Quinary
8	Octonary, or octal
10	Decimal
12	Duodecimal
16	Hexadecimal

Note that a quaternary, an octal, or a hexadecimal number corresponds, respectively, to a combination of 2, 3, or 4 bits.   These larger index numbers (particularly the octal number) are therefore sometimes used as a convenient means of writing a long binary number.   Thus, 101101101101101_2 can readily be written as 55555_8, since 101_2 corresponds to 5_8.   This shows, then, that binary-octal, binary-quaternary, and binary-hexadecimal conversions are very simple.

Some Terminology.   Additional terminology is now introduced: complement, alphanumeric character, machine word, and modulo.   The *complement* of a digit is the positive difference between the digit and the largest digit $(r-1)$ of the given radix (unless stated otherwise).   For instance, the complement of decimal digit 3 is $(9-3)$, or 6.   For binary digits, the complement of 1 is 0 and of 0 is 1.   The complement of a digit is not the complement of a number; the latter is discussed subsequently.

Alphanumeric (or *alphameric*) *characters* are symbols which include digit symbols as well as nondigit symbols, such as alphabetic letters, punctuation marks, the symbol for dollars, the symbol for per cent, etc.

A *machine word*, or *computer word*, is a group of digits (usually fixed in number for a given machine) which represents a basic unit of information. Because numbers in the computer are also commonly used to represent computer instructions, the term machine word is preferred to "machine number." A word in a large-scale general-purpose digital computer is about 10 to 15 decimal digits or 24 to 64 bits.

Modulo, or modulus, is a capacity or a unit of measurement. The number which a three-digit decimal counter can exhibit is less than 1000; it is a modulo-1000 counter. Such a counter cannot distinguish the numbers, 999 and 1999 (= 999 + 1000). In terms of the mathematical concept of congruence, this is written in the following form:

$$1999 \equiv 999 \text{ mod } 1000$$

The above is read "1999 is congruent to 999 modulo 1000." If the three-decimal-digit counter is initially 000 and a number 001 is subtracted from it, the counter shows the number 999 but not the desired answer -001. When written into a congruence, this is

$$-001 \equiv 999 \text{ mod } 1000$$

Since digital computers use counters and registers with a fixed number of digits, it is important to realize that the counters and registers cannot distinguish the numbers which differ only by an integral multiple of its modulus. Another useful term is the modulo sum. A *modulo sum* is a sum with respect to a modulus while the carry is ignored. When 8 is added to 7, the sum is 15; but assuming that the modulus is 10 in this case, the modulo sum is 5. The modulo sum and the congruence are further discussed in connection with residue number arithmetic in Chap. 2.

Negative Numbers.   In ordinary arithmetic, a number such as -12345 is represented by the sign and the magnitude. This is *sign and magnitude representation*. Two other ways of representing decimal numbers, the *10's complement* and the *9's complement*, are defined below,

$$\overline{N} = 10\text{'s complement of } N = 10^n - N \qquad (1\text{-}4)$$

$$\overline{\overline{N}} = 9\text{'s complement of } N = 10^n - N - 10^{-m} \qquad (1\text{-}5)$$

where n is the number of integral digits and m the number of fractional digits of the decimal number N. For example, the 10's complement of the number 123.45 is 876.55, and the 9's complement is 876.54. In a decimal counter having n decimal digits, the largest number that the counter can count is $10^n - 1$. For the number 10^n, the counter shows the number 0, as the former number exceeds its capacity. When such a condition occurs in a computer, expressions (1-4) and (1-5) for the 10's and 9's complements of a number N become

$$\overline{N} = 0 - N \qquad (1\text{-}6)$$

$$\overline{\overline{N}} = 0 - N - 10^{-m} \qquad (1\text{-}7)$$

Note that the negative number can also be represented by the 10's or 9's complement. For example, the 10's and 9's complements of the number -123.45 are, respectively, -876.55 and -876.54.

The 10's complement of the 10's complement of a number is the number itself;

likewise the 9's complement of the 9's complement of a number is the number itself. These statements are proved as shown:

$$10^n - \overline{N} = 10^n - (10^n - N) = N \qquad (1\text{-}8)$$

$$\text{and} \quad 10^n - 10^{-m} - \overline{\overline{N}} = (10^n - 10^{-m}) - (10^n - 10^{-m} - N) = N \quad (1\text{-}9)$$

There are three methods of obtaining the 10's complement of a decimal number. The first method is to use the relation (1-6). The second method is first to obtain the 9's complement and then to add 1 to the least significant digit of the 9's complement of the number. The third method uses the following rule: The least significant zero digits of the given number (if any) remain zero; the first and least significant nonzero digit is complemented with respect to 10; each of the remaining digits is complemented with respect to 9. These three methods are summarized into the algorithm in Table 1-1.

Table 1-1   Algorithm for Obtaining 10's Complement of a Decimal Number

Method	Algorithm
a	$\overline{N} = 0 - N$
b	$\overline{N} = \overline{\overline{N}} + 10^{-m}$
c	Keep least significant zero digits unchanged; complement first least significant nonzero digit with respect to 10; complement each of other digits with respect to 9

Example 1-1. Let the decimal number N be 23400. The steps for the three methods are:

(a) $\overline{N} = 00000 - 23400 = 76600$

(b) $\overline{N} = 76599$

   $\overline{N} = 76599 + 00001 = 76600$

(c) The two least significant zero digits remain unchanged. The first least significant nonzero digit is complemented with respect to 10; that is, 4 is changed to 6. The remaining digits are complemented with respect to 9; that is, 2 is changed to 7 and 3 to 6. The answer is 76600.

Similarly, there are three methods of obtaining the 9's complement of a decimal number. These are shown in Table 1-2. Note that the second method is merely to complement each digit with respect to 9. The first and third methods are impractical, because the 9's complement is easier to obtain than the 10's complement.

Table 1-2   Algorithm for Obtaining 9's Complement of a Decimal Number

Method	Algorithm
a	$\overline{\overline{N}} = 0 - N - 10^{-m}$
b	Complement each digit with respect to 9
c	$\overline{\overline{N}} = \overline{N} - 10^{-m}$

The 10's and 9's complements of a decimal number have their counterparts in the binary number system: the 2's *complement* and the 1's *complement*, respectively. Relations (1-4) to (1-9) and the algorithms in Tables 1-1 and 1-2 are equally valid if we simply substitute 2 for 10 and 1 for 9. In general, for an $(n + m)$ digit number N with radix r, we have the following definitions for the r's complement and the $(r - 1)$'s complement† of the number,

$$\overline{N} = r\text{'s complement} = r^n - N \tag{1-10}$$

and

$$\overline{\overline{N}} = (r - 1)\text{'s complement} = r^n - N - r^{-m} \tag{1-11}$$

when n and m are, respectively, the number of integral and fractional digits of the number N.

1-2 Number Base Conversion

Three number systems are most frequently used in digital computers: binary, octal, and decimal. Occasions arise where a number expressed in one number system must be converted to another. Thus, three kinds of number base conversion are of interest: binary-octal, binary-decimal, and octal-decimal conversions.

Binary-Octal Conversion. Binary-octal conversion, already illustrated, simply replaces each three-digit binary number with its equivalent octal digit. Similarly, in octal-binary conversion, each octal digit is replaced by an equivalent three-digit binary number.

Decimal-Binary Conversion. For decimal-binary conversion of an integral number, the *repeated-division-by-2 method* is used. Let N be the decimal integer. When it is converted into an n-digit binary number of digits b_i, it can be written in the following form:

$$N = b_{n-1}2^{n-1} + \cdots + b_1 2^1 + b_0 2^0$$

When both sides of the above equation are divided by 2, we have the quotient Q_1, which is an integer, and a remainder b_0, as follows:

$$\frac{N}{2} = Q_1 + b_0 2^{-1} \qquad \text{where } Q_1 = b_{n-1}2^{n-2} + \cdots + b_1 2^0$$

The remainder b_0 thus obtained is the desired least significant digit, because the given number N and the radix 2 are both integers; the quotients and remainders on both sides of the above equation can be, respectively, equated. Next, we divide Q_1 by 2 and thus obtain Q_2 and a remainder b_1,

$$\frac{Q_1}{2} = Q_2 + b_1 2^{-1} \qquad \text{where } Q_2 = b_{n-1}2^{n-3} + \cdots + b_2 2^0$$

The remainder b_1 thus obtained is the desired next least significant digit. This process continues until Q_n is equal to 0. The conversion is summarized in the algorithm shown in Table 1-3. The above method can also be applied in converting an integral number in radix r_1 to its equivalent in radix r_2, by dividing the number in radix r_1 by radix r_2.

---

† These two terms are also called the *radix complement* and the *diminished radix complement*, respectively.

Table 1-3   *Algorithm of Decimal-Binary Conversion of an Integral Decimal Number*

Step   *Algorithm*

a   Divide given integral decimal number N by radix 2. Resulting quotient is Q_1 and remainder b_0

b   Divide quotient Q_1 by radix 2. Resulting quotient is Q_2 and remainder b_1

c   Continue this process until Q_n is zero. Remainders are digits of converted binary number, b_0 being least significant digit

Example 1-2. Let $N = 53$.

$$
\begin{array}{ll}
2\underline{|53} & \\
2\underline{|26} & b_0 = 1 \\
2\underline{|13} & b_1 = 0 \\
2\underline{|\ 6} & b_2 = 1 \\
2\underline{|\ 3} & b_3 = 0 \\
2\underline{|\ 1} & b_4 = 1 \\
0 & b_5 = 1
\end{array}
$$

The remainders b_0 to b_5 give the equivalent binary number 110101.

For decimal-binary conversion of a fractional decimal number, the *repeated-multiplication-by*-2 method is used. Let N be the decimal fraction. When it is converted into a binary number, it can be written in the following form:

$$N = b_{-1}2^{-1} + b_{-2}2^{-2} + \cdots + b_{-m}2^{-m}$$

When both sides of the above equation are multiplied by 2, we have a product which consists of an integer part b_{-1} and a fractional part F_1 as follows:

$$2N = b_{-1} + F_1 \qquad \text{where } F_1 = b_{-2}2^{-1} + \cdots + b_{-m}2^{-m+1}$$

The integral digit b_{-1} thus obtained is the desired most significant digit, because the integral and fractional parts on both sides of the above equation can be, respectively, equated. Next we multiply F_1 by 2 and thus obtain

$$2F_1 = b_{-2} + F_2 \qquad \text{where } F_2 = b_{-3}2^{-1} + \cdots + b_{-m}2^{-m+2}$$

The integral bit b_{-2} thus obtained is the desired next most significant digit. This process continues until F_m becomes zero. This conversion is summarized into the algorithm shown in Table 1-4.

Table 1-4   *Algorithm of Decimal-Binary Conversion of a Fractional Decimal Number*

Step   *Algorithm*

a   Multiply given fractional decimal number N by radix 2. Resulting fractional part is F_1 and integral bit b_{-1}

b   Multiply fractional part F_1 by radix 2. Resulting fractional part is F_2 and integral bit b_{-2}

c   This process continues until F_m is zero. Integral bits are digits of converted binary number, b_{-1} being most significant digit

Example 1-3. Let $N = 0.4375$.

$$
\begin{array}{ll}
0.4375 \times 2 = 0.8750 & b_{-1} = 0 \\
0.8750 \times 2 = 1.7500 & b_{-2} = 1
\end{array}
$$

$$0.7500 \times 2 = 1.5000 \qquad b_{-3} = 1$$
$$0.5000 \times 2 = 1.0000 \qquad b_{-4} = 1$$

The integral bits b_{-1} to b_{-4} give the equivalent number .0111.

Example 1-4. Let $N = 0.3$.

$$0.3 \times 2 = 0.6 \qquad b_{-1} = 0$$
$$0.6 \times 2 = 1.2 \qquad b_{-2} = 1$$
$$0.2 \times 2 = 0.4 \qquad b_{-3} = 0$$
$$0.4 \times 2 = 0.8 \qquad b_{-4} = 0$$
$$0.8 \times 2 = 1.6 \qquad b_{-5} = 1$$
$$0.6 \times 2 = 1.2 \qquad b_{-6} = 1$$
$$0.2 \times 2 = 0.4 \qquad b_{-7} = 0$$

This may be continued as long as you wish. The equivalent binary number is $0.0100110 \cdots$. In general, a finite fraction in one number system cannot always be represented by a finite fraction in another number system.

Binary-Decimal Conversion. For binary-decimal conversion of an integral binary number, the repeated-multiplication-by-2 method is used. Let N be the binary integer with six digits as below:

$$N = b_5 2^5 + b_4 2^4 + b_3 2^3 + b_2 2^2 + b_1 2^1 + b_0 2^0$$

To convert this binary number into its equivalent decimal number, the above expression is rewritten as follows:

$$N = (\{[(b_5 2 + b_4)2 + b_3]2 + b_2\}2 + b_1)2 + b_0$$

The above conversion process is described by the algorithm in Table 1-5.

Table 1-5   Algorithm of Binary-Decimal Conversion of an Integral Decimal Number

Step	Algorithm
a	Start with most significant digit of binary number
b	Double this digit if second most significant digit is 0, or double and add 1 if second most significant digit is 1. Call result M_1
c	Double M_1 if third most significant digit is 0, or double and add 1 if third most significant digit is 1. Call result M_2
d	Continue this process until multiplication indicated by least significant digit is performed
e	Final decimal number is the converted decimal equivalent

Example 1-5. Let $N = 110101$.

$$b_5 \text{ (most significant digit)} = 1$$
$$M_1 = 1 \times 2 + 1 = 3$$
$$M_2 = 3 \times 2 + 0 = 6$$
$$M_3 = 6 \times 2 + 1 = 13$$
$$M_4 = 13 \times 2 + 0 = 26$$
$$N = 26 \times 2 + 1 = \underline{53}$$

The equivalent decimal number is 53, in agreement with the number in Example 1-2.

For binary-decimal conversion of a fractional binary number, the repeated-division-by-2 method is used.   Let N be the binary fractional number with four fractional digits as below,

$$N = b_{-1}2^{-1} + b_{-2}2^{-2} + b_{-3}2^{-3} + b_{-4}2^{-4}$$

To convert this binary number into its equivalent decimal number, the above expression is written as follows,

$$N = 2^{-1}\{b_{-1} + 2^{-1}[b_{-2} + 2^{-1}(b_3 + b_4 2^{-1})]\}$$

The conversion process using the above relation is described by the algorithm in Table 1-6.

Table 1-6   *Algorithm of Binary-Decimal Conversion of a Fractional Binary Number*

Step	Algorithm
a	Start with least significant digit of binary number
b	Divide this digit by 2 if next least significant digit is 0, or divide by 2 and add 1 if next least significant digit is 1. Call result R_1
c	Divide R_1 by 2 if third least significant digit is 0, or divide by 2 and add 1 if third least significant digit is 1. Call result R_2
d	Continue this process until division indicated by digit 0 at left of binary point has been performed
e	Final decimal number is the converted decimal equivalent

Example 1-6.   Let $N = 0.0111$.

$$b_{-4} \text{ (least significant digit)} = 1$$
$$R_1 = (1 \div 2) + 1 = 1.5$$
$$R_2 = (1.5 \div 2) + 1 = 1.75$$
$$R_3 = (1.75 \div 2) + 0 = 0.875$$
$$N = (0.875 \div 2) + 0 = \underline{0.4375}$$

The equivalent decimal number is 0.4375, which agrees with the number in Example 1-3.

Example 1-7.   Let $N = 0.01001$.

$$b_{-5} \text{ (least significant digit)} = 1$$
$$R_1 = (1 \div 2) + 0 = 0.5$$
$$R_2 = (0.5 \div 2) + 0 = 0.25$$
$$R_3 = (0.25 \div 2) + 1 = 1.125$$
$$R_4 = (1.125 \div 2) + 0 = 0.5625$$
$$N = (0.5625 \div 2) + 0 = \underline{0.28125}$$

The equivalent decimal number is 0.28125, which does *not* agree with the value of 0.3 of Example 1-4.   If the number N carries more digits, say, 0.01001101, the n decimal equivalent is 0.298828125.   It is thus obvious that an adequate number of digits has to be used to obtain the converted number with sufficient accuracy.

The decimal equivalents of powers of 2 for both positive and negative powers are given in Table 1-7.   The number of bits necessary for reasonably accurate conversion to decimal digits can be found from this table.   For example, to represent the largest decimal number of three digits (999), the number of bits needed is 10 (that is, the required n is 10 in Table 1-7).   Similarly, a decimal number of four, five, and six digits requires, respectively, 14, 17, and 20 bits. It can be readily shown that one decimal digit is equivalent to 3.2 (or $1/\log 2$) bits.

Table 1-7   Decimal Equivalents of Powers of 2

N	2^n	2^{-n}
0	1	1.0
1	2	0.5
2	4	0.25
3	8	0.125
4	16	0.062 5
5	32	0.031 25
6	64	0.015 625
7	128	0.007 812 5
8	256	0.003 906 25
9	512	0.001 953 125
10	1 024	0.000 976 562 5
11	2 048	0.000 488 281 25
12	4 096	0.000 244 140 625
13	8 192	0.000 122 070 312 5
14	16 384	0.000 061 035 156 25
15	32 768	0.000 030 517 578 125
16	65 536	0.000 015 258 789 062 5
17	131 072	0.000 007 629 394 531 25
18	262 144	0.000 003 814 697 265 625
19	524 288	0.000 001 907 348 632 812 5
20	1 048 576	0.000 000 953 674 316 406 25
21	2 097 152	0.000 000 476 837 158 203 125
22	4 194 304	0.000 000 238 418 579 101 562 5
23	8 388 608	0.000 000 119 209 289 550 781 25
24	16 777 216	0.000 000 059 604 644 775 390 625
25	33 554 432	0.000 000 029 802 322 387 695 312 5
26	67 108 864	0.000 000 014 901 161 193 847 656 25
27	134 217 728	0.000 000 007 450 580 596 923 828 125
28	268 435 456	0.000 000 003 725 290 298 461 914 062 5
29	536 870 912	0.000 000 001 862 645 149 230 957 031 25
30	1 073 741 824	0.000 000 000 931 322 574 615 478 515 625
31	2 147 483 648	0.000 000 000 465 661 287 307 739 257 812 5
32	4 294 967 296	0.000 000 000 232 830 643 653 869 628 906 25
33	8 589 934 592	0.000 000 000 116 415 321 826 934 814 453 125
34	17 179 869 184	0.000 000 000 058 207 660 913 467 407 226 562 5

Octal-Decimal Conversion. There are three methods for octal-decimal conversion. The first method is similar to those for binary-decimal conversion, except that multiplication by 2 and division by 2 becomes multiplication or division by 8. The second method is first to perform the simple octal-binary conversion and then the more familiar binary-decimal conversion. The third and most convenient method employs a prepared octal-decimal conversion table.

1-3   Single-digit Binary Arithmetic

Arithmetic rules for binary numbers are very simple. The rules for binary addition, subtraction, and multiplication of a single digit are shown below:

Binary addition

Augend digit	0	0	1	1
Addend digit	0	1	0	1
Sum	0	1	1	0
Carry	0	0	0	1

(1-12)

Binary subtraction

Minuend digit	0	0	1	1
Subtrahend digit	0	1	0	1
Difference	0	1	1	0
Borrow	0	1	0	0

(1-13)

Binary multiplication

Multiplicand digit	0	0	1	1
Multiplier digit	0	1	0	1
Product	0	0	0	1

(1-14)

From these rules, the following observations can be made:

1. For binary addition, the sum digit is 1 when either augend or addend but not both is 1; the carry digit is 1 only when both augend and addend digits are 1.

2. For binary subtraction, the difference digit is 1 when either minuend or subtrahend but not both is 1; the borrow digit occurs only when the minuend digit is 0 and the subtrahend digit is 1.

3. For binary multiplication, the product digit is 1 only when both multiplicand digit and multiplier digit are 1.

4. The rules for the sum digit and the difference digit are the same.

5. If 0 and 1 are used to represent, respectively, the positive and negative signs of numbers, then the modulo-2 sum of the two sign bits is the correct sign when the two numbers are multiplied.

1-4 Signed Binary Numbers

Three Representations of Signed Binary Numbers. When the sign of a binary number is denoted by one of its digits (usually the most significant digit), it is called a *signed binary number*. The 0 and 1 are usually chosen to represent, respectively, the positive and negative signs. The other digits of a signed binary number are called here the *number digits*. A signed binary number can be represented according to the three ways of representing negative numbers. We thus have:

1. Signed-magnitude representation
2. Signed-2's-complement representation
3. Signed-1's-complement representation

In the signed-magnitude representation, the number digits represent the magnitude (or absolute value) of the number, while in the other two representations the number digits are either in 2's or 1's complement when the number is negative. If the number is positive, the three representations are the same.

Example 1-8. This example shows (Table 1-8) the three representations of signed binary numbers for the given decimal numbers $+13$ and -7. *Note that a comma is employed here to indicate the sign digit.*

Table 1-8 Examples of Representation of Signed Binary Numbers

Representation	Number ($+13$)	Number (-7)
Signed magnitude........	0,1101	1,0111
Signed 2's complement....	0,1101	1,1001
Signed 1's complement....	0,1101	1,1000

The above choice of 0 and 1 in representing, respectively, the positive and negative signs is based on an important property of the signed-complement representations. Consider, for instance, the binary number 1,1001 (or -7) in signed-2's-complement representation. If the sign digit is regarded to be negative (that is, -1), we have

$$1,1001 = -1 \times 2^4 + 1 \times 2^3 + 0 \times 2^2 + 0 \times 2^1 + 1 \times 2^0$$
$$= -10000 + 1001$$
$$= -0111$$

The above number -0111 is the actual value of the given binary number. As will be proved, *the signed-2's-complement representation of a binary number gives the actual value of the binary number if the value of the sign digit is regarded as negative.* This does not affect the positive numbers, because in these numbers the sign digits are 0.

In general, if X is the given binary number of $m + n$ digits, the three representations are as follows:

Signed-magnitude Representation

$$X = -x_n 2^n + \sum_{i=-m}^{n-1} x_i 2^i \tag{1-15}$$

where x_n is 0 for a positive number and is 1 for a negative number.

Signed-2's-complement Representation

$$X = 0 \times 2^n + \sum_{i=-m}^{n-1} x_i 2^i \qquad \text{when } X \text{ is positive} \tag{1-16}$$

$$X = -1 \times 2^n + \sum_{i=-m}^{n-1} \bar{x}_i 2_i + 2^{-m} \qquad \text{when } X \text{ is negative} \tag{1-17}$$

$$\bar{x}_i = 1 - x_i \qquad \text{1's complement of digit } x_i \tag{1-18}$$

Signed-1's-complement Representation

$$X = 0 \times 2^n + \sum_{i=-m}^{n-1} x_i 2^i \qquad \text{when } X \text{ is positive} \tag{1-19}$$

$$X = -1 \times 2^n + \sum_{i=-m}^{n-1} \bar{x}_i 2^i \qquad \text{when } X \text{ is negative} \tag{1-20}$$

We now prove that the signed-2's-complement representation (1-17) truly represents the actual value of the number. A convenient identity (for example, $10000 = 1111 + 0001$) can be expressed in the general form

$$2^n = \sum_{i=-m}^{n-1} 2^i + 2^{-m} \tag{1-21}$$

When relation (1-21) is substituted into (1-17), we have

$$X = -\sum_{i=-m}^{n-1} 2^i - 2^{-m} + \sum_{i=-m}^{n-1} \bar{x}_i 2^i + 2^{-m}$$

$$= -\sum_{i=-m}^{n-1} (1 - \bar{x}_i) 2^i$$

or

$$X = -\sum_{i=-m}^{n-1} x_i 2^i \tag{1-22}$$

which was to be demonstrated. This may also be proved readily if one utilizes the fact that the number digits of representation (1-17) corresponds to the 2's complement of the number digits of the given negative number, X, or

$$\sum_{i=-m}^{n-1} \bar{x}_i 2^i + 2^{-m} = 2^n - \sum_{i=-m}^{n-1} x_i \tag{1-23}$$

The binary number X, by using the above relation, is

$$X = -\sum_{i=-m}^{n-1} x_i = -2^n + \sum_{i=-m}^{n-1} \bar{x}_i 2^i + 2^{-m} \tag{1-24}$$

Relation (1-24) is identical to relation (1-17). Similarly we can demonstrate the validity of representation (1-20) for the case of the signed-1's-complement representation.

Shifting Algorithm of Signed Binary Number. Multiplying a binary number by 2^1 or 2^{-1} is equivalent, respectively, to shifting the binary number one digit to the left or right of the binary point. For example, if the given number is 0,0101.010, the most significant digit 0 (indicated by the comma) representing a positive number, then its multiplication by 2^1 is 0,1010.100 and its multiplication by 2^{-1} is 0,0010.101. For a positive number with its sign digit represented by 0, the three representations of signed binary numbers are the same; as just illustrated, the shift of one or more digits to the right or left requires addition or removal of 0's and the sign digit 0 remains unchanged.

When the number is negative, with its sign digit represented by 1, the shift is not so simple, because the sign digit should remain unchanged and the added digits as a result of shifting should have the correct value of 0 or 1, as illustrated by the following example.

Example 1-9. This example shows the shift to the left or right of the three signed negative numbers. Let the number be X, -1101 (or -13). In the following a comma is employed to indicate the location of the sign digit. The sign bit is not to be disturbed. If the number digits are to remain as 4 bits, the digits in the parentheses should be removed and the underscored digits added.

(*a*) Signed-magnitude representation

$$X = 1,1101$$
$$X2^1 = 1,(1)101\underline{0} \qquad \text{one digit shifted to left}$$
$$X2^2 = 1,(11)01\underline{00} \qquad \text{two digits shifted to left}$$
$$X2^{-1} = 1,0110.(1) \qquad \text{one digit shifted to right}$$
$$X2^{-2} = 1,\underline{0}011.(01) \qquad \text{two digits shifted to right}$$

All added digits are 0's. Note that the number bits 11010 and 110100 are, respectively, the correct numbers 26 and 52 and that the number bits 0110.1 and 0011.01 are, respectively, 1¾ and 1¾.

(*b*) Signed-2's-complement representation

$$X = 1,0011$$
$$X2^1 = 1,(0)011\underline{0}$$
$$X2^2 = 1,(00)11\underline{00}$$
$$X2^{-1} = 1,\underline{1}001.(1)$$
$$X2^{-2} = 1,\underline{11}00.(11)$$

In shifting to the left, 0's are added. In shifting toward the right, 1's are added, because these 1's are really the complement of 0's that would be added if the number were positive. Note that the 2's complements of the numbers 00110 and 001100 are, respectively, 11010 (or 26) and 110100 (or 52); those of 1001.1 and 1100.11 are, respectively, 0110.1 (or 1¾) and 0011.01 (or 1¾). The shifted numbers are thus correct.

(*c*) Signed-1's-complement representation

$$X = 1,0010$$
$$X2^1 = 1,(0)010\underline{1}$$
$$X2^2 = 1,(00)10\underline{11}$$
$$X2^{-1} = 1,\underline{1}001.(0)$$
$$X2^{-2} = 1,\underline{11}00.(10)$$

All added digits are 1's. Note that the 1's complement of the number bits 00101 and 001011 are, respectively, 11010 (or 26) and 110100 (or 52); those of 1001.0 and 1100.10 are, respectively, 0110.1 (or 1¾) and 0011.01 (or 1¾). The shifted numbers are all correct.

The above shifting process is summarized into an algorithm in Table 1-9. The shifting algorithm is used later in describing several methods of binary multiplication and division.

Table 1-9 Algorithm for Shifting Signed Binary Numbers

	Sign digit	Number digits
Positive number.....................	Unchanged	Shifted, all added digits being 0's
Negative number in signed-magnitude representation...................	Unchanged	Shifted, all added digits being 0's
Negative number in signed-2's-complement representation	Unchanged	Shifted to left, added digits being 0's; to right, added digits being 1's
Negative number in signed-1's-complement representation..................	Unchanged	Shifted, all digits being 1's

Comparison Algorithm of the Signed Number. The comparison of two numbers determines which number is larger in accordance with the familiar logic of ordinary arithmetic. When two numbers (in either signed-magnitude or signed-complement form) with different signs are compared, the number with the positive sign is the larger number. When two signed numbers with the same sign are compared, the comparison algorithm depends on whether the signs are both positive or both negative and also on whether the corresponding digits of the two numbers are being compared from the most significant digit (m.s.d.) toward the least significant (l.s.d.) or from the l.s.d. toward the m.s.d.

When two numbers with the same sign are compared from the m.s.d. toward the l.s.d., the one with the first larger digit is the larger number if both signs are positive and the one with the first smaller digit is the larger number if both signs are negative. When two numbers with the same sign are compared from the l.s.d. toward the m.s.d., the one with the last larger digit is the larger number if both signs are positive, and the one with the last smaller digit is the larger number if both signs are negative. The above is summarized in Table 1-10. This comparison algorithm is applicable for signed binary or decimal numbers.

Table 1-10   *Algorithm for Comparing Signed Numbers*

Sign digit	Compared from m.s.d. toward l.s.d.	Compared from l.s.d. toward m.s.d.
Same:		
Both positive.....	One with first larger digit is larger†	One with last larger digit is larger†
Both negative....	One with first smaller digit is larger†	One with last smaller digit is larger†
Different..........	One with positive sign is larger	

† The two numbers are equal if this does not happen.

The comparison of two signed numbers may also be accomplished by subtraction, the larger number being determined by the sign digit of the difference. In this method, the algorithm is very simple. If the sign of the difference is positive, the minuend is larger. If it is negative, the subtrahend is larger. If the two numbers are the same, the difference is zero.

Location of the Binary Point.   The binary point of a binary number is a demarcation between the integral part and the fractional part of the number. The location of the binary point is of great concern to those who program the digital computer. It is also important to the computer designer, because it affects the logic structure of the arithmetic unit of the computer.

One particular location of the binary point for the signed binary number is widely used. This form of signed numbers uses one integral digit as the sign digit and fractional digits as the number digits. Thus, the binary point indicates not only the integral and fractional parts of the number but also the sign and number digits. Let this signed number be Y, or

$$Y = \pm y_0 2^0 + Y^* \tag{1-25}$$

where y_0 is the sign digit (the $\pm$ will be explained subsequently). Y^* is the representation of number digits as below,

$$Y^* = \sum_{i=1}^{n} y_i 2^{-i} \qquad \text{for positive } Y \text{ or negative } Y \text{ in magnitude representation} \tag{1-26}$$

$$Y^* = \bar{Y}^* = \sum_{i=1}^{n} \bar{y}_i 2^{-i} + 2^{-n} \qquad \text{for negative } Y \text{ in 2's-complement representation} \qquad (1\text{-}27)$$

$$Y^* = \bar{\bar{Y}}^* = \sum_{i=1}^{n} \bar{y}_i 2^{-i} \qquad \text{for negative } Y \text{ in 1's-complement representation} \qquad (1\text{-}28)$$

where n is the number of number digits. It should be emphasized that, in this signed number, Y^* is always less than 1, or

$$Y^* < 1 \qquad (1\text{-}29)$$

regardless of which of the three is used.

It is important to become acquainted with the significance and ranges of the binary numbers which relation (1-25) represents. Two interpretations are possible, depending on whether the value of the sign digit y_0 is positive or negative. Consider the case where the sign digit y_0 has the value either 0 or 1. In this case (in which the computer interprets the number) expression (1-25) gives the numbers in the range $0 \leq Y < 2$. To be specific, when the number is positive, relation (1-25) yields numbers in the range $0 \leq Y < 1$. When the number is negative, the relation gives the number in the range, $1 \leq Y < 2$.

Consider the case where the sign digit y_0 has the value either 0 or -1. In this case the number gives its true value, and expression (1-25) gives numbers in the range $-1 \leq Y < 1$. To be specific, when the number is positive, it gives the numbers in the range $0 \leq Y < 1$. When the number is negative, it gives the number in the range $-1 \leq Y < 0$. If, for the number range of the second case $(-1 \leq Y < 1)$, we add 2^0 to each side of this inequality, we have the number range $0 \leq Y < 2$, which is the number range in the first case.

The location of the binary point as shown in representation (1-25) provides the following important advantages:

1. The multiplication process will never cause an overflow; i.e., the result of the multiplication will not exceed the number range of the computer. (However, it can cause an "underflow," so that successive multiplication can cause a number to shift out entirely to the right.)

2. This location of the binary point is easily remembered, although the choice of location has no effect on binary addition and subtraction.

3. Since the number Y^* is always less than 1, the location of the binary point remains at the same location after binary multiplication.

Because of these advantages, this particular location of the binary point (at the right of the leftmost digit) is widely used in binary computers. It will be recalled later in the logic design of a simple digital computer in Chap. 11.

1-5   *Binary Addition and Subtraction—I*

The addition and subtraction of two binary numbers are influenced by the method of representing the negative numbers. Consequently, binary addition and subtraction are discussed in terms of the representation of signed binary numbers.

For binary numbers in signed-magnitude representation, two methods for addition or subtraction are:

1. Direct addition
2. Direct subtraction

Direct-addition Method. Let the two binary numbers X and Y and their sum Z be

$$X = x_0 2^0 + \sum_{i=-1}^{-n} x_i 2^i = x_0 2^0 + X^* \qquad (1\text{-}30)$$

$$Y = y_0 2^0 + \sum_{i=-1}^{-n} y_i 2^i = y_0 2^0 + Y^* \qquad (1\text{-}31)$$

and

$$Z = z_0 2^0 + \sum_{i=-1}^{-n} z_i 2^i = z_0 2^0 + Z^* \qquad (1\text{-}32)$$

where x_i, y_i, and z_i are either 1 or 0. The digits x_0, y_0, and z_0 are the sign digits, 0 and 1 representing, respectively, the positive and negative signs. Each number consists of n number bits and a sign bit, or a total of $n + 1$ bits. The choice of the above location of binary point does not lose generality but makes the subsequent development more convenient. The digital algorithm for addition will now be developed. If X and Y are both positive or both negative, Y is added to X; or

$$Z = X + Y = z_0 2^0 + \sum_{i=-1}^{-n} (x_i + y_i) 2^i \qquad (1\text{-}33)$$

The addition of x_i, y_i and w_i (where w_i is the carry from the adjacent, less significant digit) follows the arithmetic rule for a single digit and produces the sum bit z_i and the carry bit w_{i+1}, or

$$x_i + y_i + w_i = w_{i+1} 2 + z_i \qquad \text{for } i = -1, \ldots, -n \qquad (1\text{-}34)$$

where

$$z_i = x_i \oplus y_i \oplus w_i \qquad (1\text{-}35)$$

$$w_{i+1} = x_i y_i + y_i w_i + x_i w_i - 2 x_i y_i w_i \qquad (1\text{-}36)$$

$$w_{-n} = 0 \qquad (1\text{-}37)$$

The symbol $\oplus$ denotes the modulo sum (i.e., addition with carry ignored). The sign bit z_0 of the sum is the same as x_0 (or y_0). Thus we have the sum Z,

$$Z = x_0 2^0 + \sum_{i=-1}^{-n} z_i 2^i \qquad (1\text{-}38)$$

In the above, it is assumed that the sum of X and Y does not exceed the capacity of n bits, which means that the sum does not *overflow* (that is, $w_0 = 0$). In a digital computer, a circuit is provided to store the overflow bit in case this is needed; this circuit will then turn on an indicator or initiate some desired operation.

If X and Y are of different signs, Y is subtracted from X without any prior comparison. The difference Z can be written

$$Z = X - Y = z_0 2^0 + \sum_{i=-1}^{-n} (x_i - y_i) 2^i \qquad (1\text{-}39)$$

The subtraction of y_i from x_i follows the arithmetic rule for a single digit and produces the difference bit z_i and the borrow bit w_{i+1}, or

$$x_i - y_i - w_i = -w_{i+1}2 + z_i \qquad \text{for } i = -1, \ldots, -n \qquad (1\text{-}40)$$

where
$$z_i = x_i \oplus y_i \oplus w_i \qquad\qquad (1\text{-}41)$$

$$w_{i+1} = \bar{x}_i w_i + \bar{x}_i y_i + y_i w_i - 2\bar{x}_i y_i w_i \qquad (1\text{-}42)$$

$$w_{-n} = 0 \qquad\qquad (1\text{-}43)$$

$$\bar{x}_i = 1 - x_i$$

In determining the sign bit z_0, there are two possible cases. Consider the cas where X is positive and Y is negative. If X^* is larger than Y^*, the difference is positive and z_0 is the same as x_0. If X^* is smaller than Y^*, Z is negative an z_0 is the same as $\bar{x}_0$. Consider the case where X is negative and Y is positiv If X^* is equal to or larger than Y^*, Z is negative and z_0 is the same as x_0. X^* is smaller than Y^*, Z is positive and z_0 is the same as $\bar{x}_0$. In either case, X^* is smaller than Y^*, a borrow w_0 occurs at the bit position 2^0 and Z^* is 2's complement, indicating that Z is a negative number.

The above addition process is summarized in an algorithm shown in Table 1-1 In short, Y^* is added to or subtracted from X^*, depending on the signs x_0 and being the same or different. The sum Z is positive or negative, depending whether w_0 and x_0 are 0 or 1. If w_0 is 1, Z^* is in 2's complement. A complem tation is required to convert it into the signed-magnitude representation.

Table 1-11 *Algorithm of Binary Addition and Subtraction for Numbers in Signed-ma tude Representation*

	x_0 and y_0	Operation	Sign of sum	
Addition.............	Same	$Z^* = X^* + Y^*$	$z_0 = x_0$	
	Different	$Z^* = X^* - Y^*$	$z_0 = x_0$	if $w_0 =$
			$z_0 = \bar{x}_0$	if $w_0 =$
Subtraction............	Same	$Z^* = X^* - Y^*$	$z_0 = x_0$	if $w_0 =$
			$z_0 = \bar{x}_0$	if $w_0 =$
	Different	$Z^* = X^* + Y^*$	$z_0 = x_0$	

Note: When w_0 is 1, Z^* is in 2's-complement representation.

Example 1-10. This example shows the addition of two 4-bit numbers (plus a sign b the direct-addition method. In the following, each row of squares represents a fixed-l *register*, each square indicating a circuit to store one bit. For clarity, plus and minus are used in representing the positive and negative numbers.

Two signed binary numbers X and Y are given; $X = +1001$, and $Y = +0100$. required to perform the following eight additions:

(a) $(+X) + (+Y)$ (e) $(+Y) + (+X)$
(b) $(+X) + (-Y)$ (f) $(+Y) + (-X)$
(c) $(-X) + (+Y)$ (g) $(-Y) + (+X)$
(d) $(-X) + (-Y)$ (h) $(-Y) + (-X)$

These are the eight possible additions for the two binary numbers X and Y. As sh Table 1-11, addition (or subtraction) is carried out between number bits X^* and Y^*.

two sign bits are the same, Y^* is added to X^*; otherwise, Y^* is subtracted from X^*. The sign digit of the sum is x_0 if both sign digits x_0 and y_0 are the same. If the two sign digits are different, the sign digit of the sum is the 1's complement of x_0 when there is a borrow bit w_0 as shown in additions f and g and the sign digit of the sum is x_0 when no borrow digit occurs. In case f, for example, w_0 is 1, and the number bits are in 2's-complement representation (note that the 2's-complement of 1011 is 0101, or 5).

	(a) $X^* + Y^*$	(b) $X^* - Y^*$	(c) $X^* - Y^*$	(d) $X^* + Y^*$
Augend register	+ 1 0 0 1	+ 1 0 0 1	− 1 0 0 1	− 1 0 0 1
Addend register	+ 0 1 0 0	− 0 1 0 0	+ 0 1 0 0	− 0 1 0 0
Sum register	+ 1 1 0 1	+ 0 1 0 1	− 0 1 0 1	− 1 1 0 1

	(e) $Y^* + X^*$	(f) $Y^* - X^*$	(g) $Y^* - X^*$	(h) $Y^* + X^*$
Augend register	+ 0 1 0 0	+ 0 1 0 0	− 0 1 0 0	− 0 1 0 0
Addend register	+ 1 0 0 1	− 1 0 0 1	+ 1 0 0 1	− 1 0 0 1
Sum register	+ 1 1 0 1	− 1 1 0 1 1	+ 1 1 0 1 1	− 1 1 0 1

Borrow bit w_0

Direct-subtraction Method. The direct-subtraction method is similar to the direct-addition method, and the development of its algorithm will not be repeated. The major difference is that in the direct-subtraction method Y is added to or subtracted from X, depending on the sign bits x_0 and y_0 being different or the same. The algorithm is also shown in Table 1-11.

Example 1-11. This example shows the eight possible subtractions of one binary number from another (Table 1-12). Refer to the details of Example 1-10, and note the occurrence of a carry in examples e and h.

Table 1-12   Eight Examples of Direct-subtraction Method for Numbers in Signed-magnitude Representation

Example	Minuend X	Subtrahend Y	Difference $Z = X - Y$
a	+1001 (+9)	+0100 (+4)	+0101 (+5)
b	+1001	−0100	+1101 (+13)
c	−1001	+0100	−1101 (−13)
d	−1001	−0100	−0101 (−5)
e	+0100 (+4)	+1001 (+9)	−(1)1011 (−5)†
f	+0100	−1001	+1101 (+13)
g	−0100	+1001	−1101 (−13)
h	−0100	−1001	+(1)1011 (+5)†

† The 2's complement of 1011 is 0101, or 5.

1-6   Binary Addition and Subtraction—II

For binary numbers in signed-2's-complement representation, four methods for addition or subtraction are:

1. Direct addition
2. Direct subtraction

3. Addition by subtraction of the 2's complement
4. Subtraction by addition of the 2's complement

In any of the above methods, the sign bit is treated as a number bit. The addition or subtraction will produce a correct sign bit in the sum or difference. This is the greatest advantage of using numbers in signed-2's-complement representation.

Direct-addition Method. Let X and Y be two binary numbers and X^* and Y^* their respective magnitudes. Further, let $\overline{X}^*$ and $\overline{Y}^*$ be the respective 2's complement of X^* and Y^*. Either X or Y can be positive or negative; thus there are four possible combinations, as below.

Both X and Y Are Positive Numbers

$$X = 0 \cdot 2^0 + X^* \tag{1-44}$$

$$Y = 0 \cdot 2^0 + Y^* \tag{1-45}$$

The value of X^* or Y^* is less than 1. The sum Z is

$$Z = X + Y = 0 \cdot 2^0 + (X^* + Y^*) \tag{1-46}$$

When both X and Y are positive, Y^* should be added to X^* according to the algorithm of Table 1-11. This is correctly shown above by the quantity $X^* + Y^*$, which is the true magnitude. The sign bit is also correct as long as $X^* + Y^*$ does not exceed the value of 1 (that is, does not overflow).

X Is a Positive and Y a Negative Number

$$X = 0 \cdot 2^0 + X^* \tag{1-47}$$

$$Y = 1 \cdot 2^0 + \overline{Y}^* \tag{1-48}$$

where $\overline{Y}^*$ is the 2's complement of Y^*, or

$$\overline{Y}^* = 0 - Y^* \tag{1-49}$$

$\overline{Y}^*$ is also less than 1. The sum Z is

$$Z = X + Y = 1 \cdot 2^0 + (X^* + \overline{Y}^*) \tag{1-50}$$

As proof that the above sum Z is a correct result, consider two cases, in the first of which

$$Y^* \leq X^* \tag{1-51}$$

This means that

$$\overline{Y}^* \geq \overline{X}^* \tag{1-52}$$

As we know,

$$X^* + \overline{X}^* = 1 \tag{1-53}$$

then, if X^* is added to both sides of (1-52), we have

$$X^* + \overline{Y}^* \geq 1 \tag{1-54}$$

When X is positive and Y negative, Y^* should be subtracted from X^* as shown in Table 1-11. When X^* is added to both sides of (1-49),

$$X^* + \overline{Y}^* = X^* - Y^* \tag{1-55}$$

we actually have Y^* subtracted from X^*. Thus, the number bits in (1-50) are correct and are the true magnitude. Furthermore, $X^* + \overline{Y}^*$, as shown in (1-54), produces a carry into the bit position 2^0, which adds to the original 1 at the position 2^0 in (1-50) to produce a sign bit 0; this means that the sum is positive. This sign bit is also correct because X is larger than Y.

Consider the second case,

$$Y^* > X^* \tag{1-56}$$

This means that

$$\overline{Y}^* < \overline{X}^* \tag{1-57}$$

Similarly we have

$$X^* + \overline{Y}^* < 1 \tag{1-58}$$

When X is positive and Y negative, the term $X^* + \overline{Y}^*$ is correct because, as shown in (1-55), Y^* is subtracted from X^*; and $X^* + \overline{Y}^*$ will be in 2's complement, as (1-56) shows that Y^* is larger than X^*. Furthermore, this term $X^* + \overline{Y}^*$, as shown in (1-58), produces no carry and the sign bit remains 1, as shown in (1-50). This sign bit is also correct, because X is smaller than Y.

X Is a Negative but Y a Positive Number. This combination is similar to the preceding one, and hence the proof is not repeated.

Both X and Y Are Negative

$$X = 1 \cdot 2^0 + \overline{X}^* \tag{1-59}$$

$$Y = 1 \cdot 2^0 + \overline{Y}^* \tag{1-60}$$

The sum Z is expressed as

$$Z = X + Y = 1 \cdot 2^1 + 0 \cdot 2^0 + (\overline{X}^* + \overline{Y}^*) \tag{1-61}$$

The 1 at the bit position 2^1 can be ignored because it is beyond the register capacity. When both X and Y are negative, Y^* should be added to X^*, as shown in Table 1-11. When $\overline{X}^*$ is added to both sides of (1-49),

$$\overline{X}^* + \overline{Y}^* = \overline{X}^* - Y^* = 0 - (X^* + Y^*) \tag{1-62}$$

we actually have the addition of X^* and Y^*. Because of the negative sign in front of $X^* + Y^*$ in (1-62), the sum $\overline{X}^* + \overline{Y}^*$ is in 2's complement. The sum $X^* + Y^*$ has to be less than 1, or

$$X^* + Y^* < 1 \tag{1-63}$$

because otherwise it exceeds register capacity. Then we have

$$\overline{X}^* + \overline{Y}^* > 1 \tag{1-64}$$

This produces a carry into the bit position 2^0, which makes the sign bit 1. This sign bit is correct, because X and Y are both negative.

In conclusion, the direct addition of two binary numbers X and Y in signed-2's-complement representation results in the sum Z, or

$$Z = X + Y = \sum_{i=0}^{-n} z_i 2^i \tag{1-65}$$

The sign bit is treated as a number bit. When the sum is negative, it is in 2's-complement form. The direct-addition method is summarized into an algorithm in Table 1-13.

Table 1-13   *Algorithm of Binary Addition and Subtraction for Numbers in Signed-2's-complement Representation*

Method	Operation	Sign bit
Direct addition....................	$Z = X + Y$	Treat sign bit as a number bit as long as register capacity for number bits is not exceeded
Direct subtraction.................	$Z = X - Y$	
Addition by subtraction of 2's complement†........................	$Z = X - \overline{Y}$	
Subtraction by addition of 2's complement†........................	$Z = X + \overline{Y}$	

† $\overline{Y}$ is the 2's complement of Y.

Example 1-12. This example shows (Table 1-14) the eight possible additions of two 5-bit numbers in signed-2's-complement representation. The sign bit is treated as a number bit. The 1's in the parentheses should be ignored.

Table 1-14   *Eight Examples of Direct-addition Method for Numbers in Signed-2's-complement Representation*

Example	Augend, X	Addend, Y	Sum, $Z = X + Y$
a	0,1001 (+9)	0,0100 (+4)	0,1101 (+13)
b	0,1001	1,1100	(1)0,0101 (+5)
c	1,0111	0,0100	1,1011 (−5)
d	1,0111	1,1100	(1)1,0011 (−13)
e	0,0100 (+4)	0,1001 (+9)	0,1101 (+13)
f	0,0100	1,0111	1,1011 (−5)
g	1,1100	0,1001	(1)0,0101 (+5)
h	1,1100	1,0111	(1)1,0011 (−13)

Direct-subtraction Method. Let X and Y be the two binary numbers in signed 2's-complement representation. The difference Z is expressed as

$$Z = X - Y = \sum_{i=0}^{-n} z_i 2^i \qquad (1\text{-}66)$$

where the sign bit is again treated as a number bit. This method is similar to the direct-addition method, and its proof is not repeated. When the difference is negative, it is in 2's-complement form. The algorithm is shown in Table 1-13.

Addition Method by Subtraction of the 2's Complement. The method of binary addition by subtraction of the 2's complement is to convert the addend into the 2's-complement form and then to perform a subtraction instead of an addition. Let X and Y be, respectively, the augend and addend, and let $\overline{Y}$ be the 2's complement of Y, or

$$\overline{Y} = 0 - Y \qquad (1\text{-}67)$$

The sum Z of X and Y is

$$Z = X + Y = X - (0 - Y) \qquad (1\text{-}68)$$

When expression (1-67) is substituted in (1-68), we have

$$Z = X - \overline{Y} \qquad (1\text{-}69)$$

Since negative numbers are in 2's-complement form, the above subtraction is performed in the same manner as that in the direct-subtraction method. The sign bit is treated as a number bit. When the sign bit of the difference is 1, the number bits are in 2's-complement form. This algorithm is also shown in Table 1-13.

Subtraction Method by Addition of 2's complement. The method of binary subtraction by addition of the 2's complement is to convert the subtrahend into the 2's-complement form and then to perform an addition instead of a subtraction. The difference Z obtained by subtracting Y from X is

$$Z = X - Y = X + (0 - Y) \qquad (1\text{-}70)$$

Since $0 - Y$ is the 2's complement of Y, we have

$$Z = X + \overline{Y} \qquad (1\text{-}71)$$

Because the negative numbers are in 2's-complement form, the above addition proceeds in the same manner as in the direct-addition method. The sign bit is treated as a number bit. When the sign bit of the sum Z is 1, the number bits are in 2's-complement form. This algorithm is also shown in Table 1-13.

1-7   *Binary Addition and Subtraction—III*

For binary numbers in signed-1's-complement representation, four methods for addition or subtraction are:

1. Direct addition
2. Direct subtraction
3. Addition by subtraction of the 1's complement
4. Subtraction by addition of the 1's complement

In any of the methods listed, the sign bit is also treated as a number bit; thus the method has advantages similar to those of the signed-2's-complement representation, with the further advantage that the 1's complement of a number is easily obtained. However, the method requires addition of an end-around carry or subtraction of an end-around borrow.

Direct-addition Method. The direct addition of two binary numbers X and Y in signed-1's-complement representation results in the sum Z,

$$Z = X + Y = \sum_{i=0}^{-n} z_i 2^i \qquad (1\text{-}72)$$

where the sign bit is treated as a number bit. When the sum is negative, it is in signed-1's-complement form. Whenever a carry in the position 2^1 occurs during addition, it should be added to the 2^{-n} position of the sum.

The above result can be derived in a manner similar to that for the direct-addition method for binary numbers in signed 2's complement representation. The derivation is left to the reader. The algorithm for the direct-addition method for binary numbers in signed-1's-complement representation is shown in Table 1-15.

Table 1-15 Algorithm of Binary Addition and Subtraction for Numbers in Signed-1's-complement Representation

Method	Operation		Remarks
Direct addition	$Z = X + Y$		Treat sign bit as a number bit as long as register capacity for number bits is not exceeded
Direct subtraction	$Z = X - Y$		
Addition by subtraction of 1's complement†	$Z = X - \overline{Y}$	when $\overline{Y} \leq X$	Add (or subtract) end-around carry (or borrow), whenever it occurs, to (or from) least significant bit of sum (or difference)
	$Z = X - \overline{Y} - 2^{-n}$	when $\overline{Y} > X$	
Subtraction by addition of 1's complement†	$Z = X + \overline{Y}$	when $X + \overline{Y} < 1$	
	$Z = X + \overline{Y} + 2^{-n}$	when $X + \overline{Y} \geq 1$	

† $\overline{Y}$ is the 1's complement of Y.

Example 1-13. This example shows the direct addition of two binary numbers in signed-1's-complement representation. The sign bit is treated as a number bit. The end-around carry is added for correction. When the sum is negative, it is in 1's-complement form.

(*a*) Addition of the binary numbers $X = 0{,}1001(+9)$ and $Y = 1{,}1011(-4)$

Augend register	0 1 0 0 1
Addend register	1 1 0 1 1
Uncorrected sum	(1) 0 0 1 0 0
End-around carry	+ → 1
Sum register	0 0 1 0 1

(*b*) This example is shown in Table 1-16. There are eight possible additions of two binary numbers X and Y. The end-around carry, when occurring, has been added to the sum.

Table 1-16 Eight Examples of Direct-addition Method for Numbers in Signed-1's-complement Representation

Example	Augend X	Addend Y	Sum ZXY
a	0,1001 (+9)	0,0100 (+4)	0,1101 (+13)
b	0,1001	1,1011	0,0101 (+5)†
c	1,0110	0,0100	1,1010 (−5)
d	1,0110	1,1011	1,0010 (−13)†
e	0,0100 (+4)	0,1001 (+9)	0,1101 (+13)
f	0,0100	1,0110	1,1010 (−5)
g	1,1011	0,1001	0,0100 (+5)†
h	1,1011	1,0110	1,0011 (−13)†

† An end-around carry occurs.

Direct-subtraction Method. Let X and Y be two binary numbers in signed-1's-complement representation. The difference Z is

$$Z = X - Y = \sum_{i=0}^{-n} z_i 2^i \tag{1-73}$$

where the sign bit is treated as a number bit. This method is similar to the direct-addition method with one exception, the subtracting of the end-around borrow from the least significant bit of the uncorrected sum instead of adding the end-around carry. When the difference is negative, it is in 1's-complement form. The algorithm is also shown in Table 1-15.

Addition Method by Subtraction of 1's Complement. The method of binary addition by subtraction of the 1's complement converts the addend into the 1's-complement form and then performs a subtraction instead of an addition. Let X and Y be, respectively, the augend and addend. Then the sum is Z, where

$$Z = X + Y = X - \overline{Y} \qquad \text{when } \overline{Y} \leq X \qquad (1\text{-}74)$$

and $\overline{Y}$ is the 1's complement of Y. If $\overline{Y}$ is larger than X, the end-around borrow occurs. Under this condition, the sum should be corrected as follows:

$$Z = X + Y = X - \overline{Y} - 2^{-n} \qquad \text{when } \overline{Y} > X \qquad (1\text{-}75)$$

The proof of the above two relations is similar to that for the direct-subtraction method and therefore is not repeated.

Since negative numbers are in 1's-complement form, the foregoing subtraction is performed in the same manner as that in the direct-subtraction method. The sign bit is treated as a number bit. When the sign bit of the difference Z is 1, the number bits are in 1's-complement form. This algorithm is shown in Table 1-15.

Subtraction Method by Addition of 1's Complement. The method of binary subtraction by addition of the 1's complement first converts the subtrahend into the 1's-complement form and then performs an addition instead of a subtraction. The difference from X is Z, or

$$Z = X - Y = X + \overline{Y} \qquad \text{when } X + \overline{Y} < 1 \qquad (1\text{-}76)$$

If $X + \overline{Y}$ is equal to or larger than 1, the end-around carry occurs. Under this condition, the difference should be corrected as shown:

$$Z = X - Y = X + \overline{Y} + 2^{-n} \qquad \text{when } X + \overline{Y} \geq 1 \qquad (1\text{-}77)$$

The proof of the above relations is similar to that for the direct-addition method and thus is not repeated.

Since the negative numbers are in 1's-complement form, the above addition is performed in the same manner as that in the direct-addition method. The sign bit is treated as a number bit. When the sign bit of the sum Z is 1, the number bits are in 1's-complement form. This algorithm is also shown in Table 1-15.

1-8   Binary Multiplication

Three approaches to binary multiplication are:

1. Repeated addition
2. Multiple-digit multiplication
3. Simultaneous multiplication

Each method has many variations, intended to simplify the implementation, to reduce the steps and thus decrease the multiplication time, or to provide the necessary corrections for the case of numbers in signed-complement representation. For binary multiplication using the repeated-addition approach, the following methods will be described:

1. Direct-multiplication method
2. Burks–Goldstine–von Neumann method
3. Robertson's first method
4. Robertson's second method
5. Booth's method
6. A short-cut multiplication method

The binary multiplication of two signed numbers is influenced by the method used to represent negative numbers. In the case of signed-magnitude numbers, addition and subtraction are relatively more complicated, but multiplication is simpler. In the case of signed-complement numbers, the reverse is true. Therefore, the choice of negative number representation is a compromise. In the following description, not every method is applicable to all three representations of negative numbers.

Direct-multiplication Method. This method is used for numbers in signed-magnitude representation. Let the multiplicand be X and the multiplier be Y as below:

$$X = x_n 2^n + \sum_{i=0}^{n-1} x_i 2^i = x_n 2^n + X^* \qquad (1\text{-}78)$$

$$Y = y_n 2^n + \sum_{i=0}^{n-1} y_i 2^i = y_n 2^n + Y^* \qquad (1\text{-}79)$$

where x_i and y_i are either 0 or 1. X^* and Y^* are the number bits. Bits x_n and y_n are the sign bits, 0 and 1 representing, respectively, the positive and negative sign. Each of these two numbers has n bits plus a sign bit. Let the product be the number U. We then have

$$U = XY = u_n 2^{2n} + X^* Y^* \qquad (1\text{-}80)$$

where $\qquad X^* Y^* = X^* y_{n-1} 2^{n-1} + \cdots + X^* y_1 2^1 + X^* y_0 2^0 \qquad (1\text{-}81)$

$$u_n = x_n \oplus y_n \qquad (1\text{-}82)$$

Since the y's are merely 0 or 1, the binary multiplication is merely repeated additions, with the multiplicand properly shifted. The sign digit of the product u_n is the modulo-2 sum of the sign digits x_n and y_n.

In the pencil-and-paper method, the additions in (1-80) are done simultaneously. Here a partial product is formed with each addition. The first partial product, p_1, is

$$p_1 = X^* y_0$$

The second partial product, p_2, is

$$p_2 = p_1 2^{-1} + X^* y_1$$

and the nth partial product, p_n, is

$$p_n = p_{n-1} 2^{-1} + X^* y_{n-1} \qquad (1\text{-}83)$$

By applying (1-83) repeatedly and then multiplying both sides by 2^{n-1}, we have

$$p_n 2^{n-1} = X^*(y_{n-1}2^{n-1} + \cdots + y_1 2^1 + y_0 2^0) \qquad (1\text{-}84)$$

or $\qquad\qquad p_n 2^{n-1} = X^* Y^* \qquad\qquad\qquad\qquad\qquad\qquad (1\text{-}85)$

The final product U is then

$$U = (x \oplus y_n)2^{2n} + p_n 2^{n-1} \qquad\qquad (1\text{-}86)$$

The above multiplication process is summarized in the algorithm shown in Table 1-17.

Table 1-17   Algorithm for Binary Multiplication by Direct-multiplication Method

Sign bit.	$u_n = x_n \oplus y_n$
Number bits.	$X^* Y^* = p_n 2^{n-1}$
	$p_n = p_{n-1}2^{-1} + X^* y_{n-1}$
Product.	$U = XY = u_n 2^{2n} + X^* Y^*$

Example 1-14. This example shows how the computer actually performs the shifts and additions described in (1-83) to (1-86). Multiplication in a computer usually requires three registers: a multiplicand register, which stores the multiplicand; a multiplier-quotient register (or *MQ* register), which stores the multiplier (or the quotient during division); and an accumulator, which performs additions and stores the partial product. These three registers have the same number of bits and are shown in Fig. 1-1. In this figure the powers of 2 under each square indicate the bit locations. The multiplicand register is shown located directly above the accumulator, and additions are performed by adding the contents of the multiplicand register to corresponding digits of the accumulator.

Since the product may have twice the number of bits of the multiplier (or multiplicand), the accumulator may have to be supplemented by an additional register to store the complete product. Registers are expensive, and the need for additional storage is usually avoided by the following arrangement: After multiplication by one multiplier bit, this bit is not needed any more; at the same time, the partial product grows by 1 bit. Therefore, the accumulator is placed in tandem with the multiplier register to form a combined register, as shown in Fig. 1-1. After multiplication by each multiplier bit, the contents of both multiplier-quotient register and accumulator are shifted 1 bit to the right. In this way, the unwanted multiplier bit is shifted out of the *MQ* register at the right end, leaving room for the acquired digit of the partial product, which is shifted into the *MQ* register at the left end. The partial product, moreover, remains in proper order.

Figure 1-2 shows multiplication of two 5-bit plus sign-bit numbers in steps. The contents of the multiplicand register are not shown, as they remain unchanged during multiplication. Initially, the contents of the left half of the combined register are all zeros, and those of the

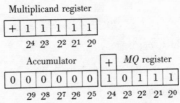

FIG. 1-1   Registers for multiplication (X = multiplicand = +11111; Y = multiplier = +10111).

Step	Operation	Accumulator and MQ register	Partial product
0		0 0 0 0 0 0 ‖ 1 0 1 1 1 y_4 y_3 y_2 y_1 y_0	
1	Add X	0 1 1 1 1 1 ‖ 1 0 1 1 1	$p_0 = 11111$
2	Shift right	0 0 1 1 1 1 ‖ 1 1 0 1 1 y_4 y_3 y_2 y_1	
3	Add X	1 0 1 1 1 0 ‖ 1 1 0 1 1	$p_1 = 1011101$
4	Shift right	0 1 0 1 1 1 ‖ 0 1 1 0 1 y_4 y_3 y_2	
5	Add X	1 1 0 1 1 0 ‖ 0 1 1 0 1	$p_2 = 11011001$
6	Shift right	0 1 1 0 1 1 ‖ 0 0 1 1 0 y_4 y_3	
7	Add 0	0 1 1 0 1 1 ‖ 0 0 1 1 0	$p_3 = 11011001$
8	Shift right	0 0 1 1 0 1 ‖ 0 1 1 1 1 y_4	
9	Add X	1 0 1 1 0 0 ‖ 1 0 0 1 1	$p_4 = 1011001001$
10	Shift right	+ 1 0 1 1 0 ‖ 0 1 0 0 1	$U = +1011001001$

FIG. 1-2 Sequential operations of the arithmetic registers during multiplication ($U =$ product $= +1011001001$).

right half are the multiplier. In the first step, bit y_0 is 1; and the contents of the multiplicand register are added to corresponding bits of the accumulator. In step 2, the contents of the combined register are shifted 1 bit to the right, and bit y_0 is shifted out of the combined register. These two steps are then performed alternately. When the multiplier digit is 0, no addition is actually required. Each right shift after each addition vacates one bit location into which the partial product may grow. The leftmost bit location in the combined register is used as a carry storage whenever a carry occurs, and the sign is inserted into this location during the last right shift in step 10. For clarity, all partial products are shown thereon. Only bit locations in the accumulator portion of the combined register are required to be capable of performing addition.

Burks–Goldstine–von Neumann Method. This method, developed by Burks, Goldstine, and von Neumann [1], multiplies binary numbers in signed-2's-complement representation. In the following, we use number representation (1-25) to (1-27). This number representation does not lose its generality if the binary point is chosen at some other location. Let the multiplicand X and the multiplier Y be

$$X = -x_0 + X^* \tag{1-87}$$
$$Y = -y_0 + Y^* \tag{1-88}$$

The negative value of sign bits x_0 and y_0 is used because in this manner the numbers give their true values. This method forms the product of the unsigned numbers X^* and Y^*, with the following result

$$X^*Y^* = (X + x_0)(Y + y_0) = XY + x_0 Y + y_0 X + x_0 y_0$$

The desired product is XY; therefore a correction has to be applied to the obtained product X^*Y^* depending on the values of x_0 and y_0. The algorithm for binary multiplication by this method is shown in Table 1-18; use of the algorithm is shown by the following example.

Table 1-18   *Algorithm for Binary Multiplication by Burks–Goldstine–von Neumann Method*

Case	x_0	y_0	Product	Correction
a	0	0	$X^*Y^* = XY$	None
b	0	1	$X^*Y^* = XY + y_0X$	$-y_0X$
c	1	0	$X^*Y^* = XY + x_0Y$	$-x_0Y$
d	1	1	$X^*Y^* = XY + x_0Y + y_0X + x_0y_0$	$-(x_0Y + y_0X + x_0y_0)$

Example 1-15

(a) When both X and Y are positive, the case is similar to that illustrated in Fig. 1-2 and thus is not repeated here.

(b) When X is positive and Y negative,

$$X = \text{multiplicand} = 0.1101 \ (+\,^{13}\!/_{16}) \qquad x_0 = 0$$
$$Y = \text{multiplier} \ \ = 1.0110 \ (-\,^{10}\!/_{16}) \qquad y_0 = 1$$

$$
\begin{array}{r l}
.1101 & = X^* \\
\times \quad .0110 & = Y^* \\
\hline
0000 & = X^*y_4 2^{-4} \\
1\ 101 & = X^*y_3 2^{-3} \\
11\ 01 & = X^*y_2 2^{-2} \\
000\ 0 & = X^*y_1 2^{-1} \\
\hline
0\ 0100\ 1110 & = X^*Y^* \\
+1\ 0011 & = -y_0X \\
\hline
1.0111\ 1110 & = XY
\end{array}
$$

$\qquad$ correction due to negative sign of Y

$\qquad$ or $-\,^{130}\!/_{256}$

In the multiplication just shown, the multiplication is performed on number bits; thus the product is X^*Y^*. The multiplication requires correction by subtracting y_0X or, equivalently, by adding the 2's complement of y_0X.

(c) When X is negative and Y positive

$$X = \text{multiplicand} = 1.0011 \ (-\,^{13}\!/_{16}) \qquad x_0 = 1$$
$$Y = \text{multiplier} \ \ = 0.1010 \ (+\,^{10}\!/_{16}) \qquad y_0 = 0$$

$$
\begin{array}{r l}
.0011 & = X^* \\
\times \quad .1010 & = Y^* \\
\hline
1\ 0000 & = x_0 2^{-4} \\
0\ 011 & = X^*y_3 2^{-3} \\
100\ 00 & = x_0 2^{-2} \\
001\ 1 & = X^*y_1 2^{-1} \\
\hline
0\ 0110\ 1110 & = X^*Y^* \text{ with } x_0Y \text{ partly corrected} \\
+1\ 0001 & = \text{remaining correction of } -x_0Y \\
\hline
1.0111\ 1110 & = XY
\end{array}
$$

Correction digits $\nearrow$ (pointing to the $1\ 0000$ and $100\ 00$ lines)

$\qquad$ or $-\,^{130}\!/_{256}$

Multiplication of X^* and Y^* just shown requires a correction: subtracting $x_0 Y$ (that is, 0.1010) or, equivalently, adding its 2's complement (that is, 1.0110). This brings about a difficulty; on completing the multiplication of X^* and Y^*, the multiplier Y is lost (as mentioned previously and shown in Fig. 1-2) and is not available for correction. The solution to this difficulty is to consider the correction number 1.0110 as the sum of 1.0000, .0101, and .0001. The question arises of how these three numbers are derived. The first number exists when x_0 is 1 (otherwise, this correction is not needed). The second number .0101 is the 1's complement of Y^*. The third number .0001 is regarded as the quantity added to convert the 1's complement of Y^* into its 2's complement; therefore it always exists as long as such a correction is needed.

The first and third numbers are added as one number 1.0001, and this addition is done as a last step. The second number is added in as many steps as the number of 0's in Y^*. In the above example, there are two 0's (y_4 and y_2). During each multiplication by digits y_4 and y_2, a 1 is added to the partial product as if the 1 were located at the position of the sign digit x_0 (shown by arrows in the above example). These are the correct positions because in each case the multiplication of x_0 and y_i locates the 1 in the final product XY at correct position if the correction number were added directly to the product X^*Y^*.

(d) When both X and Y are negative,

$$X = \text{multiplicand} = 1.0011 \ (-\tfrac{13}{16}) \qquad x_0 = 1$$
$$Y = \text{multiplier} \ \ = 1.0110 \ (-\tfrac{10}{16}) \qquad y_0 = 1$$

$$
\begin{array}{ll}
\phantom{\text{Correction}} .0011 & = X^* \\
\underline{\times \phantom{\text{Correctio}} .0110} & = Y^* \\
\text{Correction} \longrightarrow 1.0000 & = x_0 2^{-4} \\
\text{digits} 0\,011 & = X^* y_3 2^{-3} \\
 00\,11 & = X^* y_2 2^{-2} \\
\underline{{}^{\nwarrow}10000\,0} & = x_0 2^{-1} \\
 0\,1010\,0010 & = X^* Y^* \text{ with } x_0 Y \text{ partly corrected} \\
\underline{+ 1\,0001} & = \text{remaining correction of } -x_0 Y \\
 1\,0011\,0010 & = XY + y_0 X \\
\underline{+ 0\,1101} & = -y_0 X \qquad \text{correction due to negative sign of } Y \\
(1)0.1000\,0010 & = XY \qquad\quad \text{or } {}^{130}\!/_{256}
\end{array}
$$

$$\uparrow$$
$$\text{discarded}$$

The above multiplication requires a correction: subtracting the quantities $x_0 Y$, $y_0 X$, and $x_0 y_0$. The subtractions of the first two quantities are performed in a manner similar to those shown in examples b and c. Subtracting the quantity $x_0 y_0$ (which has a value of 1) is equivalent to adding 1, because any carry or borrow beyond the sign digit is disregarded. However, this addition of 1 can be shown to be unnecessary, as follows. The above correction, subtracting the quantity $x_0 Y$, is the same as adding the number 0.1010. Now examine what has been added in the above example: the quantity 1.1010. The leftmost digit of 1 is incorrect and should not have been added, but it serves admirably the purpose of correcting the quantity $x_0 y_0$. Consequently, no additional correction is really necessary, whether only the multiplicand or both the multiplicand and multiplier are negative.

Robertson's First Method. The previous method requires a simple correction when the multiplier is negative, but the correction becomes complicated when the multiplicand is negative. Robertson's first method needs only one simple correction. This method which was first used in the ORDVAC (ordnance discrete variable automatic computer) is also for numbers in signed-2's-complement representation.

In the Burks–Goldstine–von Neumann method the unsigned numbers X^* and Y^* are multiplied. By contrast, Robertson's method multiplies the signed number X and the unsigned number Y^*, shown by the algorithm in Table 1-19. Note that Y^* is equal to Y when y_0 is 0. When the multiplier is negative, the correction of subtracting y_0X is needed. No correction is necessary when the multiplicand is negative. It is important to note in the following examples that the use of the signed number X in the multiplication requires application of the shifting algorithm stated in Table 1-9.

Table 1-19 *Algorithm for Binary Multiplication by Robertson's First Method*

Case	x_0	y_0	Product	Correction
a	0	0	$XY^* = XY$	None
b	0	1	$XY^* = XY + y_0X$	$-y_0X$
c	1	0	$XY^* = XY$	None
d	1	1	$XY^* = XY + y_0X$	$-y_0X$

Example 1-16

(a) When the multiplier is positive,

$$X = \text{multiplicand} = 1.0011 \; (-13\!/\!16) \qquad x_0 = 1$$
$$Y = \text{multiplier} \;\; = 0.1010 \; (+10\!/\!16) \qquad y_0 = 0$$

$$
\begin{array}{rl}
1.0011 & = X \\
\times \qquad .1010 & = Y^* \\
\hline
0.00000000 & = Xy_42^{-4} \\
1.\underline{1}110011 & = Xy_32^{-3} \\
0.000000 & = Xy_22^{-2} \\
1.\underline{1}0011 & = Xy_12^{-1} \\
\hline
(1)1.01111110 & = XY^* = XY \qquad \text{or } -130\!/\!256
\end{array}
$$

↑
discarded

In the above, the added digits are 1's (underlined) during the shifts to the right. Since the multiplier is positive, no correction is needed.

(b) When the multiplier is negative,

$$X = \text{multiplicand} = 1.0011 \; (-13\!/\!16) \qquad x_0 = 1$$
$$Y = \text{multiplier} \;\; = 1.0110 \; (-10\!/\!16) \qquad y_0 = 1$$

$$
\begin{array}{rl}
1.0011 & = X \\
\times \qquad .0110 & = Y^* \\
\hline
0.00000000 & = Xy_42^{-4} \\
1.\underline{1}110011 & = Xy_32^{-3} \\
1.\underline{1}10011 & = Xy_22^{-2} \\
0.00000 & = Xy_12^{-1} \\
\hline
(1)1.10110010 & = XY^* \\
0.1101 & = -y_0X \qquad \text{correction} \\
\hline
(1)0.10000010 & = XY \qquad \text{or } 130\!/\!256
\end{array}
$$

↑
discarded

In the above, the correction has been the addition of the 2's complement of y_0X (or X). The leftmost carry is discarded automatically because it is beyond the capacity of the register.

Robertson's Second Method. The method in Table 1-19 requires a correction when the multiplier is negative, i.e., when y_0 equals 1; the sign digit actually means -1 and thus requires a subtraction of the multiplicand. To eliminate this correction, Robertson [6] proposed to form the product of $-X$ and $-Y$ where Y is negative. In this manner, the sign digit of $-Y$ becomes 0; cases b and d in Table 1-19 do not occur, and no correction whatever is required. The algorithm of this method is given in Table 1-20. This method fails when the multiplier Y is equal to -1. Therefore, the value of Y should be restricted to $-1 < Y < 1$.

Table 1-20 *Algorithm for Binary Multiplication by Robertson's Second Method*

Case	x_0	y_0	Product	Correction
a	0	0	$XY = XY^*$	None
b	0	1	$(-X)(-Y) = XY$	None
c	1	0	$XY = XY^*$	None
d	1	1	$(-X)(-Y) = XY$	None

Example 1-17

(a) When the multiplicand is positive,

$$X = \text{multiplicand} = 0.1101 \ (+ {}^{13}\!/_{16}) \qquad -X = 1.0011$$
$$Y = \text{multiplier} \ \ = 1.0110 \ (- {}^{10}\!/_{16}) \qquad -Y = 0.1010$$

$$
\begin{array}{r}
1.0011 = -X \\
\times \quad 0.1010 = -Y \\
\hline
0.0000\ 0000 \\
1.\underline{1110}\ 011 \\
0.0000\ 00 \\
1.\underline{1001}\ 1 \\
\hline
1.0111\ 1110 = XY \qquad \text{or} \ - {}^{130}\!/_{256}
\end{array}
$$

(b) When the multiplicand is negative,

$$X = \text{multiplicand} = 1.0011 \ (- {}^{13}\!/_{16}) \qquad -X = 0.1101$$
$$Y = \text{multiplier} \ \ = 1.0110 \ (- {}^{10}\!/_{16}) \qquad -Y = 0.1010$$

$$
\begin{array}{r}
0.1101 = -X \\
\times \quad 0.1010 = -Y \\
\hline
0.0000\ 0000 \\
0.0001\ 101 \\
0.0000\ 00 \\
0.0110\ 1 \\
\hline
0.1000\ 0010 = XY \qquad \text{or} \ {}^{130}\!/_{256}
\end{array}
$$

The relative merits of Robertson's two methods will now be noted. When the multiplier is negative, the first method requires a simple correction; the second method requires none. In both methods, circuits are required to implement the shifting algorithm for a signed binary number. Both require circuits to sense the sign digit y_0 and to complement the multiplicand X; the second method requires, in addition, a circuit to complement the multiplier Y. The choice of method depends, then, on whether it is more advantageous to apply the correction or to provide an additional complementing circuit.

Booth's Method. A. D. Booth and K. H. V. Booth [7] developed an algorithm of binary multiplication for numbers in signed-2's-complement representation. This method requires no correction and no sensing of the sign digit of the multiplicand or multiplier.

Let X and Y be the multiplicand and the multiplier, respectively. The representation of the multiplier is

$$Y = y_0 + \sum_{i=1}^{n} y_i 2^{-i} \qquad (1\text{-}89)$$

The positive value of the sign bit y_0 is used, because this is the way the computer recognizes it. The product XY is then

$$XY = y_0 X + y_1 2^{-1} X + y_2 2^{-2} X + \cdots + y_{n-1} 2^{-(n-1)} X + y_n 2^{-n} X \qquad (1\text{-}90)$$

Let us replace each y_i in the above by the difference $y_{i+1} - y_i$, which is a subtraction of two adjacent multiplier digits. Specifically,

$$y_n \text{ is replaced by } y_{n+1} - y_n \qquad \text{where } y_{n+1} = 0$$
$$y_{n-1} \text{ is replaced by } y_n - y_{n-1}$$
$$\cdots \cdots \cdots \cdots \cdots \cdots \cdots \cdots$$
$$y_2 \text{ is replaced by } y_3 - y_2 \qquad\qquad (1\text{-}91)$$
$$y_1 \text{ is replaced by } y_2 - y_1$$
$$y_0 \text{ is replaced by } y_1 - y_0$$

Note that, when the difference $y_{i+1} - y_i$ is $+1$ or -1, $y_i y_{i+1}$ is made up of two adjacent multiplier bits which are, respectively, 01 and 10; when the difference is 0, $y_i y_{i+1}$ is either 00 or 11. Let us now consider the following multiplier Y as an illustration;

$$Y = \cdots y_3 y_4 y_5 y_6 y_7 y_8 y_9 \cdots = \cdots 0111100 \cdots$$

When the multiplier bits are a series of 0's such as $y_8 y_9$, no addition is needed. When they are a series of 1's, such as y_4 to y_7, these additions can be replaced by one subtraction and one addition if the following relation is utilized:

$$Y = \cdots 1000000 \cdots - \cdots 0000100 \cdots$$

Therefore, one can examine two adjacent multiplier bits $y_i y_{i+1}$ and select one of three possible operations: an addition, a subtraction, or neither addition nor subtraction. To be specific, the rules for binary multiplication of numbers in 2's-complement representation are: when $y_i y_{i+1}$ is 01, the relation means an addition of multiplicand; when it is 10, the condition requires a subtraction of multiplicand; when it is 00 or 11, neither addition nor subtraction is needed. In examining the two adjacent multiplier bits, the right-hand bit is considered the reference; the left-hand bit is the multiplier. Note that the reference bit for the least significant multiplier bit y_n in expression (1-90) is 0.

The above replacement of each y_i by $y_{i+1} - y_i$ can be readily proved valid. If the y_i's in expressions (1-91) are substituted into expression (1-90), we have

$$XY = [-y_0 + y_1(2^0 - 2^{-1}) + y_2(2^{-1} - 2^{-2}) + \cdots$$
$$+ y_m(2^{-(m-1)} - 2^{-m}) + y_{m+1}2^{-m}]X \quad (1\text{-}92)$$

or
$$XY = \left(-y_0 2^0 + \sum_{i=1}^{n} y_i 2^{-i}\right)X \quad (1\text{-}93)$$

The value in parentheses above truly represents the value of Y whether the sign bit y_0 is 0 or 1. The first term in expression (1-90) is $y_0 X$; this shows no need of a right shift after the last step. The above multiplying process is summarized as an algorithm in Table 1-21 and is illustrated by the following example.

Table 1-21   Booth's Algorithm for Binary Multiplication

Multiplier bits $y_i y_{i+1}$	Operation†
01	Add multiplicand X, then shift partial product right 1 bit
10	Subtract multiplicand X, then shift partial product right 1 bit
00	Shift partial product right 1 bit
11	Shift partial product right 1 bit

† (1) The initial reference bit for the least significant multiplier bit is 0. (2) No shift operation is required after the last operation.

Example 1-18

(a) When the multiplier is positive,

$$X = \text{multiplicand} = 1.0011 \ (-{}^{13}\!/_{16})$$
$$Y = \text{multiplier} \ \ \ = 1.1010 \ (+{}^{10}\!/_{16})$$

```
1.0011     = X
0.1010(0)  = Y
0.00000000    initial condition in combined register
```

$y_i y_{i+1}$	Operation		
00	Shift right	0.00000000	first partial product
10	Subtract X	1.0011	
		0.11010000	second partial product
	Shift right	0.01101000	
01	Add X	1.0011	
		1.10011000	third partial product
	Shift right	1.11001100	
10	Subtract X	1.0011	
		0.10011100	fourth partial product
	Shift right	0.01001110	
01	Add X	1.0011	
		1.01111110 = XY	or $-{}^{130}\!/_{256}$

The parenthetic 0 in the multiplier is the initial referenced bit for the least significant multiplier bit. Thus, at the beginning of the multiplication process, only two possible pairs of bits exist, 00 and 10. Since the multiplicand is a signed number, the shifting algorithm should be observed; the added bits are shown underlined. No right-shift operation is needed after the operation called for by the last pair of multiplier bits.

(*b*) When the multiplier is negative,

$$X = \text{multiplicand} = 1.0011 \ (-{}^{13}\!/_{16})$$
$$Y = \text{multiplier} \ \ \ = 1.0110 \ (-{}^{10}\!/_{16})$$

$$
\begin{array}{ll}
1.0011 & = X \\
\underline{1.0110(0)} & = Y \\
0.00000000 & \text{initial condition in combined register}
\end{array}
$$

$y_i y_{i+1}$ *Operation*

00	Shift right	0.00000000	first partial product
10	Subtract X	1.0011	
		0.11010000	second partial product
	Shift right	0.01101000	
11	Shift right	0.00110100	third partial product
01	Add X	1.0011	
		1.01100100	fourth partial product
	Shift right	1.10110010	
10	Subtract X	1.0011	
		0.10000010 $= XY$	or ${}^{130}\!/_{256}$

A Short-cut Multiplication Method [9]. Booth's algorithm of binary multiplication makes use of relation (1-21). This idea can be extended by including isolated bits in a sequence of 1's or 0's. A sequence of 1's, such as 11111111, in a given multiplier requires eight additions of the multiplicand. But using relation (1-21), we see that

$$11111111 = 2^8 - 2^0$$

This multiplier calls for only one addition and one subtraction. The concept illustrated is applicable in instances other than when the multiplier consists of an uninterrupted sequence of 1's. Every multiplier, obviously, will fall into one of three categories: those containing an equal number of 1's and 0's; those which contain more 1's than 0's; those with more 0's than 1's. In the latter two cases, a certain time economy can be obtained. For example, when more 0's than 1's exist, as in the multiplier 10010000, an add sequence is used; this requires only two additions, i.e.,

$$10010000 = 2^7 + 2^4$$

Multiple shifts for the zeros are desired if the time of multiplication is to be reduced. For a sequence of more 1's than 0's such as 11101111, a subtract sequence is used; this calls for only three operations, i.e.,

$$11101111 = 2^8 - 2^4 - 2^0$$

Again, multiple shifts for the 1's are desired. Neither type of sequence offers any advantage when the number of 1's equals the number of 0's.

Although the above method can reduce the multiplication time, it requires circuits to determine whether the multiplier has more 0's or more 1's and circuits to perform multiple shifts. Adoption of this method depends on whether or not the savings in multiplication time outweigh the complexity of the extra circuits.

Multiple-digit Multiplication Method. As mentioned previously, binary multiplication merely repeats additions with a proper shift after each addition. When the multiplier digit is 0 or 1, it calls for, respectively, no addition or addition of the multiplicand. This idea can be extended by multiplying several multiplier digits at a time. For the case of multiplying a pair of multiplier digits at a time, there are four possibilities: no addition; an additon of the multplicand; an addition of twice the value of the multiplicand; an addition of thrice the value of the multiplicand. The partial product after each addition is shifted two digits to the right. Consequently, fewer additions are required, and this means faster multiplication.

Example 1-19

$$\text{Multiplier} = Y = 10010011 \qquad \text{or } 147$$
$$\text{Multiplicand} = X = 10101010 \qquad \text{or } 170$$
$$2X = 101010100$$
$$3X = 111111110$$

$$
\begin{array}{ll}
10101010 & = X \\
\underline{10010011} & = Y \\
111111110 & = 3X \cdot 2^0 \\
00000000 & = 0 \\
10101010 & = X \cdot 2^4 \\
\underline{101010100} & = 2X \cdot 2^6 \\
110000110011110 & = XY \qquad \text{or } 24{,}990
\end{array}
$$

Simultaneous-multiplication Method. Binary multiplication requires many additions of the shifted multiplicand. If the shifted multiplicand simultaneously adds to the previous multiplicand, the operation is called *simultaneous multiplication*. The implementation of simultaneous multiplication gives the fastest but also the most expensive multiplier. An example of a simultaneous multiplier will be considered in Chap. 12.

1-9 Binary Division

Three methods of binary division are:

1. Comparison method
2. Restoring method
3. Nonrestoring method

The first method makes use of repeated subtractions, while the last two utilize repeated addition-subtractions. The restoring method may be regarded as a special case of the comparison method.

As with multiplication, the binary division of two signed numbers is also influenced by the method of representing negative numbers. The comparison and restoring methods to be described apply only to signed-magnitude representation, whereas the subsequent nonrestoring method applies to both signed-magnitude and signed-2's-complement representations. Equivalent methods for numbers in signed-1's-complement representation exist but will not be described. As in binary multiplication, the algorithm of binary division for numbers in signed-magnitude representation requires no correction and is generally preferred.

Two new problems arise in division. One is the divide-stop condition, and the other is the round-off procedure. Both will be discussed later.

Comparison Method. The comparison method is the ordinary longhand, or paper-and-pencil, method. It requires a trial-and-error procedure (particularly when this method is applied to decimal division) and therefore is also known as the trial-and-error method. Let the following symbols be used:

X = dividend
Y = divisor
Q = quotient, with q's as individual quotient digits
R_n = remainder from division
r_0 = initial remainder = X
r_n = nth partial remainder

Division determines from the known X and Y the unknown Q and R_n which satisfy the relation

$$X = QY + R_n \qquad (1\text{-}94)$$

This method calls for a comparison between the partial remainder and the divisor. If the partial remainder is larger than the divisor, a subtraction is performed and the quotient digit is 1. If it is smaller, no arithmetic operation is performed and the quotient digit is 0. In either case, the result after being shifted one bit position to the left becomes the new partial remainder. This process continues until the remainder is zero or the desired number of quotient digits is obtained. To be precise, the initial remainder r_0 is X, or

$$r_0 = X \qquad (1\text{-}95)$$

The first partial remainder r_1 is

$$r_1 = 2r_0 - q_1 Y \qquad (1\text{-}96)$$

where the first quotient digit q_1 is 1 or 0, depending, respectively, on whether $2r_0$ is greater than or equal to Y or is smaller than Y. (Note that both $2r_0$ and Y are positive numbers.) If $2r_0$ is greater than or equal to Y, then we have q_1 equal to 1 and (1-96) becomes

$$r_1 = 2r_0 - Y \qquad (1\text{-}97)$$

If it is not, then we have q_1 equal to 0, or

$$r_1 = 2r_0 \qquad (1\text{-}98)$$

The next remainder r_2 is

$$r_2 = 2r_1 - q_2 Y \qquad (1\text{-}99)$$

where the second quotient digit q_2 is 1 or 0, depending, respectively, on whether $2r_1$ is larger than or equal to Y or is smaller than Y, as before. In general, the ith partial remainder is

$$r_i = 2r_{i-1} - q_i Y \qquad (1\text{-}100)$$

where q_i is 1 when $2r_{i-1}$ is larger than or equal to Y and q_1 is 0 when $2r_{i-1}$ is smaller than Y. This is the algorithm of this method. If we now multiply both sides by 2^{-i}, (1-100) becomes

$$2^{-i}r_i = 2^{-(i-1)}r_{i-1} - 2^{-i}q_i Y \tag{1-101}$$

By repeated applications of relation (1-101), we have, for n quotient digits,

$$2^{-n}r_n = -2^{-n}q_n Y \cdots - 2^{-2}q_2 Y - 2^{-1}q_1 Y + X \tag{1-102}$$

or

$$\frac{X}{Y} = \sum_{i=1}^{n} q_i 2^{-i} + \frac{2^{-n}r_n}{Y} \tag{1-103}$$

In comparison with (1-94), we have the quotient and the remainder

$$\begin{aligned} Q &= \sum_{i=1}^{n} q_i 2^{-i} \\ R_n &= 2^{-n}r_n \end{aligned} \tag{1-104}$$

Table 1-22   *Algorithm for Binary Division by Comparison or Restoring Method*

Remainder.......... $R_n = 2^{-n}r_n$

Partial remainder...... $r_n = 2r_{n-1} - q_n Y$
                       $q_n = 1$ if r_n is positive or zero
                       $q_n = 0$ if r_n is negative

Quotient.......... $Q = \sum_{i=1}^{n} q_i 2^{-i}$

The above division process is summarized in the algorithm shown in Table 1-22. Expression (1-104) shows the quotient Q to be a fraction, requiring that the dividend X be smaller than the divisor Y. This condition should be ascertained before the start of the division process. A dividend X larger than or equal to divisor Y identifies the *divide-stop* condition. Usually, the computer does not proceed with the division process but halts and sets up an indicator. If the programmer shifts the divisor enough digits to the left, the divisor will become larger than the dividend and the division can proceed. The divide-stop condition also eliminates the possibility of a number being divided by zero.

Example 1-20. This example shows how the computer performs the division process by using the comparison algorithm. Division in the computer requires three registers: a divisor register (which usually is the multiplicand register); a multiplier-quotient register (or MQ register); an accumulator (which is used for subtractions during division). The partial remainder is left and stored in the accumulator after an addition or a subtraction. This arrangement is shown in Fig. 1-3. Note that the divisor register in Fig. 1-3 is shown directly above the accumulator, so that subtraction is performed by subtracting the contents of the accumulator from the corresponding digits in the divisor register.

Figure 1-4 shows the detailed steps of the division process. It is a division of two 5-bit plus sign-bit numbers. Since the contents of the divisor register remain unchanged during division, they are not shown. Initially, as shown in step 0, the dividend is in the accumulator and the zeros in the MQ register; and the computer makes a comparison to test the divide-stop condition. Since the dividend X is smaller than the divisor Y, the division proceeds.

In the first step, the dividend shifts left one digit to form $2r_0$. During the second step, $2r_0$ is compared with Y. Since the former is larger than the latter, this calls for a subtraction and the quotient digit q_1 equal to 1 is inserted as the least significant digit in the MQ register. The first partial remainder is now in the accumulator [Eq. (1-96)]. This is followed by a left shift in step 3 to form $2r_1$. During the fourth step, $2r_1$ is compared with Y. The quotient digit q_2 is equal to 0 and is inserted in the MQ register, and the second partial remainder is now in the accumulator [Eq. (1-99)]. This process continues until the five

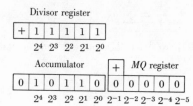

Divisor register

+	1	1	1	1	1

2^4 2^3 2^2 2^1 2^0

Accumulator   + MQ register

| 0 | 1 | 0 | 1 | 1 | 0 | | 0 | 0 | 0 | 0 | 0 |

2^4 2^3 2^2 2^1 2^0 2^{-1} 2^{-2} 2^{-3} 2^{-4} 2^{-5}

FIG. 1-3   Registers for division (X = dividend = $+10110$; Y = divisor = $+11111$).

Step	Operation	Accumulator and MQ register	Partial remainder
0	$X < Y$, proceed*	0 1 0 1 1 0 | 0 0 0 0 0	$r_0 = X = 010110$
1	Shift left	1 0 1 1 0 0 | 0 0 0 0 0	$2r_0$
2	$2r_0 > Y$, $-Y$	0 0 1 1 0 1 | 0 0 0 0 1 (q_1)	$r_1 = 001101$
3	Shift left	0 1 1 0 1 0 | 0 0 0 1 0 (q_1)	$2r_1 = 011010$
4	$2r_1 < Y$, none	0 1 1 0 1 0 | 0 0 0 1 0 (q_1 q_2)	$r_2 = 011010$
5	Shift left	1 1 0 1 0 0 | 0 0 1 0 0 (q_1 q_2)	$2r_2 = 110100$
6	$2r_2 > Y$, $-Y$	0 1 0 1 0 1 | 0 0 1 0 1 (q_1 q_2 q_3)	$r_3 = 010101$
7	Shift left	1 0 1 0 1 0 | 0 1 0 1 0 (q_1 q_2 q_3)	$2r_3 = 101010$
8	$2r_3 > Y$, $-Y$	0 0 1 0 1 1 | 0 1 0 1 1 (q_1 q_2 q_3 q_4)	$r_4 = 001011$
9	Shift left	0 1 0 1 1 0 | 1 0 1̃ 1 0 (+)	$2r_4 = 010110$
10	$2r_4 < Y$, none	0 1 0 1 1 0 | 1 0 1 1 0 (q_1 q_2 q_3 q_4 q_5)	$r_5 = 010110$

* If $Y \leq X$, this is the divide-stop condition. The computer gives a signal and usually stops unless programmed otherwise.

FIG. 1-4   Sequential operations of arithmetic registers during division (quotient = $+.10110$; remainder = $r_5 2^{-5} = 0.10110$).

quotient digits 0.10110 are generated and stored in the *MQ* register. The final remainder, 0.10110, which is $2^{-5}r_5$, is stored in the accumulator. During step 10, the quotient sign is inserted. For clarity, all partial remainders are also listed separately. Note that there is no need to have a second subtraction when the partial remainder is positive, because there can be no digit greater than 1 in the quotient. Also note that only digit locations in the accumulator portion of the combined register are required to be capable of performing subtraction.

Restoring Method. The restoring method may be regarded as a special case of the comparison method. If the method of comparison between the partial remainder and the divisor is a subtraction, it is the restoring method. This algorithm calls for a subtraction of the divisor to form the partial remainder. If the difference is positive, the quotient digit is 1 and the process continues with a one-digit left shift. If the difference is negative, the quotient digit is 0; the divisor is added to the remainder and restores the partial remainder. The algorithm remains the same as that in Table 1-22.

Example 1-21

$$X = \text{dividend} = +10110 \ (+22)$$
$$Y = \text{divisor} \quad = +11111 \ (+31)$$

$$
\begin{array}{ll}
10110 = X & \\
\underline{11111 = Y} & \\
(-)10111 = X - Y & \text{no divide-stop condition}\\
\underline{11111 = +Y} & \\
10110 = r_0 & \\
101100 = 2r_0 & \\
\underline{11111 = -Y} & \\
01101 = r_1 & q_1 = 1\\
11010 = 2r_1 & \\
\underline{11111 = -Y} & \\
(-)11011 = 2r_1 - Y & q_2 = 0\\
\underline{11111 = +Y} & \\
11010 = r_2 & \\
110100 = 2r_2 & \\
\underline{11111 = -Y} & \\
10101 = r_3 & q_3 = 1\\
101010 = 2r_3 & \\
\underline{11111 = -Y} & \\
01011 = r_4 & q_4 = 1\\
10110 = 2r_4 & \\
\underline{11111 = -Y} & \\
(-)10111 = 2r_4 - Y & q_5 = 0\\
\underline{11111 = +Y} & \\
10110 = r_5 & \\
\end{array}
$$

$$Q = .10110 = {}^{11}\!/_{16} = .6875$$

$$R_n = 2^{-5}r_5 = .10110$$

$$\frac{Y}{X} = \frac{22}{31} = .70967$$

Nonrestoring Method. For ease in demonstrating the following derivation, location of the binary point is as stated in (1-25) to (1-27). A different location, however, does not impair the generality of the method.

In the nonrestoring method [1], the divisor is either added to or subtracted from the partial remainder, depending on the sign of the divisor and that of the partial remainder. If these two signs agree, a subtraction is performed and the quotient digit is 1. The subtraction may be replaced by the addition of the 2's complement of the divisor. If the signs do not agree, an addition is performed and the quotient digit is 0. In either case, a new partial remainder is next formed by a proper shift, and the process continues until the remainder is zero or the desired number of quotient digits is obtained. To be precise, the initial remainder r_0 is X, or

$$r_0 = X \tag{1-105}$$

The first partial remainder r_1 is

$$r_1 = 2r_0 + (1 - 2q_1)Y \tag{1-106}$$

where the first quotient q_1 being 1 or 0 depends on the sign of r_0 (but not $2r_0$) and Y. If these two signs agree, q_1 is 1; and (1-106) becomes

$$r_1 = 2r_0 - Y \tag{1-107}$$

If these two signs do not agree, q_1 is 0; and (1-106) becomes

$$r_1 = 2r_0 + Y \tag{1-108}$$

The next remainder r_2 is

$$r_2 = 2r_1 + (1 - 2q_2)Y \tag{1-109}$$

where the second quotient digit q_2 being 1 or 0 depends, respectively, on the signs of r_1 (but not $2r_1$) and Y being alike or different, as discussed before. In general, the ith partial remainder is

$$r_i = 2r_{i-1} + (1 - 2q_i)Y \tag{1-110}$$

where the quotient digit q_i is 1 or 0 corresponding to the signs of r_{i-1} (but not $2r_{i-1}$) and Y being the same or not. If we multiply both sides of (1-110) by 2^{-i}, we have

$$2^{-i}r_i = 2^{-(i-1)}r_{i-1} + (2^{-i} - 2^{-(i-1)}q_i)Y \tag{1-111}$$

By repeated application of (1-111), we have for n quotient digits

$$2^{-n}r_n = X + \left(\sum_{i=1}^{n} 2^{-i} - \sum_{i=1}^{n} 2^{-(i-1)}q_i \right)Y \tag{1-112}$$

Making use of the relation (1-21), we have

$$\sum_{i=1}^{n} 2^{-i} = 1 - 2^{-n} \tag{1-113}$$

If (1-113) is substituted into (1-112), we have after rearrangement

$$\frac{X}{Y} = \left(-1 + 2^{-n} + \sum_{i=1}^{n} 2^{-(i-1)}q_i \right) + \frac{2^{-n}r_n}{Y} \tag{1-114}$$

By comparing relations (1-94) and (1-114), we have the quotient and remainder of the division,

$$Q = -1 + 2^{-n} + \sum_{i=1}^{n} 2^{-(i-1)}q_i \tag{1-115}$$

$$R_n = 2^{-n}r_n \qquad (1\text{-}116)$$

The above quotient digits q_i alone do not give the correct quotient; the true result of division requires an addition of $-1 + 2^{-n}$ from the indicated quotient Q. Note that the subtraction of 1 can be replaced by the addition of 1, as the carry beyond the sign digit is discarded.

An explanation for this correction can be offered. During the addition operation, as shown in (1-108), the quotient digit should be -1 instead of 0. However, the register digits are not capable of storing -1, and 0 is used instead. This results in the need for the above correction.

After the correction, the quotient Q is a fractional number. This required the dividend X to be smaller than the divisor Y; otherwise a divide-stop condition would have occurred as described previously.

The above division process is summarized into an algorithm in Table 1-23.

Table 1-23   Algorithm for Binary Division by Nonrestoring Method

Remainder. $R_n = 2^{-n}r_n$

Partial remainder . . . . $r_n = 2r_{n-1} + (1 - 2q_n)Y$
$q_n = 1$ if r_{n-1} and Y are of same sign
$q_n = 0$ if r_{n-1} and Y are of different signs

Quotient. . . . . $Q = (-1 + 2^{-n}) + \displaystyle\sum_{i=1}^{n} q_i 2^{-(i-1)}$

Correction. Add $(-1 + 2^{-n})$

Example 1-22

(a) When both the dividend and divisor are positive,

$$X = \text{dividend} = 0.1000 \ (\tfrac{8}{16})$$
$$Y = \text{divisor} \ = 0.1010 \ (\tfrac{10}{16})$$

$$
\begin{array}{ll}
0.1000 = X & \\
\underline{0.1010} = Y & q_1 = 1 \\
1.0000 = 2r_0 & \\
\underline{1.0110} = -Y & \\
0.0110 = r_1 & q_2 = 1 \\
0.1100 = 2r_1 & \\
\underline{1.0110} = -Y & \\
0.0010 = r_2 & q_3 = 1 \\
0.0100 = 2r_2 & \\
\underline{1.0110} = -Y & \\
1.1010 = r_3 & q_4 = 0 \\
1.0100 = 2r_3 & \\
\underline{0.1010} = +Y & \\
1.1110 = r_4 &
\end{array}
$$

$$
\begin{array}{l}
1.110 \ \ = \text{pseudo quotient digits} \\
\underline{+1.0001} = \text{correction} \\
Q = \quad 0.1101 = \tfrac{13}{16} = 0.8125
\end{array}
$$

$$R_4 = 2^{-2}r_4 = 1.11111110$$

$$\frac{X}{Y} = 0.8000$$

Note that subtractions are performed by addition of 2's complements. The shifting of r_i's 1 bit to the left in obtaining $2r_i$'s does not follow the shifting algorithm for signed binary numbers in Table 1-9. The partial remainder bits are considered all number bits. The quotient of 0.8125 is not quite accurate because of insufficient quotient digits.

(b) When the divisor is negative,

$$X = \text{dividend} = 0.1000 \ (+\tfrac{8}{16})$$
$$Y = \text{divisor} \ = 1.0110 \ (-\tfrac{10}{16})$$

$$
\begin{array}{ll}
0.1000 = X & \\
\underline{1.0110} = Y & \\
1.0000 = 2r_0 & \\
\underline{1.0110} = +Y & q_1 = 0 \\
0.0110 = r_1 & \\
0.1100 = 2r_1 & \\
\underline{1.0110} = +Y & q_2 = 0 \\
0.0010 = r_2 & \\
0.0100 = 2r_2 & \\
\underline{1.0110} = +Y & q_3 = 0 \\
1.1010 = r_3 & \\
1.0100 = 2r_3 & \\
\underline{0.1010} = -Y & q_4 = 1 \\
1.1110 = r_4 &
\end{array}
$$

$$Q = 0.001 + 1.0001 = 1.0011 = -.1101 = -\tfrac{13}{16} = -.8125$$

$$R_4 = 2^{-4}r_4 = 1.11111110$$

$$\frac{X}{Y} = -.8000$$

(c) When the dividend is negative,

$$X = \text{dividend} = 1.0111 \ (-\tfrac{9}{16})$$
$$Y = \text{divisor} \ = 0.1101 \ (+\tfrac{13}{16})$$

$$
\begin{array}{ll}
1.0111 = X & \\
\underline{0.1101} = Y & \\
0.1110 = 2r_0 & \\
\underline{0.1101} = +Y & q_1 = 0 \\
1.1011 = r_1 & \\
1.0110 = 2r_1 & \\
\underline{0.1101} = +Y & q_2 = 0 \\
0.0011 = r_2 & \\
0.0110 = 2r_2 & \\
\underline{1.0011} = -Y & q_3 = 1 \\
1.1001 = r_3 & \\
1.0010 = 2r_3 & \\
\underline{0.1101} = +Y & q_4 = 0 \\
1.1111 = r_4 &
\end{array}
$$

$$Q = 0.010 + 1.0001 = 1.0101 = -0.1011 = -\tfrac{11}{16} = -.6875$$

$$R_4 = 2^{-4}r_4 = 1.11111111$$

$$\frac{X}{Y} = -\frac{9}{13} = -.6923$$

(*d*) When both the dividend and divisor are negative,

$$X = \text{dividend} = 1.0111 \ (-\tfrac{9}{16})$$
$$Y = \text{divisor} = 1.0110 \ (-\tfrac{10}{16})$$

$$
\begin{aligned}
1.0111 &= X \\
\underline{1.0110} &= Y \\
0.1110 &= 2r_0 \\
\underline{0.1010} &= -Y \qquad q_1 = 1 \\
1.1000 &= r_1 \\
1.0000 &= 2r_1 \\
\underline{0.1010} &= -Y \qquad q_2 = 1 \\
1.1010 &= r_2 \\
1.0100 &= 2r_2 \\
\underline{0.1010} &= -Y \qquad q_3 = 1 \\
1.1110 &= r_3 \\
1.1100 &= 2r_3 \\
\underline{0.1010} &= -Y \qquad q_4 = 1 \\
0.0110 &= r_4
\end{aligned}
$$

$$Q = 1.111 + 1.0001 = 0.1111 = \tfrac{15}{16} = .9375$$

$$R_4 = 2^{-4}r_4 = 0.00000110$$

$$\frac{X}{Y} = 0.9$$

1-10 Binary Square Root

The square-root algorithms developed here are limited to positive numbers. Two algorithms for the binary square root will be derived; these are similar to those for binary division.

Comparison Method. The comparison algorithm for the square root is the ordinary paper-and-pencil method. Let the following symbols be used:

$$X = \text{radicand}$$
$$Q = \text{quotient of the square root}$$
$$R_0 = \text{initial remainder} = X$$
$$R_n = n\text{th remainder}$$

The square root is found from the known radicand X, the unknown quotient Q, and unknown remainder R_n, which satisfy the relation

$$R_n = X - Q^2 \tag{1-117}$$

This method calls for a comparison between the partial remainder and a root extractor which is a function of quotient digits. If the partial remainder is larger than the root extractor, a subtraction is performed and the quotient digit is 1. If it is smaller, no operation is performed and the quotient is 0. A new partial remainder is next found. The process continues until the remainder is zero or the desired number of quotient digits is obtained. To be precise, the initial remainder R_0 is X, or

$$R_0 = X \tag{1-118}$$

The first partial remainder R_1 is obtained by subtracting the first root extractor $q_1(0 + q_1)$ from R_0,

$$R_1 = R_0 - q_1(0 + q_1) \tag{1-119}$$

For convenience, the radicand is assumed to be less than 1. Then we have

$$q_1 = p_1 2^{-1} \tag{1-120}$$

where p_1 is either 1 or 0. When R_0 is larger than or equal to $q_1{}^2$, p_1 is equal to 1 and we have from (1-119)

$$R_1 = R_0 - q_1{}^2 \tag{1-121}$$

If R_0 is less than $q_1{}^2$, p_1 is equal to 0; and we have from (1-119)

$$R_1 = R_0 \tag{1-122}$$

The second remainder is obtained by subtracting the second root extractor $q_2(2q_1 + q_2)$ from R_1,

$$R_2 = R_1 - q_2(2q_1 + q_2) \tag{1-123}$$

where q_2 is equal to $p_2 2^{-2}$. If the difference on the right-hand side of (1-123) is greater than or equal to zero, p_2 equals 1. We then have (1-123) as shown. If not, we have

$$R_2 = R_1 \tag{1-124}$$

In general, the nth partial remainder is

$$R_n = R_{n-1} - q_n\left(2 \sum_{i=1}^{n-1} q_i + q_n\right) \tag{1-125}$$

and

$$q_i = p_i 2^{-i} \tag{1-126}$$

The value of q_n is 1 or 0 according to whether the difference on the right side of (1-125) is positive (or zero) or not. In the case of the binary square root, the trial-and-error operation of p's is easy, because p's can have only two values. This is of course not the case for decimal numbers. By repeated application of (1-125) we have for n quotient digits

$$R_n = -q_n\left(2 \sum_{i=1}^{n-1} q_1 + q_n\right) \cdots - q_2(2q_1 + q_2) - q_1(0 + q_1) + X \tag{1-127}$$

which after simplification reduces to

$$R_n = X - \left(\sum_{i=1}^{n} q_i\right)^2 \tag{1-128}$$

In comparison with (1-117) we have, with the use of (1-126), the quotient Q,

$$Q = \sum_{i=1}^{n} q_i = \sum_{i=1}^{n} p_i 2^{-i} \tag{1-129}$$

Since the radicand has been assumed a fractional number, the quotient of the binary square root is also a fractional number. The above process is summarized into the algorithm shown in Table 1-24.

Table 1-24   *Algorithm for Binary Square Root by Comparison or Restoring Method*

Remainder. . . . . $R_n = R_{n-1} - q_n(2 \sum_{i=1}^{n-1} q_i + q_n)$

$q_i = p_i 2^{-i}$
$p_i = 1$ if R_n is positive or zero
$p_i = 0$ if R_n is negative

Quotient. . . . . $Q = \sum_{i=1}^{n} q_i$

Example 1-23

$$X = \text{radicand} = .1011$$

.1011	$= X = R_0$	
$-.01$	$= -q_1{}^2$	$q_1 = .1$, and $p_1 = 1$
.0111	$= R_1$	
$-.0101$	$= -q_2(2q_1 + q_2)$	$q_2 = .01$, and $p_2 = 1$
.001000	$= R_2$	
$-.000000$	$= -q_3(2q_1 + 2q_2 + q_3)$	$q_3 = 0$, and $p_3 = 0$
.00100000	$= R_3$	
$-.00011001$	$= -q_4(2q_1 + 2q_2 + 2q_3 + q_4)$	$q_4 = .0001$, and $p_4 = 1$
.00000111	$= R_4$	

$$Q = .1 + .01 + .0001 = .1101$$
$$R_4 = .00000111$$

Restoring Method. Similar to the restoring method for binary division, the restoring method for the binary square root employs a subtraction as the method of comparison. The algorithm in Table 1-24 is applicable to this method.

Nonrestoring Method. Similar to the nonrestoring method for binary division, the nonrestoring method for the binary square root employs a root extractor which is added to or subtracted from the partial remainder. The root extractor in the nonrestoring method is a function of quotient digits and constants. The first operation is always the subtraction of a constant. The subsequent operation subtracts or adds the root extractor, depending on whether the remainders are positive or negative. This leads to a new partial remainder. The process continues until the remainder is zero or the desired number of quotient digits is obtained. To be precise, the initial remainder R_0 is equal to the radicand X (which is still assumed to be a fractional number), or

$$R_0 = X \tag{1-130}$$

The first partial remainder R_1 is obtained by subtracting from R_0 the first root extractor, which is the constant 2^{-2}, or

$$R_1 = R_0 - 2^{-2} \tag{1-131}$$

The first quotient digit q_1 is

$$q_1 = p_1 2^{-1} \tag{1-132}$$

The value of p_1 is 1 or 0, depending on whether the remainder R_1 is positive (zero is regarded as positive) or negative. If the remainder R_1 is positive, the second partial remainder R_2 is the same as (1-123). Here we use 2^{-1} for q_1 (as p_1 is 1) and 2^{-2} for q_2; and (1-123) becomes

$$R_2 = R_1 - 2^{-2}(2^0 + 2^{-2}) \qquad \text{for positive } R_1 \qquad (1\text{-}133)$$

If the remainder R_1 is negative, the second partial remainder R_2 is

$$R_2 = R_0 - q_2(2q_1 + q_2) \qquad \text{for negative } R_1 \qquad (1\text{-}134)$$

Note the difference in the two equations: (1-133) uses R_1, and (1-134) uses R_0. Here, q_1 is 0, and q_2 is again 2^{-2}; and (1-134) becomes

$$R_2 = R_0 - 2^{-2}(0 + 2^{-2}) \qquad (1\text{-}135)$$

If R_0 in (1-131) is substituted in (1-135), we have

$$R_2 = R_1 + 2^{-2}(2^0 - 2^{-2}) \qquad \text{for negative } R_1 \qquad (1\text{-}136)$$

In short, if R_1 is positive, R_2 is obtained from (1-133). If R_1 is negative, R_2 is obtained from (1-136). These two can be combined,

$$R_2 = R_1 + (1 - 2p_1)2^{-1}\{0 + 2^{-1}[2^0 - (1 - 2p_1)2^{-2}]\} \quad (1\text{-}137)$$

The second term on the right side of (1-137) is the second root extractor. The second quotient digit q_2 is

$$q_2 = p_2 2^{-2} \qquad (1\text{-}138)$$

The value of p_2 is 1 or 0, depending on whether the remainder R_2 is positive or negative.

If the remainder R_2 is positive, the third partial remainder R_3 is

$$R_3 = R_2 - 2^{-3}(2q_1 + 2q_2 + 2^{-3}) \qquad (1\text{-}139)$$

Here q_2 is 2^{-2}, as p_2 is 1; and (1-139) becomes

$$R_3 = R_2 - 2^{-2}[q_1 + 2^{-2}(2^0 + 2^{-2})] \qquad \text{for positive } R_2 \quad (1\text{-}140)$$

If the remainder R_2 is negative, the third partial remainder R_3 is

$$R_3 = R_1 - 2^{-3}(2q_1 + 2q_2 + 2^{-3}) \qquad \text{for negative } R_2 \quad (1\text{-}141)$$

Note that the difference between (1-139) and (1-141) lies in the first using R_2 and the second using R_1. In (1-141) we substitute 0 for q_2, and (1-141) becomes

$$R_3 = R_1 - 2^{-3}(2q_1 + 2^{-3}) \qquad (1\text{-}142)$$

The remainder R_1 in (1-142) is related, however, to R_2 as follows,

$$R_2 = R_1 - 2^{-2}(2q_1 + 2^{-2}) \qquad (1\text{-}143)$$

which is (1-123) with 2^{-2} for q_2. If we substitute R_1 from (1-143) into (1-142), we have

$$R_3 = R_2 + 2^{-2}[q_1 + 2^{-2}(2^0 - 2^{-2})] \qquad \text{for negative } R_2 \quad (1\text{-}144)$$

In short, if R_2 is positive, R_3 is obtained from (1-140). If R_2 is negative, R_3 is obtained from (1-144). These two can be combined into one,

$$R_3 = R_2 + (1 - 2p_2)2^{-2}\{q_1 + 2^{-2}[2^0 - (1 - 2p_2)2^{-2}]\} \quad (1\text{-}145)$$

The second term on the right side of (1-145) is the third root extractor. The third quotient digit q_3 is

$$q_3 = p_3 2^{-3} \quad (1\text{-}146)$$

The value of p_3 is 1 or 0, depending on whether the remainder R_3 is positive or negative. The process continues until the remainder is zero or the desired number of quotient digits is obtained. In general, if the nth partial remainder is positive, the $(n + 1)$st partial remainder R_{n+1} is

$$R_{n+1} = R_n - 2^{-n}\left[\sum_{i=1}^{n-1} q_i + 2^{-n}(2^0 + 2^{-2})\right] \quad \text{for positive } R_n \quad (1\text{-}147)$$

If the nth partial remainder is negative, the R_{n+1} is

$$R_{n+1} = R_n + 2^{-n}\left[\sum_{i=1}^{n-1} q_i + 2^{-n}(2^0 - 2^{-2})\right] \quad \text{for negative } R_n \quad (1\text{-}148)$$

The $(n + 1)$st quotient digit q_{n+1} is

$$q_{n+1} = p_{n+1} 2^{-n-1} \quad (1\text{-}149)$$

The value of p_{n+1} is 1 or 0, depending on whether R_{n+1} is positive or negative. The algorithms of (1-147) and (1-148) can be combined into one expression,

$$R_{n+1} = R_n + (1 - 2p_n)2^{-n}\left\{\sum_{i=1}^{n-1} q_i + 2^{-n}[2^0 - (1 - 2p_n)2^{-2}]\right\} \quad (1\text{-}150)$$

Equation (1-150) can be rewritten in the following form:

$$R_{n+1}2^n = R_n 2^n + (1 - 2p_n)\left\{\sum_{i=1}^{n} q_i + 2^{-n}[(2^0 - p_n) - (1 - 2p_n)2^{-2}]\right\} \quad (1\text{-}151)$$

In the rewritten equation, the quantity inside the braces is the shifted root extractor and is the summation of q_i's and a constant. The value of the quantity inside the bracket is 0.01 when p_n is 1 and 0.11 when p_n is 0. The quantity $1 - 2p_n$ becomes 1 or -1 when p_n is, respectively, 0 or 1 and thus shows whether the root extractor should be added to or subtracted from the shifted partial remainder.

Equations (1-130), (1-131), (1-149), and either (1-150) or (1-151) provide the nonrestoring algorithm for the binary square root. By repeated application of (1-150) we have, for n quotient digits, after simplification

$$R_{n+1} = X - \left(\sum_{i=1}^{n} q_i\right)^2 \quad (1\text{-}152)$$

In comparison with (1-117), we have

$$Q = \sum_{i=1}^{n} q_i = \sum_{i=1}^{n} p_i 2^{-i} \quad (1\text{-}153)$$

The above process is summarized into an algorithm in Table 1-25.

Table 1-25   Algorithm for Binary Square Root by Nonrestoring Method

First remainder. . . . . $R_1 = X - 2^{-2}$

Remainder. . . . . If R_n is positive or zero,

$$R_{n+1} = R_n - 2^{-n}\left[\sum_{i=1}^{n-1} q_i + 2^{-n}(2^0 + 2^{-2})\right]$$

If R_n is negative,

$$R_{n+1} = R_n + 2^{-n}\left[\sum_{i=1}^{n-1} q_i + 2^{-n}(2^0 - 2^{-2})\right]$$

Quotient. . . . . $Q = \sum_{i=1}^{n} q_i$

$q_i = p_i 2^{-i}$
$p_i = 1$ if R_{i+1} is positive or zero
$p_i = 0$ if R_{i+1} is negative

Example 1-24

$$X = \text{radicand} = .1011$$

$$
\begin{array}{ll}
.1011 & = X \\
- \; .01 & = -2^{-2} \\
\hline
.0111 & = R_1 \quad q_1 = 2^{-1}, p_1 = 1 \\
- \; .0101 & = -2^{-2}(2^0 + 2^{-2}) \\
\hline
.001000 & = R_2 \quad q_2 = 2^{-2}, p_2 = 1 \\
- \; .001101 & = -2^{-2}[q_1 + 2^{-2}(2^0 + 2^{-2})] \\
\hline
\bar{1}.11101100 & = R_3 \quad q_3 = 0, p_3 = 0 \\
+ \; .00011011 & = +2^{-3}[q_1 + q_2 + 2^{-3}(2^0 - 2^{-2})] \\
\hline
0.00000111 & = R_4 \quad q_4 = 2^{-4}, p_4 = 1
\end{array}
$$

$$Q = .1 + .01 + .0001 = .1101$$
$$R_4 = 0.00000111$$

The sequential operations of the three registers (those shown in Figs. 1-1 and 1-3) when the square root operation of the above example is performed are shown in Fig. 1-5. Notice the formulation of the root extractor before a subtraction or an addition; this is the major difference from the division process.

1-11   Round-off and Overflow

We conclude this chapter by mentioning the round-off procedure and the overflow problem. Both occur in a digital computer because of the limited digits in a machine word.

Round-off Procedure. When two n-digit numbers are multiplied, the product yields more than n digits. Similarly, division or square root may produce a quotient having an infinite number of digits. If only n digits are needed after a multiplication, division, or square root, the product or the quotient is rounded off. Round-off is a process for reducing the number of digits representing a number. A satisfactory round-off procedure becomes necessary, therefore, to reduce the possible error which would result from indiscriminate dropping of digits. Thus, the round-off attempts to produce a satisfactory n-digit approximation for

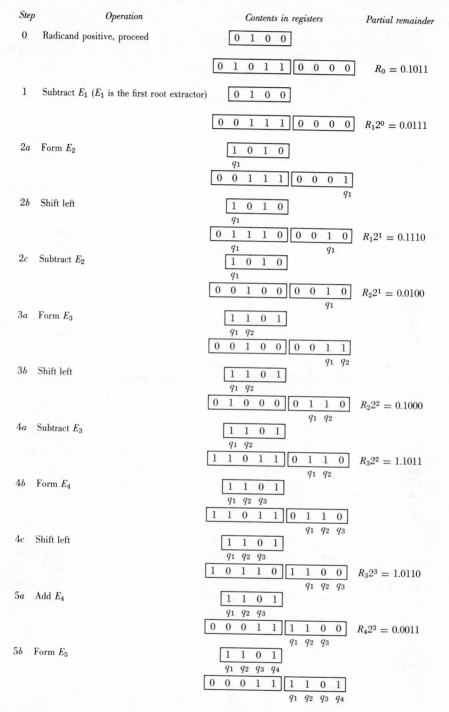

FIG. 1-5 Sequential operations of arithmetic registers during square root operation (Radicand = .1011; quotient = .1101; remainder = .0000011).

the product or the quotient. Statistically, this means that the average round-off error should be zero or unbiased; that the variance of the round-off error should be as small as practical, to prevent propagation or accumulation of round-off errors through a computation. When a round-off procedure is applied, accompanying operations are called *multiplication with round-off, division with round-off,* and *square root with round-off.*

Of various possible round-off procedures for binary numbers, two are of practical interest. The first and most familiar one is to add 1 to the $(n + 1)$st digit and to perform the carries which this may induce. Only the first n digits are kept. The other procedure replaces the nth digit by 1, regardless of whether that digit was originally 1 or 0. Since the multiplier, multiplicand, dividend, divisor, and radicand are likely to be the results of similar round-offs, directly or indirectly, these two round-off procedures have been shown to produce results which are sufficiently unbiased. The variance of the first procedure is 0.29 and that of the second is 0.58 times the nth digit. Although the first procedure produces a smaller variance, simplicity favors the second procedure (with no carries produced).

The foregoing procedures are for positive numbers as well as negative numbers in 2's-complement representation. For negative numbers in 1's-complement representation, the first procedure is to subtract 1 from the $(n + 1)$st digit and then perform the borrow if subtraction induces a borrow bit. The second procedure replaces the nth digit by 0.

Overflow. Both addition and subtraction may create new digits to the left of the original numbers, causing the number to exceed the number range of the computer. An overflow digit position is usually provided in the accumulator of the computer, such as the leftmost bit of the accumulator in Figs. 1-1 and 1-3. This is an extra digit, because there is no corresponding digit in the words stored in the memory and in the other registers of the computer. When an overflow occurs, the computer does not give correct results and usually halts, although in some cases the programmer may have anticipated the overflow and programmed the machine to ignore it and continue. It is the programmer's responsibility to anticipate such possible occurrences and to avoid stoppage by using the necessary technique in preparing the program of the computer. (Floating-point arithmetic capabilities eliminate many of the scaling difficulties and therefore circumvent several of the problems of overflow described above.)

As mentioned before, overflow may also occur in division. This is referred to as the divide-stop condition of the computer. Again, it is the responsibility of the programmer to prevent its occurrence. The programmer may find very difficult the estimating of all computer numbers and intermediate results, but if the divide-stop condition arises, the program may have to be modified and the computation carried out once again.

Problems

1. Write the 10's and 9's complements of the following decimal numbers:

(*a*) 13579   (*b*) 246.89   (*c*) 09900   (*d*) 90090

2. Write the 2's and 1's complements of the following binary numbers:

(*a*) 1010101   (*b*) 1101.011   (*c*) 0111000   (*d*) 0000001

3. Convert the following decimal numbers into binary numbers:

(a) 153   (b) .46875   (c) .469   (d) 12.0625

4. Convert the following binary numbers into decimal numbers:

(a) 1010101   (b) .110101   (c) .000001   (d) 10.10001

5. Convert the following octal numbers into decimal numbers:

(a) 125_8 (b) 101_8 (c) 470_8 (d) 700_8

6. Given two negative binary numbers -1001 and -0011:

(a) Convert them into the three representations of negative numbers.

(b) Shift the two numbers left and right two places for each of the three representations.

7. Given two binary numbers in signed-magnitude representation, 0,1010 and 0,0010, perform the eight possible additions and the eight possible subtractions (as shown in Example 1-10).

8. Given two binary numbers in signed-2's-complement representation, 0,1010 and 0,0010, perform the eight possible subtractions (as shown in Example 1-10):

(a) By the direct-subtraction method

(b) By the addition of the 2's-complement method

9. Given two binary numbers in signed-1's-complement representation, 0,1010 and 0,0010, perform the eight possible additions (as shown in Example 1-10):

(a) By the direct-addition method

(b) By the subtraction of the 1's-complement method

10. By treating the sign bit of binary number in 1's-complement representation as a number bit, derive the algorithm in Table 1-15. (This can be derived in a manner similar to that for the direct-addition method for binary number in a signed-2's-complement representation.)

11. Given the binary multiplicand ($+110011$) and multiplier (-101010), perform the binary multiplication by the direct-multiplication method in the manner shown in Fig. 1-2.

12. Given the following three pairs of binary multiplicand and multiplier:

(a) $+.1010$ and $-.0101$ (b) $-.1010$ and $+.0101$ (c) $-.1010$ and $-.0101$

Perform binary multiplications:

(a) By the Burks–Goldstine–von Neumann method   (b) Robertson's first method
(c) Robertson's second method   (d) Booth's method

13. By repeated application of relation (1-101), derive the quotient (1-104) of a binary division by the comparison method.

14. Given the following two pairs of dividend and divisor in binary numbers:

(a) $+10010$ (dividend) and $+11010$ (divisor)   (b) $+100101$ and -110101

Perform the divisions by using the comparison algorithm in the manner shown in Fig. 1-4 and by using the restoring method.

15. By repeated application of relation (1-111) derive the quotient (1-115) of a binary division by the nonrestoring method.

16. Given the following four pairs of dividend and divisor in binary numbers:

(a) $+.1001$ (dividend) and $+.1101$ (divisor)   (b) $+.1001$ and $-.1101$
(c) $-.1001$ and $+.1101$ (d) $-.1001$ and $-.1101$

Perform the divisions by the nonrestoring method.

17. Given the following binary radicands:

(a) .100001   (b) .101001

Extract binary square roots:

(a) By the comparison method   (b) By the nonrestoring method

18. By using the algorithm of (1-147) and (1-148), derive the quotient (1-152) of the binary square root by the nonrestoring method.

References

1. Burks, A. W., H. H. Goldstine, and J. von Neumann: Preliminary Discussion of the Logical Design of an Electronic Computing Instrument, *Inst. Advanced Study Rept.*, vol. 1, pt. 1, June 28, 1946.

2. Shaw, R. F.: Arithmetic Operations in a Binary Computer, *Rev. Sci. Instr.*, August, 1950, pp. 687–793.

3. Robinson, A. A.: Multiplication in the Manchester University High-speed Digital Computer, *Electronic Eng.*, January, 1953, pp. 6–10.

4. Richards, R. K.: "Arithmetic Operations in Digital Computers," D. Van Nostrand Company, Inc., Princeton, N.J., 1955.

5. Chaplin, G. B. B., R. E. Hayes, and A. R. Owens: A Transistor Digital Fast Multiplier with Magnetostrictive Storage, *Proc. IRE*, vol. 102, pt. B, no. 4, pp. 412–425, July, 1955.

6. Robertson, J. E.: Two's Complement Multiplication in Binary Parallel Digital Computers, *IRE Trans. on Electronic Computers*, September, 1955, pp. 118–119.

7. Booth, A. D., and K. H. V. Booth, "Automatic Digital Calculators," 2d ed., Academic Press, Inc., New York, 1956.

8. Phister, M.: "Logical Design of Digital Computers," John Wiley & Sons, Inc., New York, 1958.

9. Methods for High-speed Addition and Multiplication, *Natl. Bureau Standards* (*U.S.*) *Circ.* 591, sec. 1, Feb. 14, 1958.

10. Horton, A. W.: An Introduction to Computer Binary Arithmetic, *Bell Telephone Labs. Monograph* 3050, July, 1958.

11. Robertson, J. E.: A New Class of Digital Division Methods, *IRE Trans. on Electronic Computers*, September, 1958, pp. 218–222.

2

Digital Arithmetic—II

This chapter deals with the digital arithmetic primarily of decimal numbers. The binary-coded decimal number system and the signed decimal number are first discussed. A description follows of methods for decimal addition, subtraction, multiplication, and division. Later topics include floating-point arithmetic, residue number system, parity checking, and error-detecting and -correcting codes. Wherever similarity between binary and decimal numbers exists, the exposition is brief.

2-1 *Binary-coded Decimal Number Systems*

Decimal digits are usually coded in binary numbers and implemented physically by binary-state devices. A binary-coded decimal (BCD) number system is thus one in which the decimal digits are represented by a binary code.

Factors in Choosing a BCD Number System. Since n binary devices have 2^n states, the representation of 10 states of a decimal digit calls for at least 4 binary devices ($2^4 > 10$). Any 10 of the 16 states of 4 binary devices can be selected to represent one binary-coded decimal number system. However, a proper choice can greatly simplify the construction of the computing and control circuits of a digital computer. The following are factors to be considered:

1. Method for addition and subtraction
2. Need for complementing and counting
3. Conversion from input decimal digit to binary-coded digit
4. Implementation of error detection and error correction

The influence of these factors will become apparent as we proceed.

Four-bit Codes. If 10 of the 16 states of 4 bits are taken to form a binary-coded decimal digit, there are $16!/6!$, or about 2.9×10^{10}, possible codes. However, not all these are different; interchanges of bit positions or of 0's and 1's reduce the total number by a factor of 384, or about 7.6×10^7 codes. The number of possible choices of a 4-bit code is still enormous.

A number of commonly used 4-bit codes are listed in Table 2-1, together with the 16 binary numbers. The 8-4-2-1 code is chosen from the first 10 binary numbers; the 2-4-2-1 code from the first 5 and the last 5; the 8-4-$\bar{2}$-$\bar{1}$ code from the first, the last, and the middle 8; the excess-3 code from the middle 10.

Table 2-1   Several 4-bit Binary Codes for Decimal Digits

Binary number	8-4-2-1	2-4-2-1	5-2-1-1	8-4-$\bar{2}$-$\bar{1}$	Excess-3
0000	0000 = 0	0000 = 0	0000 = 0	0000 = 0	
0001	0001 = 1	0001 = 1	0001 = 1		
0010	0010 = 2	0010 = 2			
0011	0011 = 3	0011 = 3	0011 = 2		0011 = 0
0100	0100 = 4	0100 = 4		0100 = 4	0100 = 1
0101	0101 = 5		0101 = 3	0101 = 3	0101 = 2
0110	0110 = 6			0110 = 2	0110 = 3
0111	0111 = 7		0111 = 4	0111 = 1	0111 = 4
1000	1000 = 8		1000 = 5	1000 = 8	1000 = 5
1001	1001 = 9		1001 = 6	1001 = 7	1001 = 6
1010				1010 = 6	1010 = 7
1011		1011 = 5	1011 = 7	1011 = 5	1011 = 8
1100		1100 = 6			1100 = 9
1101		1101 = 7	1101 = 8		
1110		1110 = 8			
1111		1111 = 9	1111 = 9	1111 = 9	

The first four codes in Table 2-1 are called *weighted codes,* while the last one is an *unweighted code.* The weighted code can be described as follows: Let a decimal number N with n digits be represented as

$$N = \sum_{i=0}^{n-1} d_i 10^i \tag{2-1}$$

where d_i is the ith decimal digit. For the 8-4-2-1 weighted code, d_i can be expressed in the following form,

$$d_i = 8w + 4x + 2y + z \tag{2-2}$$

where w, x, y, and z represent a *code number.* The 10 code numbers are those in the second column of Table 2-1. Similar expressions can be written for the other weighted codes. Thus, in a weighted code, a value is assigned to each of the 4 bits so that the sum of the values for a given code number is equal to the value of the decimal digit represented by the given code number. For the 8-4-2-1 code, the 10 code numbers are the same as the first 10 binary numbers.

The weight of the code can be either positive or negative. If one or more of the weights is negative, as in the 8-4-$\bar{2}$-$\bar{1}$ code, the code is called *negatively weighted.* From the enormous number of possible choices of a 4-bit code, it has been found that there are 70 weighted code groups, of which 17 code groups are positively weighted. The positively weighted code groups are listed in Table 2-2. The four weights in the table are arranged in descending order, the leftmost weight being the largest. For a given set of four weights, there may be more than one way of coding the decimal digit. For example, in the 4-2-2-1 weight system, there are 32 possible ways of coding the decimal digits. As also shown in Table 2-2, there are 225 possible ways for coding the 17 positively weighted code groups.

The 2-4-2-1 code of Table 2-1, which was chosen for the Harvard Mark III Calculator, has an interesting property: If the 1's and 0's of a code number are self-complemented, the resulting code number is the 9's complement of the decimal digit which the original code number represents. For example, the code number 0011 represents 3. Complementing each of these 1's and 0's results in the code number 1100, which represents 6, or the 9's complement of 3. Such a property is called *self-complementing*. In Table 2-1, the 8-4-2-1 code is not a self-complementing code, but the negatively weighted code 8-4-$\bar{2}$-$\bar{1}$ and the un-weighted excess-3 code are self-complementing. A weighted code which is self-complementing has weights whose sum is 9. Of the 17 positively weighted code groups of Table 2-2, only the first 4 code groups can produce self-complementing codes.

Table 2-2   Positively Weighted Code Groups

Code group	Possible ways of coding decimal digits
3-3-2-1	18
4-2-2-1	32
4-3-1-1	18
5-2-1-1	32
4-3-2-1	32
4-4-2-1	8
5-2-2-1	16
5-3-1-1	16
5-3-2-1	16
5-4-2-1	8
6-2-2-1	8
6-3-1-1	4
6-3-2-1	8
6-4-2-1	4
7-3-2-1	2
7-4-2-1	2
8-4-2-1	1

The unweighted excess-3 code of Table 2-1, which was chosen for the Univac Computer, is an unweighted code. However, this may be called a *biased weighted code*, because the decimal digit d can be represented by the relation

$$d = 8w + 4x + 2y + z - 3 \tag{2-3}$$

The name excess-3 is derived from the -3 in the above expression. This code is self-complementing and was first proposed by Stibitz. It is interesting to note that if the 1's and 0's in the $\bar{2}$ and $\bar{1}$ positions in the 8-4-$\bar{2}$-$\bar{1}$ code are self-comple-mented, the resulting code is the excess-3 code.

More-than-4-bit-Codes. Although 4 bits are adequate to code a decimal digit, codes with more than 4 bits have been used for the purpose of simplifying the computing circuits or providing convenient ways of automatic checking. Several more-than-4-bit codes that have been used are listed in Table 2-3. The first four codes are positively weighted, while the last code is unweighted.

The 8-6-4-2-1 code was used in the early Harvard Mark II Calculator. In the 5-4-3-2-1-0 code, the leftmost bit determines the decimal digit's being less than 5 or not; and the existence of a 1 in the other 5 bits determines the value's being 0 to 4. Similarly the 5-1-1-1-1 code makes use of the leftmost bit to determine the decimal digit's being less than 5 or not and the number and position of 1's in other 4 bits to determine the value's being 0 to 4. The 5-1-1-1-1 code is self-complementing. The 5-0-4-3-2-1-0 code is also called a *biquinary code*. It was used in the Bell Relay Computer and in the IBM 650 Computer. In this code each coded digit has only two 1's; the position of the 1 in the leftmost 2 bits determines the decimal digit's being less than 5 or not, and the position of a single 1 in the other 5 bits determines the value's being 0 to 4. A similar situation exists in the 2-out-of-5 code. These properties are convenient for providing reliable self-checking circuits. However, the advantages of the more-than-4-bit code should be weighed against the increase in computer cost.

Table 2-3   Several More-than-4-bit Codes for Decimal Digits

Decimal digit	8-6-4-2-1	5-4-3-2-1-0	5-1-1-1-1	5-0-4-3-2-1-0	2-out-of-5
0	00000	000000	00000	0100001	00011
1	00001	000010	00001	0100010	00101
2	00010	000100	00011	0100100	00110
3	00011	001000	00111	0101000	01001
4	00100	010000	01111	0110000	01010
5	00101	100000	10000	1000001	01100
6	01000	100010	11000	1000010	10001
7	01001	100100	11100	1000100	10010
8	10000	101000	11110	1001000	10100
9	10001	110000	11111	1010000	11000

2-2   Signed Decimal Numbers

Three Representations of Signed Decimal Numbers. When a decimal number is denoted by a sign digit, it is called a *signed decimal number*. The sign digit is often a binary digit located at the most significant digit, and the values of 0 and 1 represent, respectively, the positive and negative signs. The other decimal digits are referred to as *number digits*. There are three ways of representing the number digits, depending on how the negative decimal number is represented:

1. Signed-magnitude representation
2. Signed-10's-complement representation
3. Signed-9's-complement representation

For all three representations, the number digits for a positive decimal number represent the magnitude, or absolute value, of the number. It is in regard to negative numbers that the representations differ. In the signed-magnitude representation of a negative number, the number digits still represent the magnitude, but in the other two representations the number digits represent the 10's complement or the 9's complement of the magnitude. These representations are thus similar to the three representations of a signed binary number.

Similar to the signed-2's-complement representation of a binary number, the signed-10's-complement representation of a decimal number gives the actual value of the decimal number if the value of the sign digit is regarded as negative. For example, the decimal number 1,523 (or -477) is in signed-10's-complement representation, and the value of the sign digit is regarded as $-1,000$ instead of $+1,000$ as below:

$$1,523 = -1 \times 10^3 + 5 \times 10^2 + 2 \times 10^1 + 3 \times 10^0$$
$$= -1,000 + 523$$
$$= -477$$

The value of the sign digit being regarded as negative does not affect the positive decimal number; for when the sign digit is positive, its value is zero.

Location of the Decimal Point. For reasons similar to those cited for binary numbers, it is often convenient to consider the sign digit to be an integer and the number digits to be fractional. Consequently, the decimal point serves to separate not only the integer and fractional parts of the decimal number but also the sign digit and the number digits. However, the main reason for this location of the decimal point (i.e., fractional numbers) is for its advantages in multiplication and division overflow processes, described in Chap. 1.

Shifting and Comparison Algorithms. Let the sign digit be located at the most significant digit of the decimal number. The shifting algorithm of the signed decimal number is similar to that of the signed binary number described in Chap. 1. Briefly, when a signed number is shifted, the sign digit should not be shifted. When a positive number is shifted, all added digits are 0's. When a negative number in signed-magnitude representation is shifted, all added digits are 0's. When a negative number in signed-10's-complement representation is shifted to the left, 0's are added; if it is shifted to the right, 9's are added. When a negative number in signed-9's-complement representation is shifted, all added digits are 9's. The above shifting algorithm is the same as that shown in Table 1-9, except that 2's are replaced by 10's and 1's by 9's.

The comparison algorithm for the signed decimal number is the same as that for the signed binary number as shown in Table 1-10.

2-3 Decimal Addition and Subtraction

Methods for decimal addition and subtraction may be classified according to the manner of representing the negative number. The similarity of these methods to those for binary addition and subtraction obviates the need for anything more than a summary.

Methods for Decimal Addition and Subtraction. For the case of a number represented by its sign and magnitude, two methods for addition and subtraction are:

1. Direct addition
2. Direct subtraction

The algorithm in Table 1-11 is directly applicable, except that the 2's complement is replaced by the 10's complement.

For the case where the negative number is represented in 10's complement, four methods for addition and subtraction are:

1. Direct addition
2. Direct subtraction
3. Addition by subtraction of the 10's complement
4. Subtraction by addition of the 10's complement

The algorithm in Table 1-13 is applicable by changing the 2's complement into the 10's complement.

For the case where the negative number is represented in 9's complement, four methods are:

1. Direct addition
2. Direct subtraction
3. Addition by subtraction of the 9's complement
4. Subtraction by addition of the 9's complement

This last case requires addition of the end-around carry or subtraction of the end-around borrow. The algorithm in Table 1-15 applies except that the 1's complement is replaced by the 9's complement.

In an addition or a subtraction using any of the above methods the need of complementation is unavoidable if the result has to be in the signed-magnitude representation.

Although decimal addition and subtraction methods are similar to those for binary numbers, addition and subtraction of a single decimal digit differ when decimal digits are represented by binary-coded decimal numbers. Let us illustrate this by adding two decimal numbers 759 and 683 expressed in the 8-4-2-1 code:

Decimal	Hundreds	Tens	Units
	1		
795	0111	1001	0101
	carry		
+683	+0110	+1000	+0011
1,478	1110	1,0001	1000
	+0110	+0110	
	1,0100(4)	0111(7)	1000(8)

↑
carry for thousands position

In the above, the digit sum 1000 in the units position is correct, but the digit sum 0001 in the tens position is incorrect. The digit sum 1110 in the hundreds position is not only incorrect, but the carry is missing. However, if the binary number 0110 is added to both tens and hundreds positions, all the digit sums now become correct and the carry for the thousands position also appears. Therefore, for a chosen code of decimal-digit representation, a correction algorithm should be developed. The following subsections develop the algorithm for the 8-4-2-1 code, excess-3 code, and 2-4-2-1 code.

Algorithms for Decimal Digits in 8-4-2-1 and Excess-3 Codes. Consider the case where two decimal digits and a possible carry in the 8-4-2-1 code are added. There are 20 possible correct digit sums of 0 to 19. These correct digit sums, denoted by Z, are shown in the second column of Table 2-4. The digit sums before correction, denoted by Z^*, appear in the left column of Table 2-4. (These are the digit sums from binary addition of coded digits such as the previous numbers 1110, 1,0001, and 1000.) Since the corresponding numbers in each row of the table should be the same, the problem is to find a simple set

**Table 2-4   Uncorrected and Correct Digit Sums
of Two Decimal Digits in 8-4-2-1 Code**

Uncorrected digit sum Z*	Correct digit sum Z
0000	0000 = 0
0001	0001 = 1
0010	0010 = 2
0011	0011 = 3
0100	0100 = 4
0101	0101 = 5
0110	0110 = 6
0111	0111 = 7
1000	1000 = 8
1001	1001 = 9
1010	1,0000 = 10
1011	1,0001 = 11
1100	1,0010 = 12
1101	1,0011 = 13
1110	1,0100 = 14
1111	1,0101 = 15
1,0000	1,0110 = 16
1,0001	1,0111 = 17
1,0010	1,1000 = 18
1,0011	1,1001 = 19

of rules by which the uncorrected digit sum Z^* can be corrected. In examining the contents of the table, it is apparent that for Z^* equal to or less than 1001 the correct digit sum Z is the same as Z^*; no correction is needed. For Z^* greater than 1001 but equal to or less than 1,0011, the addition of 0110 to Z^* makes the digit sum correct and the carry appears.

If one decimal digit in the 8-4-2-1 code and a possible borrow are subtracted from another also in the same code, there are 20 possible correct digit differences of 9 to -10. The uncorrected and the correct digit differences, denoted by Z^* and Z, are shown in Table 2-5. In this table, when the number has a borrow $\bar{1}$, it is in 10's complement. An examination of the table reveals that no correction is needed when Z^* is equal to or greater than 0000. When Z^* is less than 0000, the subtraction of 0110 from Z^* makes the digit difference correct and the borrow available. The addition and subtraction algorithms for two decimal digits in the 8-4-2-1 code are shown in Table 2-6.

With a similar approach, the addition and subtraction algorithms for two decimal digits in the excess-3 code can be developed and appear in Table 2-7.

The algorithms for both the 8-4-2-1 and excess-3 codes are rather simple. The excess-3 coded decimal digit has the added advantage that it is self-complementing.

Algorithm for Decimal Digits in 2-4-2-1 Code. A general approach in developing the addition (or subtraction) algorithm is to form an addition (or subtraction) matrix table consisting of 10 rows and 10 columns. Assign one coded decimal digit to one row and one column so that the 100 positions in the matrix represent all possible additions (or subtractions) of two coded decimal digits. By examining the matrix table, the algorithm may be established. When a reasonably simple algorithm cannot be established, either a different code must be chosen or the matrix table has to be implemented. The latter course is usually impractical because of the large number of components involved.

Table 2-5   *Uncorrected and Correct Digit Differences of Two Decimal Digits in 8-4-2-1 Code*

Uncorrected digit difference Z^*	Correct digit difference Z
1001	$1001 = 9$
1000	$1000 = 8$
0111	$0111 = 7$
0110	$0110 = 6$
0101	$0101 = 5$
0100	$0100 = 4$
0011	$0011 = 3$
0010	$0010 = 2$
0001	$0001 = 1$
0000	$0000 = 0$
$\bar{1},1111$	$\bar{1},1001 = -1$
$\bar{1},1110$	$\bar{1},1000 = -2$
$\bar{1},1101$	$\bar{1},0111 = -3$
$\bar{1},1100$	$\bar{1},0110 = -4$
$\bar{1},1011$	$\bar{1},0101 = -5$
$\bar{1},1010$	$\bar{1},0100 = -6$
$\bar{1},1001$	$\bar{1},0011 = -7$
$\bar{1},1000$	$\bar{1},0010 = -8$
$\bar{1},0111$	$\bar{1},0001 = -9$
$\bar{1},0110$	$\bar{1},0000 = -10$

This general approach is illustrated by developing the addition algorithm for the decimal digit in the 2-4-2-1 code. The matrix table is shown in Table 2-8. Each decimal number in the table represents, one at a time, two binary-coded numbers, the correct digit sum Z or the uncorrected digit sum Z^*. By examining every two corresponding binary-coded numbers, the table can be divided into six areas A to F, because the nature of the 2-4-2-1 code shows that the coded decimal digits 0 to 4 are the same as those in the 8-4-2-1 code; digits 5 to 9 are the same as those in excess-6 code. By applying this property it is apparent

Table 2-6   *Addition and Subtraction Algorithms for Two Decimal Digits in 8-4-2-1 Code*

Operation	Algorithm	
Addition.............................	No correction	when $Z^* \leq 1001$
	$Z = Z^* + 0110$	when $Z^* > 1001$
Subtraction...........................	No correction	when $Z^* \geq 0000$
	$Z = Z^* - 0110$	when $Z^* < 0000$

Table 2-7   *Addition and Subtraction Algorithms for Two Decimal Digits in Excess-3 Code*

Operation	Algorithm	
Addition....................	No carry correction is needed	
	$Z = Z^* - 0011$	when $1111 \geq Z^* \geq 0110$
	$Z = Z^* + 0011$	when $1,1000 \geq Z^* \geq 1,0000$
Subtraction...................	No borrow correction is needed	
	$Z = Z^* + 0011$	when $1001 \geq Z^* \geq 0000$
	$Z = Z^* - 0011$	when $\bar{1},1111 \geq Z^* \geq \bar{1},0111$

Table 2-8 Addition Matrix Table for Decimal Digit in 2-4-2-1 Code

	0	1	2	3	4	5	6	7	8	9
0	0	1	2	3	4	5	6	7	8	9
1	1	2	3	4	5	6	7	8	9	10
2	2	3	4	5	6	7	8	9	10	11
3	3	4	5	6	7	8	9	10	11	12
4	4	5	6	7	8	9	10	11	12	13
5	5	6	7	8	9	10	11	12	13	14
6	6	7	8	9	10	11	12	13	14	15
7	7	8	9	10	11	12	13	14	15	16
8	8	9	10	11	12	13	14	15	16	17
9	9	10	11	12	13	14	15	16	17	18

area A
area E
area B
area C
area F
area D

Table 2-9 Addition Algorithm for Two Decimal Digits in 2-4-2-1 Code

Condition	Correction	Remark
$0101 \leq Z^* \leq 1000$	$Z = Z^* + 0110$	Z^* equal to 1001 or 1010 does not occur
$1{,}0110 \leq Z^* \leq 1{,}1010$	$Z = Z^* - 0110$	Z^* equal to 1,0101 does not occur

that, in areas *A* to *D*, the digit sums and the carries are both correct. In area *E*, an addition of 0110 to Z^* is required. In area *F*, a subtraction of 0110 from Z^* is required. The addition algorithm for two decimal digits in the 2-4-2-1 code is shown in Table 2-9. Note that Z^* equal to 1001 or 1010 does not occur in area *E* and that Z^* equal to 1,0101 does not occur in area *F*. These "don't care" conditions are helpful in simplifying the circuits for the 2-4-2-1 coded decimal adder.

2-4 Decimal Multiplication

As in binary multiplication, methods for decimal multiplication may be classified according to the manner in which the negative number is represented. For numbers in signed-magnitude representation, methods to be described are:

1. Repeated-addition method
2. Binary-multiplication (of decimal number) method
3. Nine-multiples-of-multiplicand method
4. Doubling-and-halving method
5. Right-and-left-hand-components method

In any of these methods, the sign of the product is the modulo-2 sum of the sign digits of the two numbers.

Binary-multiplication methods for numbers in signed-2's-complement representation—such as Robertson's method—can be extended for decimal multiplication with numbers in signed-10's-complement representation. Because of the necessary correction, however, and implementation of the shifting algorithm for signed decimal numbers, it is more practical to use decimal-multiplication methods for numbers in signed-magnitude representation. The number in signed-9's-complement representation converts with relative ease from the 9's complement to its magnitude. Consequently, decimal multiplication for numbers in signed-magnitude representation is more practical. The decimal-multiplication methods to be described are the above five methods for numbers in signed-magnitude representation.

Repeated-addition Method. Quite similar to paper-and-pencil multiplication, this method for decimal multiplication requires repeated additions of the multiplicand and shifting of the partial product after multiplication by each multiplier digit. The multiplying process follows the same sequence of operations shown in Fig. 1-2, except that the required number of additions of the multiplicand should be equal to the value of the multiplier digit which is multiplying. Multiplication of two n-digit numbers requires a maximum of 9 addition times per digit of multiplier, or an average of 4½ addition times per digit of multiplier.

Binary Multiplication of Decimal Numbers [4]. This method offers an interesting variation of the repeated-addition method and applies to decimal digits in the 8-4-2-1 code. By this method, the multiplier is converted into a binary form. Consider, for example, a decimal multiplier 975 and decimal numbers in the 8-4-2-1 code. The decimal multiplier can be expressed in the following form:

$$975 = (1 \times 2^3 + 0 \times 2^2 + 0 \times 2^1 + 1 \times 2^0) \times 10^2$$
$$+ (0 \times 2^3 + 1 \times 2^2 + 1 \times 2^1 + 1 \times 2^0) \times 10^1$$
$$+ (0 \times 2^3 + 1 \times 2^2 + 0 \times 2^1 + 1 \times 2^0) \times 10^0$$
$$= (100) \times 2^3 + (011) \times 2^2 + (010) \times 2^1 + (111) \times 2^0$$

The numbers in parentheses are four decimal numbers which are located at the four binary positions of the coded decimal digit. The 1 or 0 in these four decimal numbers is the digit value of each coded decimal digit. The operations initiated by the multiplier digits are performed according to the following sequence: For the decimal number in the binary position 2^0, each 1 or 0 in the corresponding decimal number causes the multiplicand to be, respectively, added or not added, followed by shifting the partial product one *decimal* digit. After completion of additions and shifts for the decimal number at this binary position, the partial product is shifted one *binary* digit. Then begins the additions and shifts for the decimal number in the 2^1 binary position. The process continues until the decimal numbers at all binary positions are exhausted.

In this method, the additions and shifts resemble those for binary multiplication of binary numbers, because the multiplier bit determines whether the multiplicand is to be added or not added to the partial product. Points of dissimilarity are the additions performed in decimal adders and the partial-product shift in decimal and in binary digits.

Nine-multiples-of-multiplicand Method [4]. The repeated-addition method involves two operations: multiplication of the multiplicand by one multiplier digit, and shifting of the partial product. If the nine multiples of the multiplicand are made available simultaneously, each multiplier digit merely selects which multiple is added. By using this method, it is possible to reduce the multiplication time to one addition time per digit.

The generation of nine multiples takes time and is usually impractical. However, multiplication time can still be reduced by using one or more multiples. If both first and second multiples are available, the multiplication time will not exceed five addition times per digit. If both first and third multiples are available, the multiplication time will be no more than four addition times per digit. Given first, second, and fourth multiples, multiplication will not require more than three addition times per digit. As indicated by the word *available*, the foregoing multiplication time has not included the time for generating the required multiples.

Doubling-and-halving Method [4]. The doubling-and-halving method utilizes the following identities,

$$X \cdot Y = 2X \frac{Y}{2} \qquad \text{if } Y \text{ is even}$$

$$X \cdot Y = 2X \frac{Y-1}{2} + X \qquad \text{if } Y \text{ is odd} \tag{2-4}$$

where X and Y are two decimal numbers to be multiplied. The multiplication is performed by repeatedly applying these two identities, illustrated by the following multiplication of 36 by 69:

$$
\begin{aligned}
36 \times 69 &= 72 \times 34 + 36 \\
&= 144 \times 17 + 36 \\
&= 288 \times 8 + 36 + 144 \\
&= 576 \times 4 + 36 + 144 \\
&= 1{,}152 \times 2 + 36 + 144 \\
&= 2{,}304 + 36 + 144 \\
&= 2{,}484
\end{aligned}
$$

The above multiplying process can be rearranged in the following manner:

Multipliers	Multiplicands	Partial products
69	36	36
34	72	
17	144	144
8	288	
4	576	
2	1,152	
1	2,304	2,304
0	4,608	
		2,484 product

As shown, the product is the sum of those multiplicands whose corresponding multipliers are odd numbers. The 0 is taken as an even number. By this method, the multiplication requires three operations: doubling, halving, and adding. If a decimal number is in a binary code, then the doubling or halving of the number can shift each decimal digit of the number one binary digit to the left or right.

The above multiplication can also be rewritten in the following manner:

$$36 \times 69 = 36 \times (1 \times 2^6 + 0 \times 2^5 + 0 \times 2^4 + 0 \times 2^3 + 1 \times 2^2$$
$$+ 0 \times 2^1 + 1 \times 2^0)$$
$$= 36 \times 2^6 + 36 \times 2^2 + 36 \times 2^0$$
$$= 2{,}304 + 144 + 36$$
$$= 2{,}484$$

In this case, the multiplier is converted into a binary number and the multiplication carried out with decimal additions and binary shifts. Since an n-digit decimal number is equivalent to $n/\log 2$ binary digits, the multiplication time by using this method is $n/\log 2$, or about $3.3n$ addition times.

Right-and-left-hand-components Method [4]. When two decimal digits are multiplied, the product consists of two decimal digits. For example, 4×2 and 6×2 give the products 08 and 12, respectively. The decimal digits 0 and 1 are called the left-hand components, and digits 8 and 2 are the right-hand components. The multiplication of any two decimal digits produces 100 pairs of right-hand and left-hand components. These components are shown in Table 2-10, where X and Y are, respectively, the multiplicand and the multiplier. The multiplication by this method is exemplified below:

$$\begin{array}{rl} 32345 = & X \text{(multiplicand)} \\ \underline{68} = & Y \text{(multiplier)} \\ 46420 & \text{right-hand component} \\ \underline{21234} & \text{left-hand component} \\ 258760 & \text{first partial product} \\ 82840 & \text{right-hand component} \\ \underline{11123} & \text{left-hand component} \\ 2199460 & \text{product} \end{array}$$

The generation of these components is achieved by implementing Table 2-10. Multiplication by this method can be completed in n addition times if the right-hand component, the left-hand component, and the partial product are simultaneously added.

Table 2-10   *Left-hand and Right-hand Components*

Y	Left-hand component	Right-hand component
	0 1 2 3 4 5 6 7 8 9 = X =	0 1 2 3 4 5 6 7 8 9
0	0 0 0 0 0 0 0 0 0 0	0 0 0 0 0 0 0 0 0 0
1	0 0 0 0 0 0 0 0 0 0	0 1 2 3 4 5 6 7 8 9
2	0 0 0 0 0 1 1 1 1 1	0 2 4 6 8 0 2 4 6 8
3	0 0 0 0 1 1 1 2 2 2	0 3 6 9 2 5 8 1 4 7
4	0 0 0 1 1 2 2 2 3 3	0 4 8 2 6 0 4 8 2 6
5	0 0 1 1 2 2 3 3 4 4	0 5 0 5 0 5 0 5 0 5
6	0 0 1 1 2 3 3 4 4 5	0 6 2 8 4 0 6 2 8 4
7	0 0 1 2 2 3 4 4 5 6	0 7 4 1 8 5 2 9 6 3
8	0 0 1 2 3 4 4 5 6 7	0 8 6 4 2 0 8 6 4 2
9	0 0 1 2 3 4 5 6 7 8	0 9 8 7 6 5 4 3 2 1

2-5   *Decimal Division*

For the number in signed-magnitude representation, methods for decimal division to be described are:

1. Restoring method
2. Nonrestoring method
3. Nine-multiples-of-divisor method
4. Halving-the-divisor method
5. Gilman's method

In any of these the sign of the quotient is the modulo-2 sum of the sign digits of the two numbers.

Restoring Method. The restoring method for decimal division is similar to that for binary division. Let X, Y, Q, and R_n be, respectively, the dividend, the divisor, the quotient, and the nth remainder. The division process is to find the quotient Q and the remainder R_n which satisfy the following relation:

$$R_n = X - YQ \tag{2-5}$$

Assuming a dividend smaller than the divisor, or

$$X < Y \tag{2-6}$$

then the quotient Q becomes

$$Q = q_1 10^{-1} + q_2 10^{-2} + \cdots + q_n 10^{-n} \tag{2-7}$$

where q_i is the ith digit of the quotient and can have 1 of the 10 possible values $0, 1, 2, \ldots, 9$. By substituting (2-7) into (2-5), we have

$$R_n = X - Y(q_1 10^{-1} + q_2 10^{-2} + \cdots + q_n 10^{-n}) \tag{2-8}$$

Let R_n, the shifted nth remainder, be defined as

$$R_n = 10^{-n} r_n \tag{2-9}$$

The initial remainder ($n = 0$) is the first term on the right-hand side of (2-8), or

$$R_0 = r_0 = X \tag{2-10}$$

The first remainder ($n = 1$) is the first two terms on the right-hand side of (2-8),

$$R_1 = X - q_1 10^{-1} Y = R_0 - q_1 10^{-1} Y \tag{2-11}$$

or

$$r_1 = 10X - q_1 Y = 10 r_0 - q_1 Y \tag{2-12}$$

The second remainder ($n = 2$) is the first three terms on the right-hand side of (2-8),

$$R_2 = X - q_1 10^{-1} Y - q_2 10^{-2} Y = R_1 - q_2 10^{-2} Y \tag{2-13}$$

$$r_2 = 10(10X - q_1 Y) - q_2 Y = 10 r_1 - q_2 Y \tag{2-14}$$

If this continues, the nth remainder is

$$R_n = 10^{-n} r_n = 10 r_{n-1} - q_n Y \tag{2-15}$$

The preceding recursive relation (2-15) is the algorithm for the restoring-division method. The quotient digit q_i is the largest value of the 10 possible values that make the corresponding remainder still positive. When the remainder becomes negative, it is restored positive by adding the divisor. The use of this restoring algorithm is exemplified by letting the dividend X be 0.2484 and the divisor Y be 0.69. This division becomes

$$r_0 = X = 0.2484$$
$$10X = 2.484$$

Subtract $Y - 0.690$

$$\overline{1.794} \qquad q_1 = 1$$

Subtract $Y - 0.690$

$$\overline{1.104} \qquad q_1 = 2$$

Subtract $Y - 0.690$

$$\overline{0.414} \qquad q_1 = 3$$

Subtract $Y - 0.690$

$$\overline{9.724} \qquad q_1 = 4$$

Restore or add $Y + 0.690$

$$\overline{r_1 = 0.414} \qquad q_1 = 3$$
$$10r_1 = 4.140$$

Subtract $Y - 0.690$

$$\overline{3.450} \qquad q_2 = 1$$

$$. \; . \; . \; . \; .$$

$$\overline{0.690} \qquad q_2 = 5$$

Subtract $Y - 0.690$

$$\overline{0} \qquad q_2 = 6$$

$$Q = q_1 10^{-1} + q_2 10^{-2} = 0.36$$

Nonrestoring Method. The nonrestoring-division method to be shown here applies to decimal numbers in signed-magnitude representation. We begin from relation (2-5) and assumption (2-6). The initial remainder r_0 is the dividend X, or

$$r_0 = X \qquad\qquad (2\text{-}16)$$

The first remainder r_1 is obtained by shifting r_0 to the left one decimal digit and then subtracting the divisor m times (m may have a value of 1 to 10) from the shifted r_0 until the difference first becomes negative or until m equals 9,

$$r_1 = 10r_0 - mY$$

If r_1 is the first negative difference, the quotient digit q_1 is equal to $m - 1$ and the remainder is not restored; if m is 9 and r_1 is still positive, q_1 is equal to 9 and restoring is not needed. In either case, the first remainder r_1 is

$$r_1 = 10r_0 - q_1 Y - Y \qquad\qquad (2\text{-}17)$$

The r_1 is then shifted to the left one decimal digit. If the shifted first remainder was negative, the second remainder r_2 is obtained by adding the divisor m times to the shifted r_1 until the sum first becomes positive or until m has the value of 9,

$$r_2 = 10(10r_0 - q_1 Y) - 10Y + mY$$

and the second quotient digit q_2 is equal to $10 - m$. The second remainder is

$$r_2 = 10(10r_0 - q_1 Y) - q_2 Y = 10r_1 + (10 - q_2) Y \qquad (2\text{-}18)$$

Therefore, if the first remainder was negative, it has actually been restored.

If the shifted first remainder was positive, the second remainder is obtained by subtracting the divisor m times from the shifted r_1 until the difference first becomes negative or until m has the value of 9,

$$r_2 = 10(10r_0 - q_1 Y) - 10Y - mY$$

and the second quotient digit q_2 is equal to m. The second remainder is

$$r_2 = 10r_1 - q_2 Y \qquad (2\text{-}19)$$

In a comparison of (2-18) and (2-19), the former shows the quantity $(10 - q_2) Y$ added to $10r_1$, whereas in the latter $q_2 Y$ is subtracted from $10r_1$. Note that $10 - q_2$ is the 10's complement of q_2.

This process continues until the remainder is zero or until the desired number of quotient digits is obtained. The following example illustrates application of the nonrestoring-division method for decimal numbers in signed-magnitude representation. Let dividend X and divisor Y be 0.2484 and 0.69, respectively. The division process follows:

$$r_0 = X = 0.2484$$
$$10r_0 = 2.484$$

Subtract $Y - 0.690$
$$\overline{\qquad 1.794} \qquad m = 1$$
Subtract $Y - 0.69$
$$\overline{\qquad 1.104} \qquad m = 2$$
Subtract $Y - 0.690$
$$\overline{\qquad 0.414} \qquad m = 3$$
Subtract $Y - 0.690$
$$\overline{\quad r_1 = 9.724} \qquad m = 4, \quad q_1 = m - 1 = 3$$
$$10r_1 = 7.240$$
Add $Y + 0.690$
$$\overline{\qquad 7.930} \qquad m = 1$$
Add $Y + 0.690$
$$\overline{\qquad 8.620} \qquad m = 2$$
Add $Y + 0.690$
$$\overline{\qquad 9.310} \qquad m = 3$$
Add $Y + 0.690$
$$\overline{\quad r_2 = 0.0000} \qquad m = 4, \quad q_2 = 10 - m = 6$$
$$Q = q_1 10^{-1} + q_2 10^{-2} = 0.36$$

Nine-multiples-of-divisor Method. The previously developed restoring method is essentially a repeated-subtraction method; the maximum and average division times are, respectively, $10n$ and $6.3n$ addition or subtraction times, where n is the number of quotient digits. The nonrestoring method is a repeated-subtraction-addition method; the maximum and average division times are, respectively, $9n$ and $5.4n$ addition or subtraction times. The division time can be reduced if the nine multiples of the divisor are made available simultaneously. In this case, each multiple is compared simultaneously with the remainder (or the dividend in the first step). The largest multiple which makes the next remainder positive is determined and a subtraction carried out. The remainder is then shifted to the left one digit. The shifted remainder is again simultaneously compared with the nine multiples of the divisor, and so forth. This process continues until the remainder is zero or the desired number of quotient digits is obtained. If the time spent in generating the nine multiples is disregarded, the division time can be made as small as n subtraction times.

As in the nine-multiples-of-multiplicand method for decimal multiplication, the generation of the nine multiples is not too practical. If one or a few multiples of the divisor are generated, the average division time can be reduced to between n and $6.3n$ subtraction times.

Halving-the-divisor Method.   This method is similar to the doubling-and-halving method for decimal multiplication. In the division equation (2-5), the quotient Q is a decimal number. Assume that

$$X < 2Y \qquad (2\text{-}20)$$

Then the quotient Q can be written as the following binary number:

$$Q = \sum_{n=0}^{n} p_n 2^{-n} \qquad (2\text{-}21)$$

When (2-21) is substituted into (2-5), we have

$$R_n = X - Y(p_0 2^0 + p_1 2^{-1} + \cdots + p_n 2^{-n}) \qquad (2\text{-}22)$$

Division now becomes the determining of p_i, which can be achieved by forming a series of remainders. The initial remainder is the first two terms on the right-hand side of (2-22), or

$$R_0 = X - p_0 Y$$

If R_0 is positive, then p_0 is 1; this occurs when X is equal to or larger than Y. If R_0 is negative, then p_0 is 0; this happens when X is smaller than Y. In short, when X is equal to or larger than Y, R_0 is equal to X subtracted by Y; when X is smaller than Y, R_0 is equal to X.

The first remainder R_1 is the first three terms on the right-hand side of (2-22),

$$R_1 = X - p_0 Y - \frac{p_1 Y}{2} = R_0 - \frac{p_1 Y}{2} \qquad (2\text{-}23)$$

Note that the multiplier Y is halved. If R_1 is equal to or larger than R_0, p_1 is 1 and $Y/2$ is subtracted from R_0. If R_1 is smaller than R_0, p_1 is 0 and R_1 is equal to R_0. This process continues; each time the multiplier Y is further halved, p_i is determined by comparison. When the remainder becomes zero or when the desired number of quotient digits is obtained, the division is completed.

An example is shown below, X and Y being, respectively, equal to 2,484 and 36. To fulfill condition (2-20), X is scaled to 24.84, and the corresponding quotient is denoted by Q'.

Divisor	Dividend	Quotient digits of Q'
$Y2^0 = 36$	$R_0 = 24.84$	$p_0 = 0$
$Y2^{-1} = 18$	$- 18$	
	$R_1 = 6.84$	$p_1 = 1$
$Y2^{-2} = 9$	$R_2 = 6.84$	$p_2 = 0$
$Y2^{-3} = 4.5$	$- 4.5$	
	$R_3 = 2.34$	$p_3 = 1$
$Y2^{-4} = 2.25$	$- 2.25$	
	$R_4 = 0.09$	$p_4 = 1$
$Y2^{-5} = 1.125$	$R_5 = 0.09$	$p_5 = 0$
$Y2^{-6} = 0.5625$	$R_6 = 0.09$	$p_6 = 0$
$Y2^{-7} = 0.28125$	$R_7 = 0.09$	$p_7 = 0$
$Y2^{-8} = 0.140625$	$R_8 = 0.09$	$p_8 = 0$
$Y2^{-9} = 0.0703125$	$- 0.0703125$	
	$R_9 = 0.0196875$	$p_9 = 1$

The quotient Q' is then

$$Q' = 2^{-1} + 2^{-3} + 2^{-4} + 2^{-9} = {}^{353}\!/\!_{512} = 0.689$$

The quotient Q' should be multiplied by 10^2 to obtain Q. Thus, the originally sought quotient Q is 68.9. This only approximates the correct quotient of 69, because conversion of the decimal number Q from a binary number may not always be exact. Since the divisor is halved each time a new remainder is obtained, the reason for the name of the method becomes apparent.

Gilman's Method. Gilman's method [20] for decimal division is a series of successive approximations by which the divisor is made to approach 1 and the dividend to approach the quotient. This method is best explained by an example. The numbers 0.2484 and 0.36 are chosen as the dividend and the divisor, respectively. Division consists of two operations—the preliminary and the routine. The example is developed step by step.

Step 1. This is the preliminary operation. Select a multiplier which multiplies both the divisor and the dividend so that the multiplier-divisor product begins with 0.9 or 1.0. In this example the multiplier 3 is chosen.

Divisor	Dividend
0.360000000	0.248400000
1.080000000	0.745200000

The numbers 1.08 and 0.7452 become the new divisor and the new dividend, respectively.

Step 2. This and the following steps are the routine operations. This step requires the second digit (the most significant fractional digit) of the new divisor to be either 9 or 0 and requires selection of a new multiplier. If the second digit is 0, the chosen multiplier is the third digit of the new divisor, with the decimal point located at the same position as that of the new divisor. If the second digit is 9, the chosen multiplier is the 10's complement of the digit of the new divisor, with the decimal point located at the same position as that of the new divisor. In either case, the new divisor and the new dividend are both multiplied by the chosen multiplier. The products are then added to or subtracted from the new divisor and the new dividend, depending on the examined second digit being 9 or 0, respectively. In this example, the second digit of the latest divisor is 0; thus, the chosen multiplier is 0.08 (shown underlined in the above). The two products are 0.0864 (1.08 × 0.08) and 0.059616 (0.7452 × 0.08), and the following subtractions are performed:

$$
\begin{array}{ll}
1.080000000 & 0.745200000 \\
- \ 0.084600000 & - \ 0.059616000 \\
\hline
0.995\underline{4}00000 & 0.685584000
\end{array}
$$

The above divisor 0.9954 is already quite close to 1, and thus the corresponding dividend 0.685584 is also close to the correct quotient of 0.69. In general, the number of the correct digits in the quotient is equal to the number of the consecutive 9's or 0's in the divisor, beginning with the most significant fractional digit. In the last divisor, there are two 9's, and the two correct quotient digits result in a quotient 0.69 with round-off. The numbers 0.9954 and 0.685584 now become the new divisor and the new dividend, respectively.

Step 3. In this step, the second digit of the new divisor (which can be either 9 or 0) is again examined, and a multiplier is again chosen. If the digit is 0 or 9, the chosen multiplier is, respectively, the fourth and fifth digits or their 10's complement of the new divisor, with the decimal point located at the same position as that of the new divisor. The new divisor and the new dividend are again both multiplied by the chosen multiplier. The products are then added to or subtracted from the new divisor and new dividend, depending on the examined second digit being 9 or 0, respectively. In this example, the second digit of the latest divisor is 9; thus, the chosen multiplier is 0.0046 (the complement of that shown underlined in the above). The two products are 0.00457884 and 0.003153686, and the following additions are performed:

$$
\begin{array}{ll}
0.995400000 & 0.685584000 \\
0.004578840 & 0.003153686 \\
\hline
0.999978840 & 0.688737686
\end{array}
$$

The above divisor 0.99997884 is very close to 1, and thus the corresponding dividend 0.688737686 is also very close to the correct quotient of 0.69. Since there are four 9's in the latest divisor, the correct quotient digits are 0.6887.

Step 4. If a better result is desired, more routine operations have to be taken. This step is similar to Step 3 except that the multiplier is chosen from the sixth, seventh, eighth, and ninth digits or their 10's complement.

Other steps can be similarly formulated. Ordinarily, four routine operations produce an accuracy of 8 digits, five operations an accuracy of 16 digits, and so forth.

2-6   *Floating-point Arithmetic*

In a fixed-point computer, the location of the radix point, once established during design, is considered fixed, although no such point physically exists at the computer. The binary point, for example, of the number N is commonly chosen in a binary computer so that the number is always fractional, or $-1 \leq N < 1$.

Numbers outside this range require scaling or shifting operations provided for in the programming. This requires effort by the programmer, who may have difficulty keeping all numbers within machine range during computation. In any event, the programming becomes more time-consuming and painstaking.

In a floating-point computer, the radix point for each number varies automatically; this results in easier programming. Historically, it was the user of the computer who developed the "floating-point routine" in coping with the difficulty of keeping within machine range the numbers in inputs, intermediate results, and outputs. The floating-point computer has a built-in logic for floating-point arithmetic. This feature was regarded as one major advance in digital computer design. Because of the added complexity in the arithmetic unit and because floating-point operation can be programmed (at the expense of speed), not all computers in use today possess the built-in floating-point logic.

The following arithmetic is described in terms of decimal numbers, but the principle applies equally well to binary numbers.

Representation of Floating-point Numbers. The floating-point number is represented by an expression which consists of two portions, the fraction part (or *mantissa*) and the exponent part (or *characteristic*). For example, the following decimal number can be written as a fraction multiplied by a power of 10:

$$+1357.9531 = +.13579531 \times 10^{+4}$$
$$-.00246864 = -.24686400 \times 10^{-2}$$

Each of the above numbers consists of a fractional part and an exponent part. These two-part numbers appear further simplified with the omission of the symbol 10,

$$+.13579531 \times 10^{+4} = +13579531 + 4$$
$$-.24686400 \times 10^{-2} = -24686400 - 2$$

Of the 11 digits in these numbers, the first digit represents the sign, the next 8 are number digits, and the last 2 are exponent digits. Another arrangement places the exponent part at the left of the fractional part. Furthermore, the exponent part may be represented by a biased number, which is the sum of the exponent and a constant (say, 50); such representation avoids use of a positive and a negative exponent. With these two modifications, the above two decimal numbers now become

$$+.13579531 \times 10^{+4} = +5413579531$$
$$-.24686400 \times 10^{-2} = -4824686400$$

Addition of the constant 50 to the exponent part expresses in 2 digits any exponent between 10^{+49} and 10^{-50}. Thus, the floating-point number can be made to represent a very large range of numbers, enough for all practical uses. However, it should be noted that the quantity of *number* digits is reduced; for example, in the above decimal numbers, the 10 number digits (excluding the sign digit) are reduced to 8 digits. Instead of using a biased exponent to avoid the occurrence of positive and negative exponents, the exponent part may be expressed in a complement representation.

The above floating-point number representation consists of a fractional part which is smaller than 1 but equal to or larger than 0.1. This particular representation is referred to as the *normalized form,* the form in which numbers are stored in the memory unit. Operations scaling a floating-point number to the normalized form are called *normalizing.* The fractional part f of a floating-point decimal number in the normalized form lies in the following ranges:

$$0.1 \leq f < 1 \qquad \text{for positive numbers}$$
$$-0.1 \geq f > -1 \qquad \text{for negative numbers}$$

The most desirable normalized form has a nonzero most significant digit in the fractional part and also a range as large as possible. A nonzero most significant digit in the fractional part makes possible all digits' being significant in the fractional part. If a floating-point number is not in a normalized form, it is in either an overflow form or an underflow form. In the former case, there are nonzero digits to the left of the radix point. In the latter case, nonzero digits occur to the immediate right of the radix point. The decimal numbers $+1.357953 \times 10^{+4}$ and $-0.02468640 \times 10^{-2}$ are two examples.

   Addition and Subtraction.   Adding or subtracting two numbers requires first an alignment of radix points: exponent parts of the two numbers must be made equal before addition or subtraction. Let f and e be the fractional part and the exponent part, respectively, of a floating-point number, and let subscripts a and b represent the two numbers A and B, respectively. We have

$$A = f_a 10^{e_a} \tag{2-24}$$

$$B = f_b 10^{e_b} \tag{2-25}$$

Addition or subtraction of the two floating-point numbers yields

$$A \pm B = (f_a \pm f_b \times 10^{-d}) \times 10^{e_a} \qquad \text{for } e_a > e_b \tag{2-26}$$

$$A \pm B = (f_a \times 10^{+d} \pm f_b) \times 10^{e_b} \qquad \text{for } e_b > e_a \tag{2-27}$$

where
$$d = e_a - e_b \tag{2-28}$$

   The steps taken by the arithmetic unit in carrying out the addition or subtraction are derived from the above equations. The difference d of the two exponent parts is first obtained by subtracting e_b from e_a. The larger exponent is then taken as the exponent of the sum 'or difference. If d is not zero, the number with a smaller exponent part is scaled by being shifted d digits to the right. The addition or subtraction is performed on the scaled numbers. Finally, the sum or the difference is normalized.

   In scaling a number the exponent part may become overlarge and exceed its allocated digits (two decimal digits in the above example). Likewise, when the fractional parts of two numbers are added, the fractional part of the sum may exceed its allocated digits (eight decimal digits in the above example). To meet this contingency, the computer arithmetic unit often provides bit-storage elements for both exponent- and fractional-part overflows.

   Round-off may be applied after the addition or subtraction, provided that the sum or difference does not require use of exact numbers in further computation or as an end product. With round-off, the error from indiscriminate dropping of digits due to limited number digits will not become cumulative.

   Multiplication.   Multiplication of two floating-point numbers A and B requires no initial alignment of the radix point. The product can be formed directly by multiplying the two fractional parts and by adding the exponent parts, or

$$AB = (f_a f_b) 10^{e_a + e_b} \tag{2-29}$$

No overflow results, as the product of two fractions is still a fraction. When the numbers A and B, each with n fractional digits, are in normalized form, their product contains $2n$ or $2n - 1$ significant digits. In the latter case, the product is in an underflow form with one nonzero digit at the immediate right of the radix point. For this case, the product should be rounded off before normalizing. If the round-off does not yield a product of $2n$ digits, the product is shifted to the left one digit, with a corresponding change in the exponent part of the product and then is rounded off again. Improper round-off may cause the product to lose its significant digits. If the exponent part is biased by a constant, the constant should be subtracted from the sum of the two exponent parts.

Division. Division of two floating-point numbers A and B conversely parallels their multiplication. The quotient can be formed directly by dividing the fractional part of the dividend by that of the divisor and by subtracting the divisor exponent from the dividend exponent,

$$\frac{A}{B} = \frac{f_a}{f_b} 10^{e_a - e_b} \tag{2-30}$$

In fixed-point division, the dividend has to be smaller than the divisor. The divide-stop condition occurs otherwise and is indicated to the operator. Similarly floating-point division requires that the fractional part of the dividend be smaller than that of the divisor. If the fractional part of the dividend is not smaller, the dividend has to be first rescaled. When both dividend and divisor are in normalized form, all digits in both fractional parts are significant digits with no leading zeros. However, the dividend may still be larger than the divisor. This can be readily remedied by shifting the dividend before division one digit to the right (i.e., by multiplying by 10^{-1}) and by changing correspondingly the exponent part of the quotient. In this manner, the dividend now will certainly be smaller than the divisor, and the division can proceed.

2-7   *Residue Number Arithmetic* [22]

Congruences.   The residue number is based on the concept of linear congruence. An integer A is said to be congruent to an integer R mod b, or

$$A \equiv R \text{ mod } b \tag{2-31}$$

The above congruence means that A is equal to the sum of the integer R and an integral multiple m of *modulo* (or *base*) b, or

$$A = R + mb \tag{2-32}$$

Integer R is called the *residue*, the positive remainder obtained by dividing integer A by base b. For example, if A is 10 and b is 3, then three possible residues are 7, 4, and 1. When written in terms of congruence, they are

$$10 \equiv 7 \text{ mod } 3$$
$$10 \equiv 4 \text{ mod } 3$$
$$10 \equiv 1 \text{ mod } 3$$

The integers 7, 4, and 1 are said to form a residue class of 10 mod 3. The residue 1 is called the *least positive residue;* it is a positive integer but is smaller than the base, or $0 \le R < b$. As will be shown, it is the least positive residue that is used in residue number arithmetic.

Some properties of congruences are stated in the following without proof. Consider the following set of congruences all having the same base:

$$A_1 \equiv R_1 \text{ mod } b$$
$$. . . . .$$
$$A_n \equiv R_n \text{ mod } b$$

(2-33)

1. When congruences of the same modulus are added, the result is a congruence of the same modulus, or

$$\sum_{i=1}^{n} A_i \equiv \left(\sum_{i=1}^{n} R_i \right) \text{mod } b$$

(2-34)

2. As a corollary, when one congruence is subtracted from another with the same modulus, the result is a congruence of the same modulus, or

$$A_1 - A_2 \equiv (R_1 - R_2) \text{ mod } b$$

(2-35)

3. Also as a corollary, the terms in a congruence may be transferred from one side to the other by a change of sign.

4. When congruences of the same modulus are multiplied, the result is a congruence of the same modulus, or

$$\prod_{i=1}^{n} A_i \equiv \left(\prod_{i=1}^{n} R_i \right) \text{ mod } b$$

(2-36)

5. As a corollary, if both sides of the congruence are raised to the same power or multiplied by a constant, the result is a congruence of the same base.

6. Congruences are transitive. That is, if $A \equiv B$ and $B \equiv C$, then $A \equiv C$.

7. When the integer, the residue, and the modulus of a congruence are divided by a common factor, the result is a congruence.

8. When the integer and the residue of a congruence are divided by some common factor relatively prime to the modulus, the result is a congruence.

Residue Number Representation.   A residue number system can be established by choosing a set of bases which are prime numbers—such as 2, 3, 5, 7, 11, 13, 17, 19, 23, etc. Let N be the decimal number. If the four chosen bases are 2, 3, 5, and 7, then the residue number is represented by the least positive residues $R_2 R_3 R_5 R_7$ defined by the following congruences:

$$N \equiv R_2 \text{ mod } 2$$
$$N \equiv R_3 \text{ mod } 3$$
$$N \equiv R_5 \text{ mod } 5$$
$$N \equiv R_7 \text{ mod } 7$$

(2-37)

The first 19 residue numbers are shown in Table 2-11. This residue number system contains 210 states or independent representations, and this number equals the product of all the four chosen bases. If the prime base 11 is included, then

Table 2-11 2-3-5-7 Residue Number System

Decimal number	$R_2R_3R_5R_7$	Decimal number	$R_2R_3R_5R_7$
0	0000	10	0103
1	1111	11	1214
2	0222	12	0025
3	1033	13	1136
4	0144	14	0240
5	1205	15	1001
6	0016	16	0112
7	1120	17	1223
8	0231	18	0034
9	1042	19	1145

there are 2,310 states; if an additional base 13 is included, there are 30,030 states. When the prime bases include those up to 23, there are more than 223 million states. When one residue number is added to or multiplied by another residue number, the residue number system must possess sufficient states to represent the resulting sum or product. The residue representation, otherwise, of the sum or product may correspond to more than one decimal number.

In the above, prime numbers are chosen as the bases for a residue number system. The chosen set of bases need not be prime numbers. It is necessary only that the chosen bases be relatively prime. For example, numbers 20 and 21, neither of which is a prime number, can serve as bases for a residue number system. In this case, the available number of unique representations is equal to the product of all those relative prime numbers.

The *complement* representation $\bar{A}$ of a residue number A is so defined that their modulo sum is 0, or

$$A + \bar{A} = 0 \tag{2-38}$$

This formula is applicable to the residue number in its entirety as well as to each digit of the residue number. Consider the residue number A (1223) of the 2-3-5-7 residue number system. Its complement $\bar{A}$ is the residue number 1134 because the modulo sum of each corresponding pair of residues is zero, or:

Residue representation

```
  2 3 5 7

  1 2 2 3
  1 1 3 4
  2 3 5 7   sum of residues
  0 0 0 0   modulo sum
```

The *negative* residue number A can also be represented by its complement $\bar{A}$. In this way, the range of A is reduced to about one-half the total possible residue representations; the other one-half serves to represent negative residue numbers. For example, in the above 2-3-5-7 residue number system the residue number representation is divided into two parts. The positive residue numbers correspond to decimal numbers 0 to 104; the negative numbers correspond to decimal numbers 105 to 209, which are the complements of the negative decimal numbers

-105 to -1. Thus, the residue number range is the decimal numbers -105 to $+104$.

In general, one can divide the total number range into positive and negative regions for number A and its complement $\bar{A}$, respectively. However, there is no simple way in which one can determine whether a number is positive or negative, since it is not possible, for example, to look at the most significant digit of a signed binary number and determine immediately the sign of a number.

Residue Number Arithmetic. The addition of two residue numbers follows congruence (2-34), which states that the sum of the integers A_i is the sum of their residues from the same modulo b. The residue sum is not necessarily equal to the actual decimal sum. An example of adding the decimal numbers 19 to 26 in the 2-3-5-7 residue number system is shown below:

		Residue representation			
Decimal Representation	2	3	5	7	
19	1	1	4	5	
+26	0	2	1	5	
45	1	3	5	10	sum of residues
	1	0	0	3	modulo sum

Note that the sum of residues is a *modulo sum*. The modulo sum is an arithmetic sum; but the carry, which is the quotient obtained by dividing the modulo sum by the base, is disregarded if it occurs. Thus, it has the distinguishing property of *addition without carry*. Another example, of adding the decimal number 250 to 26 in the same residue number system, appears as follows:

		Residue representation			
Decimal representation	2	3	5	7	
250	0	1	0	5	
+ 26	0	2	1	5	
276	0	0	1	3	modulo sum

Since the sum 276 exceeds 209, the largest number in the 2-3-5-7 residue number system, the residue sum 0013, corresponds to decimal number 66—not 276. In other words, the decimal sum has overflowed the residue number system and actually is the residue of the integer 276 mod 210,

$$276 \equiv 66 \bmod 210$$

The subtraction of two residue numbers follows congruence (2-35). An example of subtracting the decimal number 9 from 16 in the same residue number system is shown below:

		Residue representation			
Decimal representation	2	3	5	7	
16	0	1	1	2	minuend
−9	1	0	4	2	subtrahend
7	1	1	2	0	difference of residues

Note that, during subtraction, each residue of the minuend can be increased by the value of its respective base if needed and the borrow disregarded. If the larger number 16 is subtracted from 9, the result is the residue number 1230 (or decimal number 203), which is the complement of the residue number 1120 (or decimal number 7).

Multiplication of two residue numbers follows congruence (2-36). This states that the product of the integers A_i is the product of their residues from the same modulo b. An example of multiplying two decimal numbers 13 and 11 is shown below:

	Residue representation			
Decimal representation	2	3	5	7
13	1	1	3	6
×11	1	2	1	4
143	1	2	3	24	product of residues
	1	2	3	3	modulo product

The extreme simplicity of multiplying residue numbers is a reward for using the residue number representation.

Division of the residue number corresponds to normal division only when the quotient is an integer. A satisfactory algorithm for residue number division remains to be developed.

As has been shown, the carry or borrow occurring during addition, subtraction, or multiplication of residue numbers can be ignored. This is an important advantage because the speed of current circuitry in performing addition, subtraction, and multiplication is limited by the ability of the circuit to handle carry and borrow. However, some difficulties attend the use of residue number arithmetic. One problem is that the number of independent representations from a chosen set of moduli may be exceeded as a result of arithmetic operations, and this overflow cannot be detected. Another problem is determining the correct sign of the difference in a subtraction, although this can be achieved by translating the result to a weighted number system such as the decimal number system. Lastly, no known method exists of performing division of residue numbers.

Residue-coded Decimal Numbers [15]. To avoid difficulty in representing a decimal number by a residue number, one approach uses the residue-coded decimal number in which the decimal digit is represented by 10 residue numbers. If the integers 5 and 2 are chosen as the moduli, there are 10 unique states available to represent a decimal digit. These 10 residue numbers 00, 11, 20, etc., are shown in Table 2-12. The values 0 to 4 of these residues are further coded by the binary numbers 000 to 100 also shown in Table 2-12.

When two decimal digits are added or multiplied, the operation is carried out by adding or multiplying residues of the corresponding modulus; there is no carry among the moduli, although the decimal carry may still occur. Thus the advantage of "no carry" in using residue numbers is partially retained. One way to achieve addition of the residues is to build an addition table into the computer. The addition table is shown in Table 2-13. Determination of the decimal carry from a decimal digit is not so simple. Let X and Y be two input decimal digits. A decimal carry occurs when X or Y is equal to or greater than 5 and when the modulo-5 sum of the residues of X and Y is equal to or greater than 5. Alternatively, a decimal carry occurs when the sum of X and Y is equal to 9 and when there is a carry from the next least significant decimal digit. The addition of an

Table 2-12   Residue-coded Decimal Digit and Its Binary Code

Decimal digit	Residue of modulo 5	Residue of modulo 2	Binary code
0	0	0	0000
1	1	1	0011
2	2	0	0100
3	3	1	0111
4	4	0	1000
5	0	1	0001
6	1	0	0010
7	2	1	0101
8	3	0	0110
9	4	1	1001

Table 2-13   Addition Table for Residues of Moduli 5 and 2

	Modulo 5					Modulo 2	
	0	1	2	3	4	0	1
0	0	1	2	3	4	0	1
1	1	2	3	4	0	1	0
2	2	3	4	0	1		
3	3	4	0	1	2		
4	4	0	1	2	3		

Table 2-14   9's Complement of a Residue-coded Decimal Digit

Modulo 5		Modulo 2	
Residue	Complement	Residue	Complement
0	4	0	1
1	3	1	0
2	2		
3	1		
4	0		

input decimal can be achieved by adding 1 to both the modulo-5 and modulo-2 parts of the sum.

The subtraction may be carried out by using the addition-of-10's-complement method. The 10's complement of the subtrahend can be obtained by using its 9's complement during the addition and then adding a carry to the least significant digit of the sum. The residue code for the 9's complement of the decimal digit is shown in Table 2-14. This table shows that the complement of the residue in modulo-5 is its 4's complement and that in modulo-2 is its 1's complement.

The multiplication of residue-coded decimal numbers can be performed by using the repeated-addition method and the division by using either the repeated-subtraction or the repeated-addition-subtraction method.

2-8   Error-checking Codes

The severe reliability requirements imposed on a digital computer call for the use of error-checking codes. The error-checking codes are those which can be made to self-detect and/or self-correct errors that arise as a result of an information-transfer operation or an arithmetic (or a logic) operation. Preferably an error-checking code should be capable of checking both operations. The code to be described consists of information digits and check digits. The check digits are redundancies to verify information digits by the use of checking circuits. If enough check digits are provided, it is possible actually to correct the most likely types of errors.

Forbidden-combination Check. In the previously shown 4-bit binary-coded decimal numbers, only 10 of 16 possible binary numbers are selected to represent a decimal digit. The other 6 do not occur, and these "forbidden combinations" may thus be used for error-checking purposes; this is called the *forbidden-combination check.* Similarly, the use of more-than-4-bit codes as shown in Table 2-3 makes possible the formulation of a simple rule for detecting forbidden combinations. For example, in the biquinary code and 2-out-of-5 code in Table 2-3, an error is detected whenever a coded digit has more or less than two 1's. However, the advantage of using the forbidden-combination check with more-than-4-bit codes should be weighed against the additional circuitry.

In general, the amount of redundancy introduced for the forbidden-combination check should be sufficient so that allowed combinations of binary digits are separated, one from the other, by forbidden combinations. If, for example, a single error occurs which modifies the combination of binary digits, this results in a forbidden combination, enabling one to detect the error.

On the other hand, if the redundancy is not adequate, the forbidden-combination check, though simple, is very limited. This can be demonstrated as follows: Assume that only one error occurs at a time in the 8-4-2-1 coded decimal digit 0000. The corrupted coded decimal digit would be 0001, 0010, 0100, or 1000. Since none of these 4 is a forbidden combination, a single error cannot be detected by the forbidden-combination check. Consider now the coded decimal digit 1001. For a single error, the corrupted coded decimal digit would be 1000, 1011, 1101, or 0001. Of these 4, the second and the third are the forbidden combinations, and thus an error can be detected. If all the 10 coded decimal digits are examined in this manner, the average probability of detecting a single error is 0.25. It has been shown that the best 4-bit code consists of 10 binary numbers (out of a possible 16) which include those 8 having the number of 1's all odd or all even. These best 4-bit codes can increase an average probability of detecting a single error to 0.6. But this still cannot ensure the detection of a single error. One way to increase the probability is to use more forbidden combinations, available in the previously mentioned more-than-4-bit codes.

Parity Check for Binary or Binary-coded Number. A simple way for checking errors is to use one redundant bit for the sole purpose of checking. Table 2-15 shows the 4-bit binary numbers with an added check bit called the *parity bit p.* The value of the parity bit is so chosen that the number of 1's in the 5 bits (i.e., including the parity bit) is odd; this is called the *odd parity check.* In this way, a single error in any one of 5 bits can always be detected. There are several important properties to be noticed:

1. If there is an error in the parity bit itself, the error will be detected.

2. The parity check can detect the existence of an error if an odd number of errors occurs but may not detect it if there is an even number of errors.

3. There are at least two changes of 1-to-0 or 0-to-1 between two corresponding bit of any two 5-bit numbers for detecting a single error; this condition is generally true for error-checking codes. Such 1-to-0 or 0-to-1 change between two corresponding bits is referred to as a *bit change.*

4. The parity check is invariant to the shifting of the binary number if no bits are added or deleted.

5. The parity check is independent of the binary point location.

Table 2-15   Odd Parity Bit in 4-bit Binary Number

Decimal number	Binary number with odd parity bit				
	x_3	x_2	x_1	x_0	p
0	0	0	0	0	1
1	0	0	0	1	0
2	0	0	1	0	0
3	0	0	1	1	1
4	0	1	0	0	0
5	0	1	0	1	1
6	0	1	1	0	1
7	0	1	1	1	0
8	1	0	0	0	0
9	1	0	0	1	1
10	1	0	1	0	1
11	1	0	1	1	0
12	1	1	0	0	1
13	1	1	0	1	0
14	1	1	1	0	0
15	1	1	1	1	1

6. The parity check makes use of the concept of congruence, because the value of the above parity bit makes the modulo-2 sum of the values of the 5 bits equal to 1, or

$$x_3 \oplus x_2 \oplus x_1 \oplus x_0 \oplus p = 1 \qquad (2\text{-}39)$$

where the symbol $\oplus$ denotes the modulo-2 sum. If the following two relations are utilized,

$$p \oplus p = 0 \qquad \text{and} \qquad 1 \oplus 1 = 0 \qquad (2\text{-}40)$$

relation (2-39) can be rewritten in the following form:

$$p = x_3 \oplus x_2 \oplus x_1 \oplus x_0 \oplus 1 \qquad (2\text{-}41)$$

The parity bit can be chosen so that the number of 1's in the 5 bits is even; this is called the *even parity check*. The value of the even parity bit makes the modulo-2 sum of the values of the 5 bits equal to 0, or

$$x_3 \oplus x_2 \oplus x_1 \oplus x_0 \oplus p = 0 \qquad (2\text{-}42)$$

This can be written in another form,

$$p = x_3 \oplus x_2 \oplus x_1 \oplus x_0 \qquad (2\text{-}43)$$

There are no overwhelming arguments in favor of either even or odd parity. However, odd parity is ordinarily used, for two reasons: The zero digit is often represented by the absence of signal, so that the use of odd parity ensures that some signal will be obtained; computer words often consist of an even number of digits, so that odd parity will detect the situation in which all 1's or all 0's have occurred because of a circuit malfunction. It is noted that neither odd nor even parity check will detect double errors, because a double error may leave the modulo-2 sum of the number of 1's or the number of 0's unchanged. A parity check need not necessarily include every digit of the number. Multiple parity checks may be employed so that each parity bit checks only certain allocated digits.

Parity Check for Decimal Number. The previously mentioned congruent concept of the parity check has been extended by Garner [18] to the decimal number. Consider the decimal number N,

$$N = \sum_{i=0}^{n-1} x_i 10^i \tag{2-44}$$

With respect to the decimal number, there are two types of parity checks: the *digit parity check* and the *number parity check*. First consider the digit parity check which is defined below,

$$\sum_{i=0}^{n-1} x_i \equiv p \bmod r \tag{2-45}$$

where p is the parity digit and r the radix, or base. For even-digit parity check, the parity digit p is given by

$$p = x_{n-1} \oplus \cdots \oplus x_0 \tag{2-46}$$

For odd-digit parity check, the parity digit p is given by

$$p = x_{n-1} \oplus \cdots \oplus x_0 \oplus (r - 1) \tag{2-47}$$

When the base is 2, (2-46) and (2-47) become, respectively, (2-43) and (2-41). As an example, consider the decimal number 34,567. The digit parity check, from (2-45), is

$$3 + 4 + 5 + 6 + 7 \equiv p \bmod 10$$

For even parity check, p, from (2-46), is

$$p = 3 \oplus 4 \oplus 5 \oplus 6 \oplus 7 = 5$$

For odd parity check, p, from (2-47), is

$$p = 3 \oplus 4 \oplus 5 \oplus 6 \oplus 7 \oplus 9 = 4$$

If there occurs a single error in the decimal number, for instance if the digit 3 becomes 6, then the modulo-10 sum becomes 8 for the even parity digit and becomes 7 for the odd parity digit. The parity digit may not be able to detect two or more errors, because these errors may compensate each other in the modulo-10 sum. In conclusion, the digit parity check can detect a single error in a decimal number even if this error is in the parity digit itself.

Now consider the number parity check defined as

$$N \equiv p \bmod b \tag{2-48}$$

where N is the number [Eq. (2-44)] and b is the modulus, or base, not necessarily equal to the radix 10 of N. If b is equal to 10, then (2-48) becomes

$$N \equiv x_0 \bmod 10 \tag{2-49}$$

This case has no practical interest, because it can detect an error only in the least significant digit x_0 of the number N. However, two more useful number parity checks are now introduced. The *first number parity check* is derived below:

$$x_i 10^n \equiv x_i \bmod 9 \tag{2-50}$$

If the above is applied to the number N [Eq. (2-44)], we have

$$N = \sum_{i=0}^{n-1} x_i 10^i \equiv p \bmod 9 \tag{2-51}$$

where

$$p = x_{n-1} \oplus \cdots \oplus x_0 \tag{2-52}$$

The above parity digit is for modulo $r - 1$, where r is 10; this is different from (2-46), which is for modulo r. The *second number parity check* is derived as shown,

$$
\begin{aligned}
x_i 10^n &\equiv + x_i \bmod 11 &\quad \text{if } n \text{ is even} \\
x_i 10^n &\equiv - x_i \bmod 11 &\quad \text{if } n \text{ is odd}
\end{aligned}
\tag{2-53}
$$

Applying the second check to the number N [Eq. (2-44)], we have

$$N = \sum_{i=0}^{n-1} x_i 10^i \equiv p \bmod 11 \tag{2-54}$$

where

$$p = x_0 - x_1 + x_2 - x_3 + x_4 + \cdots \tag{2-55}$$

If the subtraction in the above relation is replaced by the addition of 11's complement, the parity digit p becomes

$$p = x_0 \oplus 10x_1 \oplus x_2 \oplus 10x_3 \oplus x_4 \oplus \cdots \tag{2-56}$$

Although this has not been mentioned previously, number parity checks may also be applied to binary numbers.

Parity Check for Arithmetic Operations. As mentioned, the errors on data usually arise as a result of a data-transfer operation or an arithmetic (or a logic) operation. In the above paragraphs, the use of parity has been described to check the result of a data-transfer operation. The parity bit can also be used to check the result of an arithmetic operation [18]. Discussion of this use, however, will be limited to the checking of the sum of an addition, as the checking of other arithmetic or logic operations can be similarly developed.

A single error in the sum of an addition can be detected by using the digit parity check or either of the two number parity checks. First consider the use of the digit parity check. Let the augend X and the addend Y be represented as

$$X = \sum_{i=0}^{n-1} x_i 10^i \tag{2-57}$$

$$Y = \sum_{i=0}^{n-1} y_i 10^i \tag{2-58}$$

where n is the number of the decimal digits of the augend or addend. Let s_i and c_i be the ith digit of the sum and the carry, respectively, and let S be the sum. Then we have

$$s_i = x_i \oplus y_i \oplus c_i \tag{2-59}$$

$$x_i + y_i + c_i = s_i + c_{i+1}10 \tag{2-60}$$

$$c_0 = 0 \quad \text{and} \quad c_i = 0 \text{ or } 1 \quad \text{if } i \neq 0 \tag{2-61}$$

$$S = c_n 10^n + s_{n-1}10^{n-1} + \cdots + s_0 10^0 \tag{2-62}$$

Let p_x, p_y, and p_s be the parity digit of the augend, addend, and sum, respectively, all defined in the following manner:

$$p_x = x_0 \oplus x_1 \oplus \cdots \oplus x_{n-1} \tag{2-63}$$

$$p_y = y_0 \oplus y_1 \oplus \cdots \oplus y_{n-1} \tag{2-64}$$

and

$$p_s = s_0 \oplus s_1 \oplus \cdots \oplus s_{n-1} \oplus c_n \tag{2-65}$$

If relation (2-59) is substituted into (2-65), we have

$$p_s = x_0 \oplus y_0 \oplus \cdots \oplus x_{n-1} \oplus y_{n-1} \oplus c_{n-1} \oplus c_n \tag{2-66}$$

or

$$p_s = p_x \oplus p_y \oplus \left(\sum_{i=1}^{n} c_i \right) \tag{2-67}$$

The above relation states that the parity digit of the sum is equal to the modulo-10 sum of the parity digits of the augend, the addend and the sum of the generated carries; this provides a means of detecting a single error in addition. An example showing the parity check of an addition of the decimal numbers 34,567 and 47,357 appears below:

$$
\begin{array}{cccccc}
 & 3 & 4 & 5 & 6 & 7 \\
+ & 4 & 7 & 3 & 5 & 7 \\
\hline
 & 7 & 1 & 8 & 1 & 4 \\
+ & 1 & 0 & 1 & 1 & 0 \quad \text{carries}\\
\hline
 & 8 & 1 & 9 & 2 & 4 \\
\end{array}
$$

$$p_s = 8 \oplus 1 \oplus 9 \oplus 2 \oplus 4 = 4$$
$$p_x = 3 \oplus 4 \oplus 5 \oplus 6 \oplus 7 = 5$$
$$p_y = 4 \oplus 7 \oplus 3 \oplus 5 \oplus 7 = 6$$

$$\sum_{i=1}^{5} c_i = 1 + 1 + 1 = 3$$

The modulo-10 sum of the above P_x, P_y, and Σc_i equals 4, which agrees with the above p_s.

Next consider the use of the first number parity check. The congruences for the augend, the addend, and the sum according to (2-51) are

$$X \equiv p_x \bmod 9 \tag{2-68}$$

$$Y \equiv p_y \bmod 9 \tag{2-69}$$

$$S \equiv p_s \bmod 9 \tag{2-70}$$

where p_x, p_y, and p_s are determined by (2-52). Since linear congruences are additive, we can write

$$S = X + Y \equiv (p_x + p_y) \bmod 9 \tag{2-71}$$

Therefore we have

$$p_s = p_x \oplus p_y \tag{2-72}$$

The above relation states that the parity digit of the sum is equal to the modulo-9 sum of the parity digits of the augend and of the addend and is thus independent of the generated carries. If the decimal numbers in the above example are used, the parity digits for the modulo-9 sum are

$$p_x = 3 \oplus 4 \oplus 5 \oplus 6 \oplus 7 = 7$$
$$p_y = 4 \oplus 7 \oplus 3 \oplus 5 \oplus 7 = 8$$
$$p_s = 8 \oplus 1 \oplus 9 \oplus 2 \oplus 4 = 6$$

The modulo-9 sum of the above 7 and 8 is 6, which agrees with the above p_s.

Lastly, consider the use of the second number parity check. The derivation is similar to the case using the first number parity check except that p_x, p_y, and p_s are determined by (2-56) and the modulo sum in (2-72) is for modulo 11. The result is Eq. (2-72). If the decimal numbers in the above example are again used, the parity digits for the modulo-11 sum are

$$p_x = 7 \oplus 60 \oplus 5 \oplus 40 \oplus 3 = 5$$
$$p_y = 7 \oplus 50 \oplus 3 \oplus 70 \oplus 4 = 2$$
$$p_s = 4 \oplus 20 \oplus 9 \oplus 10 \oplus 8 = 7$$

The modulo-11 sum of the above 5 and 2 is 7, which agrees with the above p_s.

Single-error-correcting Codes. The parity check shown in Table 2-15 can detect a single error but cannot locate the error bit, and thus the error cannot be corrected. Hamming [3] has developed a single-error-correcting code; such a code for 4 information bits is shown in Table 2-16. (Ignore the column p_8 for the time being.) There are 7 bits for each number—4 number bits x_i for the 16 binary numbers and 3 parity bits p_i for the single-error correction. The parity bit p_1 is chosen to make the modulo-2 sum of p_1, x_3, x_5, and x_7 equal to 0. The parity bit p_2 makes the modulo-2 sum of p_2, x_3, x_6, and x_7 equal to 0. The parity bit p_4 makes the modulo-2 sum of p_4, x_5, x_6, and x_7 equal to 0. Consider the number 1011010, corresponding to the decimal number 10, but with the x_6 bit corrupted so that the number becomes 1011000. Let us compute the value of the 3 parity bits from the corrupted number according to the above-mentioned bit positions for each parity bit:

$$p_1 = 1 \oplus 1 \oplus 0 \oplus 0 = 0$$
$$p_2 = 0 \oplus 1 \oplus 0 \oplus 0 = 1$$
$$p_3 = 1 \oplus 0 \oplus 0 \oplus 0 = 1$$

The 3 parity bits form a *check number* $p_3 p_2 p_1$, or 110, which is the binary number 6, pointing to the sixth bit x_6 as incorrect. Correcting circuitry can be built into the computer to change x_6 automatically from the incorrect value 0 to the correct value 1. If the check number is 000, the given number is correct. As long as the error is single, the check number can determine the location of the incorrect bit.

The Hamming single-error code is formulated first by determining how many check bits are needed. Let the number of information bits be m, the number of check bits k, and the total number of bits n ($= m + k$). The k check bits give 2^k check numbers. The required check numbers are equal to the total n bits plus one number to indicate the case of no error. Thus, the check number should be equal to or larger than $n + 1$, or

$$2^k \geq n + 1 \qquad \text{where } n = m + k \qquad (2\text{-}73)$$

For a given total number of n bits, the values of m and k to the nearest integer have been reported by Hamming and are shown in Table 2-17.

Next determine those information bits to which each of the three parity bits of

Table 2-16   Single-error-correcting Code

Decimal number	p_1	p_2	x_3	p_4	x_5	x_6	x_7	p_8
0	0	0	0	0	0	0	0	0
1	1	1	0	1	0	0	1	0
2	0	1	0	1	0	1	0	1
3	1	0	0	0	0	1	1	1
4	1	0	0	1	1	0	0	1
5	0	1	0	0	1	0	1	1
6	1	1	0	0	1	1	0	0
7	0	0	0	1	1	1	1	0
8	1	1	1	0	0	0	0	1
9	0	0	1	1	0	0	1	1
10	1	0	1	1	0	1	0	0
11	0	1	1	0	0	1	1	0
12	0	1	1	1	1	0	0	0
13	1	0	1	0	1	0	1	0
14	0	0	1	0	1	1	0	1
15	1	1	1	1	1	1	1	1

Table 2-16 shall apply.   Consider the parity bit p_1, which is at the location 2^0 of the check number; it can indicate the nonzero check numbers, its least significant bit being 1.   The check numbers are 001, 011, 101, and 111 or the decimal equivalents 1, 3, 5, and 7.   Similarly, the parity bit p_2 at the location 2^1 of the check number can indicate the nonzero check numbers 010, 011, 110, and 111 or the decimal equivalents 2, 3, 6, and 7.   And the parity bit p_3 at the location 2^2 of the check number can indicate the nonzero check numbers 100, 101, 110, and 111 or the decimal equivalents 4, 5, 6, and 7.   Finally, determine which 3 bits of the 7 bits are to be chosen as the check bits.   It is desirable to choose the first digits (p_1, p_2, and p_4) of the sequences 1-3-5-7, 2-3-6-7, and 4-5-6-7 to be the check bits, because in this manner the value of each parity bit can be deter-

Table 2-17   Check Bits Required for a Single-error-correcting Code

Total bits n	Information bits m	Check bits k
1	0	1
2	0	2
3	1	2
4	1	3
5	2	3
6	3	3
7	4	3
8	4	4
9	5	4
10	6	4
11	7	4
12	8	4
13	9	4
14	10	4
15	11	4
16	11	5
. . .	. . .	. . .

Table 2-18   Positions for Information and Check Bits for Single-error-correcting Code

Bit position of check number	Position of check bit	Positions to be checked by parity bit
2^0	1	1, 3, 5, 7, 9, 11, 13, . . .
2^1	2	2, 3, 6, 7, 10, 11, 14, 15, . . .
2^2	4	4, 5, 6, 7, 12, 13, 14, 15, . . .
2^3	8	8, 9, 10, 11, 12, 13, 14, 15, . . .
. . .	. . .	. . . .

mined without regard to the values of other parity bits. In other words, the bit positions 1, 2, and 4 are the check bits, and the bit positions 3, 5, 6 and 7 are the information bits, as indicated in Table 2-16. For the number of information bits larger than 4, the selected positions for the parity bits and the positions to be checked by each parity bit have been determined by Hamming and are shown in Table 2-18.

For the single-error-correcting code of Table 2-16, there are at least three bit changes (i.e., changes of 1-to-0 or 0-to-1 between corresponding bits) of any two 7-bit numbers. Since word length in digital computers lies in the range of 20 to 64 bits, the required check bits for a single-error-correcting code are 5 to 7 bits. Incorporation of the single-error-correcting code adds more circuitry complexity and costs more than the single-parity-checking code.

Multiple-error-detecting and -correcting Codes. In two binary numbers, there is at least one bit change. In the single-error-detecting code (the single-parity-checking code), there are at least two bit changes between any two coded numbers. In the single-correcting code, there are at least three bit changes between any two coded numbers. The more bit changes between any two coded numbers, the greater the redundancy introduced. The need of bit changes for multiple-error-detecting and -error-correcting codes has been determined by Hamming and is shown in Table 2-19.

As an example, refer to the single-error-correcting code of Table 2-16. If a parity bit p_8 is added (shown in the last column) and is so chosen as to make the modulo-2 sum of all 8 bits even, there are at least four bit changes between any two 8-bit numbers. If p_8 is 0 and the check number $p_3p_2p_1$ is 000, then there is no error. If p_8 is 1 but the number is 000, then the error is p_8. If p_8 is 1 and the check number is not 000, then the error is located by the check number and is thus correctable. If p_8 is 0 and the check number is not 000, then there are at least two errors which the check number is unable to locate.

Table 2-19   Bit Changes Required for Hamming Code

Bit changes between any two coded binary numbers	Possible Hamming code
1	None
2	Single-error-detecting
3	Single-error-correcting or double-error-detecting
4	Single-error-correcting plus double-error-detecting
5	Double-error-correcting plus double-error-detecting
6	Double-error-correcting plus triple-error-detecting
7	Triple-error-correcting plus triple-error-detecting
. . .	. . . .

For a given minimum number of bit changes, the error-correcting ability can be exchanged for error-detecting ability. For example, if there are five bit changes between any two coded binary numbers, Table 2-19 shows that the code is capable of correcting two errors. The bit changes, however, can be utilized to correct a single error and detect three errors or to detect four errors.

The above codes, in which all code numbers have exactly n ($= m + k$) bits with m information bits and k check bits, are called by Hamming the systematic codes. Other codes have been developed by Elias, Reed, Golay, Muller, Slepian, and others. The reader may consult the references listed at the end of this chapter.

Problems

1. Write the following 4-bit binary codes for the decimal digit. Compare these codes, and give comments:

(a) Excess-6   (b) 3-3-2-1   (c) 4-4-2-$\bar{1}$ (d) 8-7-$\bar{4}$-$\bar{2}$

2. Convert the following negative decimal numbers into signed-10's- and signed-9's-complement representations. Shift the resulting signed-complement numbers three decimal digits to the left and three decimal digits to the right:

(a) $-34{,}567$ (b) $-91{,}019$ (c) $-55{,}500$
(d) $-00{,}000$ (e) $-99{,}999$

3. Prove the addition and subtraction algorithms for two decimal digits in the excess-3 code.

4. Establish the subtraction algorithm for two decimal digits in the 2-4-2-1 code.

5. Given two decimal numbers 258 and 491, perform the multiplication:

(a) By the binary multiplication method (assume the 8-4-2-1 code)
(b) By the doubling-and-halving method
(c) By the right-and-left-hand-components method

6. Given the decimal dividend 0.1875 and the decimal divisor 0.75, perform the division:

(a) By the restoring method
(b) By the nonrestoring method
(c) By the halving-the-divisor method
(d) By Gilman's method to a five-digit accuracy

7. Given two decimal numbers $X = 0.1234567 \times 10^{-10}$ and $Y = 0.7654321 \times 10^{-8}$, find the following by using the algorithms of floating-point arithmetic:

(a) $X + Y$ (b) $X - Y$ (c) XY (d) X/Y

8. Given two residue numbers in the modulo-210 system, $X = 1145$ and $Y = 1136$, find the following, and verify the results by the corresponding decimal arithmetic:

(a) $\bar{X}$ and $\bar{Y}$ (b) $X + Y$ (c) $X - Y$ (d) XY

9. Develop the error-checking algorithms for the following codes by inspection:

(a) 2-out-of-5 code   (b) Biquinary code
(c) 5-1-1-1-1 code   (d) 5-4-3-2-1-0 code

10. Find the sum of two decimal numbers 24,685 and 36,972. Check the sum, using:

(a) The digit parity check
(b) The first number parity check
(c) The second number parity check

References

1. Golay, M. J. E.: Notes on Digital Coding, *Proc. IRE*, June, 1949, p. 657.
2. Shannon, C. E.: A Mathematical Theory of Communication, *Bell System Tech. J.*, April, 1950, pp. 140–160.

3. Hamming, R. W.: Error Detecting and Error Correcting Codes, *Bell System Tech. J.*, vol. 29, pp. 147–160, April, 1950.

4. Staff of Harvard Computation Laboratory: "Synthesis of Electronic Computing and Control Circuits," Harvard University Press, Cambridge, Mass., 1951.

5. Keister, Ritchie, and Washburn: "The Design of Switching Circuits," D. Van Nostrand Company, Inc., Princeton, N. J., 1951.

6. White, G. S.: Coded Decimal Number Systems for Digital Computers, *Proc. IRE*, October, 1953, pp. 1450–1452.

7. Muller, D. E.: Metric Properties of Boolean Algebra and Their Application to Switching Circuits, *Univ. Ill. Digital Computer Lab. Rept.* 46, April, 1953.

8. Reed, I. S.: A Class of Multiple-error-correcting Codes and the Decoding Scheme, *IRE Trans. on Inform. Theory*, September, 1954, pp. 38–49.

9. Elias, P.: Error-free Coding, *IRE Trans. on Inform. Theory*, September, 1954, pp. 29–37.

10. Richards, R. K.: "Arithmetic Operations in Digital Computers," D. Van Nostrand Company, Inc., Princeton, N. J., 1955.

11. Gilchrist, B., J. H. Pomerene, and S. Y. Wong: Fast Carry Logic for Digital Computers, *IRE Trans. on Electronic Computers*, December, 1955, pp. 133–136.

12. Booth, A. D., and K. H. V. Booth: "Automatic Digital Calculators," Academic Press, Inc., New York, 1956.

13. Slepian, D.: A Class of Binary Signaling Alphabets, *Bell System Tech. J.*, January, 1956, pp. 203–234.

14. McCracken, D. D.: "Digital Computer Programming," John Wiley & Sons, Inc., New York, 1957.

15. McClean, M. A., and D. Aspinall: A Decimal Adder Using a Stored Addition Table, *Proceedings IEE (London)*, pt. B, pp. 129–135, March, 1958.

16. Robertson, J. E.: A New Class of Digital Division Methods, *IRE Trans. on Electronic Computers*, September, 1958, pp. 218–222.

17. Methods for High-speed Addition and Multiplications, *Nat. Bur. Standards (U.S.) Circ.* 591, sec. 1, 1958.

18. Garner, H. L.: Generalized Parity Checking, *IRE Trans. on Electronic Computers*, September, 1958, pp. 207–213.

19. Metropolis, N., and R. L. Ashenhurst: Significant Digit Computer Arithmetic, *IRE Trans. on Electronic Computers*, December, 1958, pp. 256–267.

20. Gilman, R. E.: A Mathematical Procedure for Machine Division, *Communs. ACM*, April, 1959, pp. 10–12.

21. Garner, H. L.: A Ring Model for the Study of Multiplication for Complement Codes, *IRE Trans. on Electronic Computers*, March, 1959, pp. 25–30.

22. Garner, H. L.: The Residue Number System, *IRE Trans. on Electronic Computers*, June, 1959, pp. 140–147.

23. Carr, John W., III: Error Analysis in Floating Point Arithmetic, *Communs. ACM*, May, 1959, pp. 10–15.

3

Boolean Algebra

Boolean algebra, an algebra of logic, is a symbolic method of studying logical relations. It was originated by George Boole (1815–1864), an English mathematician, who published his book "An Investigation of the Law of Thought" in 1854. Since then Boolean algebra has been extended by such workers as E. Schroder, A. N. Whitehead, and B. Russell and the power and simplicity of the algebra increased. The application of Boolean algebra to the digital computer hinges on the fact that digital computers of today employ internal signals represented by two values or two states.

3-1 Postulates

Boolean algebra is developed in three steps. The first step is to evolve fundamental concepts (or undefined symbols). The second step is to select a set of postulates which are the basis of the algebra. Postulates are mainly conditions arbitrarily imposed on the fundamental concepts. These postulates should be consistent, independent, and simple in statement. A set of postulates should be consistent so that a definite algebra can be developed by logical deductions. A set of postulates should be mutually independent and therefore free from redundancies. Furthermore, each postulate should be as nearly a simple statement as possible, not decomposable into two or more parts. The requirements of independence and simplicity primarily serve the ideal of mathematical elegance. One usually has considerable freedom in choosing the fundamental concepts and a set of postulates. The third step is to establish fundamental theorems of Boolean algebra from the postulates. These theorems are the working rules of the algebra.

Several different sets of postulates from the algebra of logic are available, each of which adopts a number of fundamental concepts. Each set of postulates, however, can be deduced from the other sets. Huntington's fourth set [4] appears to be simpler and perhaps more natural than the other sets of postulates. This set contains the following six postulates and three definitions:

Postulate 1

If A and B are two elements in class K (where class K contains at least two distinct elements), then $A + B$ is in class K.

Postulate 2

If A is in class K, then $\bar{A}$ is in class K.

Postulate 3

If A and B are in class K, then $A + B = B + A$.

Postulate 4

If A, B, and C are in class K, then

$$(A + B) + C = A + (B + C)$$

Postulate 5

If A is in class K, $A + A = A$.

Postulate 6

If A and B are in class K, then

$$(\overline{\overline{A} + \overline{B}}) + (\overline{\overline{A} + B}) = A$$

Definition 1

$$A + \overline{A} = 1 \qquad \text{universe element}$$

Definition 2

$$\overline{A + \overline{A}} = 0 \qquad \text{null element}$$

Definition 3

$$A \cdot B = \overline{\overline{A} + \overline{B}}$$

The above set of postulates employs four fundamental concepts $(K, +, ^-, =)$, all of which are subject to interpretation, while the definitions are merely imposed relations.

First Interpretation of Postulates. As mentioned, a set of postulates should be consistent, independent, and simple in statement. Since the latter two requirements are mainly for mathematical elegance, their proofs will not be sought. The consistency of the set of postulates can be established by showing the existence of a formulation in which K, $+$, $^-$, and $=$ are so interpreted that all the postulates are satisfied. For then the postulates and subsequent fundamental theorems will be simply the relations of the characteristics of this formulation.

The first formulation is the algebra of classes. By a *class* we mean a set of elements, a collection of articles, an aggregate of people: for example, the class of horses. The elements in the class may be abstractions or intangibles such as those in the class of truth. In this formulation, K is interpreted as the class of areas in a square. The three symbols $+$, $^-$, and $=$ can be graphically interpreted by using *Venn diagrams*. In Fig. 3-1a the two circular areas represent the elements A and B, respectively. The symbol $+$ is called *union*. The union of the two elements A and B in class K is the smallest area which includes them both; this is the shaded portion of Fig. 3-1a. In Fig. 3-1b there is one circle; its area represents the element A. The symbol $^-$ is called the *complement*. The complement of the element A is the shaded area outside the circle yet inside the square in Fig. 3-1b. The symbol $=$ is called *equality*. The equality of two elements A and B identifies the sameness of the area occupied by both A and B inside the square; this equality is shown by the shaded area of the circle in Fig. 3-1c.

The three definitions can similarly be interpreted by Venn diagrams. The universe element is the whole square, while the null element occupies no area. Definition 1 can be explained by noting that union of the unshaded area A and the shaded area $\bar{A}$ in Fig. 3-1b results in the whole square or the universe element. Definition 2 can be explained: the complement of the whole square is simply "no square," or the null element. Definition 3 defines the dot symbol $\cdot$,

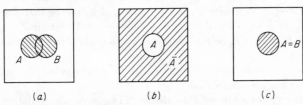

FIG. 3-1 Venn diagrams illustrating union, complement, and equality (square is universe area). (a) Shaded area is $A + B$, the union of A and B; (b) shaded area is $\bar{A}$, the complement of A; (c) shaded area is $A = B$, the equality of A and B.

which is called *intersection*. The intersection of two elements A and B is interpreted by Venn diagrams in Fig. 3-2. The vertically shaded area in Fig. 3-2a is $\bar{A}$, and the horizontally shaded area in Fig. 3-2b is $\bar{B}$. The union of $\bar{A}$ and $\bar{B}$ is the shaded area in 3-2c; this shaded area is equal to the unshaded area in Fig. 3-2d. Definition 3 states that the complement of the union of $\bar{A}$ and $\bar{B}$ is the intersection of A and B, the shaded area in Fig. 3-2d. In case the two circles A

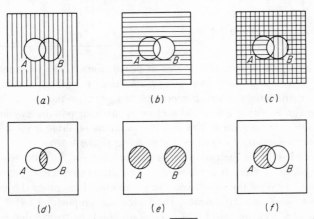

FIG. 3-2 Venn diagrams showing the composition of $\overline{\bar{A} + \bar{B}}$ or $A \cdot B$. (a) Shaded area $\bar{A}$; (b) shaded area $\bar{B}$; (c) shaded area $\bar{A} + \bar{B}$ and unshaded area $A \cdot B$; (d) shaded area $A \cdot B$ or $\overline{\bar{A} + \bar{B}}$; ($e$) A and B are disjoint; (f) shaded area $A \cdot B = \overline{\bar{A} + \bar{B}}$.

and B do not intersect as shown in Fig. 3-2e, they are called *disjoint*; the intersection of A and B does not exist.

The postulates can also be interpreted by Venn diagrams. Postulate 1 states that, if A and B are in class K, then $A + B$ is in class K. In Fig. 3-1a circle A and circle B are both in the square, and their union (the shaded area) is also in the square. Postulate 2 states that, if A is in class K, then $\bar{A}$ is in class K. In

Fig. 3-1*b*, the unshaded area A is in the square, and the shaded area $\overline{A}$ is also in the square. Interpreting Postulate 3, the shaded area in Fig. 3-1*a* does not depend on the order of forming the union $A + B$; it is immaterial whether A is united with B, or vice versa. Postulate 4 means the independence of order in forming the union among elements A, B, and C. As shown in Fig. 3-3, the shaded area can be formed from these three circles in any order. Postulate 5 is interpreted by the diagram in Fig. 3-1*b*; the union of the circle with itself results in the circle itself. Postulate 6 can be interpreted by noting that A is the union of $A \cdot B$ and $A \cdot \overline{B}$ by using Definition 3. The shaded areas in Fig. 3-2*d* and *f* represent $A \cdot B$ and $A \cdot \overline{B}$, respectively; the union of these two shaded areas is the complete circle A.

The above set of postulates has been satisfactorily interpreted by Venn diagrams; thus, its consistency is established.

Second Interpretation of Postulates. The second formulation is the calculus of propositions. A proposition is a statement such as "February 22 is Washington's birthday." Each proposition possesses one of two possible values, truth or falsehood, to be denoted by 1 or 0, respectively. Call the above proposition A. Since proposition A is true, A has a value of 1; if other than true, the value is 0.

FIG. 3-3   Venn diagram showing $A + B + C$, shaded area.

Table 3-1   Truth Table for Symbols $+$, $^-$, $=$

A	B	$A + B$	$\overline{A}$	$C = A$
0	0	0	1	0
0	1	1	1	0
1	0	1	0	1
1	1	1	0	1

In this formulation, K is interpreted as propositions. The three symbols $+$, $^-$, and $=$ can be interpreted by using *truth tables* (or tables of combination). In Table 3-1, the letters A and B represent two given propositions. Since each proposition can be either true or false (1 or 0), the four possible combinations of truth and falsehood appear in the first two columns of Table 3-1. The symbol $+$, called the *logical or*, signifies the meaning of the word *or*. The logical-*or* proposition $(A + B)$ of the two given propositions A and B is one which is false if both propositions A and B are false; its truth value is shown in the third column. The symbol $^-$, called the *logical not*, or complement, signifies the meaning of the word *negation*, or *complement*. The logical-*not* proposition $(\overline{A})$ of the given proposition A is true (or false) if A is false (or true); its truth value is shown in the fourth column. The symbol $=$, called *equal*, signifies the logical equality. Two propositions are logically equal if they have the same truth values. The truth values in the last column for proposition C are equal to those in the first column; therefore propositions A and C are equal (or $A = C$).

The three definitions can be similarly interpreted by the truth table. The universe element is a proposition whose truth value is always 1, while the null element is one whose truth value is always 0. The interpretation of Definition 1 is as follows: For a given proposition A, the new proposition $A + \overline{A}$ is formed. The new proposition is always true because either A or $\overline{A}$ is true, and its truth value is thus always 1; this agrees with Definition 1. Definition 2 means that the complement of a proposition which is always true is false, or 0. Definition 3 explains the dot symbol, ·, called the *logical and* to signify the meaning of the word *all*. The determination of its truth value is shown in Table 3-2. The first two columns show the truth values of the four possible combinations of the given propositions A and B. The truth values for proposition $\overline{\overline{A} + \overline{B}}$ is obtained by finding the truth values of propositions $\overline{A}$, $\overline{B}$, $\overline{A} + \overline{B}$, and $\overline{\overline{A} + \overline{B}}$ in sequence. From the truth values in the last column, one can state that the logical-*and* propositions $A \cdot B$ of two propositions A and B is one which is true if both A and B are true. The dot in $A \cdot B$ is usually omitted for convenience.

Table 3-2   *Truth Table for Symbol* ·

A	B	$\overline{A}$	$\overline{B}$	$\overline{A} + \overline{B}$	$\overline{\overline{A} + \overline{B}} = A \cdot B$
0	0	1	1	1	0
0	1	1	0	1	0
1	0	0	1	1	0
1	1	0	0	0	1

The postulates can similarly be interpreted by the truth table and their consistency established. Their interpretation is left to the reader.

Logical *or* is also called *logical addition,* or *logical sum;* logical *and* is also called *logical multiplication,* or *logical product.* Logical-*or,* logical-*not,* and logical-*and* symbols can be represented by blocks as illustrated in Fig. 3-4. The blocks are identified by their respective symbols: +, ⁻, and ·.

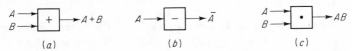

(a)   (b)   (c)

FIG. 3-4   Block representations of three logic operations. (a) Logical *or;* (b) logical *not* or complement; (c) logical *and.*

3-2   Fundamental Theorems

From the postulates, fundamental theorems of Boolean algebra can be logically deduced. These theorems are enumerated below; their logical deductions are omitted.

Theorems on Uniqueness

1*a*. The element 1 is unique.
1*b*. The element 0 is unique.

Theorems on Complementation

2*a*. $A + \overline{A} = 1$
2*b*. $A \cdot \overline{A} = 0$

Theorems on Involution (or Double Negation)

3. $\overline{\overline{A}} = A$

De Morgan's Theorems

$4a. \quad \overline{A + B} = \overline{A} \cdot \overline{B}$

$4b. \quad \overline{AB} = \overline{A} + \overline{B}$

Theorems on Absorption

$5a. \quad A + AB = A$

$5b. \quad A(A + B) = A$

Theorems on Idempotency

$6a. \quad A + A = A$

$6b. \quad A \cdot A = A$

Theorems on Union and Intersection

$7a. \quad A + 0 = A$

$7b. \quad A \cdot 1 = A$

$8a. \quad A + 1 = 1$

$8b. \quad A \cdot 0 = 0$

Theorems on Commutation, Association, and Distribution

$9a. \quad A + B = B + A$

$9b. \quad AB = BA$

$10a. \quad A + (B + C) = (A + B) + C$

$10b. \quad A(BC) = (AB)C$

$11a. \quad A + BC = (A + B)(A + C)$

$11b. \quad A(B + C) = AB + AC$

Interpretation by Venn Diagrams and Truth Tables. These theorems are the working rules of Boolean algebra. They can be interpreted by Venn diagrams. Interpretation of Theorems 10 and 11 furnishes an example, illustrated by the Venn diagrams in Fig. 3-5. The associative property of Theorem 10 is

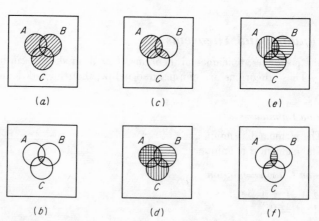

FIG. 3-5 Venn diagram for interpreting Theorems 10 and 11. (*a*) Shaded area $A + B + C$; (*b*) shaded area ABC; (*c*) shaded area $A + BC$; (*d*) double shaded area $(A + B)(A + C)$; (*e*) double shaded area $A(B + C)$; (*f*) shaded area $AB + AC$.

interpreted by noting that the shaded area $A + B + C$ in Fig. 3-5a and the shaded area ABC in Fig. 3-5b bear no relation to the order of forming the union or the intersection. The distributive property of Theorem 11 is interpreted by noting that the shaded area $A + BC$ in Fig. 3-5c is the same as the double shaded area $(A + B)(A + C)$ in Fig. 3-5d. Note also that the double shaded area $A(B + C)$ in Fig. 3-5e is the same as the shaded area $AB + AC$ in Fig. 3-5f.

These theorems can also be interpreted by truth tables. The interpretation of De Morgan's theorems is chosen as an example. The truth table is first prepared as shown in Table 3-3. Corresponding truth values in the third and fourth columns are the same, demonstrating the validity of Theorem 4a. Similarly, the

Table 3-3   Truth Table for De Morgan Theorems

A	B	$\overline{A + B}$	$\overline{A} \cdot \overline{B}$	$\overline{AB}$	$\overline{A} + \overline{B}$
0	0	1	1	1	1
0	1	0	0	1	1
1	0	0	0	1	1
1	1	0	0	0	0

sameness of truth values in the fifth and sixth columns shows the validity of Theorem 4b. The above method of verifying two sides of an equality for all possible combinations of truth values is known as the *method of perfect induction.*

Parentheses are used to indicate precedence in logic operations. The rule is the same as for ordinary algebra: *multiplication (logical-and operation) takes precedence over addition (logical-or operation) if no parentheses are used.* For example, the parentheses on the left side of Theorem 10a indicate that the logical *or* of B and C, $(B + C)$, precedes logical-*or* operation with A. As another example, the left side of Theorem 11a, $A + BC$, means $A + (BC)$ but not $(A + B)C$. If the latter is the intended relation, then parentheses should be employed. The

(a) (b)

FIG. 3-6   Venn diagrams comparing $(A + B)C$ and $A + BC$. (a) Shaded area $(A + B)C$; (b) shaded area $A + BC$.

Venn diagram in Fig. 3-6 shows the difference between the relations $(A + B)C$ and $A + BC$; the latter covers a larger area than the former.

Duality. In the fundamental theorems there exists a *duality* between logical-*and* and logical-*or* operations and between 1 and 0. *If the symbol · is replaced by symbol + (or symbol + by ·) and if 1 is replaced by 0 (or 0 by 1) in any of the above theorems, the result is the dual of the original theorem.* For example, Theorem 2a states that $(A + \overline{A}) = 1$. If the $+$ is replaced by the $\cdot$ and 1 by 0, the result is $A \cdot \overline{A} = 0$, which is the dual theorem 2b. For this reason the preceding theorems are numbered in pairs (a and b). Because of the duality in the fundamental theorems, if a new theorem is deduced, a dual theorem exists which can be written by merely applying the above rule; and the proof of the original theorem proves the dual.

3-3   *Use of Fundamental Theorems*

Several of the following examples show the fundamental theorems in use. Although unnecessary, proof of the dual will be worked out as an additional example.

Example 3-1.   Prove the following dual identities:

$$(a) \qquad\qquad AB + CD = (A + C)(A + D)(B + C)(B + D) \qquad\qquad (3\text{-}1a)$$

$$(b) \qquad\qquad (A + B)(C + D) = AC + BC + AD + BD \qquad\qquad (3\text{-}1b)$$

This two-part example shows the use of commutative, associative, and distributive theorems, which are the same as those in the ordinary algebra—with one exception, Theorem 11. This theorem is particularly useful in allowing simplification, expansion, factoring, and rearrangement of a function.

Proof

$$
\begin{aligned}
(a) \qquad AB + CD &= (AB) + CD \\
&= (AB + C)(AB + D) && \text{Theorem } 11a \\
&= (C + AB)(D + AB) && \text{Theorem } 9a \\
&= (C + A)(C + B)(D + A)(D + B) && \text{Theorem } 11a \\
&= (A + C)(A + D)(B + C)(B + D) && \text{Theorems } 9a, 9b \\
(b) \quad (A + B)(C + D) &= (A + B)C + (A + B)D && \text{Theorem } 11b \\
&= C(A + B) + D(A + B) && \text{Theorem } 9b \\
&= CA + CB + DA + DB && \text{Theorem } 11b \\
&= AC + BC + AD + BD && \text{Theorem } 9b
\end{aligned}
$$

Identities (3-1a) and (3-1b) can be drawn as the four block diagrams in Fig. 3-7. The duality is exhibited there by symmetry of the logical-*or* and logical-*and* blocks. Diagrams *a* and *b* are logically the same; so are diagrams *c* and *d*. Diagrams *a* and *c* are simpler, as

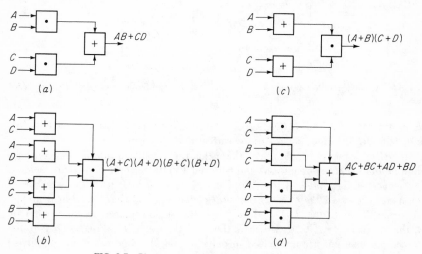

FIG. 3-7   Block diagrams for identities (3-1a) and (3-1b).

they have fewer blocks. The foregoing dual relations give rise to the following special pair:

$$AB + \bar{A}\bar{B} = (A + \bar{B})(\bar{A} + B) \tag{3-2a}$$

$$\bar{A}B + A\bar{B} = (A + B)(\bar{A} + \bar{B}) \tag{3-2b}$$

Example 3-2. Prove the following identities:

(a)
$$(A + B\bar{C} + C)\bar{C} = AB\bar{C} + ABC + \bar{A}B\bar{C} \tag{3-3}$$

(b)
$$A(\bar{A} + C)(\bar{A}B + \bar{C}) = 0 \tag{3-4}$$

This example shows the use of theorems on complementation and idempotency.

Proof

(a) $(A + B\bar{C} + C)\bar{C} = A\bar{C} + B\bar{C} + C\bar{C}$ Theorems 11b, 6b

                 $= A\bar{C} + B\bar{C}$ Theorems 2b, 7a

                 $= A(B + \bar{B})\bar{C} + (A + \bar{A})B\bar{C}$ Theorems 2a, 7b

                 $= AB\bar{C} + A\bar{B}\bar{C} + AB\bar{C} + \bar{A}B\bar{C}$ Theorem 11b

                 $= AB\bar{C} + ABC + \bar{A}B\bar{C}$ Theorem 6a

(b) $A(\bar{A} + C)(\bar{A}B + \bar{C}) = (A\bar{A} + AC)(\bar{A}B + \bar{C})$ Theorem 11b

                        $= AC(\bar{A}B + \bar{C})$ Theorems 2b, 7a

                        $= A\bar{A}BC + AC\bar{C}$ Theorems 11b, 9b

                        $= 0 + 0$ Theorems 2b, 8b

                        $= 0$ Theorem 7a

Example 3-3. Prove the following identities:

(a) $\overline{A + B + C + \cdots} = \bar{A} \cdot \bar{B} \cdot \bar{C} \cdots$ $\tag{3-5a}$

(b) $\overline{ABC \cdots} = \bar{A} + \bar{B} + \bar{C} + \cdots$ $\tag{3-5b}$

(c) $\overline{AB + BC + CA} = \overline{A}\overline{B} + \overline{B}\overline{C} + \overline{C}\overline{A}$ $\tag{3-6}$

(d) $\overline{\bar{A}[B + \bar{C}(\bar{D} + E\bar{F})]} = A + \bar{B}[C + D(\bar{E} + F)]$ $\tag{3-7}$

These statements show the use of the important De Morgan's theorems, which are very useful in complementation. The first two identities extend De Morgan's theorems to many variables.

Proof

(a) First extend Theorem 4a limited to three variables A, B, and C.

$$\overline{A + B + C} = \overline{A + (B + C)}$$ Theorem 10a

             $= A \cdot \overline{(B + C)}$ Theorem 4a

             $= \bar{A} \cdot \bar{B} \cdot \bar{C}$ Theorem 4a

(b) Next extend Theorem 4b limited to three variables A, B, and C.

$$\overline{ABC} = \overline{A(BC)}$$ Theorem 10b

        $= \bar{A} + \overline{BC}$ Theorem 4b

        $= \bar{A} + \bar{B} + \bar{C}$ Theorem 4b

Repetition of the above process extends Theorems 4a and 4b to more than three variables; therefore, identities (3-5a) and (3-5b) are proved.

(c) $\overline{AB + BC + CA} = (\overline{AB})(\overline{BC})(\overline{CA})$ Theorem 4a

                 $= (\bar{A} + \bar{B})(\bar{B} + \bar{C})(\bar{C} + \bar{A})$ Theorem 4b

                 $= (\bar{A} + \bar{B})(\bar{B}\bar{C} + \bar{B}\bar{A} + \bar{C} + \bar{C}\bar{A})$ Theorems 11b, 6b

                 $= (\bar{A} + \bar{B})(\bar{B}\bar{A} + \bar{C})$ Theorem 5a

                 $= \bar{A}\bar{B} + \bar{B}\bar{C} + \bar{A}\bar{C}$ Theorems 11b, 6b

(d) $\overline{A[B + \overline{C}(\overline{D} + E\overline{F})]} = A + [\overline{B} + \overline{\overline{C}(\overline{D} + E\overline{F})}]$ Theorem 4b
$\qquad\qquad\qquad\qquad = A + \overline{B}[\overline{\overline{C}(\overline{D} + E\overline{F})}]$ Theorem 4a
$\qquad\qquad\qquad\qquad = A + \overline{B}[C + (\overline{\overline{D} + E\overline{F}})]$ Theorem 4b
$\qquad\qquad\qquad\qquad = A + \overline{B}[C + D(\overline{E\overline{F}})]$ Theorem 4a
$\qquad\qquad\qquad\qquad = A + \overline{B}[C + D(\overline{E} + F)]$ Theorem 4b

The above four examples lead to the formulation of a simple rule: *To complement a quantity, replace all* + *symbols with* · *symbols; and replace each letter (or term) with its complement.* Note that this rule is different from that for duality, as the latter involves no complementation.

Example 3-4.   Prove the following identities on 0's and 1's:

$$0 \cdot 0 = 0 \qquad 0 + 0 = 0$$
$$0 \cdot 1 = 0 \qquad 0 + 1 = 1$$
$$1 \cdot 0 = 0 \qquad 1 + 0 = 1 \qquad\qquad (3\text{-}8)$$
$$1 \cdot 1 = 1 \qquad 1 + 1 = 1$$

These identities show the use of the theorems on union and intersection; these theorems, except Theorem 8a, established the same rules as those for ordinary multiplication and addition.

Proof

Let A in Theorems 7 and 8 be 0; we then have

$$A + 0 = 0 + 0 = 0$$
$$A \cdot 1 = 0 \cdot 1 = 0$$
$$A + 1 = 0 + 1 = 1$$
$$A \cdot 0 = 0 \cdot 0 = 0$$

Next let A in these two theorems be 1; we then have

$$A + 0 = 1 + 0 = 1$$
$$A \cdot 1 = 1 \cdot 1 = 1$$
$$A + 1 = 1 + 1 = 1$$
$$A \cdot 0 = 1 \cdot 0 = 0$$

The above eight identities were the postulates which Shannon [5] and others used in developing the fundamental theorems for relay circuits. Shannon's postulates are established on the undefined symbols of + and ·; our postulates, on the undefined symbols + and ⁻.

Example 3-5.   Prove the following identities:

(a) $\qquad\qquad\qquad (A + \overline{B})B = AB$ (3-9a)
(b) $\qquad\qquad\qquad A\overline{B} + B = A + B$ (3-9b)
(c) $\qquad\qquad\qquad AB + A\overline{B} = A$ (3-10a)
(d) $\qquad\qquad (A + B)(A + \overline{B}) = A$ (3-10b)
(e) $\qquad\qquad (A + B)(\overline{A} + C) = \overline{A}B + AC$ (3-11a)
(f) $\qquad\qquad AB + \overline{A}C = (\overline{A} + B)(A + C)$ (3-11b)

Proof of these identities provides several additional identities which are useful in later simplification and expansion of Boolean relations.

Proof

(a) $\qquad (A + \overline{B})B = AB + B\overline{B}$ Theorem 11b
$\qquad\qquad\qquad\quad = AB$ Theorems 2b, 7a

(b)
$$A\overline{B} + B = A\overline{B} + (A + \overline{A})B \qquad \text{Theorems } 2a, 7b$$
$$= A\overline{B} + AB + \overline{A}B + AB \qquad \text{Theorems } 11b, 6a$$
$$= A(B + \overline{B}) + (A + \overline{A})B \qquad \text{Theorems } 9, 11b$$
$$= A + B \qquad \text{Theorems } 2a, 7b$$

(c)
$$AB + A\overline{B} = A(B + \overline{B}) = A \qquad \text{Theorems } 2a, 7b$$

(d)
$$(A + B)(A + \overline{B}) = AA + BA + A\overline{B} + B\overline{B} \qquad \text{Theorem } 11b$$
$$= A + AB + A\overline{B} \qquad \text{Theorems } 6b, 9b, 2b, 7a$$
$$= A + A \qquad \text{Eq. (3-10}a)$$
$$= A \qquad \text{Theorem } 6a$$

(e)
$$(A + B)(\overline{A} + C) = A\overline{A} + B\overline{A} + AC + BC \qquad \text{Theorem } 11b$$
$$= \overline{A}B(C + \overline{C}) + A(B + \overline{B})C$$
$$\quad + (A + \overline{A})\,B\overline{C} \qquad \text{Theorems } 2, 7b$$
$$= \overline{A}BC + \overline{A}B\overline{C} + AB\overline{C} + A\overline{B}C \qquad \text{Theorem } 6a$$
$$= \overline{A}B + AC \qquad \text{Eq. (3-10}a)$$

(f)
$$AB + \overline{A}C = AB(C + \overline{C}) + \overline{A}(B + \overline{B})C \qquad \text{Theorems } 2a, 7b$$
$$= (ABC + AB\overline{C}) + (\overline{A}B\overline{C} + \overline{A}BC)$$
$$\quad + (ABC + \overline{A}BC) \qquad \text{Theorems } 11b, 6a$$
$$= AB + \overline{A}C + BC \qquad \text{Eq. (3-10}a)$$
$$= A\overline{A} + AB + \overline{A}C + BC \qquad \text{Theorems } 2b, 7a$$
$$= (\overline{A} + B)(A + C) \qquad \text{Theorem } 11b$$

3-4 Boolean Functions and Truth Table

A binary variable is a discrete variable which takes on two values only. *Boolean variables* are binary variables; the two values are represented by 0 and 1. Boolean variables are denoted by letters $A, B, C, \ldots, X, Y, Z$. A *Boolean function* of one or more Boolean variables is a binary variable whose value depends on the values of these Boolean variables. The symbol f is used to denote a Boolean function. For instance, $f(A,B)$ is a Boolean function of the two variables A and B. The value of variables A and B can be arbitrarily chosen; such variables are independent variables, while f is a dependent variable.

Truth Table. The value of a Boolean function depends on the values of its independent variables. For a given Boolean function, one can construct a truth table to depict the value of a Boolean function for all possible combinations of its independent variables. The following Boolean function of two variables $f(A,B)$ states that

$$f(A,B) = \overline{A}B + A\overline{B} \tag{3-12}$$

and its truth table is shown in Table 3-4. The first two columns show the four possible combinations of values of the variables A and B; they are tabulated in the order of binary numbers. The third column shows the corresponding values of the Boolean function f. The values of the complement of the function are shown in the fourth column. The value of the Boolean function f in a given row is obtained by substituting the corresponding value of A and B into the given Boolean function. For example, in the third row, $A = 1$, and $B = 0$ (or $\overline{A} = 0$ and $\overline{B} = 1$); then

$$f = 0 \times 0 + 1 \times 1 = 0 + 1 = 1$$

Table 3-4 Truth Table for Boolean Function (3-12)

A	B	f	$\overline{f}$
0	0	0	1
0	1	1	0
1	0	1	0
1	1	0	1

This agrees with the value of f in the third row. Thus, for a given Boolean function, one can construct a truth table to depict the values of a Boolean function.

Two Boolean Functions. In contrast with the preceding discussion, a Boolean function can be written representing the values of a given truth table. Exemplifying this converse relation, Table 3-4 states that the value of f is 1 when

$$A = 0 \qquad \text{and} \qquad B = 1$$

or $\qquad\qquad A = 1 \qquad \text{and} \qquad B = 0$

These conditions can be rewritten as

$$\bar{A} = 1 \qquad \text{and} \qquad B = 1$$

or $\qquad\qquad A = 1 \qquad \text{and} \qquad \bar{B} = 1$

They can further be rewritten as a logical product of $\bar{A}$ and B equal to 1 or of A and $\bar{B}$ equal to *1*,

$$\bar{A}B = 1 \qquad \text{or} \qquad A\bar{B} = 1$$

Since either of the two combinations makes the function f equal to 1, the function f is the logical sum of the two,

$$f = \bar{A}B + A\bar{B} \tag{3-13}$$

This is the required Boolean function which agrees with the function (3-12). Thus, for a given truth table, one can write a Boolean function to depict its values.

The above Boolean function (3-13) was established from Table 3-4 for those combinations of values of the variables A and B which give the value of f equal to 1. From this same table we can write, instead, the Boolean function f for those combinations of values of A and B which give the value f equal to 0. Table 3-4 states that the values of f are 0 when

$$A = 0 \qquad \text{and} \qquad B = 0$$

or $\qquad\qquad A = 1 \qquad \text{and} \qquad B = 1$

These conditions can be rewritten as

$$A = 0 \qquad \text{and} \qquad B = 0$$

or $\qquad\qquad \bar{A} = 0 \qquad \text{and} \qquad \bar{B} = 0$

They may further be written as a logical sum of A and B equal to 0 or of $\bar{A}$ and $\bar{B}$ equal to 0,

$$A + B = 0 \qquad \text{or} \qquad \bar{A} + \bar{B} = 0$$

Since either of the two combinations makes the function f equal to 0, the function f is the logical product of the two,

$$f = (A + B)(\bar{A} + \bar{B}) \tag{3-14}$$

This is the required function. Since the functions (3-13) and (3-14) have the same truth values, they are the same. As proof, follow the expansion and simplification shown,

$$\begin{aligned} f &= (A + B)(\bar{A} + \bar{B}) \\ &= A\bar{A} + \bar{A}B + A\bar{B} + B\bar{B} \\ &= \bar{A}B + A\bar{B} \end{aligned}$$

which is the expression in function (3-13).

The function (3-13) is a logical sum of logical products, while the function (3-14) is a logical product of logical sums. These are shown in the block diagrams of Fig. 3-8. One diagram makes use of *and-or* logic; the other depicts *or-and* logic.

A conclusion, drawn from the foregoing discussion, states that two Boolean functions can be written to reflect a given truth table. The functions are the same, differing only in form.

Two Complement Boolean Functions. Instead of writing the Boolean function $f(A,B)$ from Table 3-4, we can write its complement function $\bar{f}(A,B)$ whose truth values are also shown there. Using the previous approach for values of $\bar{f}$ equal to 1, we have

$$\bar{f} = \bar{A}\bar{B} + AB \tag{3-15}$$

We can also write the function $\bar{f}$ for the values of $\bar{f}$ equal to 0,

$$\bar{f} = (A + \bar{B})(\bar{A} + B) \tag{3-16}$$

Again, two complement functions are obtained which are the same, differing only in form.

An over-all conclusion states that, for a given truth table, four Boolean functions (including the two complement functions) can be written. This is important in

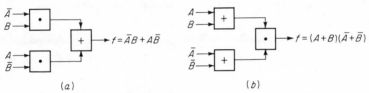

FIG. 3-8 Two-level logic. (a) *and-or*; (b) *or-and*.

application because one physical circuit may be more adaptable to one function than to the others.

3-5 Canonical Forms of Boolean Functions

Product Terms and Sum Terms. A *product term* (or *P term*) of n variables is a logical product of *all n variables*, although each variable can be the variable itself or its complement. The terms $\bar{A}B$ and $A\bar{B}$ of function (3-13) are product terms, as each term is the product of *both of the two variables*. A *sum term* (or *S term*) of n variables is a logical sum of *all n variables*, although each variable can be the variable itself or its complement. The terms $A + \bar{B}$ and $\bar{A} + B$ of function (3-16) are sum terms, as each term is the sum of both of the two variables. Either a *P* term or an *S* term is called a *canonical term*.

A Boolean function of one variable $f(A)$ comprises two terms A and $\bar{A}$ which are indistinguishable between the *P* term and the *S* term.

The Boolean function of two variables $f(A,B)$ comprises four *P* terms and four *S* terms as shown in Table 3-5. Values in the first two columns for the variables A and B are arranged in the order of the binary number. *P* terms are formed on the values of the variables which give the function *the value of* 1. *A simple rule for obtaining the P term is to represent* 1 *by an uncomplemented variable and*

102   *Digital Computer Design Fundamentals*

0 *by a complemented variable.* In the first row of Table 3-5, for example, the P term P_0 employs the variables $\bar{A}$ and $\bar{B}$ because A and B in the first two columns are 0's; and the product $\bar{A}\bar{B}$ is 1. S terms are formed on the values of the variables which give the function *the value of* 0. *A simple rule for obtaining the S term is to represent* 0 *by an uncomplemented variable and* 1 *by a complemented variable.* For example, in the first row, the S term S_0 employs variables A and B uncomplemented be-

Table 3-5   P and S Terms of Boolean Function of Two Variables

A	B	P terms	S terms
0	0	$P_0 = \bar{A}\bar{B}$	$S_0 = A + B$
0	1	$P_1 = \bar{A}B$	$S_1 = A + \bar{B}$
1	0	$P_2 = A\bar{B}$	$S_2 = \bar{A} + B$
1	1	$P_3 = AB$	$S_3 = \bar{A} + \bar{B}$

cause the corresponding values of A and B in the first two columns are 0's and the sum $A + B$ is 0. From these two rules, it is apparent that the corresponding P term and S term complement each other.

$$P_i = \bar{S}_i \qquad \text{or} \qquad S_i = \bar{P}_i \qquad (3\text{-}17)$$

A Boolean function of three variables $f(A,B,C)$ comprises eight P terms and eight S terms. They are formed by the above rules and shown in Table 3-6. In

Table 3-6   P and S Terms of Boolean Function of Three Variables

A	B	C	P terms	S terms
0	0	0	$P_0 = \bar{A}\bar{B}\bar{C}$	$S_0 = A + B + C$
0	0	1	$P_1 = \bar{A}\bar{B}C$	$S_1 = A + B + \bar{C}$
0	1	0	$P_2 = \bar{A}B\bar{C}$	$S_2 = A + \bar{B} + C$
0	1	1	$P_3 = \bar{A}BC$	$S_3 = A + \bar{B} + \bar{C}$
1	0	0	$P_4 = A\bar{B}\bar{C}$	$S_4 = \bar{A} + B + C$
1	0	1	$P_5 = A\bar{B}C$	$S_5 = \bar{A} + B + \bar{C}$
1	1	0	$P_6 = AB\bar{C}$	$S_6 = \bar{A} + \bar{B} + C$
1	1	1	$P_7 = ABC$	$S_7 = \bar{A} + \bar{B} + \bar{C}$

general, *a Boolean function of n variables comprises* 2^n *P terms and* 2^n *S terms,* because each variable has two values; thus there are 2^n possible combinations of the values of n variables.

Note that the subscripts of the P terms and S terms in Table 3-6 are the decimal equivalents of the binary numbers in the first three columns. This notation will be adopted in subsequent truth tables.

Veitch Diagram. Representation of the P terms of one, two, or three variables by a Venn diagram appears in Fig. 3-9a, b, and c, respectively. The areas which correspond to the two, four, and eight P terms of one, two, and three variables are indicated therein. Representation of the S terms can be similarly drawn.

When the circles in a Venn diagram are squared and rearranged, the resulting pattern of squares is called a *Veitch diagram.* Each square represents a P term or an S term. Veitch diagraming of the P terms of one, two, or three variables appears in Fig. 3-9d, e, and f, respectively. In these Veitch diagrams, each variable A, B, or C which brackets a number of squares represents one half the diagram, and the complement of the variable represents the other half diagram. An individual square, such as the one marked $\bar{A}B\bar{C}$ in Fig. 3-9f, represents the

P term $\bar{A}B\bar{C}$; this square is the intersection of the one-half areas $\bar{A}$, B, and $\bar{C}$ when the values of $\bar{A}$, B, and $\bar{C}$ are equal to 1. Representation of S terms can use the same Veitch diagram. In this case, each square on a Veitch diagram representing a P_i term alternately represents a corresponding S_i term. For example, the square representing $\bar{A}B\bar{C}$ (or P_2) in Fig. 3-9f may represent $A + \bar{B} + C$ (or S_2). This representation of the S term is envisaged as follows: The one-half area A (lower four squares in Fig. 3-9f), which has been considered as having the value 1 (i.e., $A = 1$), is now equivalently considered as the one-half area $\bar{A}$, having the value 0 (i.e., $\bar{A} = 0$). And the one-half area $\bar{A}$ (upper four squares), having the value 1 (i.e., $\bar{A} = 1$), is now equivalently considered as having the value 0 (i.e., $A = 0$). Adoption of this convention stems from the fact that an S term deals with 0 and that the corresponding P and S terms represented by the same square on a Veitch diagram are complements. A Veitch diagram is simpler to draw and easier to visualize than a Venn diagram and will be used hereafter.

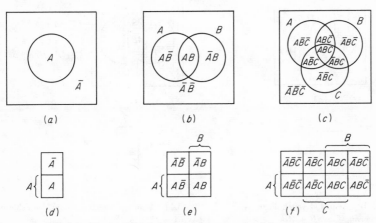

FIG. 3-9   Venn and Veitch diagrams for one, two, and three variables.

A Boolean function can also be graphically represented in either a Venn or a Veitch diagram. For instance, function (3-13) is shown as a Venn diagram in Fig. 3-10a; the shaded area represents $\bar{A}B + A\bar{B}$. Figure 3-10b illustrates the same function as a Veitch diagram; the squares representing the two P terms of the given function are marked by 1's. The 1's indicate that the value of the Boolean function is 1 when the value of the P term represented by the square becomes 1. If a Boolean function is written in S terms, it can also be graphically represented in both Venn and Veitch diagrams. Consider the function (3-14) diagramed in Fig. 3-11. The double shaded area in the Venn diagram of Fig. 3-11a represents $(A + B)(\bar{A} + \bar{B})$. In the Veitch diagram (Fig. 3-11b), the squares representing S terms $A + B$ and $\bar{A} + \bar{B}$ of the given function are marked by 0's. The 0's indicate that the value of the Boolean function is 0 when the values of the S term represented by the squares become 0. These representations on Veitch diagrams will be further described in Chap. 4.

Canonical Forms. It has been shown that from Table 3-4 one can write two Boolean functions in two forms, which can now be identified as canonical forms.

Canonical forms of a Boolean function are those functions which are written in distinct P terms or in distinct S terms. The Boolean function in P terms is called the *canonical P form,* while that written in S terms is called the *canonical S form.* Two examples are shown below:

$$f(A,B,C) = \overline{A}\overline{B}\overline{C} + \overline{A}\overline{B}C + \overline{A}B\overline{C} + \overline{A}BC + ABC + A\overline{B}C \qquad (3\text{-}18)$$

$$f(A,B,C) = (A + \overline{B} + C)(A + \overline{B} + \overline{C})(A + B + \overline{C})(\overline{A} + B + \overline{C}) \qquad (3\text{-}19)$$

The first function is a Boolean function of three variables in canonical P form, while the second function is in canonical S form.

The canonical forms of a Boolean function are important because, as will be shown later, they are unique representations of a given Boolean function. These forms may serve as a basis for comparison among various Boolean functions and also as a reference for later simplification and minimization of Boolean functions.

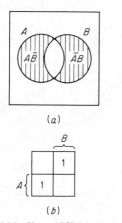

(a)

(b)

FIG. 3-10   Venn and Veitch diagrams, both showing $f = \overline{A}B + A\overline{B}$.

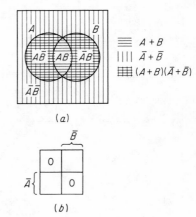

(a)

(b)

FIG. 3-11   Venn and Veitch diagrams, both showing $f = (A + B)(\overline{A} + \overline{B})$.

3-6   Theorems on Boolean Functions

Some properties of the Boolean function were discussed in the last section. Here these and other properties are formulated into a number of theorems [12].

Theorem 12a

The logical product of any two distinct P terms of a Boolean function of n variables is equal to 0, or

$$P_i P_j = 0 \qquad \text{where } i \neq j \qquad (3\text{-}20)$$

Theorem 12b

The logical sum of any two distinct S terms of a Boolean function of n variables is equal to 1, or

$$S_i + S_j = 1 \qquad \text{where } i \neq j \qquad (3\text{-}21)$$

Each of the 2^n P terms of a Boolean function is distinct from the other only in the presence or absence of the complement. By Theorem 2b, which states that $A \cdot A = 0$, the logical product of any two distinct P terms, P_i and P_j ($i \neq j$), is thus equal to 0. To illustrate, the eight P terms in Table 3-6 are all distinct; the product of the distinct P terms P_1 and P_3 is

$$P_1 P_3 = (\bar{A}\bar{B}C)(\bar{A}BC) = 0$$

Since $B\bar{B}$ is equal to 0, $P_1 P_3$ thus equals 0. As a further illustration, the sum of the distinct S terms S_3 and S_5 is

$$S_3 + S_5 = (A + \bar{B} + \bar{C}) + (\bar{A} + B + \bar{C}) = 1$$

Since $A + \bar{A} = 1$ (Theorem 2a) and $1 + A = 1$ (Theorem 8a), $S_3 + S_5$ is equal to 1.

Theorem 13a

A Boolean function of n variables can be represented by one and only one logical sum of P terms, or

$$f = \sum_{i=0}^{2^n - 1} \alpha_i P_i \tag{3-22}$$

Theorem 13b

A Boolean function of n variables can be represented by one and only one logical product of S terms, or

$$f = \prod_{i=0}^{2^n - 1} (\alpha_i + S_i) \tag{3-23}$$

The above α_i's are referred to as *characteristic numbers* of a given Boolean function. If the number of 1's in the characteristic number is equal to the number of 0's, the function is called a *neutral function*.

The proof of Theorem 13a is lengthy and has been omitted in favor of two examples. Consider the following two Boolean functions of three variables, $f(A,B,C)$:

$$f_1 = \bar{A}\bar{B}C + \bar{A}BC + A\bar{B}C$$
$$f_2 = (\bar{A} + \bar{B} + \bar{C})(\bar{A} + \bar{B} + C)(\bar{A} + B + C)(A + \bar{B} + C)(A + B + C)$$

The values of the characteristic numbers α for the above two functions are

$$\alpha_0 = \alpha_2 = \alpha_4 = \alpha_6 = \alpha_7 = 0$$
$$\alpha_1 = \alpha_3 = \alpha_5 = 1$$

By applying Theorem 13a, we have the P form,

$$f_1 = 0 \cdot P_0 + 1 \cdot P_1 + 0 \cdot P_2 + 1 \cdot P_3 + 0 \cdot P_4 + 1 \cdot P_5 + 0 \cdot P_6 + 0 \cdot P_7$$
or $\quad f_1 = P_1 + P_3 + P_5$

Applying Theorem 13b, we have the S form,

$$f_2 = (0 + S_0)(1 + S_1)(0 + S_2)(1 + S_3)(0 + S_4)(1 + S_5)(0 + S_6)(0 + S_7)$$
or $\quad f_2 = S_0 S_2 S_4 S_6 S_7$

From the above, it is noted that a Boolean function is determined by a set of values of the characteristic numbers α_i. *If the function is in canonical P form, only those P terms appear whose α_i's are equal to 1; if it is in canonical S form, only those S terms appear whose α_i's are equal to 0.*

Theorem 14a

The complement of a Boolean function of n variables can be represented by one and only one logical sum of P terms,

$$\bar{f} = \sum_{i=0}^{2^n-1} \bar{\alpha}_i P_i \tag{3-24}$$

Theorem 14b

The complement of a Boolean function of n variables can be represented by one and only one logical product of S terms, or

$$\bar{f} = \prod_{i=0}^{2^n-1} (\bar{\alpha}_i + S_i) \tag{3-25}$$

These theorems can be proved by taking complements of Theorems 13. Taking the complement of Theorem 13*b*, we have

$$\bar{f} = \overline{\prod_{i=0}^{2^n-1} (\alpha_i + S_i)} = \sum_{i=0}^{2^n-1} \bar{\alpha}_i \bar{S}_i$$

Recall identities (3-17): $\bar{S}_i = P_i$. We have the result (3-24). As an example, consider the previous two functions having the characteristic numbers

$$\alpha_0 = \alpha_2 = \alpha_4 = \alpha_6 = \alpha_7 = 0$$
$$\alpha_1 = \alpha_3 = \alpha_5 = 1$$

If these two functions are complemented, and if we apply Theorems 14*a* and 14*b*, then

$$\bar{f_1} = P_0 + P_2 + P_4 + P_6 + P_7$$
$$\bar{f_2} = S_1 S_3 S_5$$

Note that the sum of the numbers of terms in the function f_1 and $\bar{f_1}$ is constant and equal to 2^n or 8. We summarize that *the complement of a Boolean function f in a canonical form is determined by the complement of the values of characteristic numbers α_i of the given function. If the complement function $\bar{f}$ is in canonical P form, only those P terms appear whose α_i's are originally equal to 0; if $\bar{f}$ is in canonic S form, only those S terms appear whose α_i's are originally equal to 1.*

Theorem 15a

The logical sum of 2^n distinct P terms of a Boolean function of n variables is equal to 1, or

$$\sum_{i=0}^{2^n-1} P_i = 1 \tag{3-26}$$

Theorem 15b

The logical product of 2^n distinct S terms of a Boolean function of n variables is equal to 0, or

$$\prod_{i=0}^{2^n-1} S_i = 0 \qquad (3\text{-}27)$$

From Theorems 13a and 14a, we have

$$f + \bar{f} = \sum_{i=0}^{2^n-1} \alpha_i P_i + \sum_{i=0}^{2^n-1} \bar{\alpha}_i P_i = \sum_{i=0}^{2^n-1} P_i$$

Since $f + \bar{f} = 1$, Theorem 15a is proved. The following four identities are examples for Boolean functions of two and three variables:

$$\bar{A}\bar{B} + \bar{A}B + A\bar{B} + AB = 1$$
$$(\bar{A} + \bar{B})(\bar{A} + B)(A + \bar{B})(A + B) = 0$$
$$\bar{A}\bar{B}\bar{C} + \bar{A}\bar{B}C + \bar{A}B\bar{C} + \bar{A}BC + A\bar{B}\bar{C} + A\bar{B}C + AB\bar{C} + ABC = 1$$
$$(\bar{A} + \bar{B} + \bar{C})(\bar{A} + \bar{B} + C)(\bar{A} + B + \bar{C})(\bar{A} + B + C)$$
$$(A + \bar{B} + \bar{C})(A + \bar{B} + C)(A + B + \bar{C})(A + B + C) = 0$$

Theorem 16a

Any P term of a Boolean function of n variables is equal to the logical product of $2^n - 1$ S terms,

$$P_k = \prod_{i \neq k} S_i \qquad \text{where } i = 0, \ldots, 2^n - 1 \qquad (3\text{-}28)$$

Theorem 16b

Any S term of a Boolean function of n variables is equal to the logical sum of $2^n - 1$ P terms,

$$S_k = \sum_{i \neq k} P_i \qquad \text{where } i = 0, \ldots, 2^n - 1 \qquad (3\text{-}29)$$

The two functions of Theorem 13 are the same and differ only in form. Thus we have

$$\sum_{i=0}^{2^n-1} \alpha_i P_i = \prod_{i=0}^{2^n-1} (\alpha_i + S_i)$$

If there is only one P term on the left side of this equation, and if we let this term be called P_k, then the values of the α's are

$$\alpha_i = 1 \qquad \text{when} \qquad i = k$$
and
$$\alpha_i = 0 \qquad \text{when} \qquad i \neq k$$

This proves Theorem 16a. For example, consider P_1, which is a P term of a Boolean function of two variables. Then, from Theorem 16a, we have

$$\alpha_1 = 1 \qquad \text{and} \qquad \alpha_0 = \alpha_2 = \alpha_3 = 0$$
or
$$P_1 = S_0 S_2 S_3 = (A + B)(\bar{A} + B)(\bar{A} + \bar{B})$$

Instead of P_1, consider that S_1 of the same function is given. Then, from Theorem 16b, we have

$$\alpha_1 = 0 \quad \text{and} \quad \alpha_0 = \alpha_2 = \alpha_3 = 1$$

or

$$S_1 = P_0 + P_2 + P_3 = \bar{A}\bar{B} + A\bar{B} + AB$$

Theorem 17

There are 2^{2^n} distinct functions for a Boolean function of n variables.

As has been shown, there are 2^n distinct P terms; the logical sum of one or more of these terms corresponds to a distinct Boolean function. Let $m = 2^n$; m is a positive integer and also the number of distinct P terms. We can take one term at a time to form a Boolean function and similarly can take two or more terms at a time. The number of Boolean functions which can be formed by exhausting all such possibilities, including those of taking no term and of taking all terms, is the summation of all these combinations (which are binomial coefficients), or

$$\sum_{j=0}^{j=m} \frac{m!}{j!(m-j)!} = 2^m = 2^{2^n} \tag{3-30}$$

Therefore, there are 2^{2^n} distinct functions for a Boolean function of n variables. These include the function of 0 (no P terms or all S terms) and the function of 1 (no S term or all P terms). The two canonical forms of a Boolean function as shown in Theorem 13 constitute the unique representations of the given function and those in Theorem 14 the unique representation of the complement of the given function.

3-7   *Boolean Functions of Two Variables*

The number of possible Boolean functions for one to six variables is shown in Table 3-7. The number of possible Boolean functions becomes astronomical when the number of variables is six or more.

The two canonical forms for a Boolean function of one variable as obtained from Theorems 13 are

$$f(A) = \alpha_0 P_0 + \alpha_1 P_1 \tag{3-31}$$

$$f(A) = (\alpha_0 + S_0)(\alpha_1 + S_1) \tag{3-32}$$

The four possible Boolean functions of one variable in either P form or S form are all rather trivial,

$$f_0 = 0 \qquad f_1 = A \qquad f_2 = \bar{A} \qquad f_3 = 1$$

Table 3-7   *Number of Possible Boolean Functions*

Number of variables	*Number of Boolean functions*
1	4
2	16
3	256
4	65,536
5	4,294,967,296
6	18,446,744,073,709,551,616

Table 3-8   **Characteristic Numbers of Boolean Functions of Two Variables**

A	B	α	f_0	f_1	f_2	f_3	f_4	f_5	f_6	f_7	f_8	f_9	f_{10}	f_{11}	f_{12}	f_{13}	f_{14}	f_{15}
0	0	α_0	0	0	0	0	0	0	0	0	1	1	1	1	1	1	1	1
0	1	α_1	0	0	0	0	1	1	1	1	0	0	0	0	1	1	1	1
1	0	α_2	0	0	1	1	0	0	1	1	0	0	1	1	0	0	1	1
1	1	α_3	0	1	0	1	0	1	0	1	0	1	0	1	0	1	0	1

The two canonical forms for a Boolean function of *two* variables are

$$f(A,B) = \alpha_0 P_0 + \alpha_1 P_1 + \alpha_2 P_2 + \alpha_3 P_3 \tag{3-33}$$

$$f(A,B) = (\alpha_0 + S_0)(\alpha_1 + S_1)(\alpha_2 + S_2)(\alpha_3 + S_3) \tag{3-34}$$

The 16 possible functions of two variables in either P form or S form result from the 16 possible sets of the characteristic number α's ($\alpha_0\alpha_1\alpha_2\alpha_3 = 0000$, $0001, \ldots, 1110, 1111$); they are shown in Table 3-8. These functions can be simplified into those appearing in the first column of Table 3-9. This table also gives the logic explanation and the terminology.

Boolean functions of three or more variables become impractical to tabulate in all possible variations. However, they can be referred to or identified because the notation of these functions is organized in a systematic manner. Suppose, for example, that the given function comprises four variables $f(A,B,C,D)$ as follows:

$$f = \bar{A}B\bar{C}D + A\bar{B}\bar{C}D$$

The above P terms $\bar{A}B\bar{C}D$ and $A\bar{B}\bar{C}D$ refer to the binary numbers $0101(5)$ and $1001(9)$, respectively. Therefore, the characteristic numbers α_5 and α_9 are equal to 1, and all others are zero. This function can be written as

$$f = P_5 + P_9$$

Table 3-9   **Sixteen Boolean Functions of Two Variables**

Function	Explanation	Terminology
$f_0 = 0$	zero	zero
$f_1 = AB$	A and B	*and*
$f_2 = A\bar{B}$	A and (not B)	*andnot B*
$f_3 = A$	A	identity
$f_4 = \bar{A}B$	B and (not A)	*andnot A*
$f_5 = B$	B	identity
$f_6 = \bar{A}B + A\bar{B}$	($\bar{A}$ and B) or (A and $\bar{B}$)	exclusive *or*
$f_7 = A + B$	A or B	*or*†
$f_8 = \bar{A}\bar{B} = \overline{A + B}$	not (A or B)	*nor* Pierce $A \downarrow B$
$f_9 = \bar{A}\bar{B} + AB$	($\bar{A}$ and $\bar{B}$) or (A and B)	coincidence
$f_{10} = \bar{B}$	not B‡	*not* or complement
$f_{11} = A + \bar{B}$	A or (not B)	*ornot B*
$f_{12} = \bar{A}$	not A	*not*
$f_{13} = \bar{A} + B$	B or (not A)	*ornot A*
$f_{14} = \bar{A} + \bar{B} = \overline{AB}$	not (A and B)	*nand* sheffer stroke $A \uparrow B$
$f_{15} = 1$	one	one

† Also called *inclusive or*.
‡ Also called *complement of B*.

If the given function is in canonical S form,

$$f = (A + \bar{B} + C + \bar{D})(\bar{A} + B + C + \bar{D})$$

we have α_5 and α_9 equal to 0; and the function becomes

$$f = S_5 S_9$$

3-8 Elementary Terms and Elementary Forms

Simplification and Expansion. It has been shown that a Boolean function can be expressed in two canonical forms. These two canonical forms are unique; but they usually are simplified into one in which the variables appear less often. The manipulation of a Boolean function into one with fewer appearances of the variables is called *simplification*. Conversely, a Boolean function not in a canonical form can be expanded into one of the two canonical forms. Such manipulation is called *expansion*. For example, let us simplify the following Boolean function, which is in canonical P form:

$$\begin{aligned} f_1 &= \bar{A}\bar{B}\bar{C} + \bar{A}B\bar{C} + \bar{A}BC + \bar{A}BC + ABC \\ &= \bar{A}\bar{C} + \bar{A}C + BC \\ &= \bar{A} + BC \end{aligned}$$

The number of variables appearing has been reduced from 15 to only 3. Let us now expand the following Boolean function, which is in canonical S form:

$$\begin{aligned} f_2 &= (A + \bar{B})(B + \bar{C}) \\ &= (A + \bar{B} + C\bar{C})(A\bar{A} + B + \bar{C}) \\ &= (A + \bar{B} + C)(A + \bar{B} + \bar{C})(A + B + \bar{C})(\bar{A} + B + \bar{C}) \end{aligned}$$

The appearances of the variables have been increased from 4 to 12.

Elementary Terms. For a given number of variables n, there are a finite number of distinct terms in either a logical sum or a logical product of n or fewer variables. Such terms are called *elementary terms*. If the distinct term is a logical product, then it is an *elementary P term*. If the distinct term is a logical sum, then it is an *elementary S term*. The elementary P terms and S terms for one to three variables are shown in Table 3-10. The number of distinct elementary P terms and S terms for one to six variables is shown in Table 3-11. In this table, the number of canonical P terms and S terms is also shown

Table 3-10 *Elementary P and S Terms for Boolean Functions of One, Two, and Three Variables*

Number of variables	One-variable terms	P terms	S terms
1	$\bar{A}, A$		
2	$\bar{A}, A, \bar{B}, B$	$\bar{A}\bar{B}, \bar{A}B, A\bar{B}, AB$	$\bar{A} + \bar{B}, \bar{A} + B, A + \bar{B}, A + B$
3	$\bar{A}, A, \bar{B}, B, \bar{C}, C$	$\bar{A}\bar{B}, \bar{A}B, A\bar{B}, AB$ $\bar{A}\bar{C}, \bar{A}C, A\bar{C}, AC$ $\bar{B}\bar{C}, \bar{B}C, B\bar{C}, BC$ $\bar{A}\bar{B}\bar{C}, \bar{A}B\bar{C}, \bar{A}\bar{B}C,$ $\bar{A}BC, A\bar{B}\bar{C}, A\bar{B}C,$ $AB\bar{C}, ABC$	$\bar{A} + \bar{B}, \bar{A} + B, A + \bar{B}, A + B$ $\bar{A} + \bar{C}, \bar{A} + C, A + \bar{C}, A + C$ $\bar{B} + \bar{C}, \bar{B} + C, B + \bar{C}, B + C$ $\bar{A} + \bar{B} + \bar{C}, \bar{A} + \bar{B} + C, \bar{A} + B + \bar{C},$ $\bar{A} + B + C, A + \bar{B} + \bar{C}, A + \bar{B} + C,$ $A + B + \bar{C}, A + B + C$

Table 3-11   Number of Possible Elemetary P and S Terms of Boolean Functions

Number of variables	Number of elementary P terms and S terms	Number of canonical P terms and S terms
1	2	2
2	12	8
3	46	16
4	152	32
5	474	64
6	1,444	128

for comparison.   It is obvious that the number of elementary terms is larger than the number of canonical P terms and S terms, particularly when the number of variables becomes large.

Elementary Forms.   A Boolean function expressed in elementary terms is in an *elementary form.*   Boolean functions can be in either the *elementary P form* (logical sum of elementary P terms) or the *elementary S form* (logical product of elementary S terms).   Elementary forms of a Boolean function differ from canonical forms; the latter comprise only canonical P or S terms.   Thus, elementary forms are general, while canonical forms are unique.   The earlier two functions f_1 and f_2, repeated here,

$$f_1 = \bar{A} + BC$$
$$f_2 = (A + \bar{B})(B + \bar{C})$$

are examples of Boolean functions in the elementary form.   Function f_1 is in elementary P form; f_2 is in elementary S form.   An example of a *nonelementary form* is that of f_3,

$$f_3 = A + B[C + \bar{D}(A + B)]$$

For a Boolean function in a nonelementary form, there is a repeated combination of the logical sum and logical product of elementary terms.   These three functions are shown in the block diagrams of Fig. 3-12.   The variables (signals

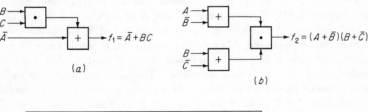

(a)

(b)

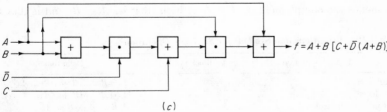

(c)

FIG. 3-12   Block diagrams showing the use of two-level and more-than-two-level logic.   (a) Two-level; (b) two-level; (c) five-level.

in actual circuits) in Fig. 3-12*a* and *b* go through two logic operations (or two levels in circuits), while some variables in Fig. 3-12*c* go through as many as five logic operations. *A Boolean function, therefore, in the elementary form requires two-level logic circuits, while that in the nonelementary form requires more-than-two-level logic circuits.* Certain types of circuits, as diode logic circuits, cause signals to suffer distortion and attenuation after passing through one or more levels. Amplification and waveform-shaping circuits, *logically* unnecessary, become a practical necessity under such conditions.

3-9   Other Basic Logic Operations

Six Other Operations. We have thus far been using the three logic operations of logical *and*, logical *or*, and logical *not* and formulating other logic operations from them. Six other basic logic operations have been mentioned in Table 3-9: exclusive *or*, coincidence, *nor*, *nand*, *andnot*, and *ornot*. Their symbols and definitions are summarized in Table 3-12. The block representation of these operations is shown in Fig. 3-13.

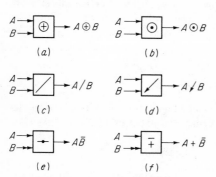

(a)   (b)

(c)   (d)

(e)   (f)

FIG. 3-13   Block representations of six logic operations. (*a*) Exclusive-*or*; (*b*) coincidence; (*c*) *nand*; (*d*) *nor*; (*e*) *andnot*-B; (*f*) *ornot*-B.

Symbols $\leftarrow$ and $\mp$ are chosen for *andnot* and *ornot* operations, respectively, because the former is composed of the symbols for logical-*and* and logical-*not* operations and the latter composed of those for logical-*or* and logical-*not* operations; furthermore, a double-headed arrow is used to indicate the complemented variable.

The exclusive-*or* operation $(A \oplus B)$ (also known as modulo-2 sum operation) means either A or B but not both; this differs from the logical-*or* operation (also known as *inclusive-or operation*), which means either A or B or both. The coincidence operation $(A \odot B)$ means both A and B or both $\bar{A}$ and $\bar{B}$; this differs from logical-*and* operation, which means only both A and B, and is the complement of exclusive-*or* operation. The *nand* operation A/B (read A per B) means either $\bar{A}$ or $\bar{B}$ or both; it also means not both A and B (that is, $\overline{AB}$) and is thus the complement of the logical-*and* operation. The *nand* operation and its symbol, first introduced by Sheffer in 1913, is also known as *Sheffer's stroke function*. The *nor* operation $A \swarrow B$ (read A peirce B, after Peirce) means both $\bar{A}$ and $\bar{B}$; it also means the complement of A or B or both (that is, $\overline{A + B}$) and is thus the

Table 3-12   Definitions and Symbols for Six Logic Operations

Logical operation	Block symbol	Definition
exclusive *or*..........................	$\oplus$	$A \oplus B = \bar{A}B + A\bar{B} = \overline{A \odot B}$
coincidence.............................	$\odot$	$A \odot B = \bar{A}\bar{B} + AB = \overline{A \oplus B}$
nand (or Sheffer stroke)..............	$/$	$A/B = \bar{A} + \bar{B} = \overline{AB}$
nor (or Peirce).......................	$\swarrow$	$A \swarrow B = \bar{A}\bar{B} = \overline{A + B}$
andnot B (inhibit)....................	$\leftarrow$	$A\bar{B}$
ornot B (implication).................	$\mp$	$A + \bar{B}$

complement of logical-*or* operation.   The *andnot-B* operation $A\bar{B}$ (or similarly *andnot-A*, $\bar{A}B$) means both A and $\bar{B}$; it is the complement of the *ornot-A* operation.   The *ornot-B* operation $(A + \bar{B})$ (or similarly *ornot-A*) means either A or $\bar{B}$ or both; it is the complement of the *andnot-A* operation and is also the logical notion of *implication*.   The values of these six logic operations on 0 and 1 together with those of logical-*and* and logical-*or* operations are shown in Table 3-13.

Table 3-13   *Logic Operations on 0 and 1*

AB	$A+B$	$A \oplus B$	$A \odot B$	A/B	$A \angle B$	$A\bar{B}$	$A + \bar{B}$
$0\cdot0=0$	$0+0=0$	$0\oplus0=0$	$0\odot0=1$	$0/0=1$	$0\angle0=1$	$0\cdot\bar{0}=0$	$0+\bar{0}=1$
$0\cdot1=0$	$0+1=1$	$0\oplus1=1$	$0\odot1=0$	$0/1=1$	$0\angle1=0$	$0\cdot\bar{1}=0$	$0+\bar{1}=0$
$1\cdot0=0$	$1+0=1$	$1\oplus0=1$	$1\odot0=0$	$1/0=1$	$1\angle0=0$	$1\cdot\bar{0}=1$	$1+\bar{0}=1$
$1\cdot1=1$	$1+1=1$	$1\oplus1=0$	$1\odot1=1$	$1/1=0$	$1\angle1=0$	$1\cdot\bar{1}=0$	$1+\bar{1}=1$
$0\cdot A=0$	$0+A=A$	$0\oplus A=A$	$0\odot A=\bar{A}$	$0/A=1$	$0\angle A=\bar{A}$	$0\cdot\bar{B}=0$	$0+\bar{B}=\bar{B}$
$1\cdot A=A$	$1+A=1$	$1\oplus A=\bar{A}$	$1\odot A=A$	$1/A=\bar{A}$	$1\angle A=0$	$1\cdot\bar{B}=\bar{B}$	$1+\bar{B}=1$
$\bar{A}\cdot A=0$	$\bar{A}+A=1$	$\bar{A}\oplus A=1$	$\bar{A}\odot A=0$	$\bar{A}/A=1$	$\bar{A}\angle A=0$	$\bar{B}\cdot\bar{B}=\bar{B}$	$\bar{B}+\bar{B}=\bar{B}$
$A\cdot A=A$	$A+A=A$	$A\oplus A=0$	$A\odot A=1$	$A/A=\bar{A}$	$A\angle A=\bar{A}$	$B\cdot\bar{B}=0$	$B+\bar{B}=1$

Some physical circuits may be more adaptable to certain basic logic operations than to others.   Relay circuits using both normally open and normally closed relays can form all these basic operations.   Circuits using diodes alone are limited to logical-*and* and logical-*or* operations.   Vacuum-tube and transistor circuits are more favorable for *nor* and *nand* operations.   Superconductor circuits are similar, with some restrictions, to relay circuits using normally closed relays. Single magnetic-core circuits are preferable for logical-*or*, *nor*, and *andnot* circuits.   Multiaperture magnetic cores can perform a number of different logic operations in one such core.   Consequently, familiarity with all these basic logic operations is useful.

Choice of Other Sets of Primitive Operations.   As mentioned earlier, Boolean algebra is developed from a chosen set of fundamental concepts.   These concepts can be regarded as primitive logic operations from which other logic operations can be formulated.   In our development of Boolean algebra, we chose logical *or* and logical *not* as primitive operations.   Another approach is to choose logical *and* and logical *not* as primitive operations.   We can also choose one or more of the six logic operations in Table 3-12 as the primitive ones.   Six possible choices are exclusive-*or* and logical-*and* operations, coincidence and logical-*and* operations, *nor* operation, *nand* operation, *andnot* operation, and *ornot* operation.   The formulation of logical-*not*, logical-*or* and logical-*and* operations from these choices of primitive operations are shown in the block representations of Fig. 3-14.   In the development of these block representations, the following identities are used:

$$A \oplus B \oplus AB = A + B$$
$$A \odot B \odot AB = A + B$$
$$(A \angle B) \angle (A \angle B) = A + B$$
$$(A / A) / (B / B) = A + B$$
$$(A \angle A) \angle (B \angle B) = AB$$
$$(A / B) / (A / B) = AB$$
$$A(\overline{A\bar{B}}) = AB$$
$$\overline{\bar{A}\bar{B}} = A + B$$
$$\overline{\bar{A} + \bar{B}} = AB$$
$$A + (\overline{A + \bar{B}}) = A + B$$

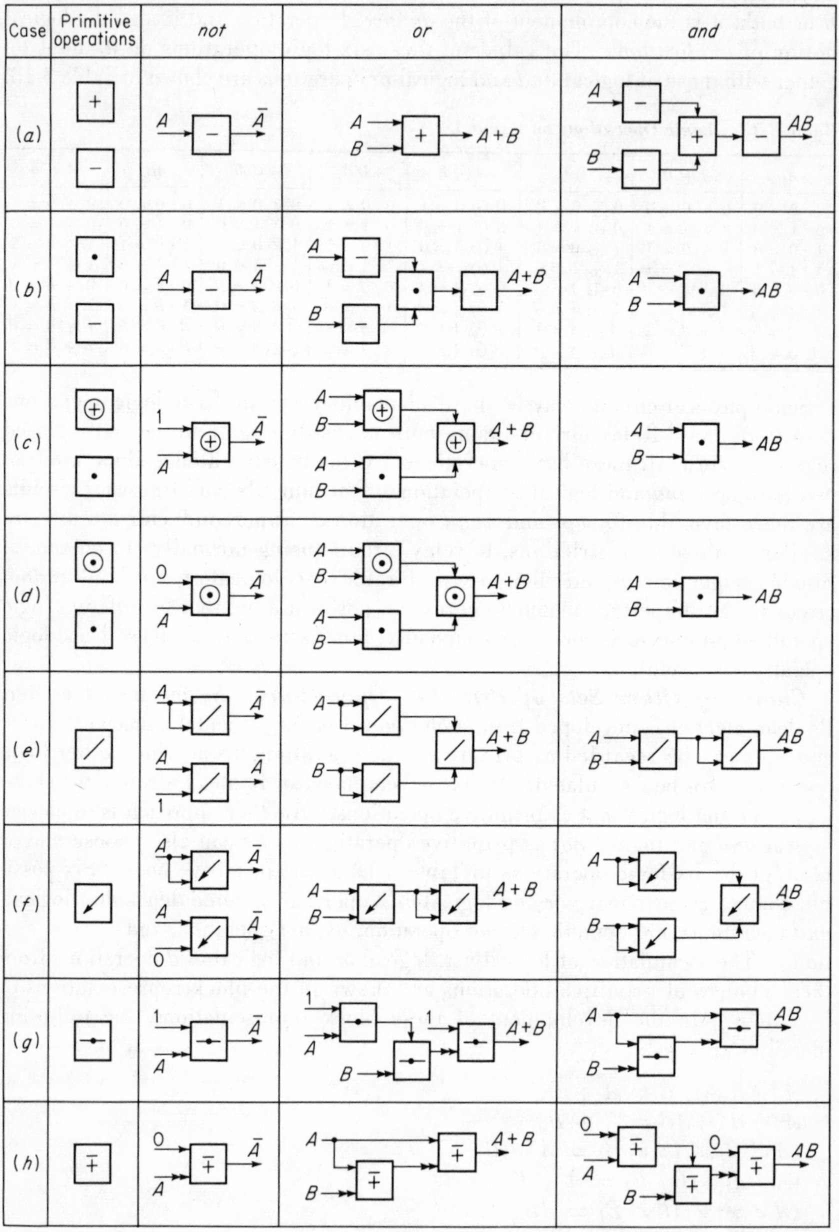

FIG. 3-14   Logical-*and*, logical-*or*, and logical-*not* operations derived from eight sets of primitive operations.

It is interesting to note that only one primitive operation is necessary if the *nor, nand, andnot,* or *ornot* operation is chosen. These operations may be called *universal operations.* The choice of the *nor* or *nand* operation has an advantage over that of the *andnot* or *ornot* operation in that the former choice requires fewer circuits.

The above choices of primitive logic operations do not exhaust all the possibilities. The selection of primitive logic operation in developing Boolean algebra is not unique. The major consideration in choosing basic logic operations lies in the realizability of more reliable and less expensive electronic circuits. Logical-*and,* logical-*or,* logical-*not,* logical-*nor,* and logical-*nand* circuits have been widely used because they can be readily realized.

Table 3-14 *Identities for Exclusive-or and Coincidence Operations* [26]

	Identity		Identity
$A \oplus 0 = A$	1a	$A \odot 0 = \bar{A}$	1b
$A \oplus 1 = \bar{A}$	2a	$A \odot 1 = A$	2b
$A \oplus A = 0$	3a	$A \odot A = 1$	3b
$A \oplus \bar{A} = 1$	4a	$A \odot \bar{A} = 0$	4b
$A \oplus A \oplus \cdots \oplus A = 0$ even number of A's	5a	$A \odot A \odot \cdots \odot A = 1$ even number of A's	5b
$A \oplus A \oplus \cdots \oplus A = A$ odd number of A's	6a	$A \odot A \odot \cdots \odot A = A$ odd number of A's	6b
$A \oplus B \oplus C \cdots = 0$ even number of variables has the value 1	7a	$A \odot B \odot C \cdots = 1$ even number of variables has the value 0	7b
$A \oplus B \oplus C \cdots = 1$ odd number of variables has the value 1	8a	$A \odot B \odot C \cdots = 0$ odd number of variables has the value 0	8b
$A \oplus B = B \oplus A$	9a	$A \odot B = B \odot A$	9b
$A \oplus (B \oplus C) = (A \oplus B) \oplus C = A \oplus B \oplus C$	10a	$A \odot (B \odot C) = (A \odot B) \odot C = A \odot B \odot C$	10b
$AB \oplus AC = A(B \oplus C)$	11a	$(A + B) \odot (A + C) = A + (B \odot C)$	11b
$A \oplus B = C$ implies $A \oplus C = B$	12a	$A \odot B = C$ implies $A \odot C = B$	12b
$B \oplus C = A$	13a	$B \odot C = A$	13b
$A \oplus B \oplus C = 0$	14a	$A \odot B \odot C = 1$	14b
$A + B = A \oplus B \oplus AB$	15a	$A + B = A \odot B \odot AB$	15b
$A \oplus B \oplus \cdots \oplus C = A + B + \cdots + C$ if $AB = \cdots = AC = \cdots = BC = 0$	16a	$A \odot B \odot \cdots \odot C = A + B + \cdots + C$ if $AB = \cdots = AC = \cdots = BC = 1$	16b
$AB \oplus \bar{A}C = AB + \bar{A}C$	17a	$AB \odot \bar{A}C = \overline{AB + \bar{A}C}$	17b
$A \oplus B = A\bar{B} + \bar{A}B = (A + B)(\bar{A} + \bar{B})$	18a	$A \odot B = AB + \overline{AB} = (\bar{A} + B)(A + \bar{B})$	18b
$\overline{A \oplus B} = \bar{A} \oplus B = A \oplus \bar{B}$	19a	$\overline{A \odot B} = \bar{A} \odot B = A \odot \bar{B}$	19b
$A \oplus B = \overline{A \odot B}$	20a	$A \odot B = \overline{A \oplus B}$	20b
$A \oplus AB = A\bar{B}$	21a	$A \odot AB = \overline{A\bar{B}}$	21b
$A \oplus (A + B) = \bar{A}B$	22a	$A \odot (A + B) = \overline{\bar{A}B}$	22b
$A \oplus \bar{A}B = A + B$	23a	$A \odot \bar{A}B = \overline{A + B}$	23b
$A \oplus (\bar{A} + B) = \overline{A}B$	24a	$A \odot (\bar{A} + B) = AB$	24b

Identities for Exclusive-or and Coincidence Operations. The exclusive-*or* and coincidence operations are very useful. Table 3-14 lists a number of identities involving these two operations. In this table, identities (9), (10), and (11) show their commutative, associative, and distributive properties, respectively. The distributive property, however, should be treated with caution. For example, the following relations are *not* correct, as indicated by the not-equal sign:

$$(A + B) \oplus (A + C) \neq A + (B \oplus C)$$
$$(A \oplus B) + (A \oplus C) \neq A \oplus (B + C)$$
$$(A \oplus B)(A \oplus C) \neq A(B \oplus C)$$
$$AB \odot BC \neq A(B \odot C)$$
$$(A \odot B) + (A \odot C) \neq A \odot (B + C)$$
$$(A \odot B)(A \odot C) \neq A(B \odot C)$$

3-10   Symmetric Boolean Functions

A Boolean function of n variables is said to be symmetric in these variables if any permutation of the variables leaves the function identically the same. This definition for a symmetric function is taken from Shannon [5]. As a case in point functions (3-35) and (3-36) of the variables A, B, and C,

$$f_1 = AB + AC + BC \tag{3-35}$$
$$f_2 = (A + B)(A + C)(B + C) \tag{3-36}$$

are symmetric functions, because if A and B (or any other two variables) were interchanged, functions f_1 and f_2 would remain unaltered. By contrast, the following two functions

$$f_3 = A\overline{B}C + \overline{A}BC + \overline{A}B\overline{C} \tag{3-37}$$
$$f_4 = (\overline{A} + B + \overline{C})(A + \overline{B} + \overline{C})(A + B + C) \tag{3-38}$$

are not symmetric in A, B, and C but are symmetric in A, B, and $\overline{C}$. Indeed, the recognition of a symmetric function is not always obvious.

The variables A, B, C or A, B, $\overline{C}$ are called *variables in symmetry*. There are two types of symmetric functions. In the first type, the variables of symmetry are either all unbarred or all barred. This type admits only two possibilities known as *m-out-of-n circuits*. In the second type, the variables of symmetry are neither all unbarred nor all barred. For this type, there are $2^n - 2$ combinations; symmetric functions of the second type are difficult to recognize.

Shannon's Theorems. Shannon [5] has formulated a number of theorems on symmetric functions in describing their properties. The first pair are the α-number theorems. Consider the above function f_1: since its value is 1 when two of the variables are 1 or when all three variables are 1, this function is said to have α numbers 2 and 3.

Theorem 18a and b (α-number Theorems)

A necessary and sufficient condition of a symmetric function may be specified by stating a set of numbers $\alpha_1, \alpha_2 \ldots, \alpha_k$ such that, if exactly α_j ($j = 1, 2, 3, \ldots, k$) of the variables are 1 (or 0), then the function is 1 (or 0) and not otherwise. These numbers are called the α *numbers* of the function.

The proofs of these theorems proceed directly from the above statement. The numbers $\alpha_1, \alpha_2, \ldots, \alpha_k$ are a set of numbers, where $0 \leq \alpha_k \leq n$, and are found by substituting $0, 1, \ldots, n$ of the n variables of the symmetric function with their values equal to 1 (or 0). Those numbers of variables which give the value of the function equal to 1 (or 0) are the α numbers. For instance, the α numbers for the above functions f_1 and f_2 are 2 and 3; and the α number for the above function f_3 or f_4 is 1.

Theorem 19a and b

There are 2^{n+1} symmetric functions of n variables.

This theorem can be proved by noting that each of the $n + 1$ numbers (0, 1, \ldots, n) may be taken or ignored in the selection of α numbers.

For a symmetric function of the n variables $X_1, X_2, \ldots, X_n$ with the

α numbers $\alpha_1, \alpha_2, \ldots, \alpha_k$, we adopt the notations $S_{\alpha 1, \ldots, \alpha k}(X_1, \ldots, X_n)$ and $M_{\alpha 1, \ldots, \alpha k}(X_1, \ldots, X_n)$ for those satisfying Theorems 18a and 18b, respectively. For example, the functions f_1 and f_2 are denoted below:

$$S_{2,3}(A,B,C) = f_1 = AB + AC + BC \tag{3-39}$$

$$M_{2,3}(A,B,C) = f_2 = (A + B)(A + C)(B + C) \tag{3-40}$$

Theorem 20a and b

The complement of a symmetric function of n variables is a symmetric function of those variables having α numbers from 0 to n which are not the α numbers of the given function.

This theorem can be proved by using α-number theorems. The α numbers of the given symmetric function are the numbers of the variables which make the given function equal to 1 (or 0) when these variables are 1 (or 0). Therefore, the α numbers from 0 to n which are not the α numbers of the given function will make the given function 0 (or 1). Thus, a symmetric function with these α numbers and with the same variables of symmetry is the complement of the given function. For example, the complements of the functions f_1 and f_2, respectively, are shown below:

$$\bar{f}_1 = \bar{S}_{2,3}(A,B,C) = S_{0,1}(A,B,C) \tag{3-41}$$

$$\bar{f}_1 = \bar{M}_{2,3}(A,B,C) = M_{0,1}(A,B,C) \tag{3-42}$$

Theorem 21a and b

A symmetric function of n variables is equal to the symmetric function in which each of the original variables is complemented and each α number α_i of the original function is replaced by the α number $n - \alpha_i$.

This theorem can be deduced from α-number theorems. A symmetric function is equal to 1 (or 0) when α_i variables of symmetry are equal to 1 (or 0) or, conversely, when $n - \alpha_i$ variables of symmetry are equal to 0 (or 1) [i.e., when $n - \alpha_i$ complemented variables of symmetry are equal to 1 (or 0)]. This proves the above theorem. Two examples are given below:

$$S_{2,3}(A,B,C) = S_{0,1}(\bar{A},\bar{B},\bar{C}) \tag{3-43}$$

$$M_{2,3}(A,B,C) = M_{0,1}(\bar{A},\bar{B},\bar{C}) \tag{3-44}$$

Theorem 22a and b

The logical sum (or product) of two given symmetric functions S (or M) with the same set of variables of symmetry is a symmetric function of these variables which has for its α numbers all α numbers appearing in either or both of the given functions.

This theorem can be proved by noting that the logical sum (or product) of the two symmetric functions is 1 (or 0) if either function is 1 (or 0). Two examples are given.

$$S_{1,2,3,5}(A, \ldots, F) = S_{1,2,3}(A, \ldots, F) + S_{2,3,5}(A, \ldots, F) \tag{3-45}$$

$$M_{1,2,3,5}(A, \ldots, F) = M_{1,2,3}(A, \ldots, F) \cdot M_{2,3,5}(A, \ldots, F) \tag{3-46}$$

Theorem 23a and b

The logical product (or sum) of two given symmetric functions S (or M) with the same set of variables of symmetry is a symmetric function of these variables which has for its α numbers those numbers common to the two given functions.

This theorem can be proved by noting that the logical product (or sum) of the two symmetric functions is 1 (or 0) if both given functions are 1 (or 0). Two examples illustrate these conditions.

$$S_{2,3}(A, \ldots, F) = S_{1,2,3}(A, \ldots, F) \cdot S_{2,3,5}(A, \ldots, F) \qquad (3\text{-}47)$$

$$M_{2,3}(A, \ldots, F) = M_{1,2,3}(A, \ldots, F) + M_{2,3,5}(A, \ldots, F) \qquad (3\text{-}48)$$

3-11   Canonical Symmetric Functions

Canonical symmetric functions have a *single α number* and are expressed in canonical terms, either in product terms (P terms) or in sum terms (S terms). The letters u and v represent these two forms, respectively, in the subsequent discussion.

Table 3-15   Canonical Symmetric Functions in Product Terms

Variable	Canonical symmetric functions
$n = 1$	$u_0 = \bar{A} = P_0$
	$u_1 = A = P_1$
$n = 2$	$u_0 = \bar{A}\bar{B} \qquad\qquad = P_0$
	$u_1 = A\bar{B} + \bar{A}B = P_1 + P_2$
	$u_2 = AB \qquad\qquad = P_3$
$n = 3$	$u_0 = \bar{A}\bar{B}\bar{C} \qquad\qquad\qquad = P_0$
	$u_1 = \bar{A}\bar{B}C + \bar{A}B\bar{C} + A\bar{B}\bar{C} = P_1 + P_2 + P_4$
	$u_2 = \bar{A}BC + A\bar{B}C + AB\bar{C} = P_3 + P_5 + P_6$
	$u_3 = ABC \qquad\qquad\qquad = P_7$

Table 3-15 shows canonical symmetric functions in P terms for one, two, and three variables. The canonical symmetric functions in product terms of n variables u_i are expressed below:

$$u_0 = \bar{X}_1\bar{X}_2 \cdots \bar{X}_n = P_0$$
$$u_1 = X_1\bar{X}_2 \cdots \bar{X}_n + \cdots + \bar{X}_1\bar{X}_2 \cdots \bar{X}_{n-1}X_n = P_1 + P_2 + P_4 + \cdots$$
$$\cdots\cdots\cdots\cdots\cdots\cdots\cdots\cdots\cdots\cdots\cdots\cdots\cdots\cdots\cdots\cdots\cdots\cdots\cdots\cdots\cdots$$
$$u_n = X_1X_2 \cdots X_n = P_{2^n-1} \qquad\qquad\qquad\qquad\qquad (3\text{-}49)$$

Subscript i of the function u_i indicates the number of *unbarred variables* of the given n variables and in turn indicates its α number; there are $n + 1$ such functions.

Table 3-16 shows canonical symmetric functions in sum terms for one, two, and three variables. Canonical symmetric functions in the sum terms of n variables v_i have the general expression

$$v_0 = X_1 + X_2 + \cdots + X_n = S_0$$
$$v_1 = (\bar{X}_1 + X_2 + \cdots + X_n) \cdots (X_1 + X_2 + \cdots + \bar{X}_n) = S_1S_2S_4 \cdots$$
$$\cdots\cdots\cdots\cdots\cdots\cdots\cdots\cdots\cdots\cdots\cdots\cdots\cdots\cdots\cdots\cdots\cdots\cdots\cdots\cdots\cdots$$
$$v_n = \bar{X}_1 + \bar{X}_2 + \cdots + \bar{X}_n = S_{2^n-1} \qquad\qquad\qquad\qquad (3\text{-}50)$$

Subscript i of the function v_i indicates the number of *barred variables* of the given n variables and in turn indicates its α numbers; again there are $n + 1$ functions. The following relations exist between the functions u_i and v_i:

$$v_i = \bar{u}_i \qquad \text{and} \qquad u_i = \bar{v}_i \qquad\qquad (3\text{-}51)$$

Several theorems concerning the properties of canonical symmetric functions are now given. Since these theorems are the results of the above, their proofs are omitted.

Table 3-16   *Canonical Symmetric Functions in Sum Terms*

Variables	*Canonical symmetric functions*
$n = 1$	$v_0 = A_1 = S_0$
	$v_1 = \bar{A}_1 = S_1$
$n = 2$	$v_0 = A + B \qquad\qquad\quad = S_0$
	$v_1 = (A + B)(\bar{A} + B) = S_1 S_2$
	$v_2 = \bar{A} + B \qquad\qquad\quad = S_3$
$n = 3$	$v_0 = A + B + C \qquad\qquad\qquad\qquad\qquad = S_0$
	$v_1 = (A + B + \bar{C})(A + \bar{B} + C)(\bar{A} + B + C) = S_1 S_2 S_4$
	$v_2 = (A + \bar{B} + \bar{C})(\bar{A} + B + \bar{C})(\bar{A} + \bar{B} + C) = S_3 S_5 S_6$
	$v_3 = \bar{A} + \bar{B} + \bar{C} \qquad\qquad\qquad\qquad\qquad = S_7$

Theorem 24a and b

When a symmetric function is expanded into its canonical product (or sum) form and when one product (or sum) term of the expanded function is identical to one product (or sum) term of a canonical symmetric function u_i (or v_i), then the given function has all product (or sum) terms of that canonical symmetric function u_i (or v_i).

For example, function (3-35) expanded into its canonical P form becomes

$$f_1 = ABC + AB\bar{C} + A\bar{B}C + \bar{A}BC \qquad\qquad (3\text{-}52)$$

The product term $AB\bar{C}$ is a product term of u_2 in Table 3-15 (for $n = 3$); hence the above function has all the product terms of u_2. Function (3-36) expanded into its canonical S form becomes

$$f_2 = (A + B + C)(A + B + \bar{C})(A + \bar{B} + C)(\bar{A} + B + C) \quad (3\text{-}53)$$

The sum term $A + B + \bar{C}$ is a sum term of v_1 in Table 3-16 (for $n = 3$); thus the above function has all the sum terms of v_1.

Theorem 25a and b

Any symmetric function f is a logical sum (or product) of canonical symmetric functions in the product (or sum) terms,

$$f = u_i + u_j + \cdots + u_n \qquad\qquad (3\text{-}54)$$

$$f = v_i \cdot v_j \cdots \cdots v_n \qquad\qquad (3\text{-}55)$$

To illustrate, function (3-52) is the logical sum of u_2 and u_3 in Table 3-15 (for $n = 3$); function (3-53) is the logical product of v_0 and v_1 in Table 3-16 (for $n = 3$).

Theorem 26a and b

The following relations express two conditions of equality:

$$u_i u_j = 0 \qquad \text{if } i \neq j \qquad (3\text{-}56)$$

$$v_i + v_j = 1 \qquad \text{if } i \neq j \qquad (3\text{-}57)$$

For example, for n equal to 3, the product of u_2 and u_3 from Table 3-15 is 0 because they are disjoint.

3-12   *Simple Symmetric Functions* [23]

Simple symmetric functions have a *single α number* and are expressed in elementary product or sum terms whose variables are all either barred or unbarred. The letters w and z represent these two forms, respectively, in this discussion. Simple symmetric functions for one, two, and three variables are shown in Table 3-17.

Table 3-17   Simple Symmetric Functions

Variables	In elementary product terms	In elementary sum terms
$n = 1$	$w_0 = 1$ $w_1 = A$ $w_2 = 0$	$z_0 = 0$ $z_1 = \bar{A}$ $z_2 = 1$
$n = 2$	$w_0 = 1$ $w_1 = A + B$ $w_2 = AB$ $w_3 = 0$	$z_0 = 0$ $z_1 = \bar{A}\bar{B}$ $z_2 = \bar{A} + \bar{B}$ $z_3 = 1$
$n = 3$	$w_0 = 1$ $w_1 = A + B + C$ $w_2 = AB + AC + BC$ $w_3 = ABC$ $w_4 = 0$	$z_0 = 0$ $z_1 = \bar{A}\bar{B}\bar{C}$ $z_2 = (\bar{A} + \bar{B})(\bar{A} + \bar{C})(\bar{B} + \bar{C})$ $z_3 = (\bar{A} + \bar{B} + \bar{C})$ $z_4 = 1$

In general, the simple symmetric functions in elementary product terms w of n variables are defined below:

$$
\begin{aligned}
w_0 &= 1 \\
w_1 &= X_1 + X_2 + \cdots + X_n \\
w_2 &= X_1 X_2 + X_1 X_3 + \cdots + X_{n-1} X_n \\
&\cdots\cdots\cdots\cdots\cdots\cdots\cdots\cdots\cdots\cdots \\
w_n &= X_1 X_2 \cdots X_n \\
w_{n+1} &= 0
\end{aligned}
\qquad (3\text{-}58)
$$

Simple symmetric functions in sum terms z of n variables are defined in the following relations:

$$
\begin{aligned}
z_0 &= 0 \\
z_1 &= \bar{X}_1 \bar{X}_2 \cdots \bar{X}_n \\
z_2 &= (\bar{X}_1 + \bar{X}_2)(\bar{X}_1 + \bar{X}_3) \cdots (\bar{X}_{n-1} + \bar{X}_n) \\
&\cdots\cdots\cdots\cdots\cdots\cdots\cdots\cdots\cdots\cdots\cdots\cdots \\
z_n &= \bar{X}_1 + \bar{X}_2 + \cdots + \bar{X}_n \\
z_{n+1} &= 1
\end{aligned}
\qquad (3\text{-}59)
$$

From the foregoing statements, the following relations exist between the functions w and z:

$$z_i = \overline{w}_i \qquad \text{and} \qquad w_i = \overline{z}_i \qquad (3\text{-}60)$$

Note that the function w_i includes w_{i+1} and that the function z_i includes z_{i-1}.

Several theorems concerning the properties of simple symmetric functions are now given. Again their proofs are omitted.

Theorem 27a and b

The logical sum (or product) of the symmetrical functions w_i (or z_i) and w_{i+1} (or z_{i+1}) is w_i (or z_i).

$$w_i + w_{i+1} = w_i \qquad (3\text{-}61)$$

$$z_i z_{i+1} = z_i \qquad (3\text{-}62)$$

The logical product (or sum) of w_i (or z_i) and w_{i+1} (or z_{i+1}) is w_{i+1} (or z_{i+1}).

$$w_i w_{i+1} = w_{i+1} \qquad (3\text{-}63)$$

$$z_i + z_{i+1} = z_{i+1} \qquad (3\text{-}64)$$

Theorem 28a and b

The canonical symmetric function u_i (or v_i) equals the logical product (or sum) of the simple symmetric functions w_i (or z_i) and z_{i+1} (w_{i+1}).

$$u_i = w_i z_{i+1} \qquad (3\text{-}65)$$

$$v_i = z_i + w_{i+1} \qquad (3\text{-}66)$$

When n equals 3, for example, the product of w_2 and z_3 from Table 3-17 is

$$w_2 z_3 = (AB + AC + BC)(\overline{A} + \overline{B} + \overline{C})$$
$$= \overline{A}BC + A\overline{B}C + AB\overline{C}$$

which agrees with the u_2 in Table 3-15. Similarly, for n equal to 3, the sum of z_2 and w_3 from Table 3-17 is

$$z_2 + w_3 = (\overline{A} + \overline{B})(\overline{A} + \overline{C})(\overline{B} + \overline{C}) + ABC$$
$$= (A + \overline{B} + \overline{C})(\overline{A} + \overline{B} + C)(\overline{A} + B + \overline{C})$$

which agrees with v_2 in Table 3-16.

Theorem 29a and b

The canonical symmetric function u_i (or v_i) is the logical exclusive-*or* (coincidence) operation of the simple symmetric functions w_i (or z_i) and w_{i+1} (or z_{i+1}), or

$$u_i = w_i \oplus w_{i+1} \qquad (3\text{-}67)$$

$$v_i = z_i \odot z_{i+1} \qquad (3\text{-}68)$$

Again, upon letting n equal 3, the logical exclusive-*or* of w_2 and w_3 is

$$w_2 \oplus w_3 = w_2 \overline{w}_3 + \overline{w}_2 w_3 = w_2 z_3 + w_3 z_2$$
$$= u_2 + ABC(\overline{A} + \overline{B})(\overline{A} + \overline{C})(\overline{B} + \overline{C}) = u_2$$

Similarly, for n equal to 3, the logical coincidence of z_2 and z_3 is

$$z_2 \odot z_3 = z_2 z_3 + w_2 w_3$$
$$= z_2 + w_3 = v_2$$

Theorem 30a and b

Any symmetric function f is a logical exclusive-*or* (coincidence) operation of the simple symmetric function w (or z),

$$f = w_i \oplus w_j \oplus \cdots \oplus w_n \qquad (3\text{-}69)$$
$$f = z_i \odot z_j \odot \cdots \odot z_n \qquad (3\text{-}70)$$

3-13   Delay and Sequential Functions

Previously discussed logic operations implied no existence of delay. This section introduces the delay operation and treats briefly the resulting sequential function.

Delay.   Delay operation holds the occurrence of a variable A after a certain time delay Δ. Symbolically, the delayed variable f is

$$f = \Delta A \qquad (3\text{-}71)$$

The block representation of the delay operation is shown in Fig. 3-15.

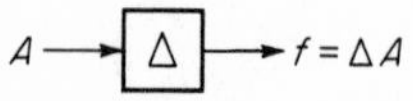

FIG. 3-15   Block representation of delay.

Table 3-18   Truth Table of Delay Operation

$A(t)$	$f(t + \tau)$
0	0
1	1

The delay operation is also described by Table 3-18. In this table, $A(t)$ is the variable A at the time t, and $f(t + \tau)$ is the variable A at a time interval τ later. Therefore, the truth values of the two columns are the same. Symbolically,

$$f(t + \tau) = A(t) \qquad (3\text{-}72)$$

The time interval τ is equivalent to the time delay Δ. In actual circuits, it can be the delay of the circuit, the clock period or the digit time in the computer, or a controlled amount of delay.

Sequential Functions.   Using the delay operation with previously described logic operations results in the *sequential function*, because time also becomes an independent variable. Consider the following sequential function:

$$f_1 = \Delta(AB) \qquad (3\text{-}73)$$

This is a delayed logical-*and* function and is shown in Fig. 3-16a. Its operation is described by the first three columns of Table 3-19. The values in these three columns are the same as the values of the truth table for a logical-*and* function, or

$$f_1(t + \tau) = A(t)B(t) \qquad (3\text{-}74)$$

As pointed out previously, functions (3-73) and (3-74) are equivalent. From the values in the last column of Table 3-19, we can write the sequential function,

$$f_2(t + \tau) = A(t) \oplus B(t) \tag{3-75}$$

or, equivalently,

$$f_2 = \Delta(A \oplus B) \tag{3-76}$$

The above function is shown in Fig. 3-16*b*. In short, one can construct from a given sequential function a truth table to describe its behavior; and, conversely, for a given truth table, one can write a sequential function to describe the operation in the table.

Table 3-19   Truth Table for Functions (3-74) and (3-75)

$A(t)$	$B(t)$	$f_1(t + \tau)$	$f_2(t + \tau)$
0	0	0	0
0	1	0	1
1	0	0	1
1	1	1	0

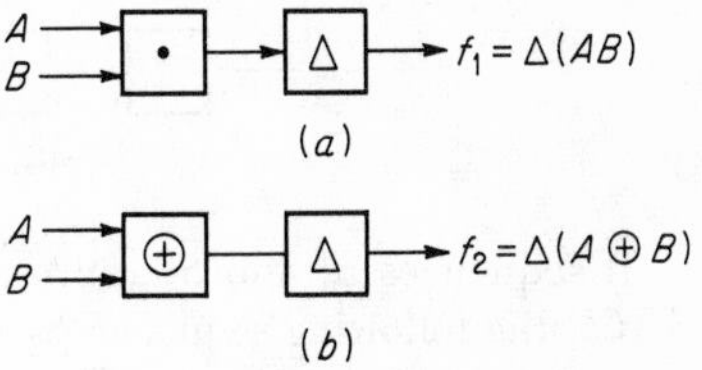

FIG. 3-16   Two delayed logic operations. (*a*) Delayed logical-*and* operation; (*b*) delayed exclusive-*or* operation.

If variable f_2 in Fig. 3-16*b* is fed back to replace variable B, the result is as shown in Fig. 3-17; the function becomes

$$f_3 = \Delta(A \oplus f_3) \tag{3-77}$$

The above shows that the present value of f_3 depends on the past values of A and f_3. This function represents one type of flipflop to be described later.

A number of cascaded delays as shown in Fig. 3-18 form a simple *shift register*. If a time sequence of values of A is shifted into these delays at one end, it will be shifted out at the other end after a delay of 4Δ. The corresponding sequential function is

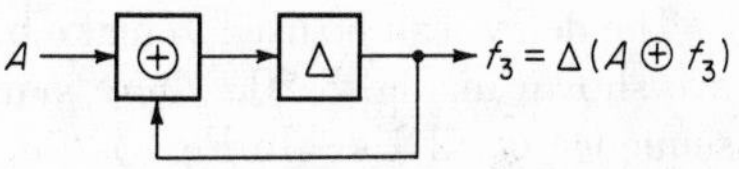

FIG. 3-17   Delayed exclusive-*or* operation with a feedback path.

$$f_4 = \Delta^4 A \tag{3-78}$$

where $\Delta^4 A$ represents a total delay of 4Δ. If f_4 in Fig. 3-18 is fed back and connected with A by a logical-*or* block as shown in Fig. 3-19, the resulting function is

$$f_5 = \Delta^4(A + f_5) \tag{3-79}$$

The result is a *circulating register*; once a time sequence of values of A is inserted, it continues to circulate and the sequence is thus stored therein.

Binary Sequence.   A binary sequence is a time sequence of 1's and 0's. The constant time interval between two adjacent bits is called *digit time* (or bit time). For example, the following S_1 and S_2 are two binary sequences,

	t_6	t_5	t_4	t_3	t_2	t_1
S_1	1	1	0	0	1	1
S_2	1	0	1	0	1	0

where t_1 occurs prior to t_2, and so forth; and the time interval between t_i and t_{i+1} is τ. If sequences S_1 and S_2 represent, respectively, the variables A and B in Fig. 3-16a, the following sequence S_3 occurs and represents f_1.

$$
\begin{array}{cccccccc}
 & t_7 & t_6 & t_5 & t_4 & t_3 & t_2 & t_1 \\
S_3 & 1 & 0 & 0 & 0 & 1 & 0 &
\end{array}
$$

The above sequence occurs with a delay of one digit time. It may be interpreted as the digits in sequence S_1 extracted by the 1's digits in sequence S_2. Since 1's occur at t_2, t_4, and t_6 of sequence S_2, the extracted digits occur at t_3, t_5, and t_7 of sequence S_3.

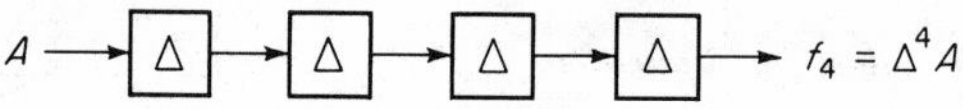

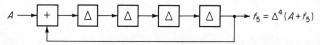

FIG. 3-18   A shift register.

If sequences S_1 and S_2 represent, respectively, the variables A and B in Fig. 3-16b, the following sequence S_4 appears and represents f_2:

$$
\begin{array}{cccccccc}
 & t_7 & t_6 & t_5 & t_4 & t_3 & t_2 & t_1 \\
S_4 & 0 & 1 & 1 & 0 & 0 & 1 &
\end{array}
$$

Each bit in sequence S_4 is the delayed arithmetic sum (but no carry) of the corresponding bits of S_1 and S_2.

FIG. 3-19   A circulating register.

The delays can be used to make binary sequence generators; two such generators are shown in Fig. 3-20, where symbol 1 represents a source which generates a sequence of all 1's. In Fig. 3-20a, it consists of a delay block, an *andnot* block, and a feedback path; the corresponding sequential function is

$$f_6 = \Delta \overline{f_6} \tag{3-80}$$

The generated sequence $\cdots 101010$ alternates with 1's and 0's. In Fig. 3-20b, there are three delay blocks, two *andnot* blocks, and two feedback paths; the

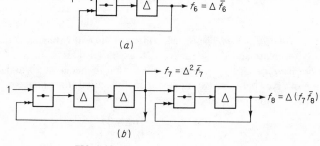

FIG. 3-20   Two binary sequence generators.

corresponding sequential function is

$$f_7 = \Delta^2 \overline{f_7}$$
$$f_8 = \Delta(f_7 \overline{f_8}) = \Delta[\overline{f_8}(\Delta^2 \overline{f_7})] \tag{3-81}$$

The generated sequence $\cdots 10001000$ has a 1 occurring at every fourth digit time.

3-14 Linear Sequential Functions

Linear Sequential Filter. Huffman [17] has formulated a class of linear sequential functions consisting of delay and modulo-2 sum (exclusive-*or*) operations. An example of such a linear sequential function is given below:

$$f = A \oplus \Delta A \oplus \Delta^3 A \oplus \Delta^4 A \oplus \Delta^5 A \tag{3-82}$$

The above function means that function f is a modulo-2 sum of Boolean variable A, the A at a time τ earlier, the A at a time 3τ earlier, and so forth. This function can be represented by the block diagram shown in Fig. 3-21.

The delay and modulo-2 sum operations are linear operations; therefore, the principle of superposition holds. Let S_1 and S_2 be two binary sequences applied to input A in Fig. 3-21. Let S_3 and S_4 be the two corresponding binary sequences

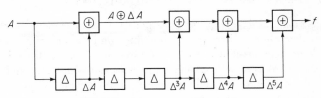

FIG. 3-21   A linear sequential network.

which emerge at output f as a result of the respective application of S_1 and S_2. If the binary sequence $S_1 \oplus S_2$ is applied to input A, then by superposition the binary sequence $S_3 \oplus S_4$ will emerge at output f. Because of its linear nature, function (3-82) can be written as a *digital transfer function*,

$$\frac{f}{A} = 1 \oplus \Delta \oplus \Delta^3 \oplus \Delta^4 \oplus \Delta^5 \tag{3-83}$$

where $1 = \Delta^0$ is the identity operator. The device of Fig. 3-21, called by Huffman a *linear sequential filter*, is a linear digital filter. Such a filter delays and operates on a binary sequence fed to the input of the filter and produces a different binary sequence at the output.

A binary sequence of 0's with the exception of a single 1 digit, as the following sequence S_1, is called the *impulse sequence:*

		t_6	t_5	t_4	t_3	t_2	t_1			
S_1	$\cdots$	0	0	0	0	0	0	0	1	0	0 $\cdots$	(3-84*a*)
S_2	$\cdots$	0	0	1	1	1	0	1	1	0	0 $\cdots$	(3-84*b*)

If an impulse sequence is applied to the input of the filter in Fig. 3-21, the corresponding sequence at the output is S_2 of (3-84*b*), which is called the *impulse response sequence* of the filter. The response consists of 6 bits. The 1's in this 6-bit sequence correspond to the terms on the right side of equality (3-83). The six digit times occupied by the 6-bit sequence is the length of the "transient" and is 1 plus the number of delays in the longest path (in time) from input to output.

Null Sequence. A binary sequence which consists only of 0's is called a *zero sequence*. If application of a sequence S_3 to input A in Fig. 3-21 produces an output sequence S_4 which is a zero sequence, sequence S_3 is called a *null sequence*. The null sequence for the filter in Fig. 3-21 can be found by substituting f equal to 0 into function (3-82), or

$$(1 \oplus \Delta \oplus \Delta^3 \oplus \Delta^4 \oplus \Delta^5)A = 0 \tag{3-85}$$

This expression means that for each digit of the null sequence the modulo-2 sum of the present and the first, third, fourth, and fifth past values is zero. The null sequence depends on the choice of initial conditions in the delays. Since there are five delays, there are $2^5 - 1$ possible choices, excluding the trivial possibility of five 0's. If the initial condition is 00001 (which in the following timing order is 10000), null sequence S_3 is found to be

$$t_{31} \qquad \text{31 digits} \qquad t_1 \qquad \text{Initial}$$
$$S_3: \overline{1000011010100100010111110110011} \, \overline{(10000)} \quad \text{condition}$$

Null sequence S_3 lasts 31 digit times, which is the null-sequence period; it repeats itself thereafter. There are 31 possible combinations of five successive digits (excluding the possibility of five successive zeros) during this null-sequence period. There are as many (31) null sequences as the possible choices of the initial condition. When the null sequence is applied, no response (or zero sequence) appears.

Linear Sequential Feedback Filter. A linear sequential network with feedback paths is shown in Fig. 3-22. The corresponding sequential function is

$$f \oplus \Delta f \oplus \Delta^3 f \oplus \Delta^4 f \oplus \Delta^5 f = A \tag{3-86}$$

The expression can be rewritten as a digital transfer function,

$$\frac{f}{A} = \frac{1}{1 \oplus \Delta \oplus \Delta^3 \oplus \Delta^4 \oplus \Delta^5} \tag{3-87}$$

The above transfer function is the reciprocal of the digital transfer function (3-83). An interesting point is revealed by comparing the diagrams of Fig. 3-21 and 3-22. Only forward paths exist in Fig. 3-21, as opposed to Fig. 3-22, which contains both forward and feedback paths. Reversing the forward path in Fig.

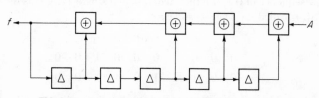

FIG. 3-22   A linear sequential network with feedback paths.

3-21 from input A to output f through all modulo-2 sum blocks and exchanging the input and output results in the diagram of Fig. 3-22.

If there is no input to the diagram of Fig. 3-22 (that is, if $A = 0$), function (3-86) becomes

$$f \oplus \Delta f \oplus \Delta^3 f \oplus \Delta^4 f \oplus \Delta^5 f = 0 \qquad (3\text{-}88)$$

If a binary sequence f exists such that, when substituted into (3-88), the modulo-2 sum of terms on the left side becomes zero, then an output sequence can be obtained without an input sequence. Since (3-88) is the same as the left side of Eq. (3-86), the previous null sequence S_3 is the sought-for null sequence f for Eq. (3-88). The presence of feedback paths permits an output sequence even without an input sequence.

The digital transfer function (3-83) has a denominator of 1, while function (3-87) has 1 as its numerator. An example of a general linear digital transfer function is given below:

$$\frac{f}{A} = \frac{\Delta^8 \oplus \Delta^5 \oplus \Delta^4 \oplus \Delta^2 \oplus \Delta}{\Delta^5 \oplus \Delta^4 \oplus 1} \qquad (3\text{-}89)$$

The corresponding diagram (Fig. 3-23) appears as a chain having more than one forward path and more than one feedback path. Note that terms in the numer-

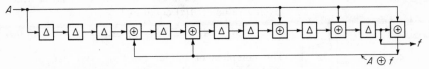

FIG. 3-23   Chain network for a linear sequential filter.

ator of (3-89) represent past values of A; the terms in the denominator represent past values of f.

3-15   *Flipflops and State Equations*

Because the digital computer operates in a time sequence, elements for storing information are necessary. Flipflop elements can store binary information as either 1 or 0. A practical flipflop circuit can exhibit and maintain a given binary state. It can also be switched by an input from one state to the other, and its state can be sensed. This section presents equations which describe the operation of several types of flipflops.

Four types of flipflops in general use appear symbolically represented in Fig. 3-24. The major difference among these four types is the number and effect of the inputs in switching the binary state of the flipflop.

Single-input Flipflop. Figure 3-24a shows a single-input flipflop or *trigger flipflop* (T flipflop). There are one input t, the output A, and the complement output $\bar{A}$. Small letters such as t represent the inputs of the flipflop; capital letters such as A represent not only the output but also the flipflop itself. For instance, letter A in the block of Fig. 3-24a also indicates the name of the flip-flop. Providing a complement output in addition to the normal output of a flip-

Table 3-20   Single-input Flipflop

$t(t_0) = t$	$A(t_0) = A$	$A(t_0 + \tau) = A(\tau)$	Flipflop state
0	0	0	Not changed
0	1	1	Not changed
1	0	1	Complemented
1	1	0	Complemented

flop eliminates subsequent use of logical-*not* circuits; this in turn avoids the transient delay in these logical-*not* circuits and contributes to circuit simplicity. All four types of flipflops in Fig. 3-24 have both normal and complement outputs.

The operation of a single-input flipflop is shown in Table 3-20. At time t_0, the input t is represented by $t(t_0)$, and the state of the flipflop by $A(t_0)$. At a time interval τ later, the state is represented by $A(t_0 + \tau)$. For convenience, these representations are simplified to t, A, and $A(\tau)$, respectively. Table 3-20 shows that the flipflop changes to its complement state when an input (i.e., 1) is applied. The input is needed only to change the state and does not have to continue.

From Table 3-20, the output function $A(\tau)$ can be written by noting the combinations of t and A which given a value of $A(\tau)$ equal to 1,

$$A(\tau) = \bar{t}A + t\bar{A} = t \oplus A \qquad (3\text{-}90)$$

The complement output function $\bar{A}(\tau)$ can also be written by noting the combinations of t and A which result in a value of $A(\tau)$ equal to 0, or

$$\bar{A}(\tau) = tA + \bar{t}\bar{A} = t \odot A \qquad (3\text{-}91)$$

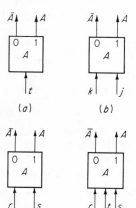

FIG. 3-24 Symbolic representations of four types of flipflops. (a) Trigger flipflop; (b) JK flipflop; (c) RS flipflop; (d) RST flipflop.

JK **Flipflop.** Figure 3-24b illustrates a *JK* flipflop having two inputs j and k. Its operation is shown in Table 3-21. The table indicates that, when no input (i.e., 0) is applied, the state of the flipflop remains unchanged. When an input is applied to j, the flipflop is switched to the 1 state. When an input is applied to k, the flipflop is switched to the 0 state. When inputs are applied to both j and k, the flipflop switches to its complement state. From Table 3-21 we have

$$A(\tau) = \bar{k}\bar{j}A + \bar{k}j\bar{A} + \bar{k}jA + kj\bar{A} \qquad (3\text{-}92)$$

$$\bar{A}(\tau) = \bar{k}\bar{j}\bar{A} + k\bar{j}\bar{A} + k\bar{j}A + kjA \qquad (3\text{-}93)$$

Simplified, these statements become

$$A(\tau) = \bar{k}A + j\bar{A} \qquad (3\text{-}94)$$

$$\bar{A}(\tau) = kA + \bar{j}\bar{A} \qquad (3\text{-}95)$$

RS **Flipflop.** Figure 3-24c shows an *RS* flipflop; the two inputs are r and s, indicating, respectively, the resetting (to the 0 state) or setting (to the 1 state) of the flipflop. The operation of an *RS* flipflop is the same as the first six possible

Table 3-21 *JK Flipflop*

$k(t_0)$	$j(t_0)$	$A(t_0)$	$A(t_0 + \tau)$	Flipflop state
0	0	0	0	Not changed
0	0	1	1	Not changed
0	1	0	1	Changed to 1 state
0	1	1	1	Changed to 1 state
1	0	0	0	Changed to 0 state
1	0	1	0	Changed to 0 state
1	1	0	1	Complemented
1	1	1	0	Complemented

combinations in Table 3-21 if r and s are identified as k and j, respectively; the other two combinations are not permitted. Thus we have

$$A(\tau) = \bar{r}\bar{s}A + \bar{r}sA + \bar{r}sA \tag{3-96}$$

$$\bar{A}(\tau) = \bar{r}\bar{s}\bar{A} + r\bar{s}\bar{A} + r\bar{s}\bar{A} \tag{3-97}$$

The two nonexistent combinations can be expressed as

$$rs = 0 \tag{3-98}$$

By using relation (3-98), functions (3-96) and (3-97) can be simplified to

$$A(\tau) = \bar{r}A + s \tag{3-99}$$

$$\bar{A}(\tau) = \bar{s}\bar{A} + r \tag{3-100}$$

RST Flipflop. Figure 3-24d shows an *RST* flipflop with three inputs r, s, and t. The operation is shown in Table 3-22. As with the *RS* flipflop, input r resets the flipflop to the 0 state; input s sets it to the 1 state. Input t complements the state of the flipflop, analogous to single-input flipflop operation. From Table 3-22, we have

$$A(\tau) = \bar{r}\bar{s}\bar{t}A + \bar{r}s\bar{t}\bar{A} + \bar{r}s\bar{t}A + \bar{r}\bar{s}t\bar{A} \tag{3-101}$$

$$\bar{A}(\tau) = \bar{r}\bar{s}\bar{t}\bar{A} + r\bar{s}\bar{t}\bar{A} + r\bar{s}\bar{t}A + \bar{r}\bar{s}tA \tag{3-102}$$

The eight nonexistent combinations in Table 3-22 can be expressed as

$$rs = rt = st = 0 \tag{3-103}$$

which means that no two inputs can occur simultaneously. By using relation (3-103), functions (3-101) and (3-102) can be simplified to

$$A(\tau) = \bar{r}\bar{t}A + t\bar{A} + s \tag{3-104}$$

$$\bar{A}(\tau) = tA + \bar{s}\bar{t}\bar{A} + r \tag{3-105}$$

Table 3-22 *RST Flipflop*

$r(t_0)$	$s(t_0)$	$t(t_0)$	$A(t_0)$	$A(t_0 + \tau)$	Flipflop state
0	0	0	0	0	Not changed
0	0	0	1	1	Not changed
0	1	0	0	1	Changed to 1 state
0	1	0	1	1	Changed to 1 state
1	0	0	0	0	Changed to 0 state
1	0	0	1	0	Changed to 0 state
0	0	1	0	1	Complemented
0	0	1	1	0	Complemented

Table 3-23   Boolean Functions of Four Types of Flipflops

Flipflop	Direct output	Complement output
T	$A(\tau) = t \oplus A$	$\bar{A}(\tau) = t \odot A$
JK	$A(\tau) = \bar{k}A + j\bar{A}$	$\bar{A}(\tau) = kA + \bar{j}\bar{A}$
RS	$A(\tau) = \bar{r}A + s$	$\bar{A}(\tau) = \bar{s}A + r$
RST	$A(\tau) = \bar{r}tA + t\bar{A} + s$	$\bar{A}(\tau) = tA + \bar{s}t\bar{A} + r$

The Boolean functions of the above four types of flipflops are shown in Table 3-23; these are *logic difference equations*. Since they describe the state of the flipflop, they are called the *flipflop-state equations*.

Dynamic Flipflop. Figure 3-25 shows a diagram having a delay block, an *andnot* block, and an *or* block. There are two inputs r and s. Let a pulse circulating in the closed loop represent the 1 state, and no pulse the 0 state. The Boolean function for output A can be written from the diagram,

$$A = \Delta(\bar{r}A + s) \qquad (3\text{-}106)$$

The above function is identical to function (3-99); hence, the diagram in Fig. 3-25

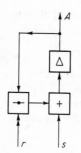

FIG. 3-25   A dynamic *RS* flipflop.

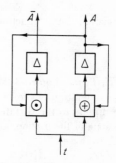

FIG. 3-26   A dynamic trigger flipflop.

also shows an *RS* flipflop. Because a circulating pulse is used to represent the state, it is known as a *dynamic flipflop*.

Another example is obtained by comparing Eqs. (3-90) and (3-77); these two equations are equivalent. Therefore, the diagram in Fig. 3-17 which corresponds to Eq. (3-77) shows a dynamic single-input flipflop. The single-input flipflop of Fig. 3-17 has only a normal output. Figure 3-26 shows a dynamic single-input flipflop which has both normal and complement outputs. It is apparent that other types of flipflops can all be realized by using delays and basic logic blocks, although they may not be practical.

3-16   *Majority and Minority Logic Operations*

Figure 3-27 shows a three-input block symbolizing a majority logic operation. The truth table for the three-input majority logic operation is Table 3-24. In a majority logic operation, the output state is the majority of input states. For example, if inputs A, B, and C are 0, 0, and 1, respectively (second row in the table), the majority of the input states is 0 and the output f_1 (fourth column in the table) is 0. A majority logic circuit which implements a majority logic operation always has an odd number of inputs (the case of one input is trivial).

Majority function f_1 in Table 3-24 is

$$f_1 = P_3 + P_5 + P_6 + P_7 \qquad (3\text{-}107)$$

or, after simplification,

$$f_1 = AB + AC + BC \qquad (3\text{-}108)$$

Function f_1 is a symmetric function because it does not depend on particular variables being 1's or 0's, but rather on the number of variables being 1's or 0's. By referring to Tables 3-15 and 3-17, majority function f_1 becomes

Table 3-24 Majority and Minority Logic Operations (for Three Inputs)

A	B	C	Majority function f_1	Minority function f_2
0	0	0	0	1
0	0	1	0	1
0	1	0	0	1
0	1	1	1	0
1	0	0	0	1
1	0	1	1	0
1	1	0	1	0
1	1	1	1	0

$$f_1 = u_2 + u_3 = w_2 \qquad (3\text{-}109)$$

The majority operation may be used as a logical-*and* or a logical-*or* operation. If C in (3-108) is equal to 1 (that is, if input C in Fig. 3-27 is connected to a 1's source), then f_1 becomes

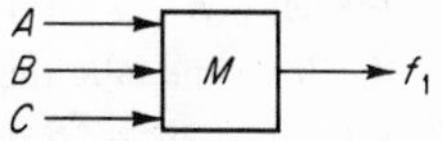

FIG. 3-27 Block representation of a majority logic operation.

$$f_1 = A + B \qquad (3\text{-}110)$$

The above is a two-input logical-*or* operation. If C is equal to 0, then f_1 becomes

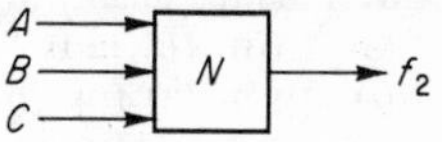

$$f_1 = AB \qquad (3\text{-}111)$$

FIG. 3-28 Block representation of a minority logic operation.

The above is a two-input logical-*and* operation.

Instead of using the idea of majority, one may use the idea of minority. Figure 3-28 shows the block symbolizing a minority logic operation. The minority logic operation is also shown in Table 3-24. In a minority logic operation, the output state is the minority of input states. For example, when inputs A, B, and C are 0, 0, and 1, respectively, the minority of the input states is 1 and output f_2 (last column in the table) is 1.

Minority function f_2 in Table 3-24 is

$$f_2 = S_3 S_5 S_6 S_7 \qquad (3\text{-}112)$$

or, after simplification,

$$f_2 = (\bar{A} + \bar{B})(\bar{A} + \bar{C})(\bar{B} + \bar{C}) \qquad (3\text{-}113)$$

Since the concept of minority here is the complement of majority, function f_2 is the complement of majority function f_1, or

$$f_2 = \bar{f_1} \qquad (3\text{-}114)$$

Minority function f_2 is also a symmetric function, as the complement of a symmetric function is again a symmetric function. By referring to Tables 3-16 and 3-17, minority function f_2 becomes

$$f_2 = v_2 v_3 = z_2 \qquad (3\text{-}115)$$

The minority function may be used as a logical-*nand* or a logical-*nor* operation. If $\bar{C}$ in (3-113) is equal to 1, then f_2 becomes

$$f_2 = \overline{AB} \tag{3-116}$$

The above is a two-input logical-*nand* operation. If $\bar{C}$ is equal to 0, then f_2 becomes

$$f_2 = \overline{A + B} \tag{3-117}$$

The above is a two-input logical-*nor* operation.

Majority and minority logic functions are symmetric functions. Such functions can be realized by tunnel diodes (Chap. 6) or by magnetic cores (Chap. 7).

Problems

1. Shade the portion of a Venn diagram which interprets the following expressions:

(a) $A + \bar{B}$ (b) $(A + \bar{B})(B + \bar{C})$ (c) $A\bar{B} + B\bar{C}$

2. Prove the following identities by using the fundamental theorems:

(a) $(A + \bar{B}C)(\bar{A}B + C) = AC + \bar{B}C$
(b) $[(AB + BC + AC) + (A\bar{B} + B\bar{C} + A\bar{C})]\overline{(\bar{A} + B + C)} = 0$
(c) $(A + B)(\bar{A} + C) = AC + \bar{A}B$
(d) $A\bar{B} + BC + AC = A\bar{B} + BC$
(e) $(A + B)(\bar{A} + C)(B + C) = (A + B)(\bar{A} + C)$

3. Find the duality of the following identities, and draw their block diagrams:

(a) $(AB)(\bar{A}\bar{B}) = 0$ (b) $(A + B + C) + (\bar{A} + \bar{B} + \bar{C}) = 1$
(c) $(\bar{A} + \bar{B})(A + \bar{B})(\bar{A} + B)(A + B) = 0$
(d) $\bar{A}\bar{B}\bar{C} + \bar{A}\bar{B}C + \bar{A}B\bar{C} + \bar{A}BC + A\bar{B}\bar{C} + A\bar{B}C + AB\bar{C} + ABC = 1$

4. Use De Morgan's theorems to expand the following expressions:

(a) $\overline{(\bar{A} + B)\bar{A}\bar{B}}$ (b) $\overline{(\overline{AB}A)(\overline{AB}B)}$
(c) $\overline{(B\bar{C} + \bar{A}D)(\bar{A}\bar{B} + C\bar{D})}$ (d) $\overline{(\overline{AC} + BD) + (\bar{A}B + \bar{C}D)}$

5. Prove the following relations:

(a) Given $A + B = B$, then $AB + A = 0$.
(b) Given $A + B = B$, then $\bar{A} + B = 1$.
(c) Given $A + B = B$, then $A\bar{B} = 0$.

6. The symbol $<$ means *inclusion*. Thus, the relation $A < B$ means "A is included in B." (Note that the symbol $<$ here is analogous to the symbol $\leq$ in ordinary algebra.) Prove that this relation is true if any of the following equalities is true:

(a) $A + B = B$ (b) $AB = A$
(c) $\bar{A} + B = 1$ (d) $A\bar{B} = 0$

7. Construct a truth table for each of the following Boolean functions:

(a) $f = (A + B)\overline{AB}$ (b) $f = A\bar{B} + B\bar{C}$
(c) $f = AB + BC + CA$ (d) $f = A\bar{B}C + B\bar{C}D$

8. Identify the equivalent binary numbers of the following P terms and S terms (which are the subscripts of P's and S's):

(a) $A\bar{B}C\bar{D}$ (b) $\bar{A}B\bar{C}DE$ (c) $A\bar{B}CD\bar{E}F$
(d) $A + B + \bar{C} + D$ (e) $A + \bar{B} + C + \bar{D} + E$
(f) $A + B + \bar{C} + D + \bar{E} + F$

Write the corresponding P terms or S terms.

9. From Tables 3-25 and 3-26 write the Boolean functions f and $\bar{f}$, both in canonical P form and in canonical S form. Determine the characteristic numbers of these functions.

10. Write all P terms and S terms for a Boolean function of four variables.

11. Expand the following Boolean functions into their canonical P forms and canonical S forms:

(a) $f(A,B,C) = A + \bar{B}C + \bar{A}BC$

(b) $f(A,B,C) = AB + BC + CA$

(c) $f(A,B,C,D) = AB + BC + CD + DA$

12. Mark 1 in the squares of Veitch diagrams which represent the following Boolean functions in P form:

(a) $f = \bar{A}B\bar{C} + A\bar{B}C + A\bar{B}\bar{C} + \bar{A}BC$

(b) $f = \bar{A}\bar{B}\bar{C} + A\bar{B}C + \bar{A}B\bar{C} + AB\bar{C} + ABC$

Table 3-25

A	B	C	f	$\bar{f}$
0	0	0	0	1
0	0	1	1	0
0	1	0	0	1
0	1	1	1	0
1	0	0	0	1
1	0	1	0	1
1	1	0	1	0
1	1	1	1	0

Mark 0 in the squares of Veitch diagrams which represent the following Boolean functions in S form:

(c) $f = (\bar{A} + \bar{B} + \bar{C})(A + \bar{B} + C)(A + B + \bar{C})$

(d) $f = (A + \bar{B} + \bar{C})(\bar{A} + B + C)(\bar{A} + \bar{B} + C)(A + B + C)$

Table 3-26

A	B	C	D	f	$\bar{f}$
0	0	0	0	0	1
0	0	0	1	0	1
0	0	1	0	1	0
0	0	1	1	0	1
0	1	0	0	1	0
0	1	0	1	1	0
0	1	1	0	0	1
0	1	1	1	1	0
1	0	0	0	1	0
1	0	0	1	0	1
1	0	1	0	0	1
1	0	1	1	1	0
1	1	0	0	1	0
1	1	0	1	0	1
1	1	1	0	1	0
1	1	1	1	0	1

13. Prove that the sum of the number of P terms and S terms of Boolean function of n variables is equal to 2^{n+1}.

14. Tabulate the distinct elementary P terms and elementary S terms for a Boolean function of four variables.

15. Use identities (3-10a) and (3-10b) to simplify the following Boolean functions into their elementary forms, and draw the corresponding block diagrams:

(a) $f(A,B,C) = P_2 + P_3 + P_6 + P_7$

(b) $f(A,B,C) = S_0 S_1 S_4 S_5$

(c) $f(A,B,C,D) = P_0 + P_3 + P_4 + P_7 + P_8 + P_9 + P_{14} + P_{15}$

(d) $f(A,B,C,D) = S_1 S_2 S_5 S_6 S_{10} S_{11} S_{12} S_{13}$

16. Expand the following Boolean functions in elementary forms into both canonical forms:

(a) $f(A,B,C) = A\bar{B} + B\bar{C}$ (b) $f(A,B,C,D) = \bar{A}B + C\bar{D}$

(c) $f(A,B,C,D) = \bar{A}B + \bar{B}C + \bar{C}D + \bar{D}A$

17. Convert the following Boolean functions in nonelementary forms into elementary forms:

(a) $f(A,B,C) = A(B + C) + \bar{A}C$

(b) $f(A,B,C) = [\bar{A} + B(A + C)](\bar{B} + C)$

(c) $f(A,B,C) = [A(B + \bar{C}) + C(\overline{A + B})](\overline{A + C}) + (A + B)C$

18. Express the Boolean function $f = \bar{A}C + B\bar{C}$ by using the following choices of primitive operations (see Fig. 3-14), and draw their block diagrams:

(a) Logical-*or* and logical-*not* operations

(b) Logical-*and* and logical-*not* operations

(c) Exclusive-*or* and logical-*and* operations

(d) Coincidence and logical-*and* operations

(e) Stroke operation

(f) Peirce operation

19. Prove the following identities:

(a) $A / (B / \bar{B}) = \bar{A}$

(b) $[\overline{A / (B / C)}] = (\bar{B} / A) / (\bar{C} / A)$

(c) $(A \swarrow C) \swarrow (A \swarrow B) = A + (\bar{B} \swarrow \bar{C})$

(d) $(A \oplus B \oplus AB)(A \oplus C \oplus AC) = A + BC$

(e) $A(A \oplus B) = A\bar{B}$

(f) $A(A \odot B) = AB$

(g) $A + (A \oplus B) = A + B$

(h) $A + (A \odot B) = A + \bar{B}$

(i) $A(\bar{A} \oplus B) = AB$

(j) $A(\bar{A} \odot B) = A\bar{B}$

(k) $A + (\bar{A} \oplus B) = A + \bar{B}$

(l) $A + (\bar{A} \odot B) = A + B$

20. Determine the α numbers of the following symmetric functions:

(a) $f(A,B,C) = A\bar{B}\bar{C} + \bar{A}B\bar{C} + \bar{A}\bar{B}C$

(b) $f(A,\bar{B},C,\bar{D}) = A\bar{B}CD + A\bar{B}C\bar{D} + ABC\bar{D} + \bar{A}\bar{B}C\bar{D}$

(c) $f(A,\bar{B},C,\bar{D}) = ABC\bar{D} + A\bar{B}CD + \bar{A}B\bar{C}\bar{D} + A\bar{B}C\bar{D} + \bar{A}BC\bar{D}$

(d) $f(A,\bar{B},\bar{C},D) = A\bar{B}\bar{C}\bar{D} + AB\bar{C}\bar{D} + \bar{A}\bar{B}C\bar{D} + \bar{A}\bar{B}\bar{C}D + \bar{A}\bar{B}C\bar{D}$
$+ A\bar{B}C\bar{D} + A\bar{B}CD + AB\bar{C}D + \bar{A}\bar{B}C\bar{D} + ABCD$

21. By using relation (3-98), simplify functions (3-96) and (3-97) to functions (3-99) and (3-100).

22. From the following equation, find the eight possible null sequences. The eight null sequences are due to eight possible initial states of the three delays.

$$1 \oplus \Delta \oplus \Delta^3 = 0$$

References

1. Boole, George: "An Investigation of the Laws of Thought," London, 1854 (reprinted by Dover Publications, New York).

2. Huntington, E. V.: The Algebra of Logic, *Trans. Am. Math. Soc.*, vol. 5, pp. 288–309, 1904.

3. Sheffer, Henry Maurice: A Set of Five Independent Postulates for Boolean Algebras, with Application to Logical Constants, *Trans. Am. Math. Soc.*, vol. 14, pp. 481–488, 1913.

4. Huntington, E. V.: New Sets of Independent Postulates for the Algebra of Logic, with Special Reference to Whitehead and Russel's Principia Mathematica, *Trans. Am. Math. Soc.*, vol. 35, pp. 274–304, 1933.

5. Shannon, C. E.: Symbolic Analysis of Relay and Switching Circuits, *Trans. AIEE*, vol. 57, pp. 713–723, 1938.

6. Montgomerie, G. A.: Sketch for an Algebra of Relay and Contactor Circuits, *J. IEE (London)*, vol. 95, pp. 303–312, 1948.

7. Shannon, C. E.: The Synthesis of Two-terminal Switching Circuits, *Bell System Tech. J.*, vol. 28, pp. 59–98, 1949.

8. Hartree, D. R.: "Calculating Instruments and Machines," University of Illinois Press, Urbana, Ill., 1949.

9. Keister, W., A. Ritchie, and S. Washburn: "The Design of Switching Circuits," D. Van Nostrand Company, Inc., Princeton, N. J., 1951.

10. Staehler, R. E.: An Application of Boolean Algebra to Switching Circuit Design, *Bell System Tech. J.*, vol. 31, pp. 280–305, 1952.

11. Birkhoff, Garrett, and Saunders MacLane: "A Survey of Modern Algebra," The Macmillan Company, New York, 1953.

12. Serrell, Robert: Elements of Boolean Algebra for the Study of Information Handling Systems, *Proc. IRE*, vol. 41, pp. 1266–1379, 1953 (corrections, *Proc. IRE*, vol. 42, pp. 475, 1954).

13. Nelson, E. C.: An Algebraic Theory for Use in Digital Computer Design, *IRE Trans. on Electronic Computers*, vol. EC-3, no. 3, pp. 12–21, September, 1954.

14. Copi, Irving M.: "Symbolic Logic," The Macmillan Company, New York, 1954.

15. Richards, R.: "Arithmetic Operations in Digital Computers," D. Van Nostrand Company, Inc., Princeton, N. J., 1955.

16. Zierler, N.: Several Binary-sequence Generators, *MIT Lincoln Lab. Tech. Rept.* 95, September, 1955.

17. Huffman, D. A.: The Synthesis of Linear Sequential Coding Networks, *Trans. Third London Symposium on Inform. Theory*, September, 1955, pp. 78–95.

18. Jeffrey, R. C.: Arithmetical Analysis of Digital Computing Nets, *J. ACM*, October, 1956, pp. 360–375.

19. McCluskey, E. J., Jr.: Detection of Group Invariance or Total Symmetry of a Boolean Function, *Bell System Tech. J.*, November, 1956, pp. 1445–1453.

20. Phister, M.: "Logical Design of Digital Computers," John Wiley & Sons, Inc., New York, 1958.

21. Grisamore, N. T., L. S. Rotolo, and Uyehara: Logical Design Using the Stroke Function, *IRE Trans. Electronic Computers*, June, 1958, pp. 181–183.

22. Caldwell, S. H.: "Switching Circuits and Logical Design," John Wiley & Sons, Inc., New York, 1958.

23. Epstein, G.: Synthesis of Electronic Circuits for Symmetric Functions, *IRE Trans. on Electronic Computers*, March, 1958, pp. 57–60.

24. Huffman, D. A.: An Algebra for Periodically Time-varying Linear Binary Sequence Transducers, *Proc. Intern. Symposium on Theory Switching*, 1959, pt. 1, pp. 180–203.

25. Seshu, S., and S. E. Hohn: Symmetric Polynomials in Boolean Algebras, *Proc. Inter. Symposium on Theory Switching*, 1959, pt. 2, pp. 225–234.

26. Huffman, D. A.: Philosophies of Sequential Circuit Behavior.

4

Minimization of the Boolean Function

Simplifying a Boolean function has been illustrated by examples in Chap. 3. The simplified function results in a simpler logic circuit. As a further step, this chapter presents methods of minimizing a Boolean function. Three "desk-top" methods which apply to a Boolean function in canonical form are described. A given function not in canonical form can always be expanded into one. The minimized function, obtained by any of these three methods, is in elementary form, with the least number of inputs (the sum of the *and* inputs and *or* inputs is least). In addition to these three methods, machine minimization is briefly discussed, and the limitations of these methods are mentioned.

4-1 Veitch-diagram Method [3]

The minimization method first described employs the Veitch diagram. Since the Veitch diagram itself was briefly mentioned in Chap. 3, we begin by describing the diagrammatic representation of a Boolean function.

Representation of Canonical Forms. The Veitch diagram consists of 2^n squares (where n is the number of Boolean variables) arranged in a specific manner so that each square can be used to represent a P term (product term) or an S term (sum term). The Veitch-diagram representation of the P terms and the S terms for two variables is shown in Fig. 4-1a and b, respectively. In representing a P or S term, the square on the Veitch diagram representing this term is marked by 1 or 0, respectively. This square is the intersection of one-half areas representing the variables (which constitute the term) when the value of each of these variables is taken to be 1 for a P term or to be 0 for an S term. It is important to note that the one-half area representing a variable in a Veitch diagram for P terms represents the complement of the variable when the diagram is for S terms. That a P or an S term is an intersection of two or more variables (which constitute the term) can be seen by recalling that, for example, quantity AB is 1 when both A and B have the value of 1 (a logical-and operation), and quantity $A + B$ is 0 when both A and B have the value of 0 (also a logical-and operation). (Alternate names for P and S terms are *minterm* and *maxterm*. Their usage has not been adopted, because both minterm and maxterm are interpreted here as intersections of one-half areas.)

Representation of a Boolean function on a Veitch diagram will now be illustrated. Consider the following Boolean function in canonical P form,

$$f_1 = \bar{A}B + A\bar{B} = P_1 + P_2 \qquad (4\text{-}1)$$

and its representation as shown in Fig. 4-1c. In this diagram, a 1 is marked in the two squares representing the two P terms. The use of 1 indicates that the value of the Boolean function is 1 when the value of the P term represented by the square becomes 1. Consider the following Boolean function in canonical S form,

$$f_2 = (A + B)(\bar{A} + \bar{B}) = S_0 S_3 \qquad (4\text{-}2)$$

and its representation in Fig. 4-1d. In this diagram, a 0 marked in the squares represents the two S terms. The use of 0 in marking the S term indicates that the value of the Boolean function is 0 when the value of the S term represented by the square becomes 0. The complements of the Boolean functions (4-1) and (4-2) are, respectively,

$$f_3 = \bar{f_1} = \overline{P_1 + P_2} = S_1 S_2 \qquad (4\text{-}3)$$
$$f_4 = \bar{f_2} = \overline{S_0 S_3} = P_0 + P_3 \qquad (4\text{-}4)$$

Their representation on Veitch diagrams is shown in Fig. 4-1e and f. In short, a Boolean function in either canonical form or in either of their complement functions can be represented on a Veitch diagram.

The relationship among functions f_1 to f_4 is clearly shown on the Veitch diagrams. Functions f_1 and f_2 or functions f_3 and f_4 are the same, each differing from the other

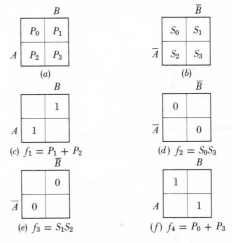

FIG. 4-1   Representation of the P terms and S terms of two variables on Veitch diagram.

only in the canonical form. Now consider f_1 and f_2 on the Veitch diagrams in Fig. 4-1c and d, respectively. Function f_1 specifies that the function is true, or 1, while function f_2 specifies that the function is false, or 0; however, the two Veitch diagrams are equivalent. A similar argument applies to functions f_3 and f_4.

Function f_1 is the complement of function f_3, and function f_2 is the complement of function f_4, each differing from the other only in the canonical form. Now consider f_1 and f_3 on the Veitch diagrams in Fig. 4-1c and e, respectively. Wherever 1 is specified in Fig. 4-1c, 0 is specified in Fig. 4-1e; the two Veitch diagrams are complements to each other. A similar situation appears in the Veitch diagrams of Fig. 4-1d and f for functions f_2 and f_4, respectively.

Functions f_1 and f_4 or functions f_2 and f_3 are in the same canonical form, each being the complement of the other. Consider f_1 and f_4 on the Veitch diagram in Fig. 4-1c and f, respectively. Wherever 1 is *not* specified in Fig. 4-1c, 1 is specified in Fig. 4-1f; the two Veitch diagrams are complements to each other.

A similar situation occurs in the Veitch diagrams of Fig. 4-1d and e for functions f_2 and f_3, except that 0 instead of 1 is used.

For three, four, five, and six Boolean variables, the representations of P terms on the Veitch diagram are shown in Figs. 4-2 and 4-3. The alternative representations of the P terms for five and six variables are shown in Fig. 4-4. Representation of the S terms, as has been shown, is the same, except that the symbol P_i in these diagrams is replaced by the symbol S_i and that the variables labeled at the sides are complemented; therefore, there is no need to show the diagrams for the S term.

Representation of Elementary Terms. Each canonical term is represented by a single square on the Veitch diagram, but each elementary term is represented by more than one square. It will be shown in the following that, the fewer the number of variables in an elementary term, the greater the number of squares represented.

Consider the Boolean function of four variables having only one elementary P term. If the elementary P term has one variable, such as

$$f_1 = C \qquad \text{and} \qquad f_2 = \overline{B} \tag{4-5}$$

that variable is represented by marking 1's in the diagrams of Fig. 4-5a and b,

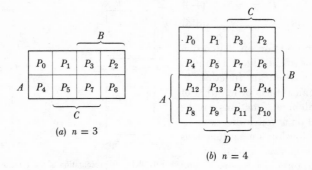

FIG. 4-2   Representation of the P terms of three and four Boolean variables on Veitch diagram.

respectively. Each one-variable term is represented by eight adjoining squares. It is important to note that the upper and the lower edges of the Veitch diagram or the left and the right edges are to be regarded as "stitched" together; for example, P_0 and P_2, P_0 and P_8, or P_3 and P_{11} in Fig. 4-2b are adjoining squares. Such two adjoining squares have only one variable (of the terms represented by them) whose value is changed from 0 to 1 or from 1 to 0; the two adjoining squares $P_0(\overline{A}\overline{B}\overline{C}\overline{D})$ and $P_2(\overline{A}\overline{B}C\overline{D})$ have only the variable C whose value is changed.

If the elementary P term has two variables, such as

$$f_3 = \overline{C}D \qquad \text{and} \qquad f_4 = \overline{B}\overline{D} \tag{4-6}$$

those variables are similarly represented in the diagrams of Fig. 4-5c and d, respectively. Each two-variable term is represented by four adjoining squares. If the elementary P term has three variables,

$$f_5 = B\overline{C}D \qquad \text{and} \qquad f_6 = \overline{A}\overline{B}\overline{D} \tag{4-7}$$

they are shown in the diagrams of Fig. 4-5*e* and *f*, respectively. Each three-variable term is represented by two adjoining squares. Apparently, from the foregoing, the least number of variables in an elementary term involves the greatest number of squares. Choosing the squares in an arbitrary manner, however, may not form an elementary *P* term. The chosen squares should adjoin and form a large square, a double square, a complete row, or a complete column; they should not form a figure such as a triple square. Such permissible adjoining squares are called the *elementary area*, an aggregate of adjoining squares

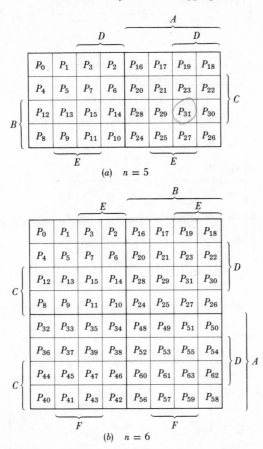

FIG. 4-3 Representation of the *P* terms of five and six Boolean variables on Veitch diagram.

capable of representing an elementary term. This geometry has its equivalent in the identity

$$XY + X\overline{Y} = X \tag{4-8}$$

applied to a logical sum of *P* terms either once or repeatedly to yield an elementary term.

Similar representation prevails for the elementary *S* terms. If the elementary *S* term has one variable, such as those below,

$$f_7 = \overline{C} \quad \text{and} \quad f_8 = B \tag{4-9}$$

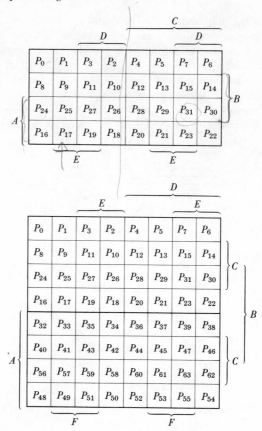

FIG. 4-4   Alternate representation of the *P* terms of five and six Boolean variables on Veitch diagram.

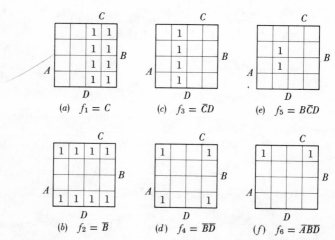

FIG. 4-5   Representation of elementary *P* terms on Veitch diagram.

they are represented by marking 0's in the squares of the diagrams in Fig. 4-6a and b, respectively. Each one-variable term is represented by eight adjoining squares. If the elementary S term has two variables, such as

$$f_9 = C + \overline{D} \quad \text{and} \quad f_{10} = B + D \qquad (4\text{-}10)$$

they are similarly represented by marking 0's in the diagrams of Fig. 4-6c and d, respectively. Each two-variable term is represented by four adjoining squares. The marking of 0's in these diagrams can be done alternatively as follows: Rewrite functions f_9 and f_{10} into a complemented form.

$$f_9 = C + \overline{D} = \overline{\overline{C}D} \quad \text{and} \quad f_{10} = B + D = \overline{\overline{B}\,\overline{D}} \qquad (4\text{-}11)$$

Mark 0's in the squares where the elementary P terms $\overline{C}D$ and $\overline{B}\,\overline{D}$ would be marked with 1's, because their complements $\overline{\overline{C}D}$ and $\overline{\overline{B}\,\overline{D}}$ are to be marked. This method of marking is the result of the earlier definition that the canonical S_i term is the complement of the canonical P_i term.

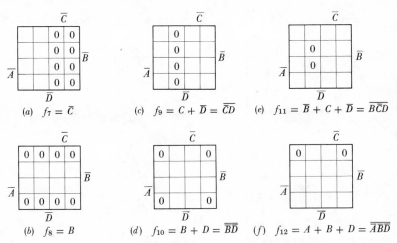

FIG. 4-6   Representation of elementary S terms on Veitch diagram.

If the elementary S term has three variables, such as

$$f_{11} = \overline{B} + C + \overline{D} \quad \text{and} \quad f_{12} = A + B + D \qquad (4\text{-}12)$$

they are shown in Fig. 4-6e and f, respectively. The 0's may again be marked by rewriting functions f_{11} and f_{12} into a complemented form,

$$f_{11} = \overline{B} + C + \overline{D} = \overline{B\overline{C}D} \quad \text{and} \quad f_{12} = A + B + D = \overline{\overline{A}\,\overline{B}\,\overline{D}} \qquad (4\text{-}13)$$

The areas where $B\overline{C}D$ and $\overline{A}\,\overline{B}\,\overline{D}$ would be marked with 1's are marked with 0's.

Comparing the patterns of 1's in Fig. 4-5a and 0's in Fig. 4-6a or the patterns of 1's in Fig. 4-5b and 0's in Fig. 4-6b shows that the functions f_1 and f_7 or the functions f_2 and f_8 complement each other. Similar comparisons can be made between Figs. 4-5c and 4-6c, and 4-5d and 4-6d, 4-5e and 4-6e, and 4-5f and 4-6f. The conclusion is that functions f_3 and f_9, f_4 and f_{10}, f_5 and f_{11}, and f_6 and f_{12} are complements of each other.

The arrangement of P terms or S terms on the Veitch diagram in Figs. 4-1 to 4-3 has been purposely chosen so that the elementary term can be represented simply. The diagrams in Figs. 4-1 to 4-3 are the form refined by Karnaugh [4].

Representation of Elementary Forms. The representation of the Boolean function in the elementary form follows closely that of the elementary term. Consider the following Boolean function in the elementary P form:

$$f_1 = A\bar{C} + \bar{A}CD + BCD \tag{4-14}$$

Representations of elementary terms $A\bar{C}$, $\bar{A}CD$, and BCD are shown, respectively, in the diagrams of Fig. 4-7a, b, and c. The representation of the function f_1, which is the logical sum of these three terms, is merely the composite diagrams of Fig. 4-7d. Note that the square for the canonical term P_7 is common to both elementary terms $\bar{A}CD$ and BCD; in such cases, only one 1 is marked in the square. Consider the following Boolean function in the elementary S form:

$$f_2 = (A + C)(\bar{C} + D)(\bar{A} + B + \bar{C}) \tag{4-15}$$

Again, representation of the function f_2 superposes the separate diagrams of its

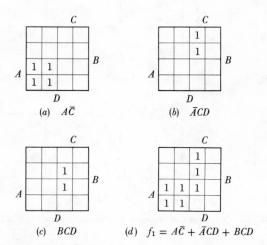

FIG. 4-7   Representation of a Boolean function in the elementary P form on Veitch diagram.

three elementary terms $A + C$, $\bar{C} + D$, and $\bar{A} + B + \bar{C}$ and is shown in Fig. 4-8.

As two additional examples, the following two Boolean functions in the elementary form are represented on the Veitch diagrams in Fig. 4-9:

$$f_3 = (\bar{A} + C)(A + \bar{C} + \bar{D})(\bar{B} + \bar{C} + \bar{D}) \tag{4-16}$$

$$f_4 = AC + C\bar{D} + A\bar{B}C \tag{4-17}$$

By comparing the diagram in Fig. 4-7d with that in Fig. 4-9a or the diagram in Fig. 4-8d with Fig. 4-9b, it is apparent that the functions f_1 and f_3 or the functions f_2 and f_4 are complements of each other.

Minimization by the Veitch Diagram. The minimization of a Boolean function in canonical form by using the Veitch diagram consists merely in visualizing the possible elementary terms from the marked diagram and then choosing those possible elementary terms which will result in a function with the least num-

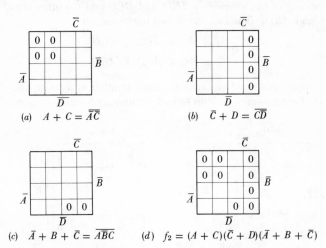

FIG. 4-8   Representation of a Boolean function in the elementary S form on Veitch diagram.

ber of total inputs. The minimization process is described by using the following Boolean functions of four variables:

$$f_1 = P_3 + P_7 + P_8 + P_9 + P_{12} + P_{13} + P_{15} \qquad (4\text{-}18)$$

$$f_2 = S_0 S_1 S_2 S_4 S_5 S_6 S_{10} S_{11} S_{14} \qquad (4\text{-}19)$$

$$f_3 = S_3 S_7 S_8 S_9 S_{12} S_{13} S_{15} \qquad (4\text{-}20)$$

$$f_4 = P_0 + P_1 + P_2 + P_4 + P_5 + P_6 + P_{10} + P_{11} + P_{14} \qquad (4\text{-}21)$$

Step 1.   Represent the given function on the Veitch diagram; these are shown in Fig. 4-10.

Step 2.   Visualize on the diagram the largest possible elementary areas, because a larger elementary area results in a lesser number of variables.

Step 3.   Choose a set of elementary terms from the available largest elementary areas. The set should be so chosen that the marked squares are all included.

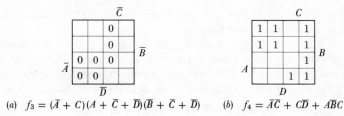

(a) $f_3 = (\bar{A} + C)(A + \bar{C} + D)(\bar{B} + \bar{C} + D)$ (b) $f_4 = \bar{A}\bar{C} + C\bar{D} + A\bar{B}C$

FIG. 4-9   Additional examples of representation of a Boolean function in elementary form on Veitch diagram.

From the diagram in Fig. 4-10*a* for the function f_1, there are four largest possible elementary areas shown by the dashed lines; they represent the elementary terms $A\bar{C}$, $\bar{A}CD$, BCD, and ABD. Two sets of elementary terms are possible choices because the elementary areas of each set cover every marked square. One set consists of the terms $A\bar{C}$, $\bar{A}\bar{C}D$, and BCD and the other set of the terms $A\bar{C}$, $\bar{A}CD$, and ABD. The two minimized functions are

$$f_5 = A\bar{C} + \bar{A}CD + BCD \qquad (4\text{-}22)$$

$$f_6 = A\bar{C} + \bar{A}CD + ABD \qquad (4\text{-}23)$$

These two minimized functions have the same number of total inputs. The terms $A\bar{C}$ and $\bar{A}CD$ are common to both sets of elementary terms; they are called *essen-*

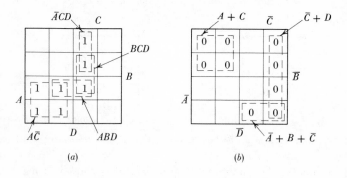

(a)   (b)

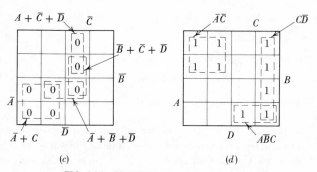

(c)   (d)

FIG. 4-10   Minimization of the Boolean functions.

tial elementary terms, as they appear in both minimized functions. The given function f_1 has two minimized functions.

From the diagram in Fig. 4-10*b* for the function f_2, there are three largest possible elementary areas which correspond to the elementary terms $A + C$, $\bar{C} + D$, and $\bar{A} + B + \bar{C}$. All three are essential elementary terms; thus, they constitute the chosen set. The minimized form of the given function f_2 is

$$f_7 = (A + C)(\bar{C} + D)(\bar{A} + B + \bar{C}) \qquad (4\text{-}24)$$

From the diagrams in Fig. 4-10*c* and *d* for the given functions f_3 and f_4, respectively, their largest possible elementary areas are visualized. For the given function f_3, two sets of elementary terms are possible; the minimized functions are

$$f_8 = (\bar{A} + C)(A + \bar{C} + \bar{D})(\bar{B} + \bar{C} + \bar{D}) \qquad (4\text{-}25)$$

$$f_9 = (\bar{A} + C)(A + \bar{C} + \bar{D})(\bar{A} + \bar{B} + \bar{D}) \qquad (4\text{-}26)$$

There is only one set of elementary terms for the given function f_4, and the minimized function is

$$f_{10} = \bar{A}\bar{C} + C\bar{D} + A\bar{B}C \qquad (4\text{-}27)$$

Diagrams in Fig. 4-10 show that the functions f_1 and f_2 or the functions f_3 and f_4 are the same but differ in canonical form and that the functions f_1 and f_3 or the functions f_2 and f_4 complement each other but also differ in canonical form. The number of inputs for the above six minimized functions f_5 to f_{10} is shown in Table 4-1. Note that functions f_7 and f_{10} require the smallest number of inputs, 10. Function f_7 requires *or-and* circuits, while function f_{10} necessitates *and-or* circuits; the final choice would be determined by circuit considerations.

From a given Boolean function in canonical form such as the function f_1, three related Boolean functions such as f_2 to f_4 can be written. The previous examples use such a set of four Boolean functions f_1 to f_4 because they illustrate an important point: merely minimizing a given Boolean function does not necessarily

Table 4-1   Number of Inputs of the Six Minimized Functions

Minimized function	Minimized from the function	Number of inputs		
		and	*or*	total
f_5	f_1	8	3	11
f_6	f_1	8	3	11
f_7	f_2	3	7	10
f_8	f_3	3	8	11
f_9	f_3	3	8	11
f_{10}	f_4	7	3	10

lead to a true minimized function; instead, minimization of each of the four functions would be needed in order to find the true minimized function. Two functions of the four, however, are complements of the other two; therefore, only two of the four functions require minimization.

Use of "Don't Care" Terms. It may happen that certain input combinations to a circuit do not occur or are prohibited. For example, a translating circuit which has 4 input lines representing the 4 bits of a binary-coded decimal digit may have as many as 16 output lines. Only 10 of the 16 outputs are needed, however, to represent the 10 states of the decimal digit; thus, 6 of the 16 input combinations do not occur. These 6 input combinations are called *"don't care"* *terms* and can be used advantageously to reduce the amount of circuitry.

The following four-variable Boolean function with four don't care terms will serve as an example:

$$f_1 = P_5 + P_9 + P_{12} + P_{13} + P_{15} \qquad (4\text{-}28)$$

Don't care terms:

$$P_2, P_7, P_8, P_{10} \qquad (4\text{-}29)$$

The P terms are represented by marking 1's and the don't care terms by marking d's in the diagram of Fig. 4-11a. Each square marked by d can be regarded as a square marked by either 1 or 0. The 1's or 0's on these d squares are so selected that they produce a set of the largest elementary areas covering all squares marked by 1. In the diagram of Fig. 4-11a, two d's are assigned 1 and the other two 0. In this way, two largest possible elementary areas are

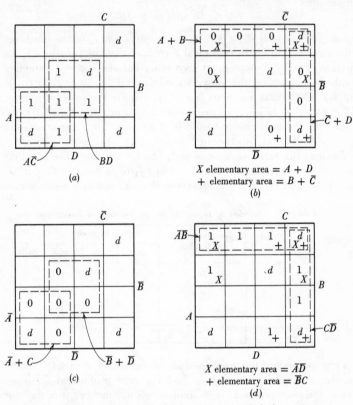

FIG. 4-11 Minimization of the Boolean functions with don't care terms.

formed, and their corresponding elementary terms are $A\bar{C}$ and BD. The minimized function for the given function f_1 is

$$f_2 = A\bar{C} + BD \tag{4-30}$$

The other three Boolean functions of the function f_1 is

$$f_3 = S_0 S_1 S_3 S_4 S_6 S_{11} S_{14} \tag{4-31}$$

$$f_4 = S_5 S_9 S_{12} S_{13} S_{15} \tag{4-32}$$

$$f_5 = P_0 + P_1 + P_3 + P_4 + P_6 + P_{11} + P_{14} \tag{4-33}$$

where the functions f_4 and f_5 are the complement functions of f_1 and f_3, respectively. Their representations on the Veitch diagrams are shown in Fig. 4-11b, c, and d. By properly assigning 1's and 0's to the d squares the largest possible elementary areas are shown there by the dashed lines, and the minimized functions are

$$f_6 = (A + B)(\bar{C} + D)(A + D)(B + \bar{C}) \qquad (4\text{-}34)$$

$$f_7 = (\bar{A} + C)(\bar{B} + \bar{D}) \qquad (4\text{-}35)$$

$$f_8 = \overline{A}\overline{B} + C\overline{D} + \overline{A}\overline{D} + \overline{B}C \qquad (4\text{-}36)$$

Comparing the number of total inputs reveals that the four minimized functions f_2, f_6, f_7, and f_8 require 6, 12, 6, and 12 inputs, respectively. Thus, the choice is either the function f_2 or the function f_7; the latter is the complement function of the given function f_1.

4-2   *Harvard-chart Method* [1]

The second minimization method utilizes the Harvard chart, the composition and properties of which will now be described.

Harvard Chart. The Harvard chart for the Boolean function with three variables is shown in Fig. 4-12. It consists of eight rows and seven columns, in addition to an index row and an index column. The first three columns contain all possible elementary P terms in one variable, the second three columns all possible elementary P terms in three variables. Each row is associated with one canonical P term, and all terms in this row have the P_i term in common. For example, the first row is associated with the P_0 term $\bar{A}\bar{B}\bar{C}$; each term in this row is a logical product of one or more of the quantities $\bar{A}, \bar{B}$, and $\bar{C}$.

Each row has an important property for the minimization process. A two-variable

P_i	A	B	C	AB	AC	BC	ABC
P_0	$\bar{A}$	$\bar{B}$	$\bar{C}$	$\bar{A}\bar{B}$	$\bar{A}\bar{C}$	$\bar{B}\bar{C}$	$\bar{A}\bar{B}\bar{C}$
P_1	$\bar{A}$	$\bar{B}$	C	$\bar{A}\bar{B}$	$\bar{A}C$	$\bar{B}C$	$\bar{A}\bar{B}C$
P_2	$\bar{A}$	B	$\bar{C}$	$\bar{A}B$	$\bar{A}\bar{C}$	$B\bar{C}$	$\bar{A}B\bar{C}$
P_3	$\bar{A}$	B	C	$\bar{A}B$	$\bar{A}C$	BC	$\bar{A}BC$
P_4	A	$\bar{B}$	$\bar{C}$	$A\bar{B}$	$A\bar{C}$	$\bar{B}\bar{C}$	$A\bar{B}\bar{C}$
P_5	A	$\bar{B}$	C	$A\bar{B}$	AC	$\bar{B}C$	$A\bar{B}C$
P_6	A	B	$\bar{C}$	AB	$A\bar{C}$	$B\bar{C}$	$AB\bar{C}$
P_7	A	B	C	AB	AC	BC	ABC

FIG. 4-12   The Harvard P chart for three variables.

term in a row implies a three-variable term, and a one-variable term implies a two-variable term. If a three-variable term is not a term of a given Boolean function, then the two-variable and one-variable terms which imply this three-variable term are not terms of the given function. On the other hand, if a three-variable term is a term of a given function, then minimization always attempts to choose the term with the least number of variables (two-variable or one-variable term) in the row where the three-variable term is located.

Each column also has an important property for the minimization process. An elementary term is placed at several locations in a column; these locations correspond to those P_i-term rows where the logical sum of these P_i terms is equal to the elementary term. For example, the elementary term $\bar{B}\bar{C}$ in the sixth column is placed at the first $\bar{A}\bar{B}\bar{C}$ row and at the fifth $A\bar{B}\bar{C}$ row, where the logical sum $\bar{A}\bar{B}\bar{C} + A\bar{B}\bar{C}$ becomes the elementary term $\bar{B}\bar{C}$; the elementary term A in the first column is placed at the last four rows, where the logical sum $A\bar{B}\bar{C} + A\bar{B}C + AB\bar{C} + ABC$ is the elementary term A.

From the above description, one may infer that the Harvard chart is equivalent to the Veitch diagram. All possible elementary terms on the Veitch diagram are visualized, while in the Harvard chart they are all tabulated.

The Harvard chart for four or more Boolean variables becomes inconveniently large. It can be condensed if elementary terms are replaced by decimal equivalents: in the chart of Fig. 4-12, the terms $\bar{A}$ and A are replaced by 0 and 1, respectively; the terms $\bar{A}\bar{B}$, $\bar{A}B$, $A\bar{B}$, and AB by 0, 1, 2, and 3; and similarly for the other columns. The condensed charts for four and five variables are shown in Figs. 4-13 and 4-14. The Harvard chart for n variables has 2^n rows and $2^n - 1$ columns or $2^n(2^n - 1)$ terms; even in the condensed form, it becomes impractically large for more than six variables.

The above Harvard charts are drawn for elementary P terms; such charts are called *P charts*. They can also be drawn for elementary S terms and are then called S charts. The Harvard S chart for four variables is shown in Fig. 4-15; the decimal digits therein are the same as those on the corresponding P chart, but the variable is taken to be 0, while the complement of the variable is taken to be 1. For example, 0 and 1 in the A column represent A and $\bar{A}$, respectively, and 0, 1, 2, and 3 in the $A + C$ column represent the terms $A + C$, $A + \bar{C}$, $\bar{A} + C$, and $\bar{A} + \bar{C}$, respectively.

P_i	A	B	C	D	AB	AC	AD	BC	BD	CD	ABC	ABD	ACD	BCD	ABCD
0	0	0	0	0	0	0	0	0	0	0	0	0	0	0	0
1	0	0	0	1	0	0	1	0	1	1	0	1	1	1	1
2	0	0	1	0	0	1	0	1	0	2	1	0	2	2	2
3	0	0	1	1	0	1	1	1	1	3	1	1	3	3	3
4	0	1	0	0	1	0	0	2	2	0	2	2	0	4	4
5	0	1	0	1	1	0	1	2	3	1	2	3	1	5	5
6	0	1	1	0	1	1	0	3	2	2	3	2	2	6	6
7	0	1	1	1	1	1	1	3	3	3	3	3	3	7	7
8	1	0	0	0	2	2	2	0	0	0	4	4	4	0	8
9	1	0	0	1	2	2	3	0	1	1	4	5	5	1	9
10	1	0	1	0	2	3	2	1	0	2	5	4	6	2	10
11	1	0	1	1	2	3	3	1	1	3	5	5	7	3	11
12	1	1	0	0	3	2	2	2	2	0	6	6	4	4	12
13	1	1	0	1	3	2	3	2	3	1	6	7	5	5	13
14	1	1	1	0	3	3	2	3	2	2	7	6	6	6	14
15	1	1	1	1	3	3	3	3	3	3	7	7	7	7	15

FIG. 4-13   The Harvard P chart for four variables.

Minimization by Harvard P Chart. A Harvard chart tabulates all possible elementary terms. Minimization of a Boolean function by using a Harvard chart is the process of eliminating impossible elementary terms and then choosing from the possible elementary terms a set of elementary terms which yields the least number of total inputs.

The minimization process may be described by using the following Boolean function of four variables as an example:

$$f_1 = P_3 + P_7 + P_8 + P_9 + P_{12} + P_{13} + P_{15} \qquad (4\text{-}37)$$

The above function is the same as (4-18).

Step 1. Cross out those rows where the P_i terms are not in the given function f_1, as shown by the horizontal lines in Fig. 4-16. This step eliminates all elementary terms in the rows where these elementary terms have in common the P_i terms not in the given function f_1.

Step 2. Cross out in each column the same decimal digits which have been crossed out during step 1; this is indicated by the slant dashes. For example, the digits 0 and 1 in the first column have been crossed out; therefore, the other 0's and 1's in the first column are all crossed out. This step eliminates all elementary terms in the columns where these elementary terms have in common the P_i terms not in the given function f_1. The remaining terms in the chart after this step are the possible elementary terms for the given function.

Step 3. In the first row not crossed out by a horizontal line, choose the possible elementary term with the least number of variables; this is the encircled digit 3 located at the fourth row. The term corresponding to the encircled digit 3 is called an *essential elementary term* because in this case there is no other choice (except the P_i term in the last column). The essential term must be a term in the minimized function. Then, in the column which has the encircled digit, encircle all digits which are the same as the encircled digit; this is the other digit 3 in the thirteenth column. Finally, cross out the remaining digits in each of those rows where a digit has been encircled during this step. This is shown by

P_i	A	B	C	D	E	AB	AC	AD	AE	BC	BD	BE	CD	CE	DE	ABC	ABD	ABE	ACD	ACE	ADE	BCD	BCE	BDE	CDE	ABCD	ABCE	ABDE	ACDE	BCDE	ABCDE
0	0	0	0	0	0	0	0	0	0	0	0	0	0	0	0	0	0	0	0	0	0	0	0	0	0	0	0	0	0	0	0
1	0	0	0	0	1	0	0	0	1	0	0	1	0	1	1	0	0	1	0	1	1	0	1	1	1	0	1	1	1	1	1
2	0	0	0	1	0	0	0	1	0	0	1	0	1	0	2	0	1	0	1	0	2	1	0	2	2	1	0	2	2	2	2
3	0	0	0	1	1	0	0	1	1	0	1	1	1	1	3	0	1	1	1	1	3	1	1	3	3	1	1	3	3	3	3
4	0	0	1	0	0	0	1	0	0	1	0	0	2	2	0	1	0	0	2	2	0	2	2	0	4	2	2	0	4	4	4
5	0	0	1	0	1	0	1	0	1	1	0	1	2	3	1	1	0	1	2	3	1	2	3	1	5	2	3	1	5	5	5
6	0	0	1	1	0	0	1	1	0	1	1	0	3	2	2	1	1	0	3	2	2	3	2	2	6	3	2	2	6	6	6
7	0	0	1	1	1	0	1	1	1	1	1	1	3	3	3	1	1	1	3	3	3	3	3	3	7	3	3	3	7	7	7
8	0	1	0	0	0	1	0	0	0	2	2	2	0	0	0	2	2	2	0	0	0	4	4	4	0	4	4	4	0	8	8
9	0	1	0	0	1	1	0	0	1	2	2	3	0	1	1	2	2	3	0	1	1	4	5	5	1	4	5	5	1	9	9
10	0	1	0	1	0	1	0	1	0	2	3	2	1	0	2	2	3	2	1	0	2	5	4	6	2	5	4	6	2	10	10
11	0	1	0	1	1	1	0	1	1	2	3	3	1	1	3	2	3	3	1	1	3	5	5	7	3	5	5	7	3	11	11
12	0	1	1	0	0	1	1	0	0	3	2	2	2	2	0	3	2	2	2	2	0	6	6	4	4	6	6	4	4	12	12
13	0	1	1	0	1	1	1	0	1	3	2	3	2	3	1	3	2	3	2	3	1	6	7	5	5	6	7	5	5	13	13
14	0	1	1	1	0	1	1	1	0	3	3	2	3	2	2	3	3	2	3	2	2	7	6	6	6	7	6	6	6	14	14
15	0	1	1	1	1	1	1	1	1	3	3	3	3	3	3	3	3	3	3	3	3	7	7	7	7	7	7	7	7	15	15
16	1	0	0	0	0	2	2	2	2	0	0	0	0	0	0	4	4	4	4	4	4	0	0	0	0	8	8	8	8	0	16
17	1	0	0	0	1	2	2	2	3	0	0	1	0	1	1	4	4	5	4	5	5	0	1	1	1	8	9	9	9	1	17
18	1	0	0	1	0	2	2	3	2	0	1	0	1	0	2	4	5	4	5	4	6	1	0	2	2	9	8	10	10	2	18
19	1	0	0	1	1	2	2	3	3	0	1	1	1	1	3	4	5	5	5	5	7	1	1	3	3	9	9	11	11	3	19
20	1	0	1	0	0	2	3	2	2	1	0	0	2	2	0	5	4	4	6	6	4	2	2	0	4	10	10	8	12	4	20
21	1	0	1	0	1	2	3	2	3	1	0	1	2	3	1	5	4	5	6	7	5	2	3	1	5	10	11	9	13	5	21
22	1	0	1	1	0	2	3	3	2	1	1	0	3	2	2	5	5	4	7	6	6	3	2	2	6	11	10	10	14	6	22
23	1	0	1	1	1	2	3	3	3	1	1	1	3	3	3	5	5	5	7	7	7	3	3	3	7	11	11	11	15	7	23
24	1	1	0	0	0	3	2	2	2	2	2	2	0	0	0	6	6	6	4	4	4	4	4	4	0	12	12	12	8	8	24
25	1	1	0	0	1	3	2	2	3	2	2	3	0	1	1	6	6	7	4	5	5	4	5	5	1	12	13	13	9	9	25
26	1	1	0	1	0	3	2	3	2	2	3	2	1	0	2	6	7	6	5	4	6	5	4	6	2	13	12	14	10	10	26
27	1	1	0	1	1	3	2	3	3	2	3	3	1	1	3	6	7	7	5	5	7	5	5	7	3	13	13	15	11	11	27
28	1	1	1	0	0	3	3	2	2	3	2	2	2	2	0	7	6	6	6	6	4	6	6	4	4	14	14	12	12	12	28
29	1	1	1	0	1	3	3	2	3	3	2	3	2	3	1	7	6	7	6	7	5	6	7	5	5	14	15	13	13	13	29
30	1	1	1	1	0	3	3	3	2	3	3	2	3	2	2	7	7	6	7	6	6	7	6	6	6	15	14	14	14	14	30
31	1	1	1	1	1	3	3	3	3	3	3	3	3	3	3	7	7	7	7	7	7	7	7	7	7	15	15	15	15	15	31

FIG. 4-14   The Harvard P chart for five variables.

the horizontal short dashes on the fourth and eighth rows. This step chooses one elementary term for the minimized function. If more than one equal choice exist (terms with the same least number of variables), the possibility of more than one minimized form should be pursued after one set of elementary terms has been chosen. The possibility of more than one equal choice should also be pursued in steps 4 and 5.

Step 4. Step 3 is repeated in the next row not crossed out by a horizontal line and having no encircled digit; the term is the encircled 2 located at the ninth row of the sixth column. Since there are three other 2's in the sixth column, they are also encircled. The remaining digits in the tenth, thirteenth, and fourteenth rows are all crossed out.

Step 5. Step 4 is repeated until each row not crossed out by a horizontal line has at least one encircled digit. This results in the encircled digit 7 in the last row. Then the elementary terms corresponding to the encircled digits are the chosen set. In this example, these are the encircled 2 in the sixth column, the encircled 3 in the thirteenth column, and the encircled 7 in the fourteenth column; their corresponding terms are $A\bar{C}$, $\bar{A}CD$, and BCD. The minimized function for the function f_1 is

$$f_2 = A\bar{C} + \bar{A}CD + BCD \tag{4-38}$$

Step 6. The other equal choice mentioned during step 3 (or during a subsequent step) should now be pursued. The other equal choice is selected, and

S_i	A B C D	$\begin{matrix}A&A&A&B&B&C\\B&C&D&C&D&D\\+&+&+&+&+&+\end{matrix}$	$\begin{matrix}A&A&A&B\\+&+&+&+\\B&B&C&C\\+&+&+&+\\C&D&D&D\end{matrix}$	$\begin{matrix}A\\+\\B\\+\\C\\+\\D\end{matrix}$
0	0 0 0 0	0 0 0 0 0 0	0 0 0 0	0
1	0 0 0 1	0 0 1 0 1 1	0 1 1 1	1
2	0 0 1 0	0 1 0 1 0 2	1 0 2 2	2
3	0 0 1 1	0 1 1 1 1 3	1 1 3 3	3
4	0 1 0 0	1 0 0 2 2 0	2 2 0 4	4
5	0 1 0 1	1 0 1 2 3 1	2 3 1 5	5
6	0 1 1 0	1 1 0 3 2 2	3 2 2 6	6
7	0 1 1 1	1 1 1 3 3 3	3 3 3 7	7
8	1 0 0 0	2 2 2 0 0 0	4 4 4 0	8
9	1 0 0 1	2 2 3 0 1 1	4 5 5 1	9
10	1 0 1 0	2 3 2 1 0 2	5 4 6 2	10
11	1 0 1 1	2 3 3 1 1 3	5 5 7 3	11
12	1 1 0 0	3 2 2 2 2 0	6 6 4 4	12
13	1 1 0 1	3 2 3 2 3 1	6 7 5 5	13
14	1 1 1 0	3 3 2 3 2 2	7 6 6 6	14
15	1 1 1 1	3 3 3 3 3 3	7 7 7 7	15

FIG. 4-15   The Harvard S chart for four variables.

P_i	A B C D	AB AC AD BC BD CD	ABC ABD ACD BCD	ABCD
0	0 0 0 0	0 0 0 0 0 0	0 0 0 0	0
1	0 0 0 1	0 0 1 0 1 1	0 1 1 1	1
2	0 0 1 0	0 1 0 1 0 2	1 0 2 2	2
3	0 0 1 1	0 1 1 1 1 3	1 1 ③ 3	3
4	0 1 0 0	1 0 0 2 2 0	2 2 0 4	4
5	0 1 0 1	1 0 1 2 3 1	2 3 1 5	5
6	0 1 1 0	1 1 0 3 2 2	3 2 2 6	6
7	0 1 1 1	1 1 1 3 3 3	3 3 ③ 7	7
8	1 0 0 0	2 ② 2 0 0 0	4 4 4 0	8
9	1 0 0 1	2 ② 3 0 1 1	4 5 5 1	9
10	1 0 1 0	2 3 2 1 0 2	5 4 6 2	10
11	1 0 1 1	2 3 3 1 1 3	5 5 7 3	11
12	1 1 0 0	3 ② 2 2 2 0	6 6 4 4	12
13	1 1 0 1	3 ② 3 2 3 1	6 7 5 5	13
14	1 1 1 0	3 3 2 3 2 2	7 6 6 6	14
15	1 1 1 1	3 3 3 3 3 3	7 7 ⑦ 7	15

Two choices

FIG. 4-16   Minimization of a Boolean function on the Harvard P chart.

steps 4 and 5 (or the remaining steps) are repeated. The resulting minimized function is compared with the previously found minimized function; the one with the smaller number of total inputs is chosen. In this example, there is an equal choice in the last row during step 5. Instead of encircling the 7 in the fourteenth column, the 7 in the twelfth column is chosen, and its corresponding elementary term is ABD. The alternative minimized function is

$$f_3 = A\bar{C} + \bar{A}CD + ABD \tag{4-39}$$

The minimized functions f_2 and f_3 agree with (4-22) and (4-23), respectively.

The minimized function f_2 (or f_3) obtained by minimizing the given function f_1 is not necessarily the true minimized function. As mentioned above, the complement of the given function should also be minimized. The complement of the function f_1 is

$$f_4 = P_0 + P_1 + P_2 + P_4 + P_5 + P_6 + P_{10} + P_{11} + P_{14} \qquad (4\text{-}40)$$

the same as (4-21). The minimization is carried out according to the above steps; the minimized P chart is shown in Fig. 4-17. One set of elementary terms (indicated by circles in Fig. 4-17) is $\overline{A}C$, $C\overline{D}$, and $A\overline{B}C$, and another set is $\overline{A}D$, $\overline{A}\overline{C}D$, $C\overline{D}$, and $A\overline{B}C$ (not shown in Fig. 4-17). Apparently, the first set will lead to a lesser number of total inputs. Accordingly the first set is chosen, and the minimized function for the given function f_4 is

$$f_5 = \overline{A}C + C\overline{D} + A\overline{B}C \qquad (4\text{-}41)$$

The above function f_5 agrees with (4-27). By comparison with function f_2 (or f_3), the function f_5 has fewer inputs.

FIG. 4-17 Minimization of another Boolean function on the Harvard P chart.

FIG. 4-18 Minimization of a Boolean function on the Harvard S chart.

Minimization by Harvard S Chart.

The above describes the minimization of a Boolean function in the canonical P form. If a Boolean function is in the canonical S form, it is minimized by using the S chart. The steps are the same. As an example, the following function of four variables is used,

$$f_6 = S_0 S_1 S_2 S_4 S_5 S_6 S_{10} S_{11} S_{14} \qquad (4\text{-}42)$$

the same as in (4-19).

Step 1. Cross out those rows where S_i terms are not in the given function f_6; this is shown by the horizontal lines in Fig. 4-18.

Step 2. Cross out in each column the same decimal digits which have been crossed out during step 1; this is indicated by slant dashes. The remaining elementary terms after this step are the possible elementary terms.

Step 3.   In the first row not crossed out by a horizontal line, choose the possible elementary term with the least number of variables; this is the encircled digit 0 located at the first row.   Then, in the column with the encircled term, encircle all digits which are the same as the encircled digit; these are the other three digits, 3, in the second, fifth, and sixth rows.   Finally, cross out the remaining digits in each of those rows where a digit has been encircled during this step; this is shown by the horizontal short dashes.

Step 4.   Step 3 is repeated in the next row not crossed out by a horizontal line and having no encircled digit; the term is the encircled 2 located at the third row of the tenth column.   Since there are three other 2's in the tenth column, they are also encircled, and the remaining digits in the rows with these encircled digits are all crossed out.

Step 5.   Step 4 is repeated until each row not crossed out by a horizontal line has at least one encircled digit.   The result is the encircled digits in the eleventh column.   Then the elementary terms corresponding to the encircled digits are the chosen set.   In this example, these are the encircled 0 in the sixth column, the encircled 2 in the tenth column, and the encircled 0 in the sixth column.   Their corresponding elementary terms are $A + C$, $\bar{C} + D$, and $\bar{A} + B + \bar{C}$.   The minimized function for the given function f_6 is

$$f_7 = (A + C)(\bar{C} + D)(\bar{A} + B + \bar{C}) \tag{4-43}$$

agreeing with (4-24).

Step 6.   The other equal choices during the above steps, if they exist, should now be pursued.   The set of elementary terms which gives the least number of total inputs is the chosen set.   In this example, there is another set, but the above chosen set gives the lesser number of total inputs.

It is noted that markings on the minimized S chart in Fig. 4-18 are the same as those on the minimized P chart in Fig. 4-17.   This occurs because the function f_6 is the complement of the function f_4 and the minimized function f_7 is the complement of the function f_5.

The complement of the function f_6 is

$$f_8 = S_3 S_7 S_8 S_9 S_{12} S_{13} S_{15} \tag{4-44}$$

The above function is the same as (4-20).   When it is minimized on the S chart, the markings are expected to be the same as those on the minimized P chart in Fig. 4-16.   The chosen set of elementary terms is $\bar{A} + C$, $A + \bar{C} + \bar{D}$, and $\bar{B} + \bar{C} + \bar{D}$; this gives the following minimized function:

$$f_9 = (\bar{A} + C)(A + \bar{C} + \bar{D})(\bar{B} + \bar{C} + \bar{D}) \tag{4-45}$$

The alternative set of elementary terms is $\bar{A} + C$, $A + \bar{C} + \bar{D}$, and $\bar{A} + \bar{B} + \bar{D}$, yielding the alternative minimized function

$$f_{10} = (\bar{A} + C)(A + \bar{C} + \bar{D})(\bar{A} + \bar{B} + \bar{D}) \tag{4-46}$$

Functions f_9 and f_{10} agree with (4-25) and (4-26), respectively.

The minimization process is the same on a P chart or on an S chart; the choice depends on the given Boolean function's being in the canonical P form or in the canonical S form.   Since the given functions in the above examples are the same as those in the examples of minimization by the Veitch diagram, it is to be expected that the functions minimized according to these two methods should agree.

4-3 Minimization by Quine-McCluskey Method

This method, first formulated by Quine [2] and later improved by McCluskey [13], consists of two operations; the first is to find the possible elementary terms by a matching process, and the second is to choose those possible elementary terms which will result in a function with the least total number of inputs. The possible elementary terms are called by Quine *prime implicants*.

Matching Process. The first operation finds the prime implicants by using a matching process. This process compares each canonical term of a Boolean function with every other canonical term. If two terms differ in only one variable, that variable is eliminated and an elementary term found. When all such elementary terms are found, the first matching cycle is completed. The matching process cycle is repeated for these elementary terms just found. Third and further cycles are continued until a single pass through a cycle yields no matches. The remaining terms and all the terms that did not match during the process comprise the prime implicants. The matching process is the repeated application of identity (4-8).

(a)		(b)		(c)	
A B C D		*A B C D*		*A B C D*	
8,	1 0 0 0 ∨	8, 9,	1 0 0 – ∨	8, 9, 12, 13,	1 – 0 –
3,	0 0 1 1 ∨	8, 12,	1 – 0 0 ∨	8, 9, 12, 13,	1 – 0 –
9,	1 0 0 1 ∨	3, 7,	0 – 1 1		
12,	1 1 0 0 ∨	9, 13,	1 – 0 1 ∨		
7,	0 1 1 1 ∨	12, 13,	1 1 0 – ∨		
13,	1 1 0 1 ∨	7, 15,	– 1 1 1		
15,	1 1 1 1 ∨	13, 15,	1 1 – 1		

FIG. 4-19   Matching cycles of the Quine-McCluskey method (*P* form). (*a*) Tabulation of the sorted binary equivalents of the P_i terms; (*b*) elementary terms after the first matching cycle; (*c*) elementary terms after the second matching cycle.

The above operation is illustrated by the Boolean function

$$f_1 = P_3 + P_7 + P_8 + P_9 + P_{12} + P_{13} + P_{15} \qquad (4\text{-}47)$$

which is the same as (4-18) and (4-37). This operation begins by replacing the P_i terms by their binary equivalents, *where the variable is taken to be 1 and the complement of the variable is taken to be 0*. These binary equivalents are sorted and placed in four sections shown in Fig. 4-19*a*. The first, second, third, and fourth sections contain those binary equivalents whose number of 1's is one, two, three, and four, respectively. The decimal equivalents are also carried along for later identification of the P_i terms.

Tabulation in sections conveniently matches any two terms. The terms in one section need to match with only those in the next section, because two terms differing by more than one 1 (that is, more than one variable) cannot match. The term in the first section, 1000, is compared with each of the three terms in the second section. Any two terms which form a match are both check-marked, and the resulting elementary term together with the decimal equivalents is listed in the table of Fig. 4-19*b*. The variable eliminated during the matching is indicated by inserting a dash in its original position. Two elementary terms are found by matching the first two sections in Fig. 4-19a, and they form the first section in Fig. 4-19b. The terms in other sections of Fig. 4-19a are similarly compared and subsequent sections formed in Fig. 4-19b. The resulting elementary terms after the first matching cycle are tabulated in Fig. 4-19b. The canonical terms unchecked in Fig. 4-19a are prime implicants; this example has none. The elementary terms in Fig. 4-19b have only three variables.

The second matching cycle results in the tabulation of elementary terms shown in Fig. 4-19c. In the table of Fig. 4-19b, there are seven three-variable elementary terms; three are unchecked. These unchecked terms are prime implicants, corresponding to the terms $\bar{A}CD$, BCD, and ABD.

The elementary terms in Fig. 4-19c have only two variables; there are two terms which are the same, and thus one can be removed. No additional matching cycle is needed, and the term $A\bar{C}$ is a prime implicant. In conclusion, four prime implicants are found.

Prime-implicant Table. The second operation chooses some of these prime implicants to form the minimized function. The selection is made from a prime-implicant table, the columns of which are indexed by the prime implicants and the rows by the given P_i terms with their decimal equivalents. The prime-implicant table for this example is shown in Fig. 4-20. There are seven rows and four columns. Crosses are placed in the table to show the composition of the prime implicants in P_i terms; this can be readily done when the composition of the prime implicants is identified by the decimal equivalents of P_i terms. When the crosses are all marked, a set of prime implicants is chosen. The chosen prime implicants are regarded as a set if, upon examining the crosses in the columns of these prime implicants, there is at least one cross in each row. If there is more than one possible set, the set having the least total number of inputs is chosen. In this example, two sets with an equal number of inputs are found. These sets result in two minimized functions,

		$A\bar{C}$	ABD	$\bar{A}CD$	BCD
3	$\bar{A}\bar{B}CD$			x	
7	$\bar{A}BCD$			x	x
8	$A\bar{B}\bar{C}\bar{D}$	x			
9	$A\bar{B}\bar{C}D$	x			
12	$AB\bar{C}\bar{D}$	x			
13	$AB\bar{C}D$	x	x		
15	$ABCD$		x		x

FIG. 4-20   Prime-implicant table of the Quine-McCluskey method (P form).

$$f_2 = A\bar{C} + \bar{A}CD + BCD \qquad (4\text{-}48)$$

$$f_3 = A\bar{C} + \bar{A}CD + ABD \qquad (4\text{-}49)$$

The two minimized functions agree with functions (4-22) and (4-23) and with functions (4-38) and (4-39) resulting from the other two methods.

If the table in Fig. 4-20 is compared with the Harvard chart in Fig. 4-16, it is obvious that the prime-implicant table is a reduced form of the Harvard chart. Instead of crossing out elementary terms from a Harvard chart, the Quine-McCluskey method achieves elimination by matching, as shown in the tables of Fig. 4-19.

Minimization of the S Form. Minimization of a Boolean function in the S form is similar to minimization in the P form, illustrated by using the Boolean function

$$f_4 = S_0 S_1 S_2 S_4 S_5 S_6 S_{10} S_{11} S_{14} \qquad (4\text{-}50)$$

equivalent to (4-19) and (4-42).

The first operation is again to find the prime implicants. The S terms are replaced by their binary equivalents, as shown in Fig. 4-21a, *where the variable is taken to be 0 and the complement of the variable is taken to be 1.* These binary equivalents are sorted and placed in four sections containing, respectively, one, two, three, and four 0's in the binary equivalents. The decimal equivalents are again carried along for later identification of the respective S terms.

The matching process employs repeated application of identity

$$(X + Y)(X + \overline{Y}) = X \tag{4-51}$$

the dual of (4-8). Matching procedure is the same as before. The elementary terms found during the first matching cycle are tabulated in Fig. 4-21b. Since every S term in Fig. 4-21a is check-marked, no prime implicant appears during the first cycle. The elementary terms found during the second matching cycle are tabulated in Fig. 4-21b. One prime implicant is found during the second cycle—one term with no check mark; this term is $\overline{A} + B + \overline{C}$. The third matching cycle, shown in Fig. 4-21c, yields no more matches; therefore, the re-

(a)						
	A	$+ B$	$+ C$	$+ D$		
14,	1	1	1	0		√
11,	1	0	1	1		√
10,	1	0	1	0		√
6,	0	1	1	0		√
5,	0	1	0	1		√
4,	0	1	0	0		√
2,	0	0	1	0		√
1,	0	0	0	1		√
0,	0	0	0	0		√

(b)						
	A	$+ B$	$+ C$	$+ D$		
14, 10,	1	–	1	0		√
14, 6,	–	1	1	0		√
11, 10,	1	0	1	–		
6, 4,	0	1	–	0		√
5, 4,	0	1	0	–		√
10, 2,	–	0	1	0		√
6, 2,	0	–	1	0		√
5, 1,	0	–	0	1		√
4, 0,	0	–	0	0		√
2, 0,	0	0	–	0		√
1, 0,	0	0	0	–		√

(c)				
	A	$+ B$	$+ C$	$+ D$
14, 10, 6, 2,	–	–	1	0
6, 4, 2, 0,	0	–	–	0
5, 4, 1, 0,	0	–	0	–

FIG. 4-21 Matching cycles of the Quine-McCluskey method (S form). (a) Tabulation of the sorted binary equivalents of the S_i terms; (b) elementary terms after the first matching cycle; (c) elementary terms after the second matching cycle.

maining elementary terms, $\overline{C} + D$, $A + D$, and $A + C$, are also prime implicants.

The second operation is to choose a set of prime implicants to form the minimized function. The prime-implicant table is shown in Fig. 4-22. The chosen set of prime implicants consists of terms $A + C$, $\overline{C} + D$, and $\overline{A} + B + \overline{C}$; and the minimized function is

$$f_5 = (A + C)(\overline{C} + D)(\overline{A} + B + \overline{C}) \tag{4-52}$$

The S-form minimized function agrees with (4-24) and (4-43). The table in Fig. 4-22 again appears as a reduced form of the Harvard chart in Fig. 4-18.

4-4 Machine Minimization

In addition to the previously described methods for minimization, there are others such as Mueller's comparison method [9] and Ghazala's algebraic method

[19].   In any of these methods, when the number of variables of a Boolean function exceeds about six, minimization becomes impractical by pencil-and-paper methods. The use of a digital computer to perform the minimization is a logical step.   In general, there are two approaches: one is to use a large-scale general-purpose machine, and the other is to use a specially built digital machine.

The *relay circuit analyzer* and the *truth-function evaluator* are two specially built machines.   The relay circuit analyzer reported by Shannon and Moore [5] verifies whether or not an input contact circuit satisfies the expected specification and makes systematic attempts to simplify the circuit by removing redundant relay contacts.   The Burroughs truth-function evaluator [12] can evaluate Boolean functions; six logical functions (*not, and, or,* exclusive *or,* coincident, *ornot*) can be directly evaluated.   It can also be used to obtain the truth table and to prove by comparison a simplified function.   However, these machines are not really designed for Boolean-function minimization.

The use of a general-purpose machine for minimization has been more successful.   The Harvard-chart method, Mueller's method, Ghazala's method, or other methods may be programmed for minimizing the Boolean function.   A program which makes use of Quine-McCluskey's technique has been recently reported by Bartee [25].   The program was written for a logic network having 12 inputs and 14 outputs.   The programmed minimizing process is very similar to that described previously.   The computer prints automatically the prime implicants, but the choice of a set of prime implicants is left separate from the computer program to permit flexibility for circuit-design considerations.   The program which was prepared for the MIT Whirlwind Computer consists of about 3,000 instructions; it requires about 40 sec to generate the canonical form for each output of a 12-input truth table and about 10 min to minimize and print the final form.   About 25,000 memory locations are required to store the partial results during the processing; for this reason, a drum storage was used during minimization.

		$A + C$	$A + D$	$\bar{C} + D$	$\bar{A} + B + \bar{C}$
0	$A + B + C + D$	x	x		
1	$A + B + C + \bar{D}$	x			
2	$A + B + \bar{C} + D$		x	x	
4	$A + \bar{B} + C + D$	x	x		
5	$A + \bar{B} + C + \bar{D}$	x			
6	$A + \bar{B} + \bar{C} + D$		x	x	
10	$\bar{A} + B + \bar{C} + D$			x	x
11	$\bar{A} + B + \bar{C} + \bar{D}$				x
14	$\bar{A} + \bar{B} + \bar{C} + D$			x	

FIG. 4-22   Prime-implicant table of the Quine-McCluskey method (*S* form).

4-5   Limitations of Minimization Methods

Minimization methods so far described simplify a Boolean function from a canonical form into an elementary form which has the least number of total inputs.   This minimization criterion is dictated by considerations of expediency, and the methods have many limitations.   A number of these limitations will now be discussed.

Circuit Limitations.   A Boolean function in the elementary form may be referred to as a two-level logic equation because it employs *or-and* or *and-or* circuits which are two-level circuits.   The minimization methods described are applicable only to two-level circuits.

The purpose of minimizing a Boolean function is to reduce the amount of circuitry. However, one may further reduce the amount of circuitry by expressing the Boolean function in a more-than-two-level logic equation, so that multiple-level circuits such as *and-or-and, or-and-or, and-or-and-or,* or *or-and-or-and* circuits could be used. One way to simplify a Boolean function into a multiple-level logic equation is to apply the Boolean theorems and the known identities to the function already in minimized elementary form.

A multiple-level circuit is usually formed by cascading two-level (or one-level) circuits. The number of levels that can be used is limited by practical considerations. As will be discussed in later chapters, signals in logic circuits (such as diode, resistor, transistor, and magnetic-core logic circuits) require a finite time to propagate through each level; this propagation time limits the operating speed. After propagating through one or a few levels, the signal may be distorted; in this case an amplifier or a restoring circuit is needed. Furthermore, each circuit is limited in its fan-in (number of inputs) and fan-out (number of outputs) capability; this is usually solved at the expense of more circuits. The problem may further be complicated by the need to consider the cost and reliability of logic circuits. For these reasons, the optimum number of levels of logic circuits is difficult to determine. In short, caution should be exerted in using the previously described minimization methods.

Different Types of Logic Circuits. Instead of using the *and-or* and *or-and* types of logic circuits, other types may merit consideration: the *nor* and *nand* circuits using transistors and resistors or transistors and diodes, and the *andnot* and *ornot* circuits using magnetic cores and diodes. These circuits may be regarded as *universal logic circuits,* because one type is theoretically sufficient to implement Boolean functions. Even if the number of a universal logic circuit exceeds the number of alternate choice of *and-or* or *or-and* type, the use of one (type) circuit (or perhaps a few in practice) confers an advantage in simplicity of circuit modules and perhaps in cost.

Multiple-output Circuits. The previously described minimization methods apply to one Boolean function at a time; they are thus limited to the single-output circuit. Many circuits in computers are multiple-output circuits which are described by a number of Boolean functions. If each of a number of Boolean functions is minimized, this does not necessarily mean that the given number of Boolean functions is minimized. The possible application of the above minimization methods to multiple-output circuits is discussed in Chap. 9.

Problems

1. Simplify the following Boolean functions into an elementary form by using known theorems and identities:

(a) $f_1(A,B,C,D) = P_0 + P_2 + P_3 + P_4 + P_5 + P_6 + P_8 + P_{10} + P_{11}$
(b) $f_2(A,B,C,D) = S_0 S_{11} S_{13} S_{14} S_{15}$
(c) $f_3(A,B,C,D) = P_0 + P_2 + P_4 + P_5 + P_6 + P_7 + P_8 + P_{10} + P_{11} + P_{12} + P_{14}$
(d) $f_4(A,B,C,D) = S_0 S_1 S_2 S_4 S_5 S_6 S_8 S_9 S_{10} S_{15}$

2. Use the Veitch diagram to minimize the following functions:

(a) $f_1(A,B,C) = P_3 + P_4 + P_7$
(b) $f_2(A,B,C) = S_0 S_1 S_3 S_6 S_7$
(c) $f_3(A,B,C,D) = P_0 + P_2 + P_5 + P_6 + P_7 + P_8 + P_{10}$
(d) $f_4(A,B,C,D) = S_0 S_4 S_5 S_6 S_7 S_8 S_9 S_{10}$

Obtain more than one minimized form if more than one exist. Compare the number of total inputs between the functions f_1 and f_2 and the functions f_3 and f_4.

3. Obtain the complements of the functions of Prob. 1, and minimize them by using the Veitch diagram.

4. Repeat Probs. 2 and 3, using the Harvard chart.

5. Repeat Probs. 2 and 3, using the Quine-McCluskey method.

6. Use the Veitch diagram to minimize the following functions, each having don't care terms:

(a) $f_1(A,B,C,D) = P_0 + P_5 + P_6 + P_7 + P_{10}$
   Don't care terms: P_2, P_3, P_{11}, P_{12}

(b) $f_2(A,B,C,D) = S_0 S_4 S_7 S_{11} S_{14}$
   Don't care terms: S_6, S_8, S_9, S_{13}

Compare the number of total inputs between these two functions.

7. Obtain the complements of the functions of Prob. 6, and minimize them, together with their don't care terms, by using the Veitch diagram.

8. Repeat Probs. 6 and 7, using the Harvard chart.

9. Repeat Probs. 6 and 7, using the Quine-McCluskey method.

10. Simplify the functions in Prob. 1 into more-than-two-level logic equations if they exist.

References

1. Staff of Harvard Computation Laboratory: "Synthesis of Electronic Computing and Control Circuits," Harvard University Press, Cambridge, Mass, 1951.

2. Quine, W. V.: The Problem of Simplifying Truth-functions, *Am. Math. Monthly*, vol. 59, pp. 521–531, 1952.

3. Veitch, E. W.: A Chart Method for Simplifying Truth Functions, *Proc. Computing Machinery Conf.*, May 2–3, 1952, pp. 127–133.

4. Karnaugh, M.: The Map Method for Synthesis of Combinational Logic Circuits, *AIEE Communs. Electronics*, November, 1953, pp. 593–599.

5. Shannon, C. E., and E. F. Moore: Machine Aid for Switching Circuit Design, *Proc. IRE*, October, 1953, pp. 1348–1351.

6. Caldwell, S. H.: The Recognition and Identification of Symmetric Switching Functions, *AIEE Communs. Electronics*, May, 1954, pp. 142–147.

7. Nelson, R. J.: Simplest Normal Truth Functions, *J. Symbolic Logic*, vol. 20, no. 2, pp. 105–108, 1955.

8. Nelson, R. J.: Weak Simplest Normal Truth Functions, *J. Symbolic Logic*, vol. 20, no. 3, pp. 232–234, 1955.

9. Mueller, R.: On the Synthesis of a Minimal Representation of a Logic Function, Report No. AFCRC-TR-55-104, *Air Force Cambridge Research Center*, April, 1955.

10. Postley, J. A.: A Method for the Evaluation of a System of Boolean Algebraic Equations, *Math. Tables and Aids for Computation*, January, 1955, pp. 5–8.

11. Quine, W. V.: A Way to Simplify Truth Functions, *Am. Math. Monthly*, vol. 62, pp. 627–631, 1955.

12. Miehle, W.: Burroughs Truth Function Evaluator, *J. ACM*, pp. 189–192, 1955.

13. McCloskey, E. J., Jr.: Minimization of Boolean Functions, *Bell System Tech. J.*, November, 1956, pp. 1417–1444.

14. Urbano, R. H., and R. K. Mueller: A Topological Method for the Determination of the Minimal Forms of a Boolean Function, *IRE Trans. on Electronic Computers*, September, 1956, pp. 126–131.

15. McCluskey, E. J., Jr.: Detection of Group Invariance or Total Symmetry of a Boolean Function, *Bell System Tech. J.*, November, 1956, pp. 1445–1453.

16. Muller, D. E.: Complexity in Electronic Switching Circuits, *IRE Trans. on Electronic Computers*, March, 1956, pp. 15–19.

17. Harris, B.: An Algorithm for Determining Minimal Representations of a Logic Function, *IRE Trans. on Electronic Computers*, June, 1957, pp. 103–108.

18. Marcus, M. P.: Minimization of the Partially-developed Transfer Tree, *IRE Trans. on Electronic Computers*, June, 1957, pp. 92–95.

19. Ghazala, M. J.: Irredundant Disjunctive and Conjunctive Forms of a Boolean Function, *IBM Research Develop. J.*, vol. 1, no. 2, pp. 171–176, 1957.

20. Hirschhorn, E.: Simplification of a Class of Boolean Functions, *J. ACM*, January, 1958, pp. 67–75.

21. Warfield, J. N.: A Note on the Reduction of Switching Functions, *IRE Trans. on Electronic Computers*, June, 1958, pp. 180–181.

22. Caldwell, S. H.: "Switching Circuits and Logical Design," John Wiley & Sons, Inc., New York, 1958.

23. Phister, M.: "Logical Design of Digital Computers," John Wiley & Sons, Inc., New York, 1958.

24. Beatson, T. J.: Minimization of Components in Electronic Switching Circuits, *AIEE Communs. Electronics*, July, 1958, pp. 283–291.

25. Bartee, T. C.: Automatic Design of Logical Networks, *Proc. Western Joint Computer Conf.*, 1959, pp. 103–107.

26. Butler, K. J., Jr., and J. N. Warfield: A Digital Computer Program for Reducing Logical Statements to a Minimal Form, *Proc. Natl. Electronics Conf.*, 1959, pp. 456–466.

5

Logic Circuits—I

Logic circuits are physical circuits that can perform logic operations and thus implement Boolean functions. They employ relays, vacuum tubes, resistors, solid-state devices, or other components. Logic circuits may be divided into two groups: magnetic and nonmagnetic. Magnetic logic circuits are described in Chaps. 7 and 8. Nonmagnetic logic circuits of the more common types are the subject of this chapter; other types are described in Chap. 6.

5-1 Logic Circuits

Basic Logic Circuits. Basic logic circuits are designed to perform elementary logic operations. They also serve as computer building blocks—fundamental units from which the logic function of a computer can be built. Most of the basic logic circuits to be described are listed in Table 5-1.

Table 5-1 *Basic Logic Circuits*

Logic operation	Terminology	Explanation
$\overline{A}$	*not*	not A
AB	*and*	A and B
$A + B$	*or* (or inclusive *or*)	A or B
$A \oplus B \ (= \overline{A \odot B})$	*exclusive or*†	(A and $\overline{B}$) or ($\overline{A}$ and B)
$A \odot B \ (= \overline{A \oplus B})$	*coincidence*	(A and B) or ($\overline{A}$ and $\overline{B}$)
$\overline{AB} \ (= \overline{A} + \overline{B})$	*nand*	not (A and B)
$\overline{A + B} \ (= \overline{A}\overline{B})$	*nor*	not (A or B)
$A\overline{B}$	*andnot* (or inhibitor)	A and (not B)
$A + \overline{B}$	*ornot*	A or (not B)

† Or modulo-2 sum or anticoincidence.

Some basic logic circuits are often called *gates*, circuits which produce an output when a specified combination of signals occurs at the inputs. For example, an *and* gate produces an output signal when there is a time coincidence of all inputs. An inhibitory gate produces an output signal in the absence of a signal at the inhibitory input.

Of the three major limitations in practical logic circuits, the first is non-instantaneous response of the circuits. The delay, sometimes called the *propagation time,* should be small in comparison with the time of each operation. The second limitation is the number of inputs and the number of outputs that may connect to the input and output, respectively, of a practical circuit; this capability is commonly referred to as the *fan-in* and the *fan-out* of the circuit.   The third limitation is the signal attenuation and distortion which make the binary identity become uncertain.   The latter two difficulties are overcome by augmenting the logic circuits with logically insignificant circuits such as amplifiers, drivers, and level restorers.

Signal Representation.   The binary state of the signals in logic circuits can be represented by either of two voltage levels or by pulses.   In the level representation the two voltages are designated as positive and negative (or upper and lower) levels, as shown in Fig. 5-1*a*.   Positive and negative denote relative levels; the actual values may be any two discrete voltages as long as the positive level is above the negative level.   Pulse representation may consist of a pulse–no-pulse combination or a positive-negative combination, as shown in Fig. 5-1*b* and *c*; it is used for a-c-coupled circuits.   Pulse representation requires a time interval

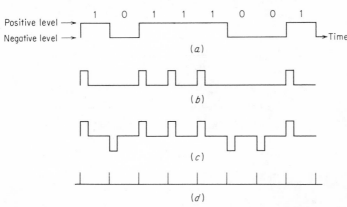

FIG. 5-1   Signal representation of binary states.   (*a*) Two-level voltage representation; (*b*) pulse and no-pulse representation; (*c*) positive-pulse and negative-pulse representation; (*d*) clock pulses.

between adjacent pulses to allow for the time tolerance.   A synchronous computer also requires clock pulses—narrow pulses with a certain repetition rate, as shown in Fig. 5-1*d*.   The clock pulses are sometimes of multiple phase; a two-phase clock pulse, for example, may produce two sequences of clock pulses occurring alternately.

The binary state of a signal may also be represented by two lines.   In this case, one line carries the signal representing the 1 state; the other line carries the 0-state signal.   Three examples of two-line signal representation are shown in Fig. 5-2.   In Fig. 5-2*a*, the positive level represents the 1 state on one line but represents the 0 state on the other line.   In Fig. 5-2*b*, the positive pulse represents the 1 state on one line, the 0 state on the other line.   In Fig. 5-2*c*, the positive pulse uses one line; the negative pulse uses the other.

D-C-coupled and A-C-coupled Logic Circuits.   Logic circuits interconnected by direct connections or resistive networks are coupled for direct current, or are d-c-coupled.   If they are connected by inductive or capacitive networks, they are coupled for alternating (or pulse) current, or are a-c-coupled.

Alternating-current-coupled circuits are limited to handling pulse-type signals. On the other hand, the d-c-coupled circuits do not necessarily require the use of two-level voltages only; either two-level voltages or pulses or both can be used. For synchronous computers, it is quite common to use both—the voltage levels from the flipflops as signals and the clock pulses for initiating the operation.

Alternating-current-coupled circuits possess the advantage that they do not have to maintain accurate voltage levels at various interconnections; this requires less design effort and perhaps fewer components.   However, a-c-coupled circuits are meaningful only during the occurrence of the pulses and require a precise coincidence of the pulses for the logical-*and* operation.   On the other hand, d-c-coupled circuits have the advantages of being less difficult to synchronize and of having better serviceability; the latter is an important practical consideration.

Positive and Negative Logic.   In representing the binary states by positive and negative signals, there are two choices in designating the binary 1 and 0.   If

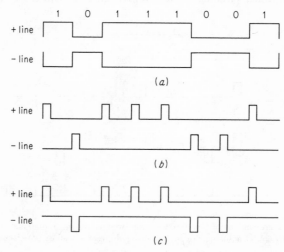

FIG. 5-2   Two-line signal representation of binary states. (*a*) Two-level voltage representation; (*b*) pulse representation; (*c*) positive-pulse and negative-pulse representation.

the positive signal is identified as 1 and the negative signal as 0, the choice is called *positive logic;* the reverse choice is called *negative logic.*   Six cases of designating positive and negative logic are shown in Table 5-2.

Table 5-2   Designation of Positive and Negative Logic

Voltage levels			Pulse states			Positive logic	Negative logic
+	+	gd†	+ pulse	+ pulse	no pulse	1	0
−	gd†	−	− pulse	no pulse	− pulse	0	1

† gd means ground.

From the above, it is apparent that identification of the logic operation of a given circuit depends on designation of the positive or negative logic.   Such possible

Table 5-3 *Identification of Complementary Circuits*

A B	Positive logic				
	and or	nand nor	exor coin	andnot A ornot A	andnot B ornot B
− −	− −	+ +	− +	− +	− +
− +	− +	+ −	+ −	+ +	− −
+ −	− +	+ −	+ −	− −	+ +
+ +	+ +	− −	− +	− +	− +
A B	or and	nor nand	coin exor	ornot A andnot A	ornot B andnot B
	Negative logic				

identification for two inputs A and B is shown in Table 5-3. This table contains five pairs of *complementary circuits*. A pair of complementary circuits are those for which the logic operation of one circuit for the positive logic is the same as the logic operation of the other for the negative logic. These five complement pairs are the *and-or, nand-nor, exor-coin, andnot-ornot A*, and *andnot-ornot B*. Since the last two pairs are essentially the same, only four complementary circuits for two inputs are unique.

Synchronous and Asychronous Operation. Operation in the digital computer is in time sequence; control of this sequence can be either synchronous

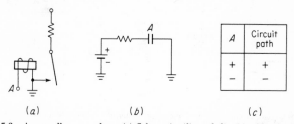

	A	Circuit path
	+	+
	−	−

(a)   (b)   (c)

FIG. 5-3   A normally open relay. (a) Schematic; (b) symbolic; (c) table of operation.

or asynchronous. In a synchronous computer, each logic operation takes place under the control of the clock—in synchronism with the clock pulses. In addition the execution of an instruction such as addition or shift occurs at a fixed time interval, usually the longest required for various operations. In an asynchronous computer, no fixed time reference exists for the operations. Completion of any one operation produces an operation-complete signal; this signal initiates the next operation. An asynchronous computer will be faster because it does not have to "use up" a fixed time interval. If most of the operations of the computer can be arranged to perform in one or more constant time intervals, then there is not much gain in asynchronous operation.

5-2   Relay Logic Circuits [47]

Relays are electromagnetically operated switches. Most relays are built with a single winding and an armature which opens or closes one or more pairs of contacts. A normally open relay closes when a voltage is applied to its winding terminal as shown in Fig. 5-3a. When the contacts close, the circuit path is completed and the load is supplied with a current. When the applied voltage is removed, the circuit path opens. Thus the relay is a binary device. Its operation is tabulated in Fig. 5-3c, where plus and minus signs indicate the circuit path closed or open, respectively, as well as the voltage applied or not applied to the terminal. For simplicity, the circuit is symbolized in Fig. 5-3b, where A identifies a pair of normally open contacts in the relay operated by the winding of Fig. 5-3a.

The schematic and symbolic diagrams of three basic relay logic circuits together with the operation tables are shown in Figs. 5-4 to 5-6. The relay *not* circuit is

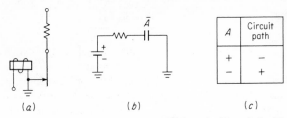

A	Circuit path
+	−
−	+

(a)   (b)   (c)

FIG. 5-4   A relay *not* circuit (normally closed relay). (a) Schematic; (b) symbolic; (c) table of operation.

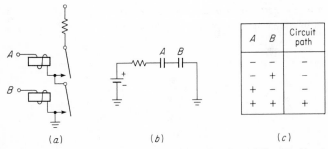

A	B	Circuit path
−	−	−
−	+	−
+	−	−
+	+	+

(a)   (b)   (c)

FIG. 5-5   A relay *and* circuit (positive logic). (a) Schematic; (b) symbolic; (c) table of operation.

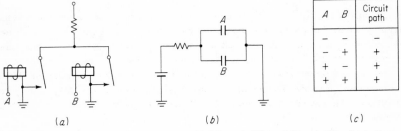

A	B	Circuit path
−	−	−
−	+	+
+	−	+
+	+	+

(a)   (b)   (c)

FIG. 5-6   A relay *or* circuit (positive logic). (a) Schematic; (b) symbolic; (c) table of operation.

a normally closed relay; the circuit path opens when voltage is applied to the terminal. It is indicated by $\bar{A}$, the complement of A. Assume that positive logic is taken here. The circuit path in the relay *and* circuit is closed only when voltages are applied to both input terminals. In the relay *or* circuit, the circuit path is closed when the voltage is applied to either of the two input terminals. It is apparent that, for positive logic, *and* circuits are contacts in series and *or* circuits are contacts in parallel.

With these three basic relay circuits, the other six basic logic operations can be readily obtained; they are shown in Fig. 5-7. For simplicity this figure eliminates the symbols for resistors, battery, and ground.

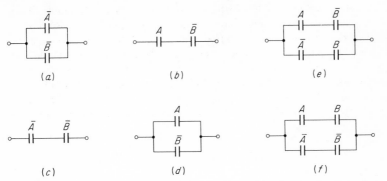

FIG. 5-7 Other relay basic logic circuits (positive logic). (*a*) *nand* circuit; (*b*) *andnot-B* circuit; (*c*) *nor* circuit; (*d*) *ornot-B* circuit; (*e*) *exor* circuit; (*f*) *coin* circuit.

Relay circuits are contact networks. A more complex contact network is shown in Fig. 5-8. The reader can readily trace the circuit from the Boolean function (which is in a nonelementary form) shown therewith.

Relays are simple but bilateral devices. Although relays have been thoroughly explored (they have been manufactured and used for a great number of years), the logic design of

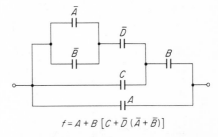

$$f = A + B\,[C + \bar{D}\,(\bar{A} + \bar{B})]$$

FIG. 5-8 A relay logic circuit.

an effective relay network can become quite complicated. For example, the relay circuit permits the use of bridge-type networks, which may lead to intricate topological configurations.

A few early digital computers used relay circuitry. A great variety of relay types are available to suit many applications. Little power is consumed when the relay is not energized; however, it is a slow-speed device. Because of their low speed, relays are now rarely used as logic circuits in digital computers.

5-3 *Vacuum-tube Logic Circuits*

After the development of relay computers, it was natural to turn to vacuum-tube circuits in an effort to increase the operating speed of digital computers. Some of the circuit techniques are described below. Description of vacuum-tube techniques will be brief, since modern machines employ solid-state circuity.

Basic Vacuum-tube Logic Circuits. A triode or a pentode can be operated in two states, either biased to cutoff or operated in an overdriven (saturated) condition. Thus, the tube is a binary device.

Basic vacuum-tube logic circuits [46] and tables of operations are shown in Fig.

5-9. For positive logic, the circuits are *not, nor, or,* and *nand* circuits. In Fig. 5-9a, the plate voltage is high or low (indicated by plus and minus signs, respectively) when the grid voltage is low or high. For positive logic, this circuit is a *not* circuit, better known as the *inverter*. Figure 5-9b shows a twin-triode circuit with a common-plate resistor. The plate voltage is high only when both grids are low, and in this condition the tube is completely cut off. For positive logic, this circuit is a *nor* circuit. The twin-cathode follower with common-cathode resistor of Fig. 5-9c, for positive logic, is an *or* circuit, as the cathode voltage is high unless both grids are low enough to cut off the twin triode completely. The pentode circuit of Fig. 5-9d conducts, and its plate voltage is low only when both control grid and suppressor grid are high. For positive logic, it is a *nand* circuit. Pentodes for this use should show a nearly equal effect on the plate current by

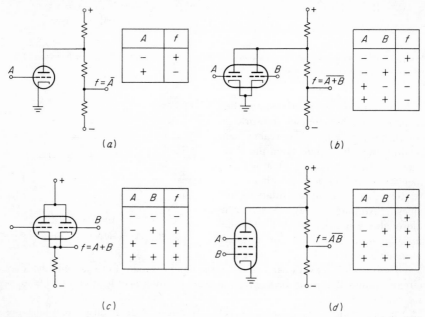

A	f
−	+
+	−

$f = \bar{A}$

(a)

A	B	f
−	−	+
−	+	−
+	−	−
+	+	−

$f = \overline{A + B}$

(b)

A	B	f
−	−	−
−	+	+
+	−	+
+	+	+

$f = A + B$

(c)

A	B	f
−	−	+
−	+	+
+	−	+
+	+	−

$f = \overline{AB}$

(d)

FIG. 5-9   Vacuum-tube basic logic circuits (positive logic).   (a) *not* circuits; (b) *nor* circuits; (c) *or* circuit; (d) *nand* circuit.

both grids. The resistor dividers in Fig. 5-9 are designed to give the same voltage swing at both input and output. Basic logic circuits with more than two inputs can be obtained similarly by connecting tubes in parallel with one common-plate or -cathode resistor.

A Half Adder. The use of vacuum-tube logic circuits is illustrated by implementing a half adder. The half adder is a logic circuit for binary addition of a single digit; its operation is shown in Table 5-4, where A, B, S, and C are the augend, addend, sum, and carry bits, respectively. Boolean functions S and C are

Table 5-4   Truth Table for Half Adder

A	B	S (sum)	C (carry)
0	0	0	0
0	1	1	0
1	0	1	0
1	1	0	1

$$S \text{ (sum)} = A\overline{B} + \overline{A}B = A \oplus B$$
$$C \text{ (carry)} = AB \tag{5-1}$$

Vacuum-tube logic circuits are well adapted to inversion operations as characterized by *nor* circuits and *nand* circuits, but they are not readily adapted to Boolean functions in *P* or *S* form such as those of Eqs. (5-1). To use these basic logic circuits, Boolean functions (5-1) are rewritten as

$$S = \overline{\overline{AB} + \overline{\overline{A}B}} = (\overline{A} + \overline{B})(A + B) = (\overline{AB})(A + B)$$
$$C = AB \tag{5-2}$$

The above functions are now directly related to these basic logic circuits. The half adder is shown in Fig. 5-10. There are one *or* circuit, two *nand* circuits, and two *not* circuits, or a total of eight grids.

Vacuum-tube circuits have high input impedance and low output impedance. If input and output voltage swings are designed to be the same, as many circuits

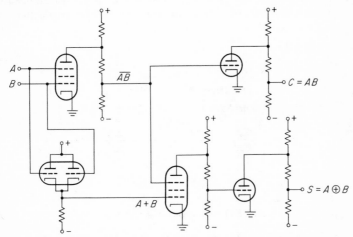

FIG. 5-10   A half adder using triodes and pentodes.

can be cascaded as cost permits. Therefore, these circuits are convenient building blocks. Unfortunately, they consume considerable power and require more space than circuits using solid-state devices.

Vacuum-tube Flipflop. Early availability of solid-state diodes eliminated the use of the above-described vacuum-tube logic circuits. However, vacuum-tube flipflops are still used in some of the existing commercial machines. Since the flipflops of modern machines use transistors, the vacuum-tube flipflop circuit is described here very briefly.

A symmetric flipflop circuit is shown in Fig. 5-11: two triodes *V* and *V′* with their cathodes grounded. Between the positive and negative supply voltages E_1 and E_2, there are two cross-coupling networks; each is a voltage divider consisting of resistors R_1, R_2, and R_3. A capacitor C_2 shunts each resistor R_2. The cross-coupling networks are so designed that, when *V* is conducting (as shown in the figure), *V′* is cut off; when *V* is cut off, *V′* is conducting. These are two stable states, designated, respectively, as the 0 and 1 states (or vice versa). The two output voltages of the flipflop are the plate voltages, complements of each other.

Two inputs r and s are connected through a capacitor to the grids, and the circuit is an *RS* flipflop.

The flipflop circuit in Fig. 5-11 is known as the Eccles-Jordan circuit, invented by Eccles and Jordan [45] in 1919. It is a two-stage inverter with the output of the second stage fed back to the grid of the first stage. Since each stage introduces a phase inversion, the feedback is positive; this situation can make the circuit such that neither both triodes would conduct simultaneously nor both would be cut off.

The design of a satisfactory flipflop circuit requires consideration of such factors as d-c stability, switching speed, triggering network, output voltage swing, and output driving capability. These considerations will be discussed at greater length in Sec. 5-7 on Transistor Flipflops.

5-4   *Diode Logic Circuits*

The diode is a two-terminal nonlinear switching device. It exhibits a binary characteristic of high forward conduction and low reverse conduction. Semi-

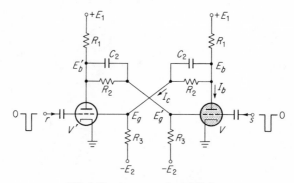

FIG. 5-11   A vacuum-tube *RS* flipflop.

conductor diodes lend themselves to computer applications because they are small and relatively inexpensive; they switch fast and operate at a low power level. The diode's inability to amplify, however, limits its use—without amplification—in a larger logic network. Practical diode logic circuits employ active components such as vacuum tubes or transistors.

Basic Diode Logic Circuits. Two basic diode logic circuits are shown in Fig. 5-12. The two supply voltages E_1 and E_4 and the two levels of input voltage E_2 and E_3 are of such magnitudes that $E_1 \geq E_2 \geq E_3 \geq E_4$. Voltage level E_2 is the high, or positive, level (plus sign), and E_3 is the low, or negative, level (minus sign). The difference $E_2 - E_3$ is the voltage swing of the input. In the circuit of Fig. 5-12a, output f will be clamped to the lower input voltage; hence, a coincidence of high input voltages is necessary to give a high output voltage. The circuit is a logical-*and* one for positive logic and a logical-*or* one for negative logic. In circuit *b*, output voltage f is high if any input voltage is high, but it is low only when both inputs are low. It is a logical-*or* circuit for positive logic and a logical-*and* circuit for negative logic. The tables of operation of both circuits are shown in Fig. 5-12.

In the above diode circuits, the forward voltage drop of the diode should be small in comparison with the voltage swing. Resistor R should be large enough to minimize power consumption, but not too large in comparison with the reverse resistance of the diode. A typical value ranges from 500 to 50,000 ohms. Diode capacitance and recovery time, as well as stray capacitance, limit the switching speed.

Two-level Diode Logic Circuits. Two-level diode logic circuits can implement a Boolean function in either canonical or elementary form. Figure 5-13 shows two examples of such diode logic circuits: one circuit for a Boolean function of three variables in canonical P form (*and-or* circuit), and the other for the canonical S form (*or-and* circuit).

The output voltage of a two-level circuit is designed to be the same as the input level so that the circuits can be cascaded. But attenuation accompanies signals passing through a two-level circuit. This situation is now analyzed for the *or-and* circuit; analysis of the *and-or* circuit is similar.

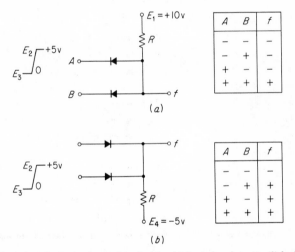

FIG. 5-12   Diode basic logic circuits (positive logic).   (*a*) Logical-*and* circuit; (*b*) logical-*or* circuit.

Let R_f and R_b be, respectively, the forward and reverse resistance of the diode; m the number of the second-level *and*-circuit inputs; and n the number of each of the first-level *or*-circuit inputs. Let supply voltages E_1 and E_4 be made equal to E_2 and E_3, respectively. Assume that $R_f \ll R_1 \ll R_b$ and $R_f \ll R_2 \ll R_b$. The analysis [2] is divided into two cases: one when the output voltage is desired to be E_2, or positive, and the other when the output voltage is E_3, or negative.

When the output voltage E_0 is the same as E_2 (or positive), all m second-level inputs (which are the first-level outputs) must be positive. This occurs when at least one of n first-level inputs of each of the first-level *or* circuits is positive. The worst condition occurs when only one of n first-level inputs of each of the first-level *or* circuits is positive. The equivalent circuit is shown in Fig. 5-14*a*. With the assumption that $R_f \ll R_2 \ll R_b$, this equivalent circuit can be simplified into that shown in Fig. 5-14*b*; and the output voltage E_{01} is

$$E_{01} = E_2 - \frac{(E_2 - E_3)R_f}{R_f + R_{e1}} \tag{5-3}$$

where

$$\frac{1}{R_{e1}} = \frac{1}{R_1} + \frac{n-1}{R_b}$$

If the diodes are ideal so that R_f is zero, then the output voltage E_{01} becomes

$$E_{01} = E_2$$

Therefore, the second term on the right-hand side of (5-3) represents the signal attenuation due to the nonideal diode.

When the output voltage E_0 is the same as E_3 (or negative), at least one of the m second-level inputs must be negative. This occurs when all n first-level inputs are negative for at least one *or* circuit. The worst condition is when n inputs for only one *or* circuit are negative but n inputs for each of the other *or* circuits are positive. The equivalent circuit is shown in Fig. 5-15a. With the assumption

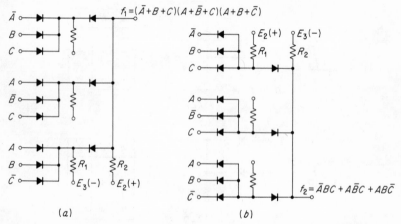

(a)   (b)

FIG. 5-13   Two-level diode logic circuits (positive logic). (a) *or-and* circuit; (b) *and-or* circuit.

that $R_f \ll R_1 \ll R_b$, this equivalent circuit is simplified into that shown in Fig. 5-15b; the output voltage E_{00} is

$$E_{00} = E_3 - \frac{(E_3 - E_2)(R_f + R_1)}{R_f + R_1 + R_{e2}} \tag{5-4}$$

where

$$\frac{1}{R_{e2}} = \frac{1}{R_2} + \frac{m-1}{R_b}$$

If the diode is ideal so that R_f is zero and R_b is infinite, then the output voltage E_{00} becomes

$$E_{00} = E_3 - \frac{(E_3 - E_2)R_1}{R_1 + R_2} \tag{5-5}$$

The above output voltage E_{00} is not equal to the desired output of E_3 but is attenuated by a quantity which is the second term on the right-hand side of (5-5), even if the diodes are ideal. This shows that *the attenuation of a two-level diode logic circuit is inherent.* For nonideal diodes, the attenuation is represented by the second term on the right-hand side of (5-4). It is important to minimize the attenuation. An examination of the above relations establishes that the following conditions can reduce the signal attenuation:

$$R_2 \leq \frac{R_b}{m - 1} \qquad \text{and} \qquad R_f \ll R_1 \ll R_2 \qquad (5\text{-}6)$$

From these conditions, it is noted that the ratio R_b/R_f of a diode is an important

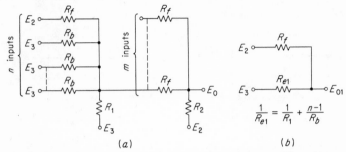

FIG. 5-14   Equivalent circuit of Fig. 5-13a for a positive output.   (a) Equivalent circuit of Fig. 5-13a; (b) equivalent circuit of (a).

quantity in selecting the diodes and that for a given diode the attenuation becomes large when the number of second-level inputs m increases.

The above signal attenuation will be worsened when the tolerance of the resistors and the forward voltage drop of the diodes are considered. However, attenuation can be minimized if the supply voltages E_1 and E_4 are not made equal to E_2 and E_3, respectively. Under this condition, the simplified equivalent

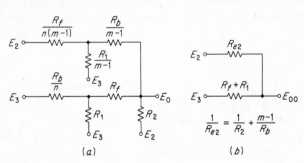

FIG. 5-15   Equivalent circuit of Fig. 5-13a for a negative output.   (a) Equivalent circuit of Fig. 5-13a; (b) equivalent circuit of (a).

circuits with a load resistance R_L are shown in Fig. 5-16. By properly choosing the supply voltages and resistances, this attenuation can be virtually eliminated.

Multiple-level Diode Logic Circuits.   A three-level diode logic circuit is shown in Fig. 5-17. For positive logic, it is an *or-and-or* circuit. For a given Boolean function, the use of more-than-two-level logic circuits may reduce the total number of diodes and is quite necessary in practice. Nonetheless, several factors deserve consideration with respect to more-than-two-level diode circuits. (1) Such circuits introduce more propagation delay. (2) Configurations of such circuits become less uniform and less simple as the number of levels increases; this requires more design effort. (3) More power from the inputs is needed to drive a multiple-level circuit. (4) The signal cross-talk and the stray capacitance increase in later stages and can seriously limit the operating speed.

NBS Diode Logic Circuit [5]. A diode logic circuit developed by the National Bureau of Standards uses pulse signals only, at a 1-Mc pulse rate, for the computers SEAC and DYSEAC. The concept was to design a universal

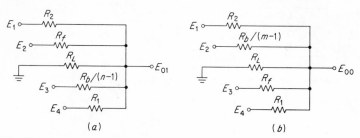

(a)   (b)

FIG. 5-16   Equivalent circuit of Fig. 5-13a with supply voltages E_1 and E_4 and load resistance R_L. (a) For positive output; (b) for negative output.

circuit capable of performing all logic operations. Such a universal logic circuit is shown in Fig. 5-18; it consists of a diode logic circuit, a beam power tube for amplification, and a transformer for coupling to subsequent levels. The pulse transformer offers several advantages: it supplies a large pulse current at low voltage; it matches impedance of tube and load; it permits the operation of all tubes with positive pulses on the grid without the need of inverters; it eliminates d-c coupling; and it allows operation of all tubes from common supply voltages.

The diode logic in Fig. 5-18 is a two-level *and-or* circuit (for positive logic).

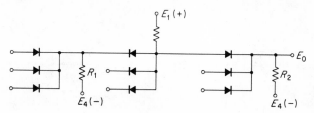

FIG. 5-17   A three-level *or-and-or* diode circuit (positive logic).

It has five *and* gates (three two-input gates, one four-input gate, and one five-input gate) and one five-input *or* gate. The diode-resistor network at the secondaries of the transformer permits the transformer to drive the gates of succeeding similar stages. There are three output terminals: the direct terminal for driving electrical delay lines and other *or* gates, the positive terminal for driving *and* gates, and the negative terminal for inhibiting *and* gates. In the absence of input pulses, the diodes of the *and* gates are conducting because their input terminals are held at slightly below -8 volts by being connected to the positive output terminals of the preceding stage. Each positive output terminal is held just below -8 volts by its limiting diodes, which are kept conducting by the (1.25- and 3.3-kilohm) resistors to −65 volts. These resistors are called the *pulldown* resistors. With the output terminals of the *and* gates at about −8 volts, the diodes in the *or* gate are nonconducting because the −5-volt clamping diode prevents the 39-kilohm resistor from pulling the grid down much below −5 volts. The 2-volt back bias on the *or*-gate diodes protects the grid from noise such as crosstalk on long leads between stages or voltage variations in the forward drop across the −8-volt limiting diodes.

The source which drives the diode *and* gate requires a low dynamic impedance. When a source pulses positive, its gate diodes simply cut off so that practically no current flows. But when a source is not pulsing, it must draw through its gate

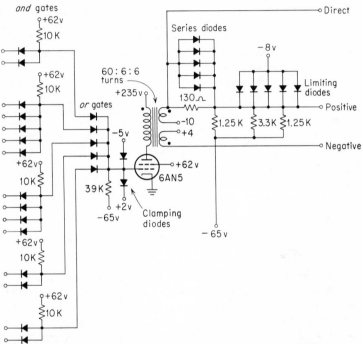

FIG. 5-18   NBS diode logic circuit using a vacuum-tube pulse amplifier.

diodes whatever current is necessary to hold the potential of the *and* gate down to about −8 volts. Only when all inputs to a gate go positive simultaneously should the 10-kilohm resistor be permitted to pull up the output voltage of the gate and (through conduction of its *or*-gate diode) to transmit a positive pulse to the grid. When some but not all of the inputs to an *and* gate are pulsed, the remaining unpulsed inputs must suddenly accept with little change in voltage a different proportion of the current supplied by the 10-kilohm resistor. Consequently, the source must have a low dynamic output impedance. A tube with a transformer does not provide such a low impedance; when not pulsed, this combination may present as much as 300 ohms impedance at 1 Mc. The required low dynamic impedance is achieved by the forward conductance of the −8-volt limiting diodes.

The output terminal of a stage may drive a number of paralleled *and* gates which are part of several succeeding stages. To keep these *and* gates conducting, even when all other sources pulse the other *and* gates of the succeeding stages, the pulldown resistors that return to −65 volts must draw more current than can be supplied by the 10-kilohm resistors connected to the *and* gates of the succeeding stages. Because the positive pulse secondary of the transformer returns to −10 volts, the series diodes in parallel with the 130-ohm resistor are cut off so that none of the pulse current remains in the transformer. When the tube is turned on, a 20-volt pulse appears at the secondary of the transformer. The series diodes conduct, and the transformer supplies the current taken by the pulldown resistors to −65 volts. Three pulldown resistors are provided to permit adjusting the load on the positive output to the number of *and* gates actually driven. Each 1.25-kilohm resistor can hold down five gates, and the 3.3-kilohm resistor can hold down two. The rest of the rated driving capacity can be used at the negative and direct outputs. One of the 1.25-kilohm resistors is permanently connected to ensure that there will be at least enough load to prevent excessive screen dissipation. The 130-ohm resistor adds no load during a pulse, but it provides somewhat less than critical damping for the negative-going transient that follows a pulse. The combination of the 130-ohm damping resistor and the permanently

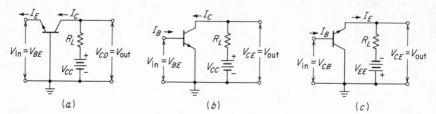

FIG. 5-19   Three configurations for connecting an *n-p-n* transistor. (*a*) Common base; (*b*) common emitter; (*c*) common collector.

connected 1.25-kilohm resistor is sufficient to prevent the underdamped transient from going above −8 volts. Inhibiting an *and* gate is accomplished by connecting the negative output terminal directly to an input diode of the gate. This diode is normally nonconducting and does not affect the operation of the gate, because the negative winding returns to +4 volts. Whenever a negative output pulse is applied to this diode, it becomes the most negative input to the gate and by conducting prevents any positive output of the *and* gate. An inhibiting connection does not necessarily have to be preceded by an *or* gate, because the connection carries current only during a pulse—when the tube and transformer present a very low impedance.

5-5   *Switching Properties of Junction Transistors*

A junction transistor comprises three elements—emitter, base, and collector—separated by two transition regions known as *p-n junctions*. Three basic configurations connect the input and output circuits, the common base, common emitter, and common collector; they are shown in Fig. 5-19. In this figure the direction of currents and the polarity of biasing voltages are for *n-p-n* transistors; they should be reversed for *p-n-p* transistors.

Three Operating Regions.   Static collector characteristics for an *n-p-n* transistor in the common-emitter configuration are shown in Fig. 5-20. It is a plot of the collector-to-emitter voltage V_{CE} against the collector current I_C with the input base current I_B as the parameter. The transistor can operate in one of three distinct regions shown in the plot, as determined by controlling the input base current.

In region I, both collector and emitter junctions are reverse-biased, and the transistor is cut off; the impedance from collector to emitter is very high. Region II is the active region: the emitter is forward-biased, and the collector is reverse-biased; the characteristics are rather linear, and the transistor conducts. In region III, both collector and emitter are forward-biased; the transistor is said to be *in saturation*, and the impedance from collector to emitter is very low.

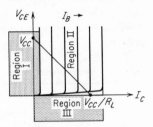

FIG. 5-20   An *n-p-n* collector characteristic in the common-emitter configuration.

The junction transistor can be used as a switch; it is open or closed when operated in regions *I* and III, respectively. When the transistor is cut off, the collector current has a leakage current I_{CO} of a few microamperes; when it is in saturation, the collector-to-emitter voltage V_{CES}, called the *saturation voltage drop*, is a few tenths of a volt. These two quantities are important characteristics of the transistor as a switching element.

Other important quantities are α and β, respectively the common-base current gain and common-emitter current gain at a given operating point,

$$\alpha = \left(\frac{\Delta I_C}{\Delta I_E}\right)_{V_C=\text{const}} \tag{5-7}$$

$$\beta = \left(\frac{\Delta I_C}{\Delta I_B}\right)_{V_C=\text{const}} \tag{5-8}$$

where ΔI_C, ΔI_E, and ΔI_B are the incremental collector, emitter, and base currents, respectively. The ratio of d-c collector current to d-c emitter current at a given operating point is called the d-c α. The relation of α to β is expressed in the equality

$$\beta = \frac{\alpha}{1 - \alpha} \tag{5-9}$$

Large values of α and β are desirable. For most transistors, α ranges from 0.9 to 0.99 and β from 10 to 100.

Large-signal Properties.   Large-signal properties of the three configurations are summarized in Table 5-5 [21]. The current relations have been derived by Ebers and Moll [8], where I_C, I_E, and I_B are the collector, emitter, and base currents, respectively; and I_{CO} is the collector cutoff current. I_{CO} is a leakage current and should preferably be very small. The common-emitter configuration exhibits both voltage and current gain as well as inversion; hence it is the most widely used configuration.

When the transistor is cut off, collector current I_C in the common-emitter configuration should be as low as possible. If the base current is zero (open base), the collector current is

$$I_C = \frac{I_{CO}}{1 - \alpha} \qquad (5\text{-}10)$$

This is obtained by substituting I_B equal to zero in the common-emitter current equation in Table 5-5. Assume that α is 0.9; then I_C is $10 \times I_{CO}$; the collector current is many times the leakage current I_{CO} and is too high to be desired. If the base current is $-I_{CO}$ (supplying a reverse current with a magnitude equal to I_{CO} to the base of p-n-p transistor), then we have $I_C \cong I_{CO}$. Therefore, when the transistor is being turned off, a small base current is made to flow in the reverse direction by applying a reverse bias to the base-emitter junction as indicated in Table 5-5.

Table 5-5   Large-signal Properties of Junction Transistors

Configuration	Common base	Common emitter	Common collector
Region II current......	$I_C = \alpha I_E + I_{CO}$	$I_C = (\alpha I_B + I_{CO})/(1-\alpha)$	$I_E = (I_B + I_{CO})/(1-\alpha)$
Current gain..........	$\alpha < 1$	$\alpha/(1-\alpha) > 1$	$1/(1-\alpha) > 1$
Voltage gain..........	>1	>1	≤ 1
Input voltage† to hold on............	$-\frac{1}{4}$ volt for Ge $-\frac{1}{4}$ volt for Si	$\frac{1}{4}$ volt for Ge $\frac{3}{4}$ volt for Si	$\frac{1}{4}$ volt for Ge $\frac{3}{4}$ volt for Si
Input voltage† to hold off............	0 volt	0 to -0.1 volt	V_{CC}
Inversion.............	No inversion	Inversion	No inversion

† Approximate voltage for n-p-n transistors.

Input and output voltage levels for switching a transistor between the cutoff and saturation states are shown in Fig. 5-21 [21]. In this figure the voltage levels are shown for the three configurations—for both p-n-p and n-p-n transistors. These voltage levels are those which appear directly at the transistor terminals. The symbols V_R and V_F represent the reverse and the forward biases at the base-emitter junction, and V_S is the reverse bias voltage which will appear across the base-collector junction if the transistor is not allowed to saturate.

Switching Time.   Analysis of the switching time of junction transistors has been made by Moll [9] and extended by Easley to include the effect of collector capacitance. Only the common-emitter configuration will be discussed here.

A transistor can be switched by applying a current pulse to the base. The waveforms when the transistor is switched from the cutoff condition to saturation and then from saturation to cutoff are shown in Fig. 5-22. I_{BS} and I_{CS} are the base and collector currents when the transistor is in saturation, and I_{BO} is the base current when the transistor is off. The time t_0 is the rise time, t_1 the delay time, and t_2 the fall time. The peak collector current I_{CS} is approximately equal to V_{CC}/R_L as the transistor is driven to saturation.

It has been shown [9,21] that rise time t_0 is

$$t_0 = \frac{1}{(1-\alpha)\omega_t} \ln \left(1 - 0.9 \frac{1-\alpha}{\alpha} \frac{I_{CS}}{I_{BS}} \right)^{-1} \qquad (5\text{-}11)$$

where

$$\omega_t = \frac{\omega_c}{1 + \omega_c R_L C_c} \qquad (5\text{-}12)$$

where ω_c is the α cutoff frequency in radians per second and C_c is the collector junction capacitance. The above relation is plotted in Fig. 5-23, which shows that rise time can be reduced by decreasing the actual circuit gain I_{CS}/I_{BS} and by increasing α and ω_t. ω_t can be made close to ω_c if the circuit is operated at a low impedance level; this also causes the rise time to be little affected by varia-

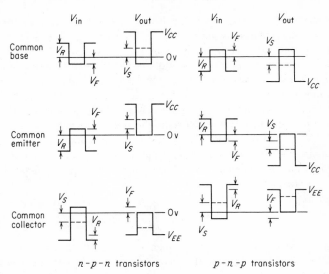

FIG. 5-21   Input and output waveforms of *n-p-n* and *p-n-p* transistor switches.

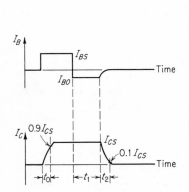

FIG. 5-22   Transient response of an *n-p-n* transistor in the common-emitter configuration.

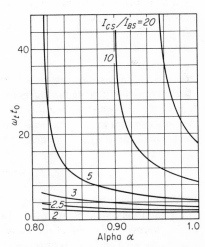

FIG. 5-23   Rise-time characteristic.

tions of α. If the circuit gain is small compared with $\alpha/(1 - \alpha)$, the rise time can be approximated as follows:

$$t_0 \cong \frac{0.9I_{CS}}{I_{BS}} \frac{1 + \omega_c R_L C_c}{\omega_c} \qquad (5\text{-}13)$$

This relation represents the nearly straight lines in Fig. 5-23 when $\omega_t t_0$ is about 5 or less.

It has also been shown that the fall time t_2 is

$$t_2 = \frac{1}{(1 - \alpha)\omega_t} \ln \frac{I_{CS}/I_{BO} - \alpha/(1 - \alpha)}{0.1\ I_{CS}/I_{BO} - \alpha/(1 - \alpha)} \tag{5-14}$$

A plot of the above relation is similar to that in Fig. 5-23 with the forward current gain I_{CS}/I_{BS} replaced by the reverse current gain $[I_{BO}/I_{CS} + (1 - \alpha)/\alpha]^{-1}$. Therefore, the fall time can be reduced, as was the rise time.

The delay time t_1 is due to the storage of the minority carrier (holes in the base of *p-n-p* and electrons in the *n-p-n* transistor). When a transistor is in saturation, minority carriers are emitted faster than they are collected and they become a surplus stored in the base region. When the transistor is being switched from the saturated state to the cutoff state, the stored minority carriers have to be removed. This removal causes the delay time. To reduce switching time, nonsaturating circuits have been developed to prevent transistor saturation.

Switching time depends on α, which—in turn—is frequency-dependent. α is usually approximated by the relation

$$\alpha = \frac{\alpha_0}{1 + j\omega/2\pi f_{co}} \tag{5-15}$$

where α_0 is the α at a very low frequency and f_{co} is the α *cutoff frequency*. Thus, the α cutoff frequency is the frequency at which α is equal to $0.707\alpha_0$. Another frequency, the *maximum frequency of oscillation* $f_{os(max)}$, is sometimes used to indicate the frequency dependence of the transistor. The maximum frequency of oscillation is found by the relation

$$f_{os(max)} = \sqrt{\frac{\alpha_0 f_{co}}{8\pi r_b C_c}} \tag{5-16}$$

where r_b is the base-layer spreading resistance.

Power Dissipation and Breakdown Voltage. The total power dissipation P_s (in milliwatts) of a transistor is related to the junction temperature T_j (in degrees centigrade) and the ambient temperature T_a (in degrees centigrade) by the factor K (in degrees centigrade per milliwatts) as shown below:

$$P_s = \frac{T_j - T_a}{K} \tag{5-17}$$

If the operating junction temperature is at its maximum, the resulting calculation is the total maximum power dissipation. The K factor, which may be regarded as the thermal resistance of the transistor, depends not only on the transistor but also on the package and environment.

Maximum allowable collector and emitter voltages are generally limited by avalanche breakdown. These maxima are called the *breakdown voltages* BV_{CBO} and BV_{EBO}. The breakdown condition itself is seldom destructive, but the resulting high collector dissipation is harmful.

Temperature Effects. Because of the nature of the semiconductor, many transistor parameters are temperature-dependent. An upper limit on the temperature is imposed by the semiconductor's tending to act as a conductor, while a lower limit is set by the opposing tendency to act as an insulator. The upper limit may exceed $85°C$ for germanium transistors and $150°C$ for silicon transistors. At too high a junction temperature, known as runaway temperature, the transistor may heat itself regeneratively until it destroys itself. The lower limit for germanium transistors approaches $-150°C$; the current gain, however, of most transistors drops to 50 per cent from its $25°C$ value when the junction temperature reaches $-55°C$.

Collector cutoff current I_{CO} very nearly doubles with every $6°C$ rise in junction temperature for silicon transistors and every $10°C$ rise for germanium transistors. The variation of I_{CO} causes an undesired variation of collector voltage in the off state of the transistor switch, because when the base is reverse-biased to keep the collector cutoff current to its lowest value, the base bias increases with the temperature and has to be designed for the highest operating temperature. The variation of current gain at high temperatures is also significant; it decreases with the decrease of ambient temperature in the silicon transistor and, to a lesser extent, in the germanium transistor.

5-6 Resistance-coupled Transistor Logic (RCTL) Circuits [19]

Resistance-coupled transistor logic circuits derive from two basic transistor circuits, the inverter and emitter follower. We first describe these two circuits and then their logic circuits.

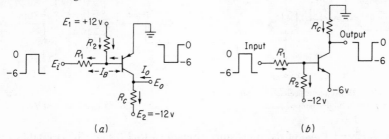

FIG. 5-24 Resistance-coupled transistor inverters. (*a*) *p-n-p* transistor; (*b*) *n-p-n* transistor.

Inverter. A *p-n-p* transistor inverter is shown in Fig. 5-24*a*. The input and output voltage levels are preferably the same. Assume that the two levels are 0 and -6 volts. The circuit parameters are so chosen that the input voltage E_i can switch the transistor on and off and the output voltage can deliver a load current I_o at the selected level E_o. When the transistor is on, the input circuit consisting of resistors R_1 and R_2 and supply voltage E_1 should be able to draw the required base current I_{BS} from the transistor, or

$$I_{BS} \leq \frac{V_{BES} - E_i}{R_1} - \frac{E_1 - V_{BES}}{R_2} \qquad (5\text{-}18)$$

where V_{BES} is the base-to-emitter saturation voltage. Furthermore, the output draws the desired load current $I_{o(on)}$,

$$I_{o(on)} = \frac{V_{CES} - E_2}{R_c} - I_{CS} \qquad (5\text{-}19)$$

$$E_{o(on)} = V_{CES}$$

where V_{CES} is the saturation voltage drop and I_{CS} is the saturated collector current.

When the transistor is off, the input circuit should be able to supply the required base current I_{BO} to the off transistor:

$$I_{BO} \leq \frac{E_1 - V_{BEO}}{R_2} - \frac{V_{BEO} - E_i}{R_1} \qquad (5\text{-}20)$$

where V_{BEO} is the emitter-to-base voltage at the cutoff condition. In addition, the output can draw the desired load current $I_{o(\text{off})}$,

$$I_{o(\text{off})} = \frac{V_{CEO} - E_2}{R_c} - I_{CO}$$

$$E_{o(\text{off})} = V_{CEO} \qquad (5\text{-}21)$$

where V_{CEO} is the collector-to-emitter voltage at the cutoff condition and I_{CO} the collector cutoff current. Relations (5-18) and (5-20) establish, respectively, the turn-on condition and the turn-off condition by using the proper values of I_{BS},

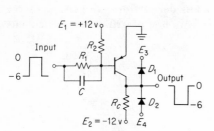

FIG. 5-25   Resistance-capacitance-coupled *p-n-p* inverter with a diode-clamped load.

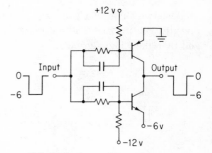

FIG. 5-26   A complemented inverter.

V_{BS}, I_{BO}, and V_{BEO} of the transistor. Relations (5-19) and (5-21) establish the required load current and voltages. An *n-p-n* transistor inverter is shown in Fig. 5-24*b*; its operation is similar.

When the transistor is on, it is operated in saturation. There are several reasons for using saturating circuits. Among them are simplicity of circuit design, better-defined on level or off level at the collector, lower transistor dissipation during conducting, and immunity to stray voltage pulses. However, the major disadvantage is that, when the transistor is driven deep into saturation, the turn-off time is increased owing to the delay time from minority carrier storage.

The switching time can be reduced by shunting resistance R_1 with a capacitor C_1 as shown in Fig. 5-25. The capacitor provides the overdrive current during the turn-on and turn-off time. It is possible to increase the operating speed by a factor of 3 or more, but the noise of the circuit is thereby increased.

Another scheme to increase the operating speed is to use a diode-clamped load, also shown in Fig. 5-25. The transistor is prevented from going into saturation if the collector is clamped by diode D_1 at a voltage E_3 (say, $-\frac{1}{2}$ volt) whose magnitude is larger than the saturation voltage drop. If the collector is also clamped by another diode D_2 at the off-state level (say, $E_4 = -6$ volt), this level becomes well defined; and the fall time is reduced because the load discharges toward -12 volts, but the discharge stops at the off-state level.

When one *p-n-p* inverter and one *n-p-n* inverter are connected as shown in Fig. 5-26, the arrangement is called a *complemented* inverter. When the input is negative-going, the *p-n-p* transistor is turned on, but the *n-p-n* transistor is turned on when the input is positive-going. These two transistors act in a push-pull manner to provide a positive drive at the output. Since no load resistor is needed at the output except the load being driven, all output current is available for driving the load itself.

Emitter Follower. Figure 5-27 shows a *p-n-p* and an *n-p-n* emitter follower. The transistor, operated in the active region, is conducting (except during a certain transient condition). Emitter output voltage at the *p-n-p* transistor is slightly positive with respect to the input signal at the base because of the emitter-base diode drop, but the dividers R_1 and R_2 compensate for this drop by slightly shifting the input level. An emitter follower has the properties of a voltage gain of less than 1, a large current gain, no inversion, and a low output impedance of tens of ohms at large signals.

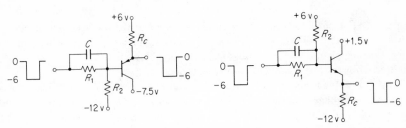

FIG. 5-27   *p-n-p* and *n-p-n* emitter followers.

An emitter follower is often used to drive a capacitive load. When the input goes positive, the *p-n-p* emitter follower is driven temporarily to cutoff because the rise time at the input is shorter than that at the load. The cutoff condition continues until the load capacitance is charged to the input level through the collector resistor.

A single emitter is unable to drive in both directions. This can be overcome by using the complemented emitter follower shown in Fig. 5-28. When the input goes negative, the *n-p-n* follower is cut off and the *p-n-p* follower draws current from the load. When the input goes positive, the *p-n-p* follower is cut off and the *n-p-n* follower conducts and supplies current to the load. The complemented emitter follower is a power driver commonly used to drive a large load.

In using the emitter follower, oscillations of large overshoots on the output waveform frequently arise because negative resistance occurs under certain conditions owing to the feedback from the capacitive load on the output. This can be damped by using a resistor larger than the negative resistance, in series with either the base

FIG. 5-28   A complemented emitter follower.

or the emitter. The oscillation problem of emitter followers makes them difficult to design; thus, emitter-follower logic circuits are less preferable than inverter logic circuits.

Emitter-follower Logic Circuits. Resistance-coupled transistor circuits are much like vacuum-tube logic circuits. However, there are two types of transistors (*p-n-p* and *n-p-n*) which are complementary to each other. If two *p-n-p* emitter followers are connected with a common-emitter resistor as shown in Fig. 5-29, the output becomes positive only when both inputs *A* and *B* are positive. If one or both inputs are negative, one or both transistors conduct and the output remains

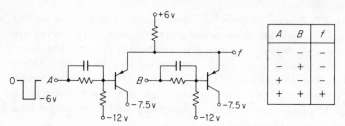

A	B	f
−	−	−
−	+	−
+	−	−
+	+	+

FIG. 5-29   *p-n-p* emitter-follower *and* circuit (positive logic).

negative. For positive logic this is an *and* circuit. If the *n-p-n* transistor emitter followers of Fig. 5-30 are used instead, the output is negative only when both inputs are negative. For positive logic this is a logical-*or* circuit. These two emitter followers are a pair of complementary circuits.

Logic circuits are commonly cascaded in a number of stages. As emitter followers have no voltage gain and there is a shift in the output voltage (which depends on the tolerances of the input network and of the transistor), there is a limit to the number of stages that can be cascaded. An inverter or a restoring circuit has to be employed to reestablish the proper signal level.

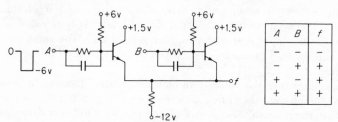

A	B	f
−	−	−
−	+	+
+	−	+
+	+	+

FIG. 5-30   *n-p-n* emitter-follower *or* circuit (positive logic).

Inverter Logic Circuits. If two *p-n-p* inverters are connected with a common-collector resistor as shown in Fig. 5-31, the output is negative only when both transistors are cut off; this occurs when both inputs are positive. For positive logic this is a logical-*nand* circuit. If *n-p-n* inverters are used instead, as shown in Fig. 5-32, the output is positive only when both transistors are cut off; this happens when both inputs are negative. For positive logic this is a logical-*nor* circuit. These two inverters are a pair of complementary circuits.

Instead of having the transistors connected in parallel they can be connected in series. When two *p-n-p* transistors and a collector resistor are connected in series as shown in Fig. 5-33, the output behaves like that shown in Fig. 5-32. For positive logic this is a logical-*nor* circuit. When *n-p-n* transistors are used instead, as shown in Fig. 5-34, the output behaves like that shown in Fig. 5-31. For positive logic this is a logical-*nand* circuit. These two serial circuits are again a pair of complements.

It is possible in any of the above circuits to have more than two transistors in parallel or in series.

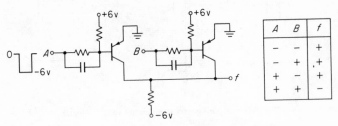

A	B	f
–	–	+
–	+	,+
+	–	+
+	+	–

FIG. 5-31 *p-n-p* inverter *nand* circuit (positive logic).

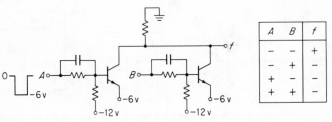

A	B	f
–	–	+
–	+	–
+	–	–
+	+	–

FIG. 5-32 *n-p-n* inverter *nor* circuit (positive logic).

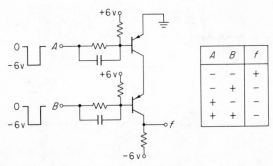

A	B	f
–	–	+
–	+	–
+	–	–
+	+	–

FIG. 5-33 *p-n-p* inverter *nor* circuit (positive logic).

Other RCTL Circuits. If a *p-n-p* emitter follower and an *n-p-n* inverter are connected to a common resistor as shown in Fig. 5-35, the output is positive only when both transistors are cut off. This occurs when the input is positive to the emitter follower and negative to the inverter. For positive logic this is a logical-*andnot-B* circuit. Interchanging *A* and *B* establishes a logical-*andnot-A* circuit.

The complementary version of the above circuit is shown in Fig. 5-36. This circuit uses an *n-p-n* emitter follower and a *p-n-p* inverter. The output is negative only when both transistors are cut off; this occurs when the input to the emitter follower is negative and that to the inverter is positive. For positive logic this is a logical-*ornot-B* circuit. When the inputs *A* and *B* are interchanged, the arrangement becomes a logical-*ornot-A* circuit.

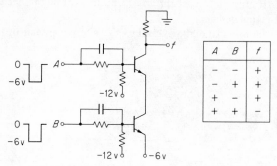

A	B	f
−	−	+
−	+	+
+	−	+
+	+	−

FIG. 5-34   *n-p-n* inverter *nand* circuit (positive logic).

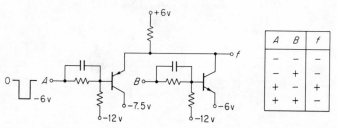

A	B	f
−	−	−
−	+	−
+	−	+
+	+	−

FIG. 5-35   *andnot-B* circuit using *p-n-p* emitter follower and *n-p-n* inverter (positive logic).

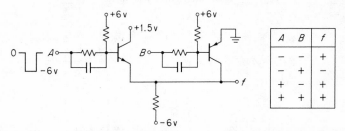

A	B	f
−	−	+
−	+	−
+	−	+
+	+	+

FIG. 5-36   *ornot-B* circuit using *n-p-n* emitter follower and *p-n-p* inverter (positive logic).

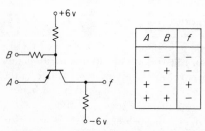

A	B	f
−	−	−
−	+	−
+	−	+
+	+	−

FIG. 5-37   Single-transistor *andnot-B* circuit (positive logic).

The logical-*andnot-B* circuit (for positive logic) can be achieved by using a single transistor as shown in Fig. 5-37. In this circuit the output is positive only when the transistor is in saturation. This occurs when the input to the emitter is positive and when the input to the base is negative.

If two such circuits are cross-coupled as shown in Fig. 5-38, the output can be positive when either transistor is in saturation. This occurs either when input A is positive and input B negative or when input A is negative and input B positive. When the two inputs are either both positive or both negative, both transistors are cut off and the output is negative. Thus, this is an *exclusive-or* circuit for positive logic. The disadvantage of this circuit is that the emitters must be driven and there is no current gain.

Methods of Preventing Saturation. For faster switching speed the transistor is prevented from going into saturation, minority carrier storage time being thus avoided. One method of preventing saturation uses the diode clamp, as is shown in Fig. 5-25. Another method utilizes nonlinear feedback to divide the

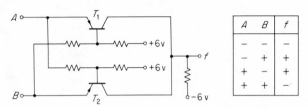

A	B	f
−	−	−
−	+	+
+	−	+
+	+	−

FIG. 5-38   Two-transistor exclusive-*or* circuit (positive logic).

input base resistor into two resistors, as shown in Fig. 5-39. When the input goes negative, the collector voltage goes more positive until the diode conducts and clamps the base to prevent any further increase in base and collector currents. Since the current in the base is much smaller than that in the collector, the minority carrier storage is less in the diode than in the transistor. A third method is known as *back clamping* (Fig. 5-40). A silicon diode D_1 is inserted in the base lead, and a germanium diode D_2 is connected to the collector. The silicon diode has a threshold voltage of 0.7 volt; the germanium diode, of 0.2 volt. When the base is driven negative, the emitter junction diode and the silicon diode are in series and a potential of 0.7 volt is established at the junction of the

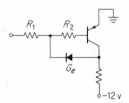

FIG. 5-39   Nonlinear feedback for preventing saturation.

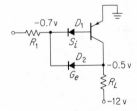

FIG. 5-40   Back clamping in preventing saturation.

two diodes. This prevents the collector from becoming more positive than $-0.7 + 0.2$, or -0.5, volt with respect to the emitter.

5-7   Transistor Flipflops

A symmetric *p-n-p* transistor flipflop of the Eccles-Jordan type is shown in Fig. 5-41. This circuit configuration is similar to that of the vacuum-tube flipflop, with the tubes replaced by transistors. When transistor T_1 is conducting, T_2 is cut off; this is taken as state 1. When transistor T_2 is conducting, T_1 is cut off;

this is taken as state 0, the state shown in the figure. There are two output voltages V_{c1} and V_{c2}, which are the collector voltages of the transistors at cutoff and at saturation, respectively.

D-C Stability [12]. The circuit of Fig. 5-41 is in a steady-state condition; thus, the capacitors can be disregarded. In this figure, T_1 is cut off, and T_2 is in saturation. Assume that no current flows in the off transistor; therefore, the

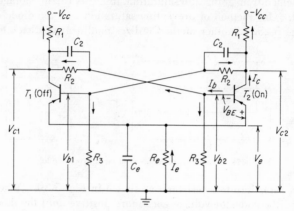

FIG. 5-41   A symmetric *p-n-p* transistor flipflop.

three terminals of T_1 can be regarded as being isolated. The known relations among the collector, base, and emitter currents I_C, I_B, and I_E are

$$I_B = I_E(1 - \alpha) \tag{5-22}$$

$$I_C = \alpha I_E \tag{5-23}$$

The base current I_B of the conducting transistor T_2 is

$$I_B = \frac{V_{b2}}{R_3} + \frac{V_{b2} + V_{cc}}{R_1 + R_2}$$

which can be rewritten into

$$V_{b2} = \frac{I_E(1 - \alpha)R_3(R_1 + R_2) - V_{cc}R_3}{R_1 + R_2 + R_3} \tag{5-24}$$

The collector current I_C of T_2 is

$$I_C = \frac{V_{c2}}{R_2 + R_3} + \frac{V_{c2} + V_{cc}}{R_1}$$

or $$V_{c2} = \frac{I_C R_1(R_2 + R_3) - V_{cc}(R_2 + R_3)}{R_1 + R_2 + R_3} \tag{5-25}$$

From the coupling network between the collector of the conducting transistor T_2 and the base of the off transistor T_1, we have

$$\frac{V_{c2} - V_{b1}}{R_2} = \frac{V_{b1}}{R_3}$$

which can be rewritten as

$$V_{b1} = \frac{\alpha I_E R_1 R_3 - V_{cc} R_3}{R_1 + R_2 + R_3} \qquad (5\text{-}26)$$

From the resistance network between the collector of the cutoff transistor T_1 and the base of the conducting transistor T_1, we have

$$\frac{V_{c1} + V_{cc}}{R_1} = \frac{V_{b2} - V_{c1}}{R_2}$$

which can evolve into

$$V_{c1} = \frac{I_B R_1 R_3 - V_{cc}(R_2 + R_3)}{R_1 + R_2 + R_3} \qquad (5\text{-}27)$$

Emitter voltage V_E bears the following relation to emitter current I_E and the base voltage V_{b2}:

$$V_E = -I_E R_e = V_{b2} - V_{BE} \qquad (5\text{-}28)$$

where V_{BE} is the base-to-emitter voltage of the saturating transistor T_2. By using (5-24) and simplifying, the emitter current I_E in (5-28) becomes

$$I_E = \left(\frac{V_{cc} R_3}{R_1 + R_2 + R_3} + V_{BE} \right) \div \left[R_e + \frac{(1 - \alpha) R_3 (R_1 + R_2)}{R_1 + R_2 + R_3} \right] \qquad (5\text{-}29)$$

Since V_{BE} is about 0.2 volt for germanium transistors and 0.7 volt for silicon transistors, it is small in comparison with V_{b2}.

The d-c stability of a flipflop requires that the transistor T_1 remain cut off. This means that base voltage V_{b1} must be more positive than emitter voltage V_E. The d-c stability also requires that transistor T_2 remain conducting. This means that the base voltage V_{b2} must be more negative than V_E. Thus, for the two stable states, the condition for d-c stability is

$$V_{b1} > V_E > V_{b2} \qquad (5\text{-}30)$$

By using (5-24) and (5-26), we obtain, for the first stability condition $V_{b1} > V_{b2}$,

$$\frac{-V_{cc} R_3 + \alpha I_E R_1 R_3}{R_1 + R_2 + R_3} > \frac{-V_{cc} R_3 + I_E (1 - \alpha) R_3 (R_1 + R_2)}{R_1 + R_2 + R_3}$$

which becomes after simplification

$$\frac{R_2}{R_1} < \frac{2\alpha - 1}{1 - \alpha}$$

If the minimum value of α (or rather a value slightly lower than this value) is used, we have

$$\frac{R_2}{R_1} = \frac{2\alpha_{\min} - 1}{1 - \alpha_{\min}} \qquad (5\text{-}31)$$

which represents one condition for d-c stability. Since α is slightly less than 1, the quantity $(2\alpha - 1)/(1 - \alpha)$ increases with α and is equal to 4 for $\alpha = 0.83$. Since $\alpha = 0.83$ is fairly low for currently available transistors, the resistance R_2 would be as much as four times larger than the resistance R_1.

Examining the stability condition (5-30) reveals the other stability condition to be $V_E > V_{b2}$. Relation (5-28) shows this condition fulfilled [note that V_E, V_{b2}, and V_{BE} in (5-28) are all negative quantities], although only by a small margin owing to V_{BE} being small. If a resistance is connected in series with the base terminal, a larger margin for this stability can be achieved.

The output voltage swing ΔV is the difference between the collector voltages when the transistor is on and off,

$$\Delta V = V_{c2} - V_{c1} \tag{5-32}$$

Substituting (5-27) and (5-25) into the above, we have the output voltage swing

$$\Delta V = \frac{I_{CS}R_1(R_2 + R_3) - I_{BS}R_1R_3}{R_1 + R_2 + R_3} \tag{5-33}$$

The procedure to design the flipflop in the steady-state condition may now be formulated by using the five relations (5-22), (5-23), (5-29), (5-31), and (5-33). These five relations involve 10 quantities: R_1, R_2, R_3, R_e, α, I_e, I_b, I_c, ΔV, and V_{cc} (V_{BE} and α_{min}, which are known, being excluded). When 5 of the 10 quantities are chosen, the others can be calculated. The calculation is not difficult but may be laborious. A check of transistor power dissipation should be made to ensure the calculated result within the rated value.

The above design procedure does not consider resistance tolerances, supply-voltage fluctuation, and variations of transistor characteristics. An exhaustive design should incorporate these factors into the above derivation. For such a design, the calculations are quite involved, and a digital computer is often resorted to.

Nonsaturated Mode. If it is desired to operate the transistor in a nonsaturated mode, the voltage V_{b2} must be equal to or less negative than the voltage V_{c2}, or

$$V_{b2} \geq V_{c2} \tag{5-34}$$

Since V_E is greater than V_{b2} as shown in (5-30), the above condition can be changed to

$$V_E \geq V_{c2} \tag{5-35}$$

By substituting (5-25) and (5-28) into this condition, we have

$$-I_ER_e \leq \frac{\alpha I_E R_1(R_2 + R_3) - V_{cc}(R_2 + R_3)}{R_1 + R_2 + R_3}$$

from which we obtain the maximum emitter current $I_{E(max)}$,

$$I_{E(max)} \geq \frac{V_{cc}(R_2 + R_3)}{R_1 + R_2 + R_3} \div \left[R_e + \frac{\alpha R_1(R_2 + R_3)}{R_1 + R_2 + R_3} \right] \tag{5-36}$$

Maximum emitter current decreases with the increase of α, while operating emitter current I_E [(5-29)] increases with the increase of α. Furthermore, operating emitter current should be less than maximum emitter current for $\alpha < 1$. To achieve this condition, certain relations should be established. First, we calculate emitter current [(5-29)] by using $\alpha = 1$. This emitter current will be at its highest value, while the maximum emitter current [(5-36)] calculated by using $\alpha = 1$ will be at its lowest value. Then, if we require these two currents to be equal, we shall meet the requirements that operating emitter current will always be less than maximum emitter current for all values of $\alpha < 1$. These relations will now be derived. Use $\alpha = 1$ in (5-29), and solve for the emitter resistance R_e; we then have

$$R_e = \frac{V_{cc}R_3}{I_E(R_1 + R_2 + R_3)} + \frac{V_{BE}}{I_E} \tag{5-37}$$

By substituting the above R_e into (5-36) and making $I_{E(\text{max})}$ equal to I_E we have, after simplification,

$$I_E R_1 R_3 = V_{cc}R_2 - I_E R_1 R_2 - V_{BE}(R_1 + R_2 + R_3) \tag{5-38}$$

In this relation, the last term involving V_{BE} seems small in comparison with other terms; thus, this term may be neglected in the interests of obtaining a simpler result. We then have

$$R_3 = \frac{V_{cc}R_2}{I_E R_1} - R_2 \tag{5-39}$$

Relations (5-37) and (5-39) are the conditions to operate the transistor in a non-saturated mode.

The procedure to design a flipflop in the steady-state condition with the transistors in a nonsaturated mode may now be formulated by using relations (5-22), (5-23), (5-31), (5-33), (5-37), and (5-39). These six relations again include 10 quantities: R_1, R_2, R_3, R_e, α, V, I_C, I_B, I_E, and V_{cc} (V_{BE} and $\alpha_{\min}$, which are known, being excluded). When 4 of the 10 quantities are chosen, the others can be calculated.

Triggering. To change the flipflop from one stable state to the other, a triggering pulse is applied. The triggering pulse merely initiates the switching process, usually through a coupling capacitor. For transistor circuits the value of this capacitor lies between 5 and 5,000 $\mu\mu f$, depending on the frequency. The low-frequency transistor operated in a saturated mode requires a larger capacitance, while the high-frequency transistor operated in a nonsaturated mode requires a smaller capacitance. If the transistor is operated in a saturated mode, the switching process will be delayed by the minority carrier storage.

The switching process can be initiated by triggering the off transistor on or by triggering the on transistor off. For *p-n-p* transistors the appropriate triggering pulses are a negative pulse at the base of the off transistor, a positive pulse at the base of the on transistor, a negative pulse at the collector of the on transistor, or a positive pulse at the collector of the off transistor. For *n-p-n* transistors the appropriate triggering pulses are a positive pulse at the off base, a negative pulse at the on base, a positive pulse at the on collector, or a negative pulse at the off collector.

In the selection of a triggering location in the circuit, factors to be considered are pulse polarity, loading on the triggering-pulse source, and initial change of direction of the charge on the coupling capacitor. The choice of the pulse polarity is related to the pulse availability and pulse (or voltage-level) representation of the logic circuits. In general, triggering the off transistor on is preferable because of the smaller loading on the pulse source; triggering the on transistor off causes the pulse source to be heavily loaded. Triggering at the base of the transistor tends initially to decrease the charge on the coupling capacitor connecting the off base to the on collector, whereas an increase is more compatible with the final steady-state potentials of the circuit. Thus, triggering at the collector is preferable because of the change of the charge direction of the coupling capacitor.

The triggering pulse should have sufficient amplitude and duration. The amplitude should be large enough to trigger the transistor either on or off. The duration should be long enough to sustain the change of the state after triggering occurs, despite the storage delay due to saturation. Thus, the pulse duration should be as long as the switching time. The requirements for pulse amplitude and duration are more severe for the t type of input than for the r or s type of input. For the r or s type of input, a too large and too long triggering pulse is not harmful. For a t type of input, a long pulse may cause the flipflop circuit to flip again; a too large amplitude may spoil the directivity of the input diode network.

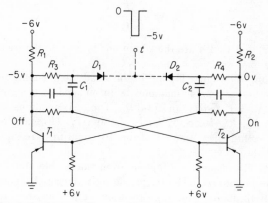

FIG. 5-42   Diode input steering circuit of a *p-n-p* transistor flipflop.

As with the vacuum-tube flipflop, crystal diodes are used in transistor triggering networks for the purpose of isolation or steering. A device often used is the resistance-gated-diode steering circuit illustrated in Figs. 5-42 and 5-43. In the first schematic (Fig. 5-42) transistor T_1 is off, with its collector voltage at about -5 volts, while transistor T_2 is on, with its collector voltage nearly at 0. Resistors R_3 and R_4 are the sensing resistors, which sense the collector voltage and thus sense the state of the flipflop. The sensing resistors are cross-coupled so that diode D_2 is near to conduction and D_1 is back-biased. When the input signal goes negative, D_2 conducts and transistor T_1 is turned on through coupling capacitor C_2. A single trigger input can be formed by connecting the two input diodes together as shown by the dashed lines. The circuit of Fig. 5-43 uses a capacitor-input steering circuit. In this figure the locations of the gating diodes and the capacitors have been changed. Instead of a negative-going input pulse, the circuit will now be triggered by a positive-going input pulse. Transistor T_1 is off, while T_2 is on. Diode D_2 is almost forward-biased by sensing resistor R_4, while diode D_1 is back-biased by sensing resistor R_3. When the input signal goes positive, the pulse goes through C_2 and D_2 and turns off the on transistor T_2. A single trigger input can be formed by connecting the two input capacitors as shown by the dashed lines.

Nonsaturated Transistor Flipflops. Minority carrier storage delay of a saturated transistor may be avoided by proper circuit design, as described previously. Several methods employ crystal diodes to prevent saturation. One such method clamps the collector of the conducting transistor to a supply voltage

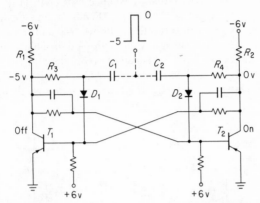

FIG. 5-43 Capacity input steering circuit of a *p-n-p* transistor flipflop.

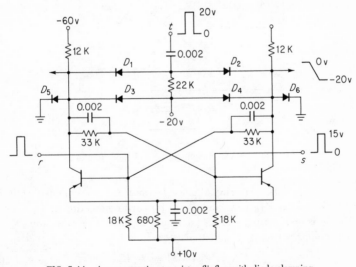

FIG. 5-44 A nonsaturating transistor flipflop with diode clamping.

at a level above that at the base, as shown in Fig. 5-44. In this circuit, when the transistor conducts, its collector is clamped by diodes D_5 and D_6 to the ground. Since available diodes have a smaller storage delay, a substantial improvement in switching time may result.

A second method uses nonlinear diode feedback from collector to base, as previously shown in Fig. 5-39. An *n-p-n* transistor flipflop circuit using nonlinear diode feedback by diodes D_1 and D_2 appears in Fig. 5-45. In this circuit, emitter followers T_3 and T_4 drive the cross-coupling networks to relieve the cross-coupling loading. When transistor T_2 is on and T_1 is off, the collector voltage of T_2 is maintained above its base potential by the amount of the voltage drop $I_B R_4$ less the forward voltage drop of diode D_2. As the base circuit is normally overdriven, saturation of T_2 is prevented as long as voltage drop $I_B R_4$ is larger than the forward voltage drop of diode D_2.

A third method uses a novel circuit developed by Linvill [14]. Consider first, however, the six-diode circuit of Fig. 5-44. Diodes D_5 and D_6 are used for low-voltage clamping to prevent saturation, diodes D_3 and D_4 for high-voltage clamping to make the output voltage swing highly predictable, and diodes D_1 and D_2 for steering the trigger input. Instead of six diodes, Linvill's flipflop circuit (Fig. 5-46) uses only four silicon diodes. In his circuit the coupling resistors are replaced by diodes D_3 and D_4, which are operated at all times in reverse

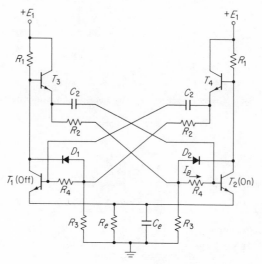

FIG. 5-45   A nonsaturating flipflop with diode feedback.

breakdown at V_1 volts. Steering diodes D_1 and D_2 are operated with D_2 in reverse breakdown at V_{TR} volts and D_1 in forward conduction at V_{TF} volts. In Fig. 5-46, T_2 is conducting, and T_1 is cut off; D_1 is at V_{TF} volts and D_2 at V_{TR} volts. The collector voltage V_{on} of transistor T_2 is

$$V_{\text{on}} = V_{\text{off}} - V_{TF} - V_{TR} \qquad (5\text{-}40)$$

where V_{off} is the collector voltage of T_1. The two base voltages V_{B1} and V_{B2} are

$$V_{B1} = V_{\text{off}} - V_{TF} - V_{TR} - V_1 \qquad (5\text{-}41)$$

$$V_{B2} = V_{\text{off}} - V_1 \qquad (5\text{-}42)$$

The condition for transistor T_2 being operated in a nonsaturated mode is

$$V_{\text{on}} > V_{B2} \qquad (5\text{-}43)$$

Using relations (5-40) and (5-42), we have

$$V_1 > V_{TF} + V_{TR} \qquad (5\text{-}44)$$

Thus we establish the condition governing operating voltages of diodes for a nonsaturating transistor mode. The output voltage swing is

$$V_{\text{off}} - V_{\text{on}} = V_{TF} + V_{TR} \qquad (5\text{-}45)$$

Since the voltages V_{TF} and V_{TR} are stable, the output voltages are predictable. These silicon diodes should be selected with matched breakdown characteristics.

A Complementary Transistor Flipflop. Figure 5-47 shows a saturated complementary current-demanded flipflop reported by Baker [15,20]. There are two *p-n-p* transistors T_1 and T_2 and two *n-p-n* transistors T_3 and T_4. As shown in the circuit, T_2 and T_3 are on, and T_1 and T_4 are off; this represents one state. When T_2 and T_3 are off and T_1 and T_4 are on, this represents the other state. The resistances R_b are the base resistances. There is no internal load resistance or collector resistance. Load resistances R_L are always connected almost

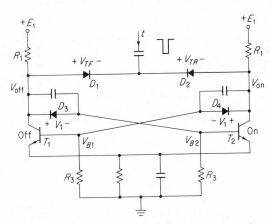

FIG. 5-46   A nonsaturating trigger flipflop using diode coupling.

directly through a conducting transistor to a fixed supply voltage. The two output voltage levels are nearly the supply voltages $-V_{cc}$ and $+V_{ee}$. As shown in the circuit, R_L at the right side is drawing current from supply voltage V_{ee} through transistor T_2, while a current is flowing through R_L at the left side to supply voltage $-V_{cc}$ through conducting transistor T_3.

The above circuit is designed for maximum energy-conversion efficiency and for minimum power drain. Essentially all the output current (collector current) is available to drive the load R_L. When there is no load, the required standby power is virtually only the dissipation in the base resistors. Both the high and low voltages are clamped, as the conducting *p-n-p* and *n-p-n* transistors are saturated. Circuit operation is less dependent on transistor parameters and can take larger resistor tolerances. The stability is rather insensitive to supply voltages. If the characteristics of the *p-n-p* transistors are matched with those of *n-p-n* transistors, the output waveform can be made nearly symmetrical because the conducting collector is not loaded by the base.

5-8   *Transistor-Diode Logic (TDL) Circuits*

In diode logic circuits, the transistor amplifier commonly restores the voltage level and provides the current gain for driving other levels. The transistor amplifier also performs an inversion. Transistor-diode logic circuits are small in size, fast in operation, and relatively inexpensive in cost; this explains their wide use.

A Transistor-Diode nor Circuit.   When diodes perform the *or* operation and a transistor the inversion, the combination results in a transistor-diode *nor*

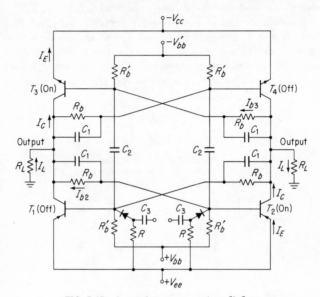

FIG. 5-47   A complementary transistor flipflop.
$$R_b = R_b' = 10 \text{ kilohms}$$
$$C_1 = 510 \ \mu f$$
$$C_2 = 0.022 \ \mu f$$
$$C_3 = 0.01 \ \mu f$$
$$-V_{cc} = -5 \text{ volts}$$
$$-V_{bb}' = -6.5 \text{ volts}$$
$$+V_{bb} = +6.5 \text{ volts}$$
$$+V_{ee} = +5 \text{ volts}$$

circuit (positive logic). Such a circuit is shown in Fig. 5-48. The diodes and resistor R_3 form the *or* circuit. Resistors R_1 and R_2 and capacitor C form the input to the transistor; the input circuit, similar to the RCTL circuit, provides proper voltage levels for switching the transistor. The transistor is cut off and the output low if one or more inputs to the diodes are high. When all inputs are low, the transistor is on and the output high. For positive logic, this is a *nor* circuit. If a diode *and* circuit and an *n-p-n* transistor are used instead, the resulting circuit, for positive logic, is a transistor-diode *nand* circuit.

A Transistor-Diode not and-or Circuit.   If a two-level diode *and-or* circuit is cascaded with a transistor amplifier, the resulting circuit is a transistor-diode *not and-or* circuit. One version of such a circuit is shown in Fig. 5-49 [7]. In this circuit, ground potential and -2 volts represent, respectively, the binary 1 and 0; this is a positive logic designation. The input diodes function as an *or* circuit and the output diodes as an *and* circuit. Transistor T_1 provides an inversion, and T_2 is an emitter follower for driving more diode circuits. The fan-in of this circuit is up to 6, and the fan-out is 8.

A Transistor-Diode Circuit Using Current Switching. Instead of using voltage switching in the previous two transistor-diode circuits, another approach

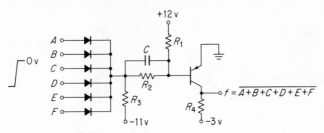

FIG. 5-48   A transistor-diode *nor* circuit (positive logic).

switches a current into or out of the base of the transistor by allowing the output voltage of a diode circuit to swing only a fraction of a volt.

In the circuit of Fig. 5-50, voltage E_1 and resistor R_1 form a current source; voltage E_2 and resistor R_2 form a current sink. When voltage V_1 is slightly more negative than voltage V_2 by an amount (say, -0.3 volt) determined by the base characteristic for a selected collector current, diode D_2 becomes back-biased; the current sink draws current from the transistor base, and the transistor is turned

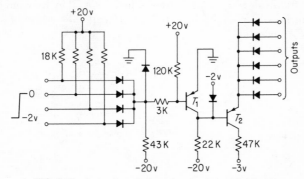

FIG. 5-49   A transistor-diode *and-or* circuit (positive logic).

on. When voltage V_1 is slightly more positive than the ground potential by an amount equal to the forward drop of diode D_2 (say, $+0.3$ volt), voltage V_2 is at ground; the current sink draws current through diode D_2, and the transistor is turned off. Therefore, with a voltage swing at V_1 between -0.3 to $+0.3$ volt, the transistor is turned on and off. Voltage V_1 may be more negative than -0.3 volt, but the succeeding turn-on time will be increased.

The voltage swing at V_1 can be provided by the current source formed by E_1 and R_1, together with a proper swing of input voltage E_i. When voltage E_i is sufficiently low, current I_{R1} is switched to flow through diode D_1 instead of through diode D_2; diode D_2 thus becomes disconnected, and the transistor is turned on. This is indicated by the solid-line current flow of Fig. 5-50, and voltage E_i must be -0.6 volt or lower to offset the forward drop of diode D_1. When voltage E_i is sufficiently high, current I_{R1} flows into diode D_2; voltage V_2 is raised to ground potential or to a slightly positive potential, and the transistor is turned off. This is indicated by the dashed-line current flow. The current source formed by E_1 and R_1 should be slightly larger than the current sink formed by E_2 and R_2 if voltage V_2 is to be raised to a slightly positive potential. In a positive

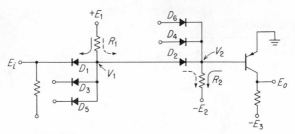

FIG. 5-50   A transistor diode using current switching.

logic, diodes D_1, D_3, and D_5 form an *and* circuit; diodes D_2, D_4, and D_6 form an *or* circuit. The transistor amplifier performs an inversion. Therefore, the circuit is a logical-*not and-or* circuit for positive logic.

5-9   Transistor-Resistor Logic (TRL) Circuits

Two basic transistor-resistor logic circuits, first reported by Row and Royer [24], are shown in Figs. 5-51 and 5-52. In these circuits, the resistors perform the

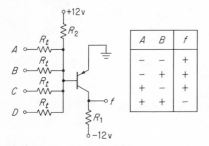

FIG. 5-51   Transistor-resistor *nor* circuit (negative logic).

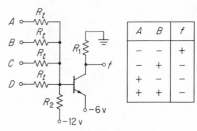

FIG. 5-52   Transistor-resistor *nand* circuit (negative logic).

logic operation, while the transistor is an inverter. The output voltage swing is designed to be the same as the input voltage swing so that they can be readily cascaded or branched out. Resistor R_t is called the *transfer* resistor because it is the output resistor of one stage as well as the input resistor of the succeeding stage. In Fig. 5-51, the transistor is cut off and the collector voltage negative when all input voltages are at ground potential (positive). If one or more inputs are negative, the transistor is turned on and the collector voltage grounded. For negative logic this is a *nor* circuit. In Fig. 5-52, the transistor is turned off and the collector voltage at the ground potential (positive) when all input voltages are negative. For negative logic this is a *nand* circuit.

The circuit in Fig. 5-51 must be so designed that when all preceding m stages are in saturation, this stage is cut off; also, when this stage is cut off, its collector voltage should be sufficiently negative to ensure saturation in all succeeding n stages. This worst condition is shown in Fig. 5-53a, and the above-stated conditions can be obtained by writing the following nodal equations:

$$I_{BO} = \frac{E_2 - V_{BEO}}{R_2} - \frac{m(V_{BEO} + V_{CES})}{R_t} \tag{5-46}$$

$$\frac{E_1 - V_{CEO}}{R_1} = I_{CO} + \frac{n(V_{CEO} - V_{BES})}{R_t} \tag{5-47}$$

where m and n are, respectively, the number of input and output resistors; V_{BEO}

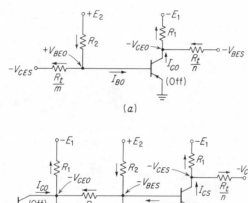

FIG. 5-53   The worst conditions of the *p-n-p* transistor-resistor circuit. (*a*) Transistor off; (*b*) transistor on.

and V_{CEO} are, respectively, the base-to-emitter and the collector-to-emitter voltages at the cutoff condition; V_{BES} and V_{CES} are, respectively, the base-to-emitter and the collector-to-emitter voltages at the saturated condition; and I_{BO} and I_{CO} are, respectively, the required base current and the collector current at the cutoff condition. The unused inputs are considered to be nearly grounded to keep the voltage V_{BEO} low. In the above equations the off condition is fulfilled by using the proper values of I_{BO} and V_{BEO} of the transistor.

On the other hand, this stage is turned on when as few as one preceding stage is cut off and does not turn on any of the n succeeding stages, although all succeeding stages can be on because they can have one of their other inputs connected to an *off* transistor. This worst condition is shown in Fig. 5-53*b*, and the above-stated conditions can be obtained by writing the following three nodal equations:

$$I_{CS} = \frac{E_1 - V_{CES}}{R_1} + \frac{n(V_{BES} - V_{CES})}{R_t} \tag{5-48}$$

$$I_{BS} = \frac{(V_{CEO} - V_{BES})}{R_t} -$$

$$\frac{(m-1)(V_{BES} - V_{CES})}{R_t} - \frac{E_2 + V_{BES}}{R_2} \tag{5-49}$$

$$\frac{E_1 - V_{CEO}}{R_1} = I_{CO} + \frac{V_{CEO} - V_{BES}}{R_t} + \frac{(n-1)(V_{CEO} - V_{BES})}{R_t} \tag{5-50}$$

where I_{CS} and I_{BS} are, respectively, the collector and the base current of the on transistor. In the above equations the on condition is fulfilled by using the proper values of I_{BS} and V_{BES} of the transistor. Since there are more parameters than there are equations, this may impose additional constraints, such as maximizing the fan-in (m) or fan-out (n) or optimizing the switching time.

The transistor-resistor logic circuit is simple, realizable, and low in cost. The major limitations are small fan-in or fan-out and low operating speed owing to a high degree of minority carrier storage brought about by a deep saturation of the transistor when two or more inputs are negative. By using transistors with a cut-off frequency of 5 Mc, a propagation time of less than 10 μsec per stage can be achieved.

Transistor-Resistor Flipflop.   A transistor-resistor flipflop, shown in Fig. 5-54, consists of two cascaded three-input TRL circuits, with the output of the second stage fed back to the first stage. As indicated in the figure, transistor T_1 is off, and T_2 is in saturation; call this the 1 state. The two inputs r and s normally are at ground potential. In this way, transistor T_1 is off because the collector potential of T_2 is at ground, and T_2 is on because the collector potential of T_1 is at a positive potential.

If a positive pulse (say, $+6$ volts) is applied to the s input, no change of the flipflop state occurs, because transistor T_2 is already on. If the positive pulse is applied to the r input, this resets the flipflop to the 0 state. The positive pulse at the r input makes the off transistor T_1 conduct; this in turn lowers the T_1 collector to ground potential. Since the input s is at ground potential, lowering the collector potential of T_1 switches T_2 into the off condition. Thus, transistor T_1 is now on and T_2 off; this is the 0 state.

The transistor-resistor flipflop is rather slow because of the deep saturation of the on transistor. Its speed can be readily improved by using coupling capacitors between the collectors and the bases; in this way it appears to become an *RC*-coupled transistor flipflop. However, the inputs are coupled to the transistor bases without using capacitors.

5-10   *Direct-coupled Transistor Logic (DCTL) Circuits*

In the previous transistor logic circuits the collector of one transistor is coupled to the base of a succeeding transistor by means of resistors (and capacitors).

Direct-coupled transistor logic circuits differ from these circuits in that the collector of one circuit is directly connected to the base of a succeeding circuit without using any resistors.

Direct-coupled Transistor Inverters [31]. Figure 5-55 shows three stages of direct-coupled transistors; transistors T_1 and T_3 are in saturation, and T_2 is cut off. Direct coupling requires that the collector voltage V_{CE1} of T_1 (-0.02 volt) should also be the base voltage V_{BE2} of T_2 and that the collector voltage V_{CE2} of T_2 (-0.49 volt) should also be the base voltage V_{BE3} of T_3, or

$$V_{CE1(on)} = V_{BE2(off)} \qquad \text{and} \qquad V_{CE2(off)} = V_{BE2(on)} \qquad (5\text{-}51)$$

When the transistor is in saturation, as T_1, resistor R_1 is the load resistor of the collector of T_1; and I_1 furnishes the collector current of T_1 and a negligible base current of T_2. When the transistor is cut off, as T_2, its collector resistor R_1 is the load resistor of the base of T_3; I_2 supplies the current to the base of T_3 and a leakage current to the collector of T_2. These currents can be expressed as

$$I_1 = I_{CS1} + I_{BO2} \qquad \text{or} \qquad I_1 \cong I_{CS1} \qquad (5\text{-}52)$$

$$I_2 = I_{CO2} + I_{BS3} \qquad \text{or} \qquad I_2 \cong I_{BS3} \qquad (5\text{-}53)$$

Load resistor R_1 and the supply voltage (-3 volts) act as a current sink which draws the current either from the collector or from the base.

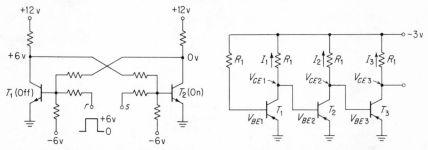

FIG. 5-54   A transistor-resistor *RS* flipflop.   FIG. 5-55   Three stages of direct-coupled transistors.

Early transistors suitable for direct coupling are surface barrier transistors [32]. A typical output collector characteristic (I_C versus V_{CE}) and input base characteristic (I_B versus V_{BE}) of a surface-barrier transistor are superimposed in one plot and shown in Fig. 5-56. The load line for resistance R_1 is the same for each characteristic. The ordinate scale for the collector or base current is the same; similarly, the abscissa scale for the collector or base voltage is the same. These combined characteristics serve the purpose of determining the operating condition of direct-coupled transistors. The base voltage and current of T_1 are established by the intersection (point A) of the load line and the base characteristic, where a base voltage V_{B1} of -0.49 volt and a base current of -2.5 ma are shown. The collector characteristic for a base current of -2.5 ma intersects the load line at point B. The collector voltage at point B is -0.02 volt and is the collector voltage of T_1. Transistor T_1 is in saturation, and its operating condition is thus established.

The operating condition for T_2 is now determined. The base voltage of T_2 is the collector voltage of T_1: -0.02 volt. From the base characteristic, it can be seen that the base current corresponding to this base voltage (-0.02 volt) of T_2 is essentially zero. Transistor T_2 is practically at cutoff, having no appreciable current in either its base or its collector. The collector voltage of T_2 is determined entirely by the base characteristic of T_3. Determination of the base voltage of T_3 is the same as for T_1: it is the intersection (point A) of the base characteristic and the load line. The collector voltage of T_3 is similarly at point B. The operating conditions of T_3 are the same as for T_1; transistor T_3 is in the condition

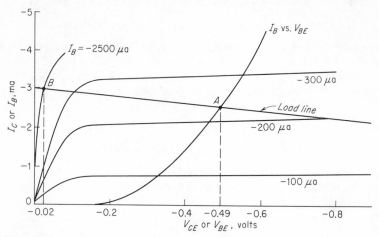

FIG. 5-56   Combined collector and base characteristics for a surface-barrier transistor in the common-emitter configuration.

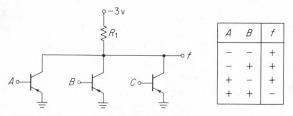

A	B	f
−	−	+
−	+	+
+	−	+
+	+	−

FIG. 5-57   Direct-coupled transistor *nor* circuit (negative logic).

of saturation. The transistor operating condition, either saturation or cutoff, is the same for every alternate stage.

In conclusion, the basic requirement for a direct-coupled *p-n-p* transistor is that the collector-to-emitter voltage V_{CES} when the transistor is on be equal to or less than the base-to-emitter voltage V_{BEO} when the transistor is off, or

$$V_{CES} \leq V_{BEO} \qquad (5\text{-}54)$$

Logic Circuits. If two or more *p-n-p* transistors are connected in parallel with a common-collector resistor, as shown in Fig. 5-57, the common-collector voltage becomes negative when all transistors are cut off; this occurs only when all inputs are positive (near ground potential). For negative logic this is a *nor* circuit. One transistor is needed for each input. If *n-p-n* transistors are used instead, for negative logic, it is a *nand* circuit.

If two or more *p-n-p* transistors and a load resistor are connected in series as shown in Fig. 5-58, the collector potential is positive (near ground potential) when all transistors are in saturation; this occurs only when all inputs are negative. For negative logic this is a *nand* circuit. The number of transistors that can be connected in series is limited because each saturated transistor contributes a voltage drop; the sum of these drops may cause the output voltage to be insufficiently positive to turn off the succeeding transistors. Therefore, the saturation voltage drop of each transistor must be small. Input *C* requires a more negative signal to turn on the transistor than that required at input *B*, which (in turn) requires a more negative signal than that at input *A*. Therefore, the serial configuration is limited to a few transistors.

Fan-in and Fan-out [37,39]. Figure 5-59 shows a common node to which *m* collectors and *n* bases are connected; this represents a general configuration of a parallel DCTL circuit. The fan-in and fan-out capability, represented by *m*

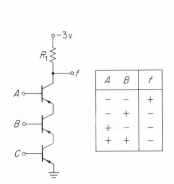

FIG. 5-58   Direct-coupled transistor *nand* circuit (negative logic).

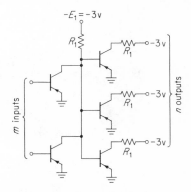

FIG. 5-59   A DCTL circuit showing a current node at the load resistor.

and *n*, can be established by two conditions. The first condition is that, when all the input transistors are turned off, all the output transistors must be on; or

$$\frac{E_1 - V_{BES}}{R_1} \geq mI_{CO} + nI_{BS} \qquad (5\text{-}55)$$

The second condition is that, when one input transistor is turned on, all the output transistors must be turned off; or

$$I_{CS} \geq \frac{E_1 - V_{BEO}}{R_1} \qquad (5\text{-}56)$$

The above node voltages V_{BES} and V_{BEO} are determined from the base characteristic of the transistor. By solving the above two inequalities for the current ratio I_{CS}/I_{BS}, we have

$$\beta_S = \frac{I_{CS}}{I_{BS}} \geq \frac{n(E_1 - V_{BEO})}{(E_1 - V_{BES}) - mI_{CO}} \qquad (5\text{-}57)$$

This shows that the allowable number of bases *n* is proportional to the common-emitter saturated current gain β_S and that the allowable number of collectors m depends (among other things) on how small the collector leakage current I_{CO} is.

Relay-circuit Analogy.   Direct-coupled transistor logic circuits need not be limited to a simple series circuit or a simple parallel circuit.   A series-parallel DCTL circuit is analogous to a relay network.   The path for the load resistance in a DCTL circuit is the circuit path of a relay network, and each direct-coupled transistor is a relay contact.   A DCTL circuit similar to the relay circuit of Fig. 5-8 is shown in Fig. 5-60.   The difference is that the output f in Fig. 5-8 represents the circuit path, while the output f in Fig. 5-60 represents the potential of the node of the load resistor and the collectors.

A Full Adder [34].   A single-bit full adder is now used as an example of the series-parallel DCTL circuit.   A full adder has three inputs X, Y, and C_i, which are, respectively, the augend bit, addend bit, and input carry bit.   The two outputs S and C_o are, respectively, the sum bit and the output carry bit.   The block

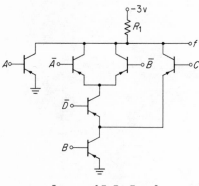

$$\bar{f} = A + B\left[\bar{D}(\bar{A}+\bar{B})+C\right]$$

FIG. 5-60   A DCTL circuit in series-parallel connections.

Table 5-6   Truth Table of Full Adder

X	Y	C_i	S	C_o
0	0	0	0	0
0	0	1	1	0
0	1	0	1	0
0	1	1	0	1
1	0	0	1	0
1	0	1	0	1
1	1	0	0	1
1	1	1	1	1

diagram of a full adder is shown in Fig. 5-61a.   Operation of the full adder is shown in Table 5-6.   The complement Boolean functions $\bar{S}$ and $\bar{C}_o$ are

$$\begin{aligned} \bar{S} &= C_i(\bar{X}Y + X\bar{Y}) + \bar{C}_i(\bar{X}\bar{Y} + XY) \\ \bar{C}_o &= \bar{C}_i(\bar{X}Y + X\bar{Y}) + \bar{X}\bar{Y} \end{aligned} \qquad (5\text{-}58)$$

Direct-coupled transistor logic circuits to implement functions (5-58) are shown in Fig. 5-61b.   Twelve transistors and two resistors are used.   The serial transistors for $X\bar{Y}$ and for $\bar{X}Y$ are shared for both inputs.   In connecting such circuits, caution should be exercised to avoid the possible "sneak path" which may occur as in the analogous relay network.   Because of the inversion at the load resistor, the above Boolean functions are written for $\bar{S}$ and $\bar{C}_o$ instead of for S and C_o.

Direct-coupled Transistor Flipflop.   A direct-coupled transistor flipflop [31] is shown in Fig. 5-62.   It is extremely simple because of the absence of the RC-coupling network.   As shown in the figure, T_1 is conducting, and T_2 is cut off.   Load current I_1 for the conducting transistor T_1 is essentially determined by load resistance R and supply E_1.   Load current I_2 for the off transistor T_2 is essentially determined by the base input characteristic of the conducting transistor

T_1. Both I_1 and I_2 are indicated by the dashed line. In the absence of external loads the collector-emitter voltage V_{CE} of the conducting T_1 is about 0.02 volt above ground, which is smaller than the base-emitter voltage V_{BE} of T_2 that is required to hold T_2 in the off state; the V_{CE} of the off T_2 is about 0.5 volt, which is larger than the V_{BE} of T_1 that is required to drive T_1 into saturation. Because of very small voltage swing at the collector of T_1, the load resistor and

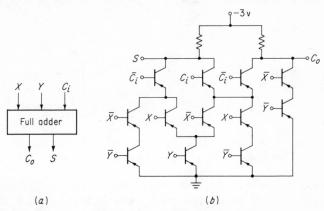

(a)   (b)

FIG. 5-61   A full adder using DCTL circuit.   (a) Block diagram; (b) schematic circuit.

the supply voltage form essentially a constant current source with a magnitude of E_1/R; thus the current I_1 or I_2 is switched between the collector of one transistor and the base of the other.

Figure 5-63 shows the triggering method for a direct-coupled transistor RS flipflop. In this circuit, two additional transistors T_3 and T_4, known as *pullover* transistors, are provided for the set and the reset inputs; these inputs can be either voltage levels or pulses. As shown in the figure, T_1 is conducting, and T_2 is at

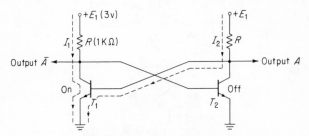

FIG. 5-62   A direct-coupled transistor flipflop.

cutoff. When a positive signal of sufficient magnitude is applied to the base of T_4, T_4 becomes saturated and pulls its collector voltage toward the ground. The collector of T_4 is tied directly to the collector of T_2 and the base of T_1. When T_4 becomes saturated, T_1 is cut off. The collector voltage of T_1 rises and drives T_2 into saturation; this will cause T_1 to remain off, and the initial positive input signal to T_4 may now be removed. In the end, T_1 is cut off, and T_2 is conducting. There is a similar sequence when a positive signal is applied to the base of T_3.

Figure 5-64 shows a direct-coupled transistor trigger-flipflop circuit. In this circuit, a clock-pulse input p is provided. The transistors T_3, T_4, and T_6 form a logical-*and* circuit; T_4, T_5, and T_6 form another *and* circuit. As shown in the figure, T_1 is conducting, and T_2 is cut off. The collector of T_4 will be pulled toward ground only when output voltage A is high and positive signals are applied to both inputs t and p. In the end, T_1 becomes cut off, and T_2 is conducting. Likewise, the switching to the other state requires that output voltage $\bar{A}$ be high

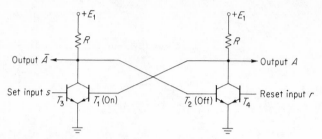

FIG. 5-63 A direct-coupled transistor *RS* flipflop.

and positive signals applied to both inputs t and p. The required delay (because output voltage A or $\bar{A}$ is needed during the switching) is provided by capacitors C.

Advantages and Disadvantages. The advantages of DCTL circuits are circuit simplicity, a single voltage source, and low power supply. These circuits are simple because only transistors and resistors are used and only about half as many resistors as transistors are needed; this results in fewer connections. Although the number of transistors required is more than with other types of

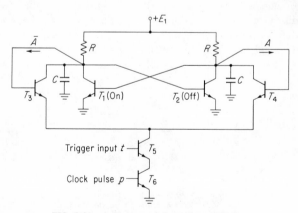

FIG. 5-64 A direct-coupled transistor *T* flipflop.

transistor logic circuits, the total component count in a computer using DCTL circuits is drastically reduced. All these advantages contribute to reduction of size and weight and to greater reliability. An arithmetic and control unit of a large-scale computer with a 20-bit word was built and reported; this computer uses 1,700 transistors and 500 resistors (and 20 capacitors) and occupies a volume of $\frac{1}{6}$ ft^3. It may require a power of no more than 8 watts with a single voltage supply of -3 volts.

On the other hand, the disadvantages are low signal voltages, a small signal swing, the transistors being in saturation during the on condition, and special transistor characteristics. The low signal level permits interference from locally generated noise, and the small signal swing makes good grounding mandatory. When the transistor is turned on, it is in saturation; this results in a reduction of switching speed by the minority carrier storage effect. However, computer speed of a few hundred thousand additions per second was achieved by using high-frequency surface-barrier transistors. The d-c characteristics of the direct-coupled transistor must fulfill relation (5-54). Such transistors must have sufficient uniformity in characteristics and sufficient current gain in the saturation condition. The lack of practical transistors that fulfill these requirements has left DCTL circuits in a rather disadvantageous position. However, direct-coupled transistors of recent planar construction are now commercially available.

5-11   *Transistor-current-switch Logic (TCSL) Circuits* [41]

The power consumption of a transistor switching circuit is proportional to the square of the voltage swing. For high speed and low power consumption, nonsaturating switching by a small voltage swing is advantageous. The TCSL circuit is designed to function in this manner.

Transistor Current Switch. A *p-n-p* transistor current switch is shown in Fig. 5-65. A 6-ma current from a current source is steered into either transistor T_1 or transistor T_2 by having a proper voltage V_e at the common-emitter node. The base of transistor T_2 is grounded. If the base voltage of transistor T_1 is $+0.6$ volt (slightly more positive than ground potential), V_e will reach this 0.6-volt potential. When this occurs (as shown in Fig. 5-65a), T_2 conducts and T_1 is cut off. If the base voltage of T_1 is -0.6 volt (slightly more negative than ground potential), V_e will reach ground potential. When this occurs (as shown in Fig. 5-65b), T_1 conducts and T_2 is cut off. A possibility exists, during a transient period, that emitter current will flow in both transistors. The input voltage need be large enough only to ensure that the voltage at the emitter node rises slightly above or below the reference ground potential.

Figure 5-65 shows two 3-ma current sinks and two output terminals f_1 and f_2.

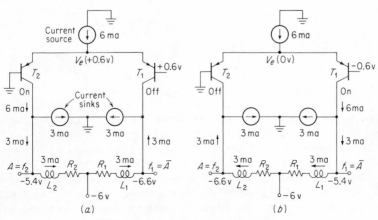

FIG. 5-65   A *p-n-p* transistor current switch.

The collectors of T_1 and T_2 return to the -6-volt supply through resistors R_1 and R_2 (200 ohms each). When T_2 is conducting and T_1 is cut off, the 6-ma current branches equally to the two paths shown in Fig. 5-65a; the output voltages at f_1 and f_2 become, respectively, -6.6 and -5.4 volts. When T_1 is conducting and T_2 is off, a similar situation occurs, as shown in Fig. 5-65b; the output voltages at f_1 and f_2 become, respectively, -5.4 and -6.6 volts. Out-

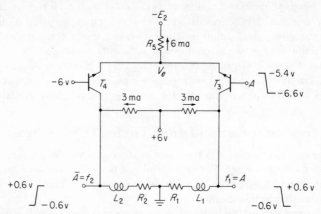

FIG. 5-66   An *n-p-n* transistor current switch.

puts f_1 and f_2 are complementary to each other. The current sinks center the output voltage swing at -6 volts. Inductances L_1 and L_2 provide a transient drive to improve the switching speed.

Because of a 6-volt difference between the input and the output, a *p-n-p* current switch cannot drive another *p-n-p* switch. This difficulty is overcome by constructing the complementary *n-p-n* switch shown in Fig. 5-66. The reference voltage at the base of T_4 is -6 volts instead of ground potential, so that T_4 can

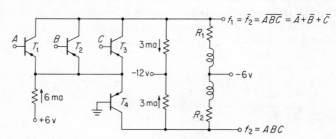

FIG. 5-67   A TCSL logical-*and* and *nand* circuit (positive logic).

be driven by the *p-n-p* switch; and the output, referenced to ground, can drive a *p-n-p* switch. The *n-p-n* and *p-n-p* switches are connected alternately.

Logic Circuits. If transistor T_1 of Fig. 5-65 is replaced by a number of paralleled *p-n-p* transistors with a common collector as shown in Fig. 5-67, transistor T_4 conducts; and the 6-ma current flows into T_4 only when all inputs A, B, and C are slightly positive. When this occurs, a 3-ma current flows into resistor R_2 and output f_2 swings to a more positive voltage of -5.4 volts; a 3-ma

current now flows out of resistor R_1, and output f_1 swings to a more negative
voltage of -6.6 volts. For positive logic, output f_2 is the logical *and* of the
three inputs, while output f_1 is the complement of f_2. Note that f_1 is the in-
verted output. Similarly, if transistor T_3 of Fig. 5-66 is replaced by a number
of paralleled *n-p-n* transistors with a common-collector resistor (Fig. 5-68),
transistor T_8 conducts and a 6-ma current flows into T_8 only when all inputs A,
B, and C are slightly more negative than -6 volts. As this happens, a 3-ma
current flows out of resistor R_2 and output f_2 swings to -0.6 volt; a 3-ma cur-

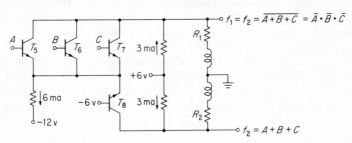

FIG. 5-68 A TCSL logical-*or* and *nor* circuit (positive logic).

rent flows into resistor R_1, and output f_1 swings to $+0.6$ volt. For positive logic,
output f_2 is the logical *or* of the three inputs, while output f_1 is again the complement of f_2.

Figure 5-69 shows a TCSL exclusive-*or* circuit. It consists of two two-input
and circuits such as that of Fig. 5-67. One *and* circuit performs the *andnot-$\overline{B}$*
operation; the other, the *andnot-$\overline{A}$* operation. The outputs of the *and* circuits
are connected to form the *or* circuit. For any of the four possible combinations
of inputs A and B, only two of the four input transistors conduct, and the other
two are cut off. When the input is $\overline{A}\overline{B}$ or AB, both T_9 and T_{10} do not conduct

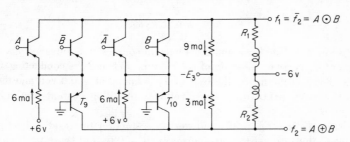

FIG. 5-69 A TCSL exclusive-*or* and coincidence circuit (positive logic).

and no current flows from the collectors of T_9 and T_{10} toward output f_2.
A 3-ma current flows out of resistor R_2 (200 ohms), and output f_2 is at a potential of -6.6 volts, which is more negative than -6 volts. But a 12-ma current
flows from the collectors of the input transistors toward output f_1. A 9-ma current sink is provided; so only a 3-ma current flows into load resistor R_1 (200
ohms). Output f_1 is at a potential of -5.4 volts, which is more positive than
-6 volts. When the input is $\overline{A}B$, T_{10} conducts and T_9 does not. When the
input is $A\overline{B}$, T_9 conducts and T_{10} does not. Under either of the two input con-

ditions, a 6-ma current flows toward output f_2. A 3-ma current sink is provided; so a 3-ma current flows into load resistor R_2. Output f_2 is at a potential of -5.4 volts, which is more positive than -6 volts. A 6-ma current also flows toward output f_1 from the collectors of the input transistors. With the 9-ma current sink, a -3-ma current flows out of load resistor R_1. Output f_1 is at a potential of -6.6 volts, which is more negative than -6 volts.

The TCSL circuit has the advantage of switching at a high speed and operating the transistor out of saturation. A good noise tolerance and a tendency to generate less noise are other advantages. On the other hand, this circuit requires a relatively large number of transistors and more than one power-supply voltage.

Transistor Current-switching Flipflop Circuit. Figure 5-70 shows a transistor current-switching RS-flipflop circuit [42]. The common-emitter 6-ma current source, transistors T_1 and T_2, and the resistors R_1 and R_2 are the same as those shown in Fig. 5-65. The two stable states are when T_1 is on and T_2 off and when T_1 is off and T_2 on. This stability is achieved by two feedbacks: one from the collector of T_1 to the base of T_2 and the other from the collector of T_2

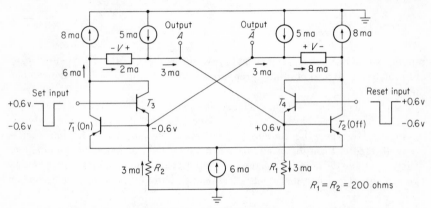

FIG. 5-70   A TCSL *RS* flipflop.

to the base of T_1. The 8-ma and 5-ma current sources and voltage drops V provide the proper current condition of the circuit. When T_1 is conducting and T_2 cut off as shown in the figure, the base of T_1 is biased at -0.6 volt and the base of T_2 is biased at $+0.6$ volt. These voltages and other currents are indicated in the figure.

Transistors T_3 and T_4 are the pullover transistors for the reset and set inputs. The bases of these transistors are normally at $+0.6$ volt; these transistors are normally cut off. When a reset input pulse of -0.6 volt is applied to the base of T_4, T_4 begins to conduct. The current in emitter resistor R_1 reduces and reverses; this in turn makes the base voltage of T_2 negative and T_2 conducts. The flow of collector current in T_2 reverses the direction of the current from output terminal $\bar{A}$ to resistor R_2. This raises the base voltage of T_1 and cuts off the collector current of T_1. The flow of collector current in T_1 reverses the direction of the current from output terminal A to resistor R_1; this sustains the new state of the circuit. A similar situation occurs when the transistor T_1 is being turned off and T_2 turned on.

5-12 Clocking Configuration

In a digital computer, information stored in one set of flipflops (called a *register*) is transferred through logic circuits to another set of flipflops. When the operation is synchronous, a clock pulse initiates the information transfer. When a series of information transfers among registers (including memory registers) is initiated by the clock pulse and controlled by the command signals, this series constitutes an internal sequence of computer operation. The logic significance of information transfer is described in Chap. 10, while several clocking schemes are shown here.

Clocking is a switching operation initiated by the clock pulse to transfer information among groups of flipflops. Assume that there are two groups of flipflops A and B interconnected by a logic circuit. Information is to be transferred from flipflops A to B. Four clocking configurations are shown in Fig. 5-71. In Fig. 5-71a, the clock pulse is applied to the input of flipflops A, and flipflops A in turn generate pulses to the input of logic circuits. The input and output of flipflops in this configuration, for example, can be transformer-coupled. Figure 5-72b shows the configuration where the clock pulse is applied to the input of logic circuits. The outputs of flipflops A are voltage levels. The clock pulse is applied to an *and* input, and this clock *and* circuit may be a special one. In Fig. 5-71c the clock pulse acts also as the supply voltage of a two-level *and-or* diode logic circuit. This configuration has the advantage that the power of the logic circuit is dissipated only during the time when the clock pulse is present. Figure 5-71d shows two examples of the configuration where the clock pulse is applied to the input of flipflops B. One example uses a coupling circuit consisting of a resistor, capacitor, and diode. The coupling circuit (which can be a part of the input network of flipflop B) is connected to the input of each of flipflops B. When the input at point X is low, the application of a negative-going clock pulse produces no pulse at point Y, as the diode is reverse-biased. When the input at X is high, the application of a negative-going clock pulse causes the diode to conduct and to discharge the capacitor; this produces a pulse at Y. The other example employs a gated pulse amplifier, which is discussed in the next section. The clock pulse enables the amplifier and initiates the information transfer.

The choice of a clocking configuration is an important one. It hinges on many considerations such as the type of logic circuits, the switching speed, the length of connecting wires, the cost, etc.

5-13 Other Digital Circuits

Delay Element. The delay element delays its input for a certain time interval. If it is used to match the unequal delays in several parallel paths for proper timing, it is not considered as a logic operation. Our discussion here is limited to the use of delay elements for logic operation.

Two types of delay circuit are in common use: the electrical delay line, and the one-shot multivibrator. The electrical delay line may be either the distributed-parameter type or the lumped-constant type. The important factors to be considered in choosing an electrical delay line are delay time, characteristic impedance, output-pulse rise time, and pulse distortion.   The one-shot multivibrator is a circuit which when triggered by an input pulse generates a rectangular pulse with a duration τ.   The trailing edge of the pulse, through a differentiating circuit, generates a pulse which occurs at a time τ later than the input pulse; thus,

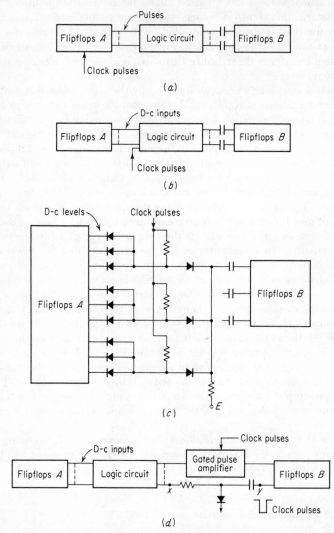

FIG. 5-71   Examples of clocking configuration.

the output is effectively a delayed input.   Delays can be either fixed or variable; in the latter case, the amount of variation can be either discrete or continuous.

There are many applications for delay elements.   If the output of an electrical delay line n bit times long (bit time is the time interval between two adjacent pulses) reenters at the input as shown in Fig. 5-72, the arrangement is an *n-bit circulating register.*   In this circuit an output amplifier with pulse-shaping circuits is needed, and an *andnot* circuit is provided for clearing the register. If the delay is one bit time long and the output again reenters at the input as shown in Fig. 5-73, this device becomes a *pulse generator* with a pulse period equal to the bit time.   If a pulse generator is connected to a number of delays with different bit times, the outputs of these delay lines form a multiple-phase clock generator shown in Fig. 5-74.   Again, pulse amplifiers are required if electrical delay lines are employed.   If a logical-*or* circuit connects the output of these delay lines (Fig. 5-75), the total circuit becomes a binary sequence gen-

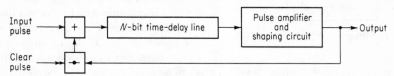

FIG. 5-72   A delay-line circulating register.

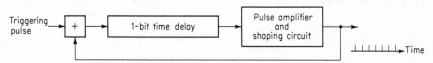

FIG. 5-73   A pulse generator.

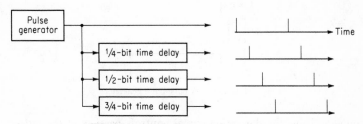

FIG. 5-74   A multiple-phase pulse generator.

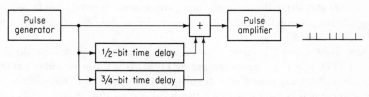

FIG. 5-75   A binary sequence generator using delay elements.

erator.   The binary number in the sequence depends on the number and the bit time of the delays.

Another circuit which makes use of a delay element is shown in Fig. 5-76. Pulses from a generator are fed to the set input of an *RS* flipflop and are also fed through a delay (with a delay time τ) to the reset input of the flipflop.   In this manner, alternate pulses from the generator set and reset the flipflop; the output of the flipflop in a sequence of rectangular pulses, each of a duration equal to the delay time.   Instead of being fed by a pulse generator, the flipflop may be actuated by a triggering pulse, and the normal output of the flipflop is utilized to control the pulses from a pulse generator through a logical-*and* circuit; this is shown in Fig. 5-77. In this circuit, a burst of pulses is obtained.

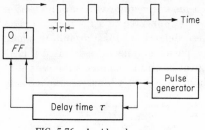

FIG. 5-76   A wide-pulse generator.

Gated Pulse Amplifiers. A gated pulse amplifier is a pulse amplifier provided with a control gate at the input of the amplifier so that information transfer can be initiated by applying a gating signal (often a clock pulse) at the gate.

A vacuum-tube gated pulse amplifier which makes use of a pentagrid amplifier is shown in Fig. 5-78. In this circuit the information signals are pulses, while the gating signal is a voltage level. Pulses to be gated are fed to the control grid, while the d-c gating signal is applied to the suppressor grid. Normally the tube conducts only during the coincidence of the positive gating signal and the positive

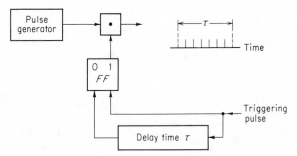

FIG. 5-77   A burst-pulse generator.

input pulse. Thus, the d-c gating signal controls passage of the pulses. The gated pulse amplifier performs a logical-*and* operation; however, a gated pulse amplifier can also shape the pulse and drive succeeding circuits. Not to be ignored is a significant propagation delay due to recovery of the control grid after being held below its cutoff voltage.

Figure 5-79 shows a transistor gated pulse amplifier reported by Booth and Bothwell [17]. In this circuit the gating signal is a 0.5-μsec pulse having an amplitude of 2.6 volts biased at -6 volts, and it is applied to the emitter. The information signal is the output of a two-level *or-and* (for negative logic) diode circuit. The inputs to the diode circuit come from flipflops whose output is either 0 or -6 volts. A pulse output from the transistor amplifier occurs only when the base potential is more negative than -3.4 volts, because otherwise the emitter will not be forward-biased. This condition exists when all inputs to the *and* diodes have at least one input of their *or* diodes at -6 volts. If one input to the *and* diodes is at ground, the voltage division among resistors R_1, R_2, R_3, and R_5 raises the base to -3 volts. The base becomes more positive when more than one input to the *and* diodes are grounded.

When the base potential is more negative than -3.4 volts actuated by the diode circuit, the transistor is driven from cutoff to saturation. Capacitor C_1

offers an increase in effective frequency response by allowing the circuit to operate as a grounded-base circuit during the turned-on and turned-off period of the
transistor. The turn-on and turn-off time is 0.1 μsec. The shunt diode at the
lower output winding of the transformer provides a low-resistance path to damp
the overshoot of the transformer at the trailing edge of the pulse.

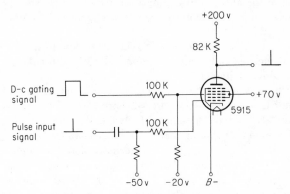

FIG. 5-78 A pentagrid gated pulse amplifier.

Special-purpose Digital Tubes. A number of special-purpose tubes have
been developed for digital applications. They may be classified according to
their use: counting tubes, coding tubes, arithmetic tubes, and indicating tubes.

There are two types of tubes for decimal counting—the gas tube and cathode-
ray tube. The gas tube utilizes the cold-cathode glow-discharge phenomenon.

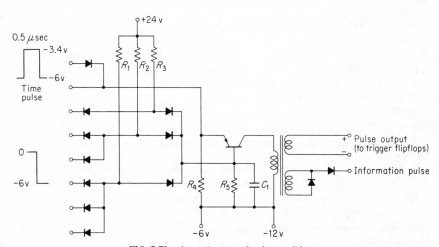

FIG. 5-79 A transistor gated pulse amplifier.

A glow discharge once started requires a less-than-initial voltage to sustain the
glow. Several cathodes are placed in the tube; the glow between the anode and
one of these cathodes represents one state. The important feature of this type of
counting tube lies in the means by which the glow is transferred from one
cathode to the next when a pulse train is counted. In a cathode-ray-tube type,

there are a number of anodes and one cathode. The electron beam is focused by an electrostatic or a magnetic field on one of these anodes. Different states are represented by deflecting the beam to different anodes. The counting is achieved by shifting the beam from one anode to the next upon the receipt of an input pulse. In the cathode-ray type, the counting can be operated at a high speed because of the absence of deionization time. Other shifting or transfer schemes include the use of secondary-emission phenomena, multiple grids, and others.

Coding tubes are used to code input signals into some form of binary output. Most of the geometries and focusing schemes described for the counting tubes may also be used for coding tubes.

Arithmetic tubes are those which can perform binary arithmetic operations. An adder tube has been reported on by Maynard [49]. The tube structure consists of a central flat cathode surrounded by two half sections of grids and plates. The three grid inputs A, B, and C are internally connected to control grids in both halves of the tube. These grids are externally biased to cutoff, each through a grid resistor. Two outputs are provided at the two plates. One plate produces a negative sum pulse when A, B, or C is pulsed by a positive signal. The other plate produces a positive carry pulse identical to the input signal when any two or all three of the inputs are applied. During a double coincidence, however, no sum signal is produced. On a triple coincidence, both sum and carry signals are produced.

Many types of numerical or alphanumerical indicators are available; they are used as output devices and will not be described further.

Problems

1. Draw a relay network for each of the following functions:

(a) $f = A(B\bar{C} + \bar{B}C)$ (b) $f = ABC + A\bar{B}C + \bar{A}BC$

(c) $f = AD + BC + (B + C)(A + D)$ (d) $f = (AB + C)(BC + D)(CD + A)$

(e) $f(A,B,C,D) = P_0 + P_2 + P_6 + P_{15}$ (f) $f(A,B,C,D) = S_1 \cdot S_5 \cdot S_{10} \cdot S_3$

2. Draw a vacuum-tube logic circuit for a full adder.

3. Draw logic diagrams for the functions in Prob. 1:

(a) By using *nor* circuits alone   (b) By using *nand* circuits alone

4. Draw diode logic circuits for the functions in Prob. 1.

5. Use diode logic circuits to design a circuit which generates a constant 3.1416 (π). Assume that the binary-coded decimal digit is used and that the clock pulse is available.

6. Design a full subtractor by using the transistor-diode logical-*nor* circuits (positive logic).

7. Draw RCTL circuits for the following functions by using inverters (positive logic):

(a) $f = \bar{A}B + \bar{B}C + \bar{C}D$ (b) $f = (A + B)(B + C)(C + D)$

(c) $f = A \oplus B \oplus C$ (d) $f = A \odot B \odot C$

8. Design a translating circuit to convert an 8-4-2-1 binary-coded decimal digit into the excess-3 code:

(a) By using TRL circuits   (b) By using DCTL circuits

9. Design a full adder by using TCSL circuits.

10. For the following function,

$$f = A \oplus B \oplus C$$

draw logic circuits using

(a) Relays   (b) DCTL circuits   (c) TRL circuits

and comment on their similarities and dissimilarities.

References

Diode Circuits

1. Chen, Tung Chang: Diode Coincidence and Mixing Circuits in Digital Computers, *Proc. IRE,* May, 1950, pp. 511–514.
2. Wang, An: Miniature Rectifier Computing and Controlling Circuits, *Proc. IRE,* August, 1952, pp. 931–935.
3. Gluck, S. E., H. J. Gray, Jr., and C. T. Lenodes: The Design of Logical OR-AND-OR Pyramids for Digital Computers, *Proc. IRE,* October, 1953, pp. 1388–1392.
4. Hussey, L. W.: Semiconductor Diode Gates, *Bell System Tech. J.,* vol. 32, pp. 1137–1154, September, 1953.
5. Elbourn, R. D., and R. P. Witt: Dynamic Circuit Techniques Used in SEAC and DYSEAC, *Proc. IRE,* October, 1953, pp. 1380–1387.
6. Yokelson, B. J., and W. Ulrich: Engineering Multistage Diode Logic Circuits, *AIEE Communs. Electronics,* September, 1955, pp. 466–475.
7. Raymond, G. A.: A Transistor-circuit Chassis for High Reliability in Missile-guidance Systems, *Procs., Eastern Joint Computer Conf.,* 1957, pp. 132–135.

Transistor Circuits

8. Ebers, J. J., and J. L. Moll: Large-signal Behavior of Junction Transistors, *Proc. IRE,* December, 1954, pp. 1761–1772.
9. Moll, J. L.: Large-signal Transient Response of Junction Transistors, *Proc. IRE,* December, 1954, pp. 1773–1784.
10. Wanlass, C. L.: Transistor Circuitry for Digital Computers, *IRE Trans. on Electronic Computers,* March, 1955, pp. 11–16.
11. Moll, J. L.: Junction Transistor Electronics, *Procs. IRE,* December, 1955, pp. 1807–1819.
12. McMahon, R. E.: Designing Transistor Flip-flops, *Electronic Design,* October, 1955, pp. 24–26.
13. Prugh, T. A.: Junction Transistor Switching Circuits, *Electronics,* Jan. 28, 1955, pp. 168–171.
14. Linvill, J. G.: Nonsaturating Pulse Circuits Using Two Junction Transistors, *Proc. IRE,* July, 1955, pp. 826–834.
15. Baker, R. H.: Maximum Efficiency Transistor Switching Circuits, *MIT Lincoln Lab. Tech. Rept.* 110, Mar. 22, 1956.
16. Bothwell, T. P., and L. Kolodin: A Bistable Symmetrical Switching Circuit, *Proc. Natl. Electronic Conf.,* 1956, pp. 655–667.
17. Booth, G. W., and T. P. Bothwell: Logical Circuits for a Transistor Digital Computer, *IRE Trans. on Electronic Computers,* September, 1956, pp. 132–138.
18. Olsen, K. H.: Transistor Circuitry in the Lincoln TX-2, *Proc. Western Joint Computer Conf.,* 1957, pp. 167–171.
19. Henle, R. A.: and J. W. Walsh: The Application of Transistors to Computers, *Proc. IRE,* June, 1958, pp. 1240–1254.
20. Baker, R. H.: Symmetrical Transistor Logic, *Proc. Western Joint Computer Conf.,* 1958, pp. 27–33.
21. Yokelson, B. J., W. B. Cagle, and M. D. Underwood: Semiconductor Circuit Design Philosophy for the Central Control of an Electronic Switching System, *Bell System Tech. J.,* September, 1958, pp. 1125–1160.
22. Cloot, P. L.: A Basic Transistor Circuit for the Construction of Digital-computing Systems, *Proc. IEE (London),* vol. 105, pt. B, no. 21, pp. 213–220, May, 1958.
23. Pressman, A. I.: "Design of Transistorized Circuits for Digital Computers," John F. Rider Publisher, Inc., New York, 1959.

Transistor-Resistor Logic Circuits

24. Rowe, W. D., and G. H. Royer: Transistor NOR Circuit Design, *AIEE Communs. Electronics,* July, 1957, pp. 263–267.

25. Marcovitz, M. W., and E. Seif: Analytical Design of Resistor-coupled Transistor Logical Circuits, *IRE Trans. on Electronic Computers,* June, 1958, pp. 109–119.

26. Rowe, W. D.: The Transistor Nor Circuit, *IRE Wescon Conven. Record,* 1957, pp. 231–245.

27. Finch, T. R.: Transistor Resistor Logic Circuits for Digital Data Systems, *Proc. Western Joint Computer Conf.,* 1958, pp. 17-22.

28. Dunnet, W. J., and E. P. Auger, and A. C. Scott: Analysis of TRL Circuit Propagation Delay, *Proc. Eastern Joint Computer Conf.,* 1958, pp. 99–107.

29. Wray, W. J., Jr.: DC Design of Resistance Coupled Transistor Logic Circuits, *IRE Trans. on Circuit Theory,* September, 1959, pp. 304–310.

30. Dunnet, W. J., E. P. Anger, and A. C. Scott: Analysis of Transistor–Resistor–Logic Circuit Propagation Delay, *Sylvania Technologist,* October, 1959,

Direct-coupled Transistor Logic Circuits

31. Beter, R. H., W. E. Bradley, R. B. Brown, and M. Robinoff: Direct-coupled Transistor Circuits, *Electronics,* June, 1955, pp. 132–136.

32. Beter, R. H., W. E. Bradley, R. B. Brown, and M. Robinoff: Surface-barrier Transistor Switching Circuits, *IRE Natl. Conv. Record,* 1955, pp. 139–145.

33. Renwick, W., and M. Phister: A Design Method for Direct-coupled Flipflops, *Electronic Eng.,* June, 1955, pp. 246–250.

34. Cavaliers, A. L.: What's inside Transac, *Electronic Design,* pt. 1, July 1, 1956, pp. 22–25, pt. 2, July 15, 1956, pp. 30–33.

35. Githens, J. A.: The Tradic Leprechaun Computer, *Proc. Eastern Joint Computer Conf.,* 1956, pp. 29–33.

36. Clark, E. G.: Direct Coupled Transistor Logic Complementing Flip-flop Circuits, *Electronic Design,* pt. 1, pp. 24–27, June 15, 1957, pt. 2, pp. 34–47, Aug. 1, 1957.

37. Harris, J. R.: Direct-coupled Transistor Logic Circuitry, *IRE Trans. on Electronic Computers,* March, 1958, pp. 2–6.

38. Easley, J. W.: Transistor Characteristics for Direct-coupled Transistor Logic Circuits, *IRE Trans. on Electronic Computers,* March, 1958, pp. 6–16.

39. Angell, J. B.: Direct-coupled Logic Circuitry, *Proc. Western Joint Computer Conf.,* 1958, pp. 22–27.

40. Kudlich, R. A.: Circuit Considerations and Logical Design with Direct-coupled Transistor Logic, *Proc. Intern. Symposium on Theory Switching,* pt. II, pp. 201, 210, 1959.

Transistor-current-switch Logic Circuits

41. Yourke, H. S., E. J. Slobodzinski: Millimicrosecond Transistor Current Switching Techniques, *Proc. Western Joint Computer Conf.,* February, 1957, pp. 68–72.

42. Walsh, J. L.: IBM Current Mode Transistor Logical Circuits, *Proc. Western Joint Computer Conf.,* 1958, pp. 34–36.

43. Buelow, F. K.: Improvement to Current Switching, Digest of Technical Papers, *Solid State Circuits Conf.,* 1960, pp. 30–31.

44. Jarvis, D. B., L. P. Morgan, and J. A. Weaver: Transistor Current Switching and Routing Techniques, *IRE Trans. on Electronic Computers,* September, 1960, pp. 302–308.

Other Circuits

45. Eccles, W. H., and F. W. Jordan: A Trigger Relay Utilizing 3-electrode Thermionic Vacuum Tubes, *Radio Rev.* (Dublin, Ireland), vol. 1, pp. 143–146, 1919.

46. Staff of Harvard Computation Laboratory: "Synthesis of Electronic Computing and Control Circuits," Harvard University Press, Cambridge, Mass., 1951.

47. Keister, W., A. E. Ritchie, and S. H. Washburn: "The Design of Switching Circuits," D. Van Nostrand Company, Inc., Princeton, N. J., 1951.

48. Kandiah, K.: Decimal Counting Tubes, *Electronic Eng.*, February, 1954, pp. 56–63.

49. Maynard, F. B.: Binary Adder Tube for High Speed Computers, *Electronics*, September, 1955, pp. 161–163.

50. Bugbee, L. F., and C. H. Davidson: A Survey of the Characteristics of Currently Used Bistable Multivibrators, *Univ. Wis. Eng. Expt. Sta. Rept.* 7, September, 1956.

51. Richards, R. K.: "Digital Computer Components and Circuits," D. Van Nostrand Company, Inc., Princeton, N. J., 1957.

52. Kuchinsky, A.: Special-purpose Tubes for Computer Applications, *Proc. Western Joint Computer Conf.*, May, 1958, pp. 96–102.

6

Logic Circuits—II

6-1   Switching Characteristics of Cryotrons

Superconductivity.   When some metals are placed at a very low temperature such as that of liquid helium, their electrical resistance drops to zero.   This phenomenon is called *superconductivity* [1].   It was discovered by H. K. Onnes, a Dutch physicist, in 1911, three years after he suceeded in liquefying helium. The temperature at which superconductivity begins to occur is called the *transition temperature*.   Materials which show the phenomenon of superconductivity in the cryogenic condition (temperature slightly above absolute zero) are called *superconductors*.   Some 22 elements have been found to be superconductive and are listed in Table 6-1 in the order of decrease of transition temperature.   In addition to these elements, many alloys and compounds are superconductive at some transition temperature between 0 and 17°K.

The resistivity of many superconductive materials is relatively high at room temperature but drops as the materials are cooled.   Relatively poor conductors such as niobium and lead become superconductors at a very low temperature, whereas good conductors such as gold, silver, and copper do not.   The resistivity of superconductors is truly zero below the transition temperature.   Professor S. C. Collins of MIT demonstrated zero resistivity by an experiment.   A persistent current of several hundred amperes was induced in a lead ring immersed in liquid helium on Mar. 16, 1954, and the current continued to flow until the experiment was voluntarily terminated on Sept. 11, 1956. During the experiment, there was no observable change in the magnitude of the current.   This phenomenon of *persistent current* has been utilized in several ways to make cryogenic memory elements.

When a superconductor is in its superconducting state, a magnetic field of

Table 6-1   Transition Temperatures of Superconducting Elements

Elements	Transition temperature, °K
Technetium	11.2
Niobium	8.0
Lead	7.22
Vanadium	5.1
Tantalum	4.4
Lanthanum	4.37
Mercury	4.15
Tin	3.73
Indium	3.37
Thallium	2.38
Thorium	1.39
Aluminum	1.20
Gallium	1.10
Rhenium	1.0
Zinc	0.91
Uranium	0.8
Osmium	0.71
Zirconium	0.70
Cadmium	0.56
Ruthenium	0.47
Titanium	0.4
Hafnium	0.35

sufficient intensity can destroy its superconductivity and cause normal resistance to reappear. The sharpness of the change in resistance during transition is an important characteristic. This binary property of normal resistance and no resistance under the influence of a magnetic field is the basis for superconductor logic circuits.

The magnetic field at which the normal resistance just reappears from the superconducting state is called the *critical magnetic field*. The relation between the transition temperature and its corresponding critical magnetic field for the superconductor lead is shown in Fig. 6-1. In this figure, the area under the curve is the superconducting region, whereas that above is the normal conducting region. If lead is held at 4.2°K, it is in the superconducting state, as indicated by point A. When a magnetic field is applied with its magnitude increasing, the condition changes from point A and moves to the right as indicated by the dashed line. When the field is at about 550 oersteds, the metal changes from the superconducting to the normal conducting state. The curve shows that, the lower the temperature

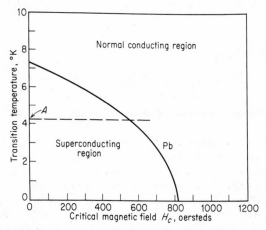

FIG. 6-1   Superconducting and normal conducting regions of a superconductor.

being held, the greater the critical magnetic field. If only a small magnetic field (50 to 100 oersteds) is available, the operating temperature is about 0.2°K below the zero-field transition temperature. Similar curves for several other superconductors are shown in Fig. 6-2. Tantalum has been used in early experiments because its transition temperature is slightly above the boiling point of helium at 1 atm (4.2°K).

When a superconductor is cooled below its transition temperature in a magnetic field, the total magnetic flux inside the superconductor becomes zero. The superconducting current flows on the surface of the superconductor. This phenomenon is called the *Meissner effect*, as it was discovered by Meissner and Ochsenfeld in 1933.

Cryotron. The feasibility of using the phenomenon of superconductivity to make a switching device for the computer application was demonstrated by Buck [2,3] in 1954. This superconductive switching device is called a *cryotron*. Figure 6-3 shows a wire-wound cryotron made of a short superconductive wire (called the *gate*) and a superconductive winding (called the *control coil*). The gate is normally in a superconductive state. When a current is applied to the coil to produce a magnetic field, the gate is switched from a superconductive to a resistive state.

A typical cryotron has a gate of tantalum wire, 9 mils in diameter and 1 in. in length and a single-layer insulated control coil of 3-mil niobium wire. The cryotron is operated at a temperature slightly below the zero-field transition

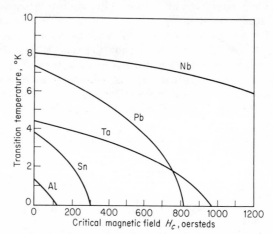

FIG. 6-2 Transition temperature and critical magnetic field of several superconductors.

temperature of the gate material. The control coil is selected of material having a transition temperature sufficiently higher than that of the gate. In such a combination the control coil remains superconductive even when the magnetic field is applied to the gate. This confers the advantage that there is no resistance in the control coil. Once the magnetic field is established in the control coil, no further energy is needed for the continuation of the field. Because of this advantage, interconnecting wires are all operated in a superconductive state.

The switching characteristic† of a cryotron is described by a family of curves of resistance vs. control-coil current I_c, with the gate current I_g as the parameter. Figure 6-4 shows two such curves for a tantalum-niobium cryotron wherein d_c, d_g, L_c, and N are the diameter of the control-coil wire, the diameter of the gate wire, the length of the control coil, and the number of turns of the coil, respectively.

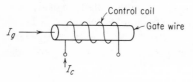

FIG. 6-3 A cryotron.

The slope of the curve in the transition region depends on the homogeneity of the gate wire as well as the gate current. For a given cryotron, a sharper transition occurs when the gate current is large enough to produce a pronounced Joule heating effect when the gate wire starts to become resistive.

Silsbee established in 1916 that the critical field at which the change of

† Also called the *quenching characteristic*, where quenching means the switching from a superconductive to a normal state.

resistance occurs depends not only on the field produced by the control coil but also on the field produced by the current in the gate; the latter field is called the *self-field* of the gate. This phenomenon is known as the *Silsbee hypothesis*. The self-field of the gate allows a reduction of the control-coil field switching the cryotron. It is even possible to control a large current in the gate by a small current in the coil.

The direction of the control-coil field H_0 is along the longitudinal axis of the gate, and the magnitude (in ampere-turns per meter†) is

$$H_0 = \frac{I_c N}{L_c} \qquad (6\text{-}1)$$

where I_c and L_c are in amperes and meters, respectively. The direction of the gate self-field H_g is tangential (circular along the wire), and the magnitude is

$$H_g = \frac{I_g}{\pi d_g} \qquad (6\text{-}2)$$

where I_g and d_g are in amperes and meters, respectively. The two fields add

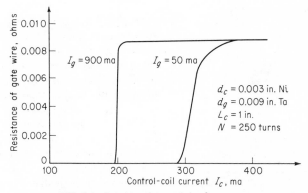

FIG. 6-4   Switching characteristic of a cryotron.

vectorially. When the vector sum reaches the value of the critical field H_c, the transition, or switching, occurs. Thus, the net field causing the switching is

$$H_c = \sqrt{H_0^2 + H_g^2} \qquad (6\text{-}3)$$

Using the above three relations, we have, after simplification,

$$(\pi d_g H_c)^2 = K^2 \left(\frac{I_c}{I_{cm}}\right)^2 + \left(\frac{I_g}{I_{cm}}\right)^2 \qquad (6\text{-}4)$$

where

$$K = \frac{\pi d_g N}{L_c} \qquad (6\text{-}5)$$

$$I_{cm} = \frac{H_c L_c}{N} \qquad (6\text{-}6)$$

I_{cm} is the minimum control-coil current to quench the gate. Equation (6-4) de-

† 1 oersted (emu) is equal to $10^3/4\pi$ amp-turns per meter.

scribes the quenching by the combined magnetic fields due to the gate and coil currents. Since d_g, H_c, and K are all constant for a given cryotron, the plot of Eq. (6-4) is an ellipse, shown in Fig. 6-5; such an ellipse is called the *control characteristic* of the cryotron. The measured control characteristic appears quite close to an ellipse, though somewhat distorted. The orientation angle α due to the two magnetic fields is

$$\tan \alpha = \frac{H_g}{H_0} = \frac{I_g}{KI_c} \qquad (6\text{-}7)$$

The above equation indicates that the flow lines of magnetic-field intensity are helices around the wire.

Cryotron Current Gain. Equation (6-5) defines the quantity K, called the *current gain* of the cryotron. It can be seen from Fig. 6-5 that the effect of magnetic field due to the control-coil current I_c is K times that due to gate current I_g. The current gain K in (6-5) can be readily written as

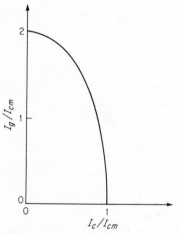

$$K = \frac{I_{gm}}{I_{cm}} \qquad (6\text{-}8)$$

where I_{gm} is the maximum gate current without quenching (called the *critical current*) and I_{cm} is the minimum control-coil current to quench the gate. Thus, the current gain is the ratio of the value on the ordinate (major axis) to the value on the abscissa (minor axis) of the ellipse of Fig. 6-5. In cryotron logic circuits the current gain should be larger than 1 so that the gate current of a cryotron can drive the control coil of another cryotron without any intermediate amplification. In practice, current gain is made equal to 2 or 3 to provide a margin against nonuniformity in cryotrons.

FIG. 6-5   Control characteristic of a cryotron.

The current gain is proportional to the product of the diameter of the gate wire and the number of turns of the control coil per unit length (or pitch of the control coil). If the control coil is a closely wound one, then the pitch N/L_c is equal to $1/d_c$. The current gain in expression (6-5) now becomes

$$K = \frac{\eta \pi d_g}{d_c} \qquad (6\text{-}9)$$

where η, called the *gate efficiency*, makes up the smaller observed current gain. The gate efficiency for tantalum and tin gate wires are about 50 to 80 per cent, respectively.

Cryotron Switching Time. During switching from a superconductive to a normal state when a step magnetic field is applied, the field is sweeping through the superconductor from the outside toward the center, leaving behind a normal region. Eddy currents flow circumferentially around the wire in the normal region and limit the rate at which the boundary region can move. As the normal region grows at the expense of the superconducting region, the normal resistance returns. A plot of the reciprocal of this switching time versus the control current is given in Fig. 6-6. The curve shows a straight-line relationship for short switching times and a departure from the straight line, presumably due to Joule heating, for long switching times. Upon removal of the magnetic field, switching from the normal to the superconductive state occurs rapidly. Experimental results have shown that the superconductive state is reestablished in about 1 μsec. To reduce the switching time, a larger resistivity of the gate wire is desired because of the Joule heating effect.

In cryotron circuitry, the gate wire of one cryotron can be used to drive the control coil of another. When cryotrons are used in this manner, there is a time constant associated with a pair of identical cryotrons. The time constant τ is

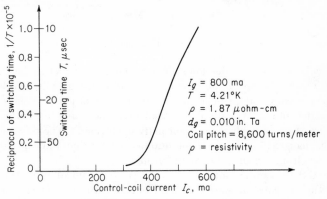

FIG. 6-6 Switching time of a cryotron.

the ratio of the control-coil inductance L_{coil} to the gate-wire normal resistance R_{gate},

$$r = \frac{L_{\text{coil}}}{R_{\text{gate}}} \tag{6-10}$$

The wire-wound cryotron has a time constant of 40 μsec and a current gain of 3. The above time constant is useful in calculating the circuit time constant and in comparing the merits of different designs of cryotrons.

6-2   Cryotron Logic Circuits

The cryotron is a switching device. Its binary states are the superconductive and the normal resistive conditions of the gate. They may be defined, respectively, as the condition in which the gate path is closed (gate current flowing) and as the condition in which the gate path is open (no gate current flowing) and are symbolized by the plus and minus signs, respectively. The logic designation is shown in Table 6-2.

Basic Cryotron Logic Circuits. Figure 6-7 shows the simplest cryotron circuit: the gate wire in series with a resistance and a battery. The cryotron, a

Table 6-2   Logic Designation for Cryotron Circuits

Symbol	Gate current	Gate path	Cryotron state	Positive logic	Negative logic
+	Flowing	Closed	Superconducting	1	0
−	Not flowing	Open	Normal conducting	0	1

low-impedance device, is operated from a current source symbolized by the battery and the resistor. The current input to the control coil represents a Boolean variable. When there is a current input A, the cryotron is in the normal conducting state and the gate current in the circuit path f is low; otherwise, the

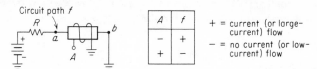

FIG. 6-7   A cryotron logical-*not* circuit.

cryotron is in the superconducting state, and the gate current in the circuit path f is high. This is a logical-*not* circuit. Instead of the gate current being considered as the output, the voltage across the cryotron at points a and b may also be used as the output. The simple cryotron circuit is similar to a normally closed relay; there is no equivalent for a normally open relay. The difference is that a cryotron changes its resistance from zero to a small value, while a relay changes its resistance from a small value to almost infinity.

Figure 6-8 shows a circuit having two cryotrons controlled by two inputs A and B. The two gate wires are connected in series with the current source; these two gates can be made one long gate wire. The gate current in the circuit path

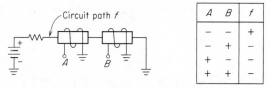

FIG. 6-8   A cryotron logical-*nor* circuit (positive logic).

f is high only when both inputs are absent. The current is low in the presence of either input or both inputs. For a positive-logic designation, it is a *nor* circuit. Other basic logic circuits can be formed by using the *nor* circuit alone; they are shown in Figs. 6-9 to 6-12. The *not* circuit is a single-input *nor* circuit.

Cryotron Two-line Logic Circuits. In the above cryotron circuits, there is more than one path, each path being connected to the battery by a resistor. These circuits may be referred to as *multiple-serial-path circuits*. Circuits can also be formed by using multiple parallel paths. Fig. 6-13 shows a circuit with two parallel paths f_1 and f_2; the paths are connected to one common resistor. When either input is applied, one path is in the superconducting state and the other in the resistive state because the ratio of these two resistances is

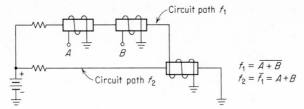

FIG. 6-9   A cryotron logical-*or* circuit (positive logic).

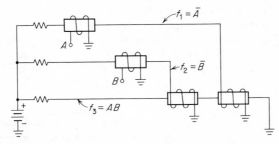

FIG. 6-10   A cryotron logical-*and* circuit (positive logic).

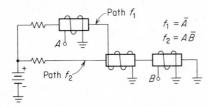

FIG. 6-11   A cryotron logical-*andnot-B* circuit (positive logic).

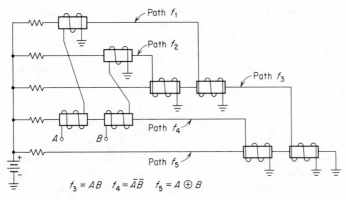

FIG. 6-12   A cryotron logical-exclusive-*or* circuit (positive logic).

infinite. If both inputs are applied or not applied, the current from the current source is divided between the two paths. The divided current may become too low a value to switch other cryotrons. This situation may become more serious when there are multiple parallel paths. Furthermore, in the presence of multiple parallel paths, the current would initially divide inversely as the ratio of the inductance but then would redistribute slowly because of possible minute parasitic resistance among the parallel paths.

One approach in using multiple parallel paths is to form the circuits in such a way that one and only one path of a number of parallel paths is superconductive and the other paths are all resistive. In this manner, the current from the constant current source is merely being switched from one path to another. This confers the additional advantage that there are no currents in the resistive paths. Consequently no power is consumed during the steady-state condition, and less liquid helium is evaporated. To achieve this kind of circuit operation, two-line signal representation is used (as in Fig. 5-2). In Fig. 6-13 one input represents input A and the other its complement $\bar{A}$. Then only one path is superconductive at one time. This is the circuit for one Boolean variable, the paths f_1 and f_2 representing $\bar{A}$ and A, respectively.

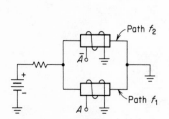

FIG. 6-13   A cryotron two-line circuit for one Boolean variable.

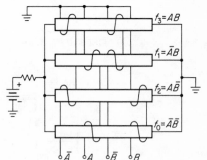

FIG. 6-14   A cryotron two-line circuit for two Boolean variables.

A cryotron two-line circuit for two Boolean variables A and B is shown in Fig. 6-14. Four long cryotrons, each with two control coils, provide four circuit paths representing the four P terms of two Boolean variables. Only one path is in the superconductive state at any one combination of the two inputs.

Let us use the single-bit full adder as an example of a multiple-parallel-path circuit. From Table 5-6, the Boolean functions for the sum S and the output carry C_o and their complement functions $\bar{S}$ and $\bar{C}_o$ are reconstructed as follows:

$$
\begin{aligned}
S &= \bar{A}\bar{B}C_i + ABC_i + A\bar{B}\bar{C}_i + \bar{A}B\bar{C}_i \\
C_o &= \bar{A}BC_i + A\bar{B}C_i + ABC_i + AB\bar{C}_i \\
\bar{S} &= \bar{A}BC_i + A\bar{B}C_i + AB\bar{C}_i + \bar{A}\bar{B}\bar{C}_i \\
\bar{C}_o &= \bar{A}\bar{B}C + A\bar{B}\bar{C} + \bar{A}B\bar{C} + ABC
\end{aligned}
\tag{6-11}
$$

The cryotron full adder is shown in Fig. 6-15. Circuit paths f_0 to f_7 for the eight long cryotrons (at the right half of the figure) represent the eight P terms of three Boolean variables. These terms are formed by using the coil currents of the eight long cryotrons to represent inputs A and B (and their complements) and by using their gate currents to represent input C_i (and its complement). These eight paths control 16 cryotrons (at the left half of the figure); the 16 gates are connected to form four circuit paths S, C, $\bar{S}$, and $\bar{C}_o$, representing the four Boolean functions (6-11).

To demonstrate the operation, trace circuit path S. (Since the cryotron circuit

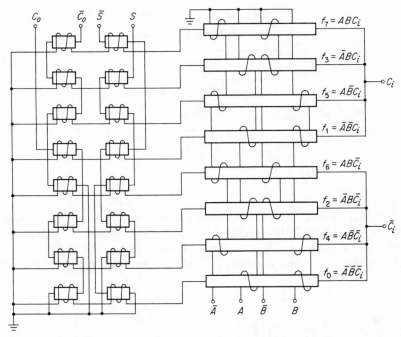

FIG. 6-15   A full adder using two-line cryotron circuits.

performs a *nor* operation, the four P terms are used for complement function $\bar{S}$.) Circuit path S is the gate path of the four serially connected cryotrons controlled by circuit paths f_3, f_5, f_6, and f_0, as no current flows in path S if any one of these four terms becomes 1.

Cryotron Flipflops. Figure 6-16 illustrates a cryotron flipflop consisting of two cryotrons. The gate wire of one cryotron is connected in series to the con-

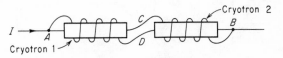

FIG. 6-16   A cryotron flipflop.

trol coil of the other. There are two parallel paths between points A and B for current I. When one cryotron is in a superconductive state, the other is not, and vice versa; these are the two stable states. These two states are equivalent to having a current flowing in one path and no current flowing in the other path. For example, when a current is flowing in path ACB, cryotron 2 is in a resistive state; the path *ADB* is resistive, and no current flows in it. These states wherein both paths are resistive or superconductive are either unstable or do not occur.

A cryotron *RS* flipflop is shown in Fig. 6-17. Cryotrons 1 and 2 are the two cryotrons of Fig. 6-16. Cryotrons 3 and 4 are input cryotrons for reset and set inputs, respectively. Cryotrons 5 and 6 are output cryotrons for normal and

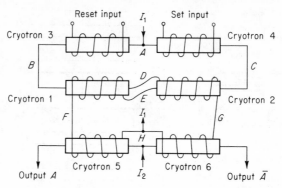

FIG. 6-17   A cryotron *RS* flipflop.

complement outputs. I_1 and I_2 indicate two current sources. When a current flows in path *ABDGH*, this condition is regarded here as state 1 and a current is available at output *A*. When a current flows in path *ACEFH*, this is state 0 and a current is available at output $\bar{A}$. When a current is applied to the reset

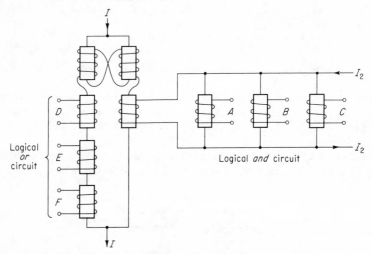

FIG. 6-18   A cryotron flipflop having serial and parallel inputs.

input, the flipflop changes from state 1 to 0; similarly the flipflop changes state from 0 to 1 with a set input.

Additional input cryotrons can be employed to form a multiple-input cryotron flipflop. Figure 6-18 illustrates the use of a logical-*and* circuit (positive logic) as one input circuit and the use of a logical-*or* circuit (positive logic) as the other input circuit. Cryotrons can be similarly used at the outputs. In either case, the added cryotrons in a serial path increase the switching time and thus reduce the operating speed.

One disadvantage of cryotron circuitry is the need for a cryostat, a low-temperature refrigerator. Cryostats of today are not reliable enough for computer application. Development of a small and reliable cryostat is being undertaken, and it may be ready for use when cryotrons are beyond the present research stage.

6-3   Thin-film Cryotrons

A cryotron, as described above, is a switching device in which one current controls another current. Three important characteristics of a cryotron are the critical field of the gate, which determines the control-coil current necessary to perform the switching; the current gain, which determines the amount of gate current that can be controlled; and the time constant, which determines the switching speed. Because of the low switching speed and tedious interconnections of wire-wound cryotrons, thin-film cryotrons are being developed by vacuum deposition of successive layers of superconductive and insulation material.

Superconductive Thin Film. Thin films are prepared by conventional vacuum deposition techniques. In a vacuum bell jar, pure tin is evaporated from a heated molybdenum boat in a vacuum of approximately 10^{-6} mm Hg. The vaporized tin condenses as a thin-film deposit on a substrate of glass, quartz, or sapphire. A metal mask on the substrate forms the desired shape of the film.

In thin-film cryotrons now being developed, tin has been commonly used as the gate material and lead as the control-coil material, in addition to an insulating material such as silicon monoxide. Since only tin changes its state during operation, several of its characteristics will now be briefly described: critical field, critical current, resistivity, and switching characteristic.

The critical field in a thin film is higher than the critical field in bulk metal. For example, as reported by Newhouse et al. [8], the critical field for tin, as a 3,000 Å film at 0.2° K below the zero-field transition temperature, is about 60 oersteds, twice the critical field of bulk tin. The critical field of a thin film consists of two components, tangential and normal. Both tangential and normal components are inversely proportional to film width, but the normal component further depends on the ratio of film width to thickness. This ratio for typical film is $10^3 : 10^5$; for these values, the maximum normal field is 2.5 to 4 times the tangential field.

As mentioned before, the critical current of a superconductor below its transition temperature is the maximum current that the superconductor can carry before the magnetic field produced by the current causes quenching. Smallman [13] has shown that the critical current I_{gm} of a film with a thickness t is related to the penetration depth λ. (The penetration depth is roughly equal to the thickness of the surface layer in which the current flows in a bulk superconductor.) For thin films, the critical current I_{gm} can be approximated by

$$I_{gm} = \frac{H_c t w_g}{0.4\pi\lambda} \qquad \text{for small } \frac{t}{2\lambda} \qquad (6\text{-}12)$$

Thus, the critical current for a thin film is directly proportional to the width w_g

and thickness t of the film and the critical magnetic field H_c. For thick films, the critical current I_{gm} can be approximated by

$$I_{gm} = \frac{H_c w_g}{0.4\pi} \quad \text{for large } \frac{t}{2\lambda} \qquad (6\text{-}13)$$

The critical current for a thick film is proportional to film width w_g and the critical field H_c but is independent of film thickness. Relations (6-12) and (6-13) assume a uniform current distribution in the film; this is quite close when there is a ground plane to be described subsequently. The boundary between thin and thick films may be taken in the region of thickness where $t/2\lambda$ is 1; for tin, this is a film thickness of about 3,000 Å at a temperature 0.25° K below the transition temperature. Note that the critical field can be increased by operating the film at a lower temperature below the transition temperature.

The critical current is significantly increased when a film of tin is deposited on top of an insulated lead shield plane, called a *ground plane*. Induced surface currents in the ground plane prevent flux penetration, and current distribution in the film of tin becomes more uniform. The insulation can be a silicon monoxide layer about 3,000 Å thick. It is highly desirable to use a ground plane in thin-film-cryotron logic circuits.

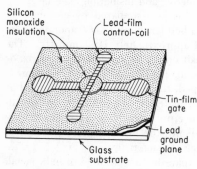

FIG. 6-19   A thin-film cryotron.

The low-temperature resistivity of tin as a film is much greater than the resistivity of pure bulk tin. This increased resistivity may be traceable to factors such as strain, impurity, and inhomogeneity which affect bulk material but have a more pronounced influence on films. However, high resistivity in films is desirable because it reduces the time constant and thus increases the switching speed of a cryotron.

The sharp transition switching characteristic holds good for a thin film of tin to which a short pulse current is applied; this is essentially an isothermal process. When a low-rising current is applied to cause switching, Joule heating causes thermal propagation of resistive areas in the film. Switching-characteristic behavior is hysteresislike in the transition region, and the slope in that region becomes sharper. For this reason, the switching characteristic depends on film resistivity and on substrate thermal conductivity.

Thin-film Cryotron.   Figure 6-19 shows a thin-film cryotron described by Slade [13]; it is also called a *planar* cryotron or *crossed-film* cryotron. On a glass substrate are deposited under vacuum a superconducting layer of lead as a ground plane and then an insulation layer of silicon monoxide. On the insulation layer are deposited a gate film of tin, an insulation layer again, and then a narrower control film. The lead, tin, and silicon monoxide layers are all 3,000 Å thick. The gate film of tin is 0.125 in. wide, and the lead control film is 0.006 in. wide. The common area between the gate and the control is called the *quenched area*. The quenched area is considered the effective portion of the cryotron; remaining portions of the films are considered as interconnecting leads.

Deposition of cryotrons and interconnections can be made simultaneously. Film deposition is amenable to large-scale fabrication at a possible low cost. However, the serious problem of uniformity and reproducibility has not been satisfactorily solved.

The current gain of a thin-film cryotron (with a ground plane) will now be determined. The current gain, as defined in relation (6-8), is the ratio I_{gm}/I_{cm}. The critical current I_{gm} for a thick film is shown in (6-13). The minimum current in the control film to quench the gate I_{cm} is approximated, as in relation (6-13), by

$$I_{cm} = \frac{H_0 w_c}{0.4\pi} \qquad \text{for large } \frac{t}{2\lambda} \qquad (6\text{-}14)$$

where w_c is the control-film thickness and H_0 is the surface field (between the control film and the ground plane) whose tangential component reaches the magnitude of the critical field H_c. By taking the ratio of (6-13) and (6-14) the current gain of a thick thin-film cryotron is

$$K = \frac{w_g H_c}{w_c H_0} \qquad (6\text{-}15)$$

Thus, the current gain is directly proportional to the ratio of gate width to control width. This also explains why the control width of the cryotron of Fig. 6-19 is narrower than the gate width. The current gain of the cryotron of Fig. 6-19 is 1 at about 3.7°K. At 3.73°K, the current gain is 1.3; at 3.55°K, it is 1.6; the current gain increases with lower operating temperature.

Superconducting Ground Plane. The ground plane is a superconductive layer and, as mentioned before, increases the critical current of the gate. The normal component of the field at the surface of the ground plane must be zero, since flux cannot penetrate a superconducting material; the ground plane achieves this by generating eddy currents (which do not decay with time) that produce a field exactly opposing the applied field.

The ground plane greatly affects the inductance of a cryotron. The inductance without a ground plane is proportional to the distance between the film and its return path. The inductance with a ground plane is proportional to the distance between the film and the ground plane. As a result, the inductance can be greatly reduced. For example, the inductance per unit length of a superconducting film 0.2 mm wide without a superconducting plane is 10^{-8} henry per cm if the return path is assumed to be 1 cm. The inductance per unit length for the same film with a ground plane is 10^{-11} henry per cm. This possible reduction is important, as the switching time of cryotrons is proportional to the inductance. The large reduction of cryotron inductance has made possible a great improvement in switching time.

The ground plane also affects the resistance of a cryotron during switching. When there is no ground plane, the portion of the gate film quenched and the restored gate resistance are proportional to the control current. When there is a ground plane, the normal component of the field is canceled. The gate resistance is restored by the tangential component in the quenched area, and it approaches a constant value when the control current becomes large. Experimental results show that, when there is no ground plane, a gate resistance exists even with no control current; this residual resistance does not occur with a ground plane.

Switching Time. The time required to switch a current from one path to another in a cryotron circuit is determined by the ratio of the inductance of the cryotrons and their interconnecting leads to the resistance which is causing the change to occur. The inductance of a current loop with its current changing depends, not on the area enclosed by the loop, but on the length and width of the leads involved. Therefore, all leads should be short and wide; otherwise, leads may contribute more inductance than cryotrons.

Slade [13] has given the calculation for a thin-film cryotron, as shown in Fig. 6-19. The calculation is based on the quenched area of the cryotron. The inductance of the control film L_{cf} [9] and the resistance of the gate R_{gate} are

$$L_{cf} = \frac{4\pi d l_c}{w_c} \times 10^{-9} \text{ henry} \qquad (6\text{-}16)$$

$$R_{\text{gate}} = \frac{\rho l_g}{t w_g} \quad \text{ohms} \qquad (6\text{-}17)$$

where d = distance between control and ground plane = 10^{-4} cm
l_c = length of control = 0.31 cm (0.125 in.)
w_c = width of control = 0.015 cm (0.006 in.)
ρ = resistivity of tin gate = 3×10^{-7} ohm-cm
l_g = length of gate = 0.015 cm = w_c
w_g = width of gate = 0.31 cm = l_c
t = thickness of gate = 3×10^{-5} cm

The calculated value of L_{cf} is about 3×10^{-11} henry. A similar calculation of the inductance of the gate L_{cg} is 2×10^{-14} henry and can therefore be neglected. The calculated value of R_{gate} is 5×10^{-14} ohm. The time constant τ as defined in Eq. (6-10) is

$$\tau = \frac{L_{cf}}{R_{\text{gate}}} = \frac{4\pi d t}{\rho} \left(\frac{w_g}{w_c}\right)^2 \times 10^{-9} \text{ sec} \qquad (6\text{-}18)$$

The time constant τ of a thin-film cryotron is proportional to the square of the ratio of gate width to control width. The calculated τ is 6×10^{-8} sec, about 1,000 times smaller than a typical wire-wound cryotron. As shown in relation (6-18), the time constant can be reduced further by using a thinner insulation layer between the gate and ground plane and a higher gate resistivity, as well as by operating the cryotron at a lower temperature.

6-4 Tunnel-diode Logic Circuits

The tunnel diode, invented by Esaki of Japan [14], is an extremely narrow p-n junction (of the order of 100 Å) consisting of a heavily doped (about 5×10^{19} atoms per cm^3) semiconductor material such as germanium or silicon. The doping is so heavy that both p and n regions become degenerate; i.e., the Fermi level must be within the conduction band in the n region and within the valence band in the p region, or vice versa. When forward-biased, the device exhibits a negative-resistance region; when reverse-biased, it is highly conducting. Owing to quantum-mechanical tunneling of electron waves across the space-charge layer of the *p-n* junction, these waves propagate with a speed comparable with that of light; thus, the high-frequency response is mainly limited by the junction capacity which exists across the junction. Tunnel-diode characteristics are virtually independent of the lifetime of minority carriers or of the surface treatment of the semiconductor material; consequently, a tunnel diode is very tolerant of nuclear radiation and of a very wide range of temperature variation.

Tunnel-diode Characteristic. The typical current-voltage characteristic of a germanium tunnel diode is the N-shaped curve in Fig. 6-20. In the forward-biased region, where the voltage is low (below 55 mv), the current, called *tunnel* current, consists of majority carriers; at a high voltage (about 400 mv), the diffusion current of an ordinary diode (i.e., the minority carriers injected across the junction) occurs. At an intermediate voltage, the current is called excess current—larger than the sum of the minority and majority carrier currents—and is not yet fully explained. The negative resistance occurs between the peak and

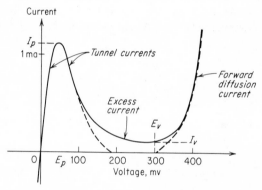

FIG. 6-20   Characteristic of a typical germanium tunnel diode.

valley of the forward-biased region and has a value of about 100 ohms. The peak and valley voltages are about 50 to 350 mv, respectively. The peak current I_p can be made from tens of a microampere to a few amperes. For a given peak current, the ratio of peak current I_p to valley current I_v is an important characteristic. The difference of the two voltages at the peak and valley currents is the voltage swing. Germanium tunnel diodes have been made with a peak-to-valley ratio as high as 14:1, a voltage swing as large as 0.5 volt, and an operating frequency as high as several kilomegacycles. A silicon tunnel diode with a voltage swing of 0.75 volt has been reported. Tunnel diodes have also been made from III-V compounds such as gallium antimonide and gallium arsenide. Gallium arsenide has been reported to have a peak-to-valley ratio of 60:1, a voltage swing of 1.2 volts, and an operating frequency exceeding 4 kMc.

In summary, the tunnel diode is an extremely rapid low-power bilateral semiconductor device with a negative-resistance region. It has a wide temperature range and is highly tolerant to nuclear radiation.

Backward Tunnel Diode. The backward tunnel diode consists also of an extremely narrow *p-n* junction made from a semiconductor, but slightly less heavily doped than the tunnel diode. In a backward diode, tunneling occurs in one direction but not the other. The current-voltage characteristic is shown in Fig. 6-21. When the device is reverse-biased, the current at a low voltage appears as a leakage current of tens of microamperes. There is no negative-resistance region, but a rectification region (zero current) exists in the forward-biased condition. The current which flows in the rectification region is still produced by tunneling and therefore is extremely rapid.

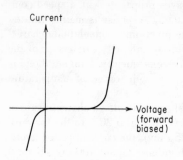

FIG. 6-21   Characteristic of a backward diode.

Single-diode Bistable Logic Circuit.
Figure 6-22 shows a single-diode bistable logic circuit which operates with two stable states at points *a* and *b*. Both states are stable, as they are located in the two positive regions of the characetristic. Supply voltage *E* and resistor *R* form a current bias for the diode. The input resistors form a current summing network. As shown in Fig. 6-22, the bias is chosen at

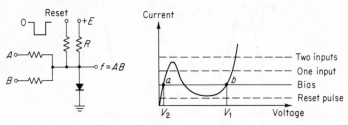

FIG. 6-22   A single tunnel-diode logical-*and* circuit (bistable operation).

such a level that a single current input keeps the diode current remaining in the low-voltage positive-resistance region, while two inputs are sufficient to switch the diode to the high-voltage positive-resistance region. The two possible levels of the output are voltages V_1 and V_2. For positive logic, this is an *and* circuit.

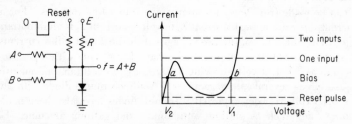

FIG. 6-23   A single tunnel-diode logical-*or* circuit (bistable operation).

If the bias is at such a level that either one current input or both inputs can switch the diode to the high-voltage positive-resistance region, the circuit becomes for positive logic an *or* circuit, shown in Fig. 6-23.

In the above logic circuits, the peak-current portion of the characteristic is utilized as a threshold; these circuits are called *threshold logic circuits.* They are analogous to magnetic-core logic circuits, not only in having a threshold property, but also in having storage capability. Similar to magnetic-core logic circuits, these tunnel-diode threshold logic circuits require a rest input (shown in Figs. 6-22 and 6-23) to reset the tunnel diode to its initial state. The reset input is a negative current pulse, while the inputs are positive current pulses.

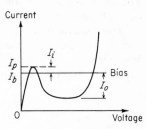

FIG. 6-24   Current gain $[=I_o/I_i = I_o/(I_p - I_b)]$.

The output current of the above logic circuits should be larger than the input current so that the output can drive other stages; this calls for a current gain greater than 1. As shown in Fig. 6-24, the current gain is the ratio of the output current I_o to the input current I_i, or $I_o/(I_p - I_b)$, where I_p and I_b are peak and bias currents, respectively. The bias level I_b should be chosen to maximize the current gain with due consideration to the characteristic variation of the tunnel diode.

Single-diode Monostable Logic Circuit. Figure 6-25 shows a single-diode monostable logic circuit which operates at one stable state at point a. The loca-

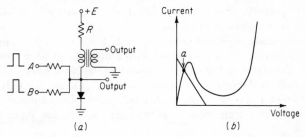

(a)   (b)

FIG. 6-25   A single tunnel-diode logic circuit with a pulse output (monostable operation).

tion of this bias level is determined by the load line. The choice of bias level determines either the *and* circuit or the *or* circuit, similar to the circuits in Figs. 6-22 and 6-23. The input resistors form a current summing network. The input or output is either a pulse or no-pulse. Inputs should occur simultaneously. The output pulse is fixed in duration when the input (or inputs) exceeds the threshold. In addition to a normal output a complement output is supplied by the transformer in Fig. 6-25. This monostable logic circuit resets itself after each operation.

Two-diode Logic Circuit. Figure 6-26a shows a pair of serially connected tunnel diodes, called a *Goto pair* [21]. If the proper levels of the two symmetrical voltages $+E$ and $-E$ are applied to terminals a and b of the pair, the current-voltage characteristics of each tunnel diode are superimposed and the resulting characteristic is shown in Fig. 6-26b. There are three points of intersection: A, B, and C. Point C is an unstable state because both diodes are in the negative-resistance region; but points A and B are both stable states because at either point A or B both diodes are in the positive-resistance regions. At point A or B, one diode is at a high voltage and the other at a low voltage. Let voltages at points A and B be $+V$ and $-V$, respectively; they represent the binary states. If a symmetric pair of clock pulses with magnitudes of $+E$ and $-E$ as shown in Fig. 6-26 are applied to terminals a and b, a voltage pulse with an amplitude of either $+V$ or $-V$ appears at output terminal c, depending on the initial voltage at terminal c being slightly positive or slightly negative.

Figure 6-27a shows a parallel network with an odd number of resistors connected to terminal f of the diode pair. The input resistors form a voltage summing network. When input pulses with an amplitude of either $+V$ or $-V$ are applied to the input terminals of the resistors, an output signal appears. The

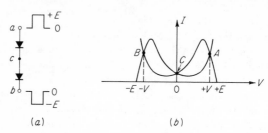

(a)   (b)

FIG. 6-26   A pair of tunnel diodes.   (a) A diode pair; (b) two stable states.

output signal has an amplitude of either $+V$ or $-V$, depending on the majority of input-pulse polarity. Such a circuit is called a *majority circuit;* majority logic operation has been described in Chap. 3.

In the tunnel-diode logic circuits of Fig. 6-27 there are three input terminals. If one input terminal is always excited with a negative pulse as shown in Fig. 6-27a, a positive pulse appears at the output terminal only when positive pulses are applied to both the other two input terminals. The output pulse occurs at the application of a pair of symmetrical clock pulses simultaneously with input pulses. For positive logic, this is an *and* circuit. If one input terminal is

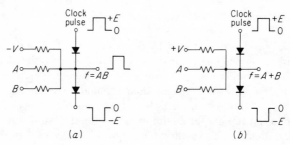

(a)   (b)

FIG. 6-27   Two tunnel-diode logic circuits (positive logic).   (a) *and* circuit; (b) *or* circuit.

always excited with a positive pulse as shown in Fig. 6-27b, a positive pulse appears at the output terminal when a positive pulse is applied to either or both of the other two input terminals and when the pair of clock pulses are simultaneously applied. For positive logic, this is an *or* circuit.

Interstage Coupling.   The tunnel-diode logic circuit, whether using a single diode or two diodes, is bilateral. The direction of information flow is controlled either by unilateral coupling or by gating with proper clock pulses.

Conventional diodes permit simple, unilateral coupling—but lower the speed capability of the tunnel diode.   The previously described backward tunnel diode switches rapidly.   Figure 6-28 illustrates an example of backward diode unilateral coupling for single-diode circuits.   Although this is not shown in Fig. 6-28, backward diode coupling is also applicable to two-diode circuits.

Interstage coupling can also be achieved by a three-phase symmetric clock system shown in Fig. 6-29.   The tunnel-diode logic circuits are divided into three groups, each group excited in turn by one phase.   For example, in Fig. 6-30, the leftmost two-diode *and* circuit belongs to the first group and is gated by the

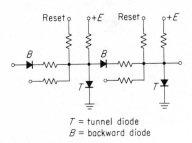

T = tunnel diode
B = backward diode

FIG. 6-28   Interstage coupling by using backward diodes.

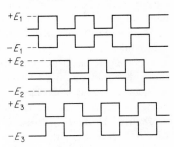

FIG. 6-29   Three-phase symmetric clock pulses.

E_1-phase clock; the middle *or* circuit belongs to the second group and is gated by the E_2-phase clock; the rightmost *and* circuit belongs to the third group and is gated by the E_3-phase clock.   The direction of information flow is determined by the relative timing of the three phases of clock pulses; in Fig. 6-29, it moves to the right.   A two-phase clock is not sufficient, and a three-phase clock is necessary for isolating adjacent diode pairs.   Although not shown in Fig. 6-30, a three-phase clock system is also applicable to single-diode logic circuits.

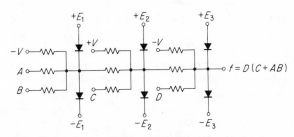

FIG. 6-30   Interstage coupling by using three-phase clock pulses.

Logical-not Circuits.   A tunnel-diode logical-*not* circuit which uses a pulse transformer was shown earlier, in Fig. 6-25.   Figure 6-31*a* illustrates another tunnel-diode logical-*not* circuit [18]; its operation is given in Fig. 6-31*b*.   As indicated, resistor R and supply voltage E are chosen to establish stable states at points a and b.   At point a, both voltage and current are high; at point b, both are low.   The circuit is normally at point a, and the output voltage is high.   If there is no input pulse, the output voltage remains high.   If an input current pulse triggers the diode current to exceed the threshold, the diode changes its state from point a to b and the output voltage is changed from high to low.

Another solution to the logical-*not* circuit is to use a two-line representation, as shown in Fig. 5-2; in this case, signals in one series of cascaded diode logic circuits represent the normal quantities, and those in the other series represent their respective complements.   This method doubles the required number of diodes, but it offers two advantages.   One is that the corresponding location of two lines can be compared for checking any malfunctioning of the circuit.   The other occurs if two corresponding diode pairs are placed nearby so that the current in one diode pair, flowing in one direction, supplies to the other pair the current which flows in the opposite direction.   In this way, the clock pulse need only initiate the current flow and then supply a small unbalanced current.

Backward-tunnel-diode Logic Circuit.   As shown in Fig. 6-21, the characteristic of a backward tunnel diode is similar in shape to that of a normal diode. Therefore, the backward diode can be used to form diode logic circuits such as those shown in Fig. 5-12.   One exception is that the backward diode should be connected in a reversed manner, since the forward-biased region of a backward diode is similar to the reversed region of an ordinary diode.

Tunnel-diode Flipflops.   Figure 6-32 shows several tunnel-diode flipflops. Circuit *a* is a single-diode flipflop similar to the circuit of Fig. 6-23.   Supply

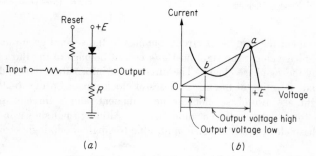

(a)   (b)

FIG. 6-31   A single-diode logical-*not* circuit.

voltage E and resistor R form a current source to bias the diode to a level shown in Fig. 6-23.   When a positive current pulse is applied to the set input, the flipflop is switched so that the output terminal is at voltage V_1 (Fig. 6-23); this is chosen here as state 1.   Applying a negative current pulse to the reset input switches the flipflop to have a voltage V_2 at its output terminal; this is state 0. The flipflop of Fig. 6-32*a* is an *RS* flipflop.

Circuit *b* is a three-stage single-diode flipflop.   The supply voltage is a three-phase clock having pulses E_1, E_2, and E_3 (but not $-E_1$, etc.), as was shown in Fig. 6-29; so the stored information is circulated.   Operation at the input employs the majority principle.   Let I be the magnitude of the current bias resulting from a pair of E_i and R.   To circulate the stored information, a current pulse of $+I$ is applied to terminal *a* and of $-I$ to terminal *b* at each circulation.   To store 1 into the flipflop, both terminals are supplied a current pulse of $+I$; to store 0, a current pulse of $-I$.

Circuit *c* is a flipflop consisting of three stages of two diodes each.   The flipflop is operated by the three-phase clock system of Fig. 6-29.   The setting and resetting of the flipflop are likewise achieved by the majority principle.

Circuit d of Fig. 6-32 is a single-input flipflop, reported by Chow [23] and having two tunnel diodes connected in series. Supply voltage E is d-c and of such magnitude that only one of the two diodes can be in the high-voltage low-current state and the other in the low-voltage high-current state. The difference

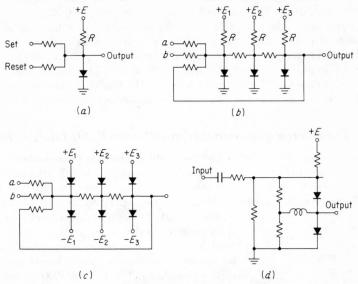

FIG. 6-32   Tunnel-diode flipflops.

between the two diode currents flows through the inductance and returns to the voltage supply. The input pulse always triggers the diode in the low-voltage high-current state into the high-voltage low-current state. Then the voltage appearing across the inductance triggers the other diode into the low-voltage high-current state.

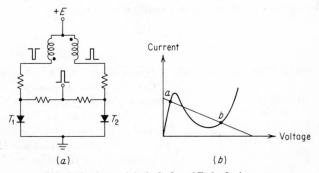

FIG. 6-33   A tunnel-diode flipflop of Eccles-Jordan type.

Figure 6-33a shows a tunnel-diode single-input flipflop, reported by Lockhart [22] and analogous to the Eccles-Jordan flipflops described in Chap. 5. There are two branches in the flipflop; each branch appears similar to the monostable circuit of Fig. 6-25. Each branch is biased, however, to have two stable states at points *a* and *b*, as in Fig. 6-33*b*. The two inductors are windings of a transformer, their polarities being shown by the dots. When diode T_1 is biased at point *a* and diode T_2 at point *b*, the condition obtained is referred to here as state 1. Reversing the bias condition establishes the 0 state.

Assume that the flipflop is at state 1. When a fast-rise pulse is applied to the input terminal, diode T_2 momentarily increases its current (i.e., point *b* moves to the right) but at the same time diode T_1 is triggered over the threshold and switches from point *a* to *b*. The switching of T_1 from point *a* to *b* causes a high rate of current change, which induces a large negative pulse across the transformer. This negative pulse in the branch with diode T_2 inhibits the input pulse; moreover, it switches T_2 from point *b* to *a*. The flipflop is thus changed from state 1 to 0. Each subsequent input pulse complements the flipflop state.

6-5   *Parametric-phase-locked-oscillator (PLO) Logic Circuits*

There are two approaches in the use of the parametric phase-locked subharmonic oscillators (PLO) as logic circuits, one using a varying inductance, and the other using a varying capacitance. Available variable inductors have losses which increase with frequency; hence, the upper operating frequency is limited.

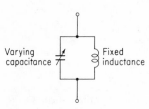

Varying capacitance   Fixed inductance

FIG. 6-34   A varying-capacitance tank circuit.

Available variable capacitors have low loss, even at frequencies in the kilomegacycle region. One version of the varying-inductance circuit is the Parametron, which makes use of ferrite cores; this will be described in Chap. 7. A PLO circuit using variable capacitance is described here.

Varying-capacitance Parametric Phase-locked Oscillator. The parametric phase-locked oscillator (PLO) consists essentially of a tank circuit, as shown in Fig. 6-34. This circuit is turned to a frequency f_o, and the capacitance is made to vary at different frequency f_p called the *pump frequency*. If these two frequencies bear the following relation (*n* is a positive interger).

$$f_o = \frac{n f_p}{2} \qquad (6\text{-}19)$$

the circuit can oscillate parametrically at frequency f_o. Usually, *n* is taken to be 1; then, the pump frequency f_p is twice the frequency of the parametric oscillation f_o.

The parametric oscillation can be locked to the pump oscillation in one of two possible phases which are 180° apart —phases *A* and *B* of Fig. 6-35. Phases *A* and *B* represent the binary states of the circuit. When the circuit is initially at rest and then the pump suddenly applied, both phases have an equal chance to occur. The circuit can be initiated into one or the other phase during the buildup time by applying a *locking signal*.

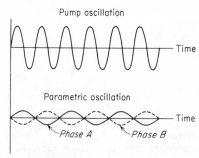

Pump oscillation

Time

Parametric oscillation

Time

Phase A   Phase B

FIG. 6-35   Pump and parametric oscillation frequencies.

A practical PLO circuit is shown in Fig. 6-36. It consists of a balanced tank circuit and a pump. The pump frequency signal is fed into the tank circuit through a transformer. The two back-biased diodes are used as capacitors; their connection is in series for the pump signal but in parallel for the parametric signal. Thus, the parametric oscillation in the tank circuit is decoupled from the pump; only parametric oscillation appears at terminals *a* and *b*. Terminals *a* and *b* are time-shared for both input locking signal and output signal. Another way to couple the input and the output is to use resistors; this arrangement is also shown in Fig. 6-36.

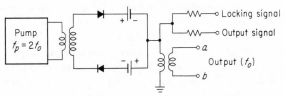

FIG. 6-36   A varying-capacitance balanced PLO circuit.

Phase Locking. As mentioned, a PLO can oscillate in either one of two phases. One method enabling the PLO to oscillate in a desired phase, called *forced phase locking*, uses the locking signal, which is a burst of oscillations at the parametric frequency f_o with a desired phase. This locking signal is injected into an oscillating PLO and forces the parametric oscillation to be in phase with the locking signal. In this method, the locking signal has to be large, and the buildup time is long if the PLO is oscillating at a different phase.

Another method, called *guided phase locking* (Fig. 6-37), makes use of a

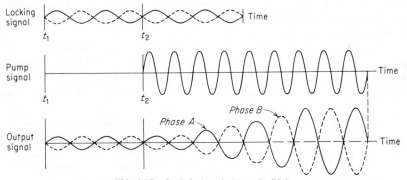

FIG. 6-37   Guided phase locking of a PLO.

pump which generates an oscillating signal intermittently. Initially the pump and the PLO are both not oscillating. At time t_1 the locking signal with a desired phase is applied to the PLO. At time t_2 the pump starts; this starts the PLO oscillating in the same phase as the locking signal. The buildup time ranges from 4 to 20 cycles of parametric oscillations. This method requires only a small locking signal, and the PLO becomes an amplifying device, although a pulsed pump is required.

The PLO Logic Circuits. The PLO logic circuit is formed by using a majority circuit as for the tunnel-diode logic circuit of Fig. 6-27. The majority circuit can be either resistive or inductive. Input signals to the majority circuit are either in phase A or in phase B and are added algebraically so that the resulting locking signal is a phase-A or a phase-B signal. Since the PLO is a bilateral circuit, information flow is achieved by the previously mentioned three-phase clock system. The PLO logic circuit is similar to the tunnel-diode logic circuit in its use of the majority principle; hence, it will not be further described.

In PLO circuits there are two frequencies, pump frequency and parametric frequency; neither is the frequency of information flow. Because there is a time interval for a PLO to change from one state to the other, the information frequency is much lower than the parametric frequency. For example, consider a microwave PLO with a pump frequency and a parametric frequency of 4,000 and 2,000 Mc, respectively. If at least 10 cycles of parametric oscillation is required for each change of PLO state, the information frequency is 200 Mc or lower. In the Japanese Parametron computer, MUSASINO I, the pump and the parametric frequencies are 2.4 and 1.2 Mc, respectively; and the information frequency is 10 kc, which is 120 times lower than the parametric frequency.

6-6   *Microwave Logic Circuits*

Microwave logic circuits are those which make use of microwave techniques for the purpose of achieving extremely high speed. There are two approaches, one using a baseband system and the other using a carrier system. In a baseband system, the signal occupies a frequency band starting at or near zero and extending to as high as a microwave frequency. In the carrier system, only a passband is required: a passband centered about a carrier frequency and as wide as 1,000 Mc. Although the baseband system is more directly comparable with conventional logic circuits, available microwave components such as the traveling-wave amplifier, parametric oscillator, hybrid ring, ferrite isolator, and others are better adapted to the carrier system.

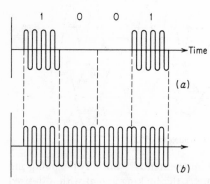

FIG. 6-38   Binary representation of microwave signals.

Signal Representation. Two methods of binary representation of signals in microwave circuits are shown in Fig. 6-38: r-f pulse representation and r-f phase representation. These two representations can be converted from one to the other by using a hybrid ring. Radio-frequency pulse representation is a carrier modulated by rectangular pulses; the presence or absence of an r-f pulse represents 1 or 0 (or vice versa). Radio-frequency phase representation has been described in connection with PLO circuits.

Microwave PLO Circuits. One favorable way of using the microwave circuit is the microwave parametric phase-locked subharmonic oscillator. A microwave PLO reported by Sterzer [29] is shown in Fig. 6-39. It is built from a strip transmission line and is thus quite compact. It consists of a 2,000-Mc (parametric-frequency) quarter-wave resonator having a variable-capacitance diode attached at one end, a 4,000-Mc (pump-frequency) half-wave resonant bar which permits the pump power to enter the resonator but prevents parametric oscillation power escaping from it, and a loosely coupled output arm. A locking signal of 60 db below the full output of the oscillator is sufficient to start the parametric oscillation in the desired phase. The amplitude of oscillations increases at the rate of 6 and 7 db per mμsec at low levels and falls to 3 db per mμsec at saturation. These rates were measured by first biasing the diode into conduction and then applying a d-c pulse to change the bias to a value which permits maximum power output. The time for the output to decay from saturation to a value too small to be measured is less than 1.5 mμsec. Coupling for PLO circuits may be by means of hybrid rings. The use of a three-phase clock system for controlling the information flow is generally quite complex and introduces significant delays. Unidirectional coupling may be achieved by using ferrite circulators or isolators, but they are usually quite bulky and may not be available at the desired frequency.

Logic circuits have been built from the above microwave PLO. The logical-*not* circuit in r-f phase representation is simply a transmission line one-half wavelength long. Logical-*and* and logical-*or* circuits are built by using the

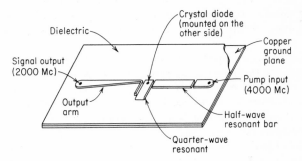

FIG. 6-39   A microwave parametric phase-locked subharmonic oscillator.

majority principle. A binary full adder has been made from these logic circuits and can be operated at a clock rate of 100 Mc.

Microwave Logic Circuits Using Detectors and Modulators. Microwave logic circuits using detectors and modulators have been reported by Ortel [31]. These circuits employ r-f pulse representation for the binary states. They are operated with a carrier frequency of 11,000 Mc (*X* band) and a pulse rate as high as 480 Mc. The basic logic circuit is essentially an r-f pulse generator, and amplification is achieved by using a traveling-wave amplifier.

The basic microwave circuit is shown in Fig. 6-40. It consists of a waveguide hybrid junction with four arms. Input r-f power C to arm 1 divides between arms 2 and 4. Arms 2 and 4 are terminated in diodes M_a and M_b, which form the modulators; these diodes are respectively controlled by diodes D_a and D_b, which form the detectors. The r-f output from arm 3 is simply the vector difference of the reflected waves in arms 2 and 4. When M_a and M_b are forward-biased in the absence of signals A and B, they have high admittances Y_a' and Y_b'; if these two admittances are equal, the reflected waves cancel and there is no output. When M_a is reverse-biased in the presence of signal A and thus has a low admittance

Y_a, and when M_b is forward-biased in the absence of the signal B and thus has a high admittance Y_b', there is a power output. A similar condition occurs when M_a is forward-biased and when M_b is reverse-biased.

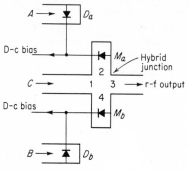

FIG. 6-40   A basic microwave logic circuit.

The bias to both diodes D_a and M_a comes from an external constant-current source. In the absence of r-f signals, the current from the external source divides equally between them, and these two diodes are both forward-biased. When an r-f signal is incident on diode D_a, conduction takes place during the peak of the r-f cycle and provides a d-c current to reverse the bias on M_a. When M_a is reverse-biased, the rectified current through D_a is equal to the current from the external source. The values of the forward bias and reverse bias supplying M_a must be large enough so that any r-f signal on M_a does not cross the zero-bias point during any part of the r-f cycle. Therefore, the r-f signal to D_a must be larger than the signal on M_a so that M_a never acts as a rectifier. Similar biasing occurs at D_b and M_b, and M_b never acts as a rectifier.

When Y_a and Y_a' are equal to Y_b and Y_b', respectively, the modulator is of a balanced type. In this case, the r-f power from C is transmitted to the output if only one, but not both, of signals A and B is present; the output is an exclusive-*or* operation of A and B. If B is made always absent, the output is a logical-*and* operation of A and C. If B and C are made always present, the output is a logical-*not* operation of A.

When Y_a' is equal to Y_b' but Y_a is not equal to Y_b, the modulator is not balanced. In this case, if C is made always present, the output is a logical-*or* operation of A and B.

Thus, the basic microwave circuit of Fig. 6-40 can be made into a number of basic logic circuits.

6-7   *Electroluminescent-Photoconductor Logic Circuits*

The phenomenon of electroluminescence, first reported by Destriau [39] in 1936, is a sustained emission of light by a phosphor subjected to an alternating electric field. An electroluminescent phosphor contains a small portion of impurity atoms (called *activators*); it becomes luminescent when the activators become ionized by absorbing sufficient energy from an externally applied electric field. An example of electroluminescent phosphor is zinc sulfide activated with copper and chlorine, which emits a predominantly green light at very low frequencies to a predominantly blue light at high frequencies. When an electroluminescent element is used in conjunction with a light-sensitive photoconductor such as cadmium sulfide, the resulting electroluminescent-photoconductor logic circuits offer the advantages of compactness, potentially low cost, low power consumption, and the unique property of light coupling. However, they are relatively slow at the order of 100 msec owing to the slow response of the photoconductor.

Electroluminescent-photoconductor circuits are sometimes called *optoelectronic* circuits or *photoelectronic* circuits. For convenience, an abbreviated term, EL-PC circuits, is used here.

Basic EL-PC Circuits. An electroluminescent element, shown in Fig. 6-41, consists of three layers. A layer of electroluminescent material suspended in a clear insulating plastic is sandwiched between two conductive layers; these three layers are deposited in turn on a glass substrate. An EL element is essentially a capacitor with the electroluminescent layer functioning as a dielectric. At least

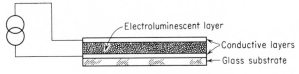

FIG. 6-41   An electroluminescent element.

one of the two conductive layers (such as tin oxide, bismuth oxide, or gold) is transparent so that the luminescence becomes visible. The EL layer must be very thin so as to have a large enough electric field to produce a sufficient intensity of light.

One basic EL-PC circuit is shown in Fig. 6-42. It consists of an electroluminescent element, a photoconductor element, and an a-c source; all are connected in series. The input to the circuit is a light with a spectrum sensitive to the photoconductor, as is indicated by another EL element shown in Fig. 6-42. When the input light is off, the resistance of the PC element is so large that the EL element does not become luminescent. When the input light is on, the re-

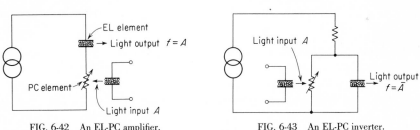

FIG. 6-42   An EL-PC amplifier.   FIG. 6-43   An EL-PC inverter.

sistance is so small that the EL element does become luminescent. This device is an amplifier with no inversion; the amount of gain depends on the relative sizes of the two EL elements.

When a pair of EL-PC elements are connected in parallel and then connected in series with a resistor as shown in Fig. 6-43, this arrangement constitutes another basic EL-PC circuit. The output light is off if the input light is on, and vice versa. This circuit provides an inversion. The relative sizes of the input and output EL elements again determine the gain. Thus, the EL-PC circuit of Fig. 6-43 is an inverting amplifier or a logical-*not* circuit.

Logic Circuits. Figures 6-44 and 6-45 are two logic circuits derived from the circuit of Fig. 6-42. In Fig. 6-44, there are two PC elements connected in parallel. The output light occurs when either input light appears. The table of operation is also shown in the figure, where + and − indicate that the light is on and off, respectively. For positive logic, this is a logical-*or* circuit. In Fig. 6-45, the two PC elements and the EL element are connected in series. The

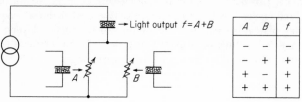

FIG. 6-44   An EL-PC logical-*or* circuit (positive logic) (+ and − represent the light being on and off, respectively).

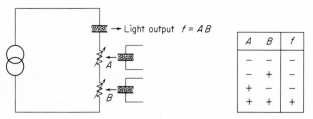

FIG. 6-45   An EL-PC logical-*and* circuit (positive logic).

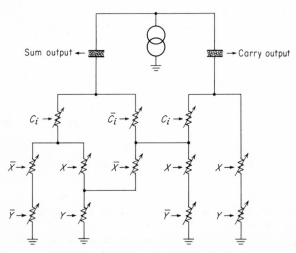

FIG. 6-46   Full adder using EL-PC logic circuit.

output light occurs only when both input lights appear. For positive logic, this is a logical-*and* circuit.

The serial and parallel aspects of the above logical-*and* and logical-*or* circuits are illustrated by a single-bit full adder shown in Fig. 6-46, where X, Y, and C_i

are the augend bit, addend bit, and input carry bit, respectively.   This adder is similar to that using DCTL circuits (Fig. 5-61).

Figures 6-47 and 6-48 are two logic circuits derived from the circuit of Fig. 6-43.   The tables of operation are also shown in the figures.   For positive logic, they are logical-*nor* and logical-*nand* circuits.

The serial resistor of Figs. 6-43, 6-47, and 6-48 can be replaced by a capacitor in order to save power.   This capacitor can be another EL element if no light coupling is permitted.

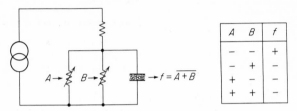

FIG. 6-47   An EL-PC logical-*nor* circuit (positive logic).

A	B	f
−	−	+
−	+	−
+	−	−
+	+	−

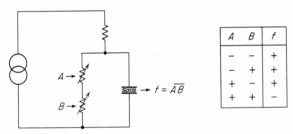

FIG. 6-48   An EL-PC logical-*nand* circuit (positive logic).

A	B	f
−	−	+
−	+	+
+	−	+
+	+	−

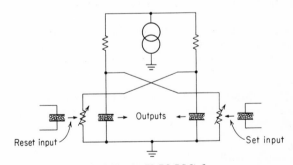

FIG. 6-49   An EL-PC *RS* flipflop.

Flipflop Circuits.   When the two logical-*not* circuits of Fig. 6-34 are cascaded, with the light output of the second stage fed back to the input of the first stage, the resulting circuit is as shown in Fig. 6-49.   There are two possible states: one EL element is on and the other is off, and vice versa.   The circuit of Fig. 6-49 is an *RS* flipflop, as there are two inputs, one for resetting and the other for setting the flipflop.

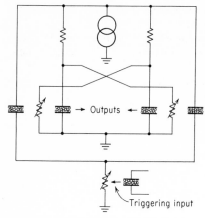

FIG. 6-50   An EL-PC trigger flipflop.

If the two input EL elements are connected in the manner shown in Fig. 6-50, the resulting flipflop becomes a trigger flipflop.   When an input light is applied, the flipflop changes its state to 1 if it is 0 or to 0 of it is 1.

References

Superconductor Logic Circuits

1. Schoenberg, D.: "Superconductivity," Cambridge University Press, New York, 1952.

2. Buck, D. A.: The Cryotron: A Superconductive Computer Component, *Proc. IRE,* April, 1956, pp. 482–493.

3. Buck, D. A.: A Magnetically Controlled Gating Element, *Proc. Eastern Joint Computer Conf.,* 1956, pp. 47–50.

4. Slade, A. E., and H. O. McMahon: A Cryotron Catalog Memory System, *Proc. Eastern Joint Computer Conf.,* 1956, pp. 115–120.

5. McMahon, H. O.: Superconductivity and Its Application to Electric Circuits, *Proc. Symposium on Role of Solid State Phenomena in Elec. Circuits,* 1957, pp. 187–195.

6. Slade, A. E., and H. O. McMahon: A Review of Superconductive Switching Circuits, *Proc. Natl. Electronics Conf.,* 1957, pp. 574–582.

7. Slade, A. E., and H. O. McMahon: Superconductive Devices, *Proc. Western Joint Computer Conf.,* 1958, pp. 103–107.

8. Newhouse, V. L., J. W. Bremer, and H. H. Edwards: The Crossed-film Crytron and Its Application to Digital Computer Circuits, *Proc. Eastern Joint Computer Conf.,* 1959, pp. 255–260.

9. Mendelssohn, K.: "Progress in Cryogenics," vol. 1, Academic Press, Inc., New York, 1959.

10. Smallman, C. R.: An Evaporated-film Cryotron Circuit, Digest of Technical Papers, *Solid State Circuits Conf.,* 1960, pp. 26–27.

11. Symposium on Superconductive Techniques for Computing Systems, *ONR Symposium Rept.* ACR-50, May 17–19, 1960.

12. Crittenden, E. C., Jr., J. N. Cooper, and F. W. Schmidlin: The Persistor: A Superconducting Memory Element, *Proc. IRE,* July, 1960, pp. 1233–1246.

13. Smallman, C. R., A. E. Slade, and M. I. Cohen: *Proc. IRE,* September, 1960, pp. 1562–1582.

Tunnel-diode Logic Circuits

14. Esaki, L.: New Phenomenon in Narrow Ge *p-n* Junctions, *Phys. Rev.,* vol. 109, pp. 603, 1958.

15. Lesk, I. A., N. Holonyak, Jr., U. S. Davidsohn, and M. W. Aarons: Germanium and Silicon Tunnel Diodes: Design, Operation, and Application, *IRE Wescon Conv. Record,* pt. 3, 1959.

16. Sommers, H. S.: Tunnel Diodes as High-frequency Devices, *Proc. IRE,* July, 1959, pp. 1201–1206.

17. Hall, R. N.: Tunnel Diodes, paper presented at IRE PGEC meeting, Oct. 29, 1959, Washington, D.C.

18. Lewin, M. H.: Negative-resistance Elements as Digital Computer Components, *Proc. Eastern Joint Computer Conf.*, 1959, pp. 15–27.

19. Lewin, M. H., A. G. Samusenko, and A. W. Lo: The Tunnel Diode as a Logic Element, *Digest of Technical Papers*, Solid State Circuits Conf., 1960, pp. 10–11.

20. Neff, G. W., S. A. Butler, and D. L. Critchlow: Esaki Diode Logic Circuits, *Digest of Technical Papers*, Solid State Circuits Conf., 1960, pp. 16–17.

21. Goto, E., K. Murata, K. Nakazaws, T. Moto-Oka, Y. Matsuoka, Y. Ishibashi, H. Ishida, T. Soma, and E. Wada: Esaki Diode High-speed Logical Circuits, *IRE Trans. on Electronic Computers*, March, 1960, pp. 25–29.

22. Lockhart, R. K.: Tunnel Diode Computer Logic Circuits, paper presented to IRE PGEC meeting, April, 1960, Washington, D.C.

23. Chow, W. F.: Tunnel Diode Digital Circuitry, *IRE Trans. on Electronic Computers*, September, 1960, pp. 295–301.

24. Gummel, H. K., and F. M. Smits: Margin Consideration for an Esaki Diode-resistor Or Gate, *Bell System Tech. J.*, January, 1961, pp. 213–232.

PLO and Microwave Logic Circuits

25. Edson, W. A.: Frequency Memory in Multi-mode Oscillations, *Stanford Univ. Electronics Research Lab. Tech. Rept.* 16, July 19, 1954.

26. Non-linear Capacitance or Inductance Switching, Amplifying and Memory Organs, U.S. patent 2,815, 477, Dec. 3, 1957.

27. Wigington, R. L.: A New Concept in Computing, *Proc. IRE*, April, 1959, pp. 516–523.

28. Lewis, W. D.: Microwave Logic, *Proc. Intern. Symposium on Theory of Switching*, 1959, pt. II, pp. 334–342.

29. Sterzer, F.: Microwave Parametric Subharmonic Oscillators for Digital Computing, *Proc. IRE*, August, 1959, pp. 1317–1324.

30. Meagher, R. E.: History and Introduction: Microwave Techniques for Computers, *IRE Trans. on Electronic Computers*, September, 1959, pp. 263–265.

31. Ortel, W. C. G.: Nanosecond Logic by Amplitude Modulation at X band, *IRE Trans. on Electronic Computers*, September, 1959, pp. 265–271.

32. Onyshkevych, L. S., W. F. Kosonocky, and A. W. Lo: Parametric Phase-lock Oscillator: Characteristics and Applications to Digital Systems, *IRE Trans. on Electronic Computers*, September, 1959, pp. 277–286.

33. Hilibrand, J., C. W. Mueller, C. F. Stocker, and R. D. Gold: Semiconductor Parametric Diodes in Microwave Computers, *IRE Trans. on Electronic Computers*, September, 1959, pp. 287–297.

34. Blattner, D. J., and F. Sterzer: Fast Microwave Logic Circuits, *IRE Trans. on Electronic Computers*, September, 1959, pp. 297–301.

35. Sauter, W., and P. J. Isaacs: Microwave Logic Circuits Using Diodes, September, 1959, pp. 302–307.

36. Rajchman, J. A.: Solid-state Microwave High Speed Computers, *Proc. Eastern Joint Computer Conf.*, 1959, pp. 38–47.

37. Eckhardt, W., and F. Sterzer: A Modulation-demodulation Scheme for Ultrahigh-speed Computing and Wideband Amplification, Digest of Technical Papers, *Solid State Circuits Conf.* 1960, pp. 24–35.

38. McIsaac, P. R., and I. Itzkan: A New Class of Switching Devices and Logic Elements, *Proc. IRE*, July, 1960, pp. 1264–1271.

Electroluminescent-Photoconductor Logic Circuits

39. Destriau, G.: Experimental Studies on the Action of an Electric Field on Phosphorescent Sulfides. *J. chim. phys.*, vol. 33, p. 620, 1936.

40. Ghandhi, S. R.: Photoelectronic Circuit Applications, *Proc. IRE*, January, 1959, pp. 4–11.

41. Bray, T. E.: An Electro-optical Shift Register, *IRE Trans. on Electronic Computers,* June, 1959, pp. 113–117.

42. Domenico, R. J., and R. A. Henle: All-purpose Computer Circuits, *Electronics,* Aug. 19, 1960, pp. 56–58.

43. O'Connell, J. A., and B. Narken: Increasing the Brightness-voltage Nonlinearity of Electroluminescent Devices, *IBM J. of Research Develop.,* October, 1960, pp. 426–429.

44. O'Connell, J. A.: An Electroluminescent-Photoconductor Device for Variable Pattern Recognition, *IBM Data Systems Div. TR* 00.762, 1960.

45. Low, P. R., and G. A. Maley: Flow Table Logic, *Proc. IRE,* January, 1961, pp. 221–228.

46. Smith, D. H.: Electroluminescence, Its Characteristics and Applications, *Electronic Eng.,* pt. 1, pp. 68–72, 1961, pt. 2, pp. 164–170, March, 1961.

47. Greenberg, I.: Electroluminescent Display and Logic Devices, *Electronics,* Mar. 24, 1961, pp. 31–36.

7

Magnetic-core Logic Circuits

All physical circuits have delays. The delay in the logic circuits of the last two chapters is made small in comparison with the time for each digital operation. The delay in magnetic logic circuits is different in that it can be made indefinite because of the permanent storage property of magnetic material. As will be seen, such a permanent delay can become advantageous in certain applications, as digital circuits are operated in a time sequence.

Magnetic logic circuits using toroidal cores are the subject of this chapter. Those using multiaperture cores are described in Chap. 8.

7-1   Magnetic-core Characteristics

Magnetic-core Switching.   Magnetic-core material exhibits a rectangular hysteresis loop (Fig. 7-1), which relates the applied magnetic field H and the flux density, or induction, B in the material. There are two unique values of flux density at zero applied field, $\pm B_r$, called *remanence*, or *residual induction*. These are the binary states of the core. The positive remanence $+B_r$ may be designated as the *binary* 1, or *set, state* and $-B_r$ as the *binary* 0, or *reset, state*. To change the remanence, a field, called *coercive force H_c*, must be applied in reverse. A core can be switched from one state to the other by applying a current pulse through its winding, shown in Fig. 7-2a. The dynamic paths during the switching are indicated by the dashed lines *rabs* and *scdr* in Fig. 7-1. The nearly

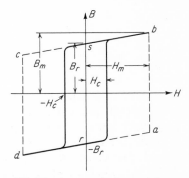

FIG. 7-1   A rectangular hysteresis loop.

horizontal paths *ra* and *sc* are traversed during the rise time of the applied pulse and the paths *bs* and *dr* during the fall time. Along the vertical paths *ab* and *cd*, most of the switching time is taken up, and most of the flux change (or flux reversal) takes place. The voltage waveform on the output winding of the core when it is switched by a rectangular current pulse applied to the input winding is shown in Fig. 7-2. This output voltage is proportional to the rate of flux change. Figure 7-2b shows the output voltage waveform when the core is switched from one state to the other (paths *rabs* or *scdr*). It may be called the *switching voltage*. The initial peak occurs during the rise time and is caused by the rapid traversal of the horizontal path *ra* or *sc*. The remainder of the positive waveform is generated on the vertical path *ab* or *cd*. A short negative peak occurs during the fall of the applied pulse and is caused by the traversal of the horizontal path *bs* or *dr*. Figure 7-2*c* shows the output voltage waveform when the core is switched without changing its state. This waveform may be called the *nonswitching voltage*. The state of a core which is being "non-switched" follows the horizontal path *sb* or *rd* on the rise of the applied current and returns to its starting point *s* or *r* on the fall of the current. The nonswitching voltage is much smaller than the switching voltage and is regarded as noise. The equal areas under the positive and negative peaks testify to no net change in flux.

For computer application, the area under the positive nonswitching voltage peak should be negligible so that the output is either a distinct switching pulse or no-pulse. This requires the two flat portions of the hysteresis loop to be nearly

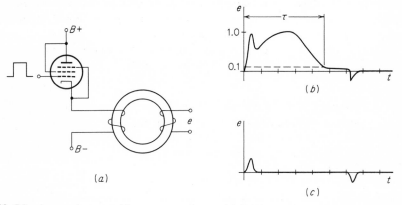

FIG. 7-2 A magnetic core and its output waveforms. (*a*) Switching core; (*b*) switching voltage; (*c*) nonswitching voltage.

horizontal, a characteristic described by the *squareness ratio* B_r/B_m, where B_m is the saturation flux density. Available cores have a squareness ratio in the range 0.85:0.98; this means that a signal-to-noise ratio of about 20 is feasible. A small coercive force H_c is desired because then a small drive current is required. The quantity B_r should be large because this occasions a large flux change during the switching, which in turn gives a large signal output. The loop area should be small for a small eddy-current loss.

Domain Theory of Magnetization. Magnetization of a material can be explained by Weiss's domain theory, which postulates that a ferromagnetic material consists of many small regions, called *domains*. Each domain is composed of numerous magnetic moments. The magnetic moment of a domain is determined by the magnitude and direction of its magnetization. Each domain is magnetized to saturation and is oriented to a certain direction, called the *direction of easy magnetization*. In the absence of an external field, these domains are aligned at random so that the total magnetization of the material is zero.

The domain size depends on composition and treatment of the material; its linear dimensions range from 10^{-2} to 10^{-5} cm. The boundary between domains which can orient in different directions is called a *Bloch wall*. The wall volume is small compared with the volume of the domain. The domain wall is not sharp, as orientation of atoms in the wall changes gradually. The wall is quite thin; for example, it is about 1,000 atoms thick in iron.

Domains rearrange themselves in the presence of an external magnetic field. Favorably oriented domains grow in a field at the expense of those opposed to the field; thus, the domain walls move, and the domain volumes change. The wall motion can be reversible (in a weak field) or irreversible (in a stronger field). When a weak field is applied, the domain walls move but return to their original position on removal of the field. Under the influence of a stronger field the domain walls move but do not return. The magnetization reversal in switching a magnetic core is attributed to this irreversible wall motion.

Another possible domain motion is a reversible domain rotation in a strong field; the domain tends to align with the field. When the dimensions of a ferromagnetic material approach the domain wall thickness, change in magnetization is possible, not by wall motion, but by domain rotation. The domain rotation occurs favorably in a strong field when there is a direction of easy magnetization.

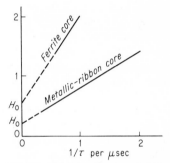

FIG. 7-3   Switching-time characteristic of magnetic core.

Switching Time. Four important magnetic-core characteristics are the d-c coercive force H_c, the squareness ratio B_r/B_m, the flux reversal $B_r + B_m$, and the switching time. The first three have already been discussed.

The switching time τ of a magnetic core may be defined as the time required for the output voltage to go from 10 per cent of its maximum value through the maximum and down to 10 per cent. It is the flux-reversal characteristic of the core. If the applied magnetic-field intensity H is plotted against the reciprocal of switching time, the resulting graph is nearly a straight line, as indicated by Fig. 7-3. This line extrapolated would intercept the ordinate at a value H_0. Actually, as the H axis is approached, the core begins to cycle minor hysteresis loops and the line in Fig. 7-3 bends toward the origin. This straight line is described by the following relation,

$$\tau = \frac{S_w}{H - H_0} \qquad \text{for } H \geq 2H_c \qquad (7\text{-}1)$$

where S_w, the switching coefficient, is the slope of the straight line. The switching characteristics of metal-ribbon core and ferrite core are exemplified in Table 7-1 [19]. The lower switching coefficient of the 4-79 molybdenum-permalloy core permits it to switch nearly twice as fast as the ferrite core at a given applied field difference $(H - H_0)$.

Magnetic-core Types. Magnetic cores with a rectangular-loop characteristic have been developed in two types: the metal-ribbon core and the molded ferrite core. The ribbon-type core is made of a grain-oriented alloy and consists of a

Table 7-1   Switching Characteristics of Metal-ribbon and Ferrite Cores

Material	S_w, oersted-sec (emu)	H_0, oersteds (emu)
⅛-mil 4-79 molybdenum-permalloy..........	0.55×10^{-6}	0.14
¼-mil 4-79 molybdenum-permalloy..........	0.63×10^{-6}	0.14
Ferramic MF-1312B.....................	1.02×10^{-6}	0.52

number of wraps of an ultrathin ribbon wound on a bobbin. The last wrap is usually spot-welded in place. The whole unit is then heat-treated in a dry hydrogen atmosphere to maximize the squareness ratio. The annealing process is critical and must be carefully controlled if an optimum result is to be achieved. The use of ultrathin ribbon, 1 mil (0.001 in.) to ⅛ mil, reduces the eddy current. Ceramic bobbins are used because they can withstand annealing temperatures. Ribbon-type cores may be fabricated in other ways and packaged in plastic bobbins. The two alloy materials most commonly used in computer applications are 4-79 molybdenum-permalloy and 48 per cent nickel-iron alloy. A typical core might have 20 wraps of ⅛-mil molybdenum-permalloy ribbon on a ⅛-in.-wide and 0.2-in. mean-diameter bobbin.

Ferrites are magnetic ceramics, fabricated in a manner similar to that used in making ceramics. A finely powdered mixture containing magnetite, various bivalent metals, and an organic binder is pressed into a small toroidal shape. Sintering these molded cores in a reducing atmosphere results in a ferromagnetic compound. Since some ferrites have d-c resistivities nearly 10^{12} times that of metals, the eddy-current loss is negligible and laminations are not required.

Cores are made in different sizes. The larger cores have been used in circuits where numerous turns are wound on the core, while the tiny ferrite cores (50 or 80 mils outside diameter) have been used primarily for magnetic-core memories, where only a very few copper wires pass through the toroid itself. Both types of cores have been plagued with nonuniformity in their characteristics. The metal-ribbon cores are either manually wound or machine-wound and vary according to the tension of ribbon, thickness of ribbon, etc. It is thus difficult to achieve good uniformity at low cost. Fabrication techniques have been improved, however, and greater uniformity can now be obtained.

Three major energy losses attending irreversible magnetization are hysteresis, eddy-current, and relaxation loss. Menyuk and Goodenough [14] have expressed the energy loss per cubic centimeter per cycle for the grain-oriented material as

$$\text{Hysteresis loss + eddy-current loss + relaxation loss} = 4H_0I_m + S_w \frac{4I_m}{\tau} \tag{7-2}$$

and
$$S_w = S_{we} + S_{wr} \tag{7-3}$$

where I_m is equal to $B_m/4\pi$. The switching coefficient S_w is made up of two parts: S_{wr}, contributed by relaxation loss, and S_{we} contributed by eddy-current loss. For thin metal ribbons and ferrites, S_{we} is very much smaller than S_{wr}. Relaxation loss is essentially a damping loss manifested by the delay of the electron-spin vectors in aligning themselves in the direction of the applied field.

The power dissipation of a core is proportional to the repetition frequency if the peak amplitude of the applied field remains constant. The heating effects which may result from operation at high repetition frequency limit the operation of the magnetic core as a switching device. The power dissipation per core is somewhat smaller in metal cores, because the higher flux density of metal ribbon permits the use of a smaller cross section and hence a smaller volume of metal than of ferrite to achieve the same amount of flux change; also the metal requires less magnetomotive force (mmf) to obtain the same time-rate of flux change. Furthermore, the high thermal conductivity of molybdenum-permalloy permits any cooling scheme applied to the surface of the core to be effective in cooling the entire volume. The metal core is less sensitive to small temperature changes at room temperature, because molybdenum-permalloy has the higher Curie temperature of 460°C, while ferrite has a lower value of 300°C.

In conclusion, magnetic cores offer great reliability and long life. Ferrite cores are more widely used in memories such as the coincident-current type because of better uniformity and lower cost. Switching time for this application can approach 1 μsec. Metal-ribbon cores have two attractive features, having a very square hysteresis loop, which reduces the noise, and requiring a relatively small driving current for switching. They are better for switching circuits and shift registers. Their practical switching time has been about 10 μsec; for shorter switching times, the driving power would become excessive. Recent fabrication techniques have improved the switching time to about 2 μsec.

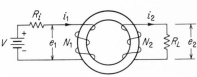

FIG. 7-4   A simple magnetic-core circuit.

Basic Relations of Magnetic-core Switching Circuits. The basic relations of a simple magnetic-core switching circuit shown in Fig. 7-4 are now developed as an illustration. There are two windings on the core, the input winding with N_1 turns and the output winding with N_2 turns. The reactance effect of the two windings in this case is considered negligible. The input winding is driven by a voltage source V with an internal resistance R_i that includes the resistance of winding N_1. The output winding is connected to a load R_L. The resistance of winding N_2 is included in R_L. The input mmf F_{in} is equal to the sum of core mmf F_{core} and load mmf F_{load},

$$F_{in} = F_{core} + F_{load} \qquad (7\text{-}4)$$

The input and load mmfs are equal to their respective ampere-turns, or

$$F_{in} = N_1 i_1 \qquad (7\text{-}5)$$

$$F_{load} = N_2 i_2 \qquad (7\text{-}6)$$

The core mmf F_{core} bears the following relation to applied field H in oersteds (emu),

$$F_{core} = 2.5Hd \qquad (7\text{-}7)$$

where d is the core mean diameter in centimeters. By substituting (7-5) to (7-7) into (7-4) we have

$$N_1 i_1 - N_2 i_2 = 2.5Hd \qquad (7\text{-}8)$$

In (7-8), H should be larger than H_c for the flux reversal to occur. The two currents i_1 and i_2 can be determined from the input and load circuits as follows:

$$V = i_1 R_1 + e_1 \tag{7-9}$$

$$e_2 = i_2 R_L \tag{7-10}$$

It is assumed that the exciter voltage e_1 and the induced voltage e_2 are square pulses and that e_2 is generated during the switching time τ. This implies that the rate of change of flux with time is a constant, or

$$e_1 = \frac{(\emptyset_r + \emptyset_m) N_1 \times 10^{-8}}{\tau} \tag{7-11}$$

$$e_2 = \frac{(\emptyset_r + \emptyset_m) N_2 \times 10^{-8}}{\tau} \tag{7-12}$$

where $\emptyset_r$ and $\emptyset_m$ are, respectively, the residual flux and maximum flux in maxwells. The above two relations and that for the switching time [(7-1)] enables one to design a simple switching core. If the output winding is connected to

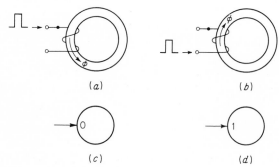

(a)   (b)

(c)   (d)

FIG. 7-5   Reset and set windings. (a) Reset winding and reset state; (b) set winding and set state; (c) symbolic representation of reset winding; (d) symbolic representation of set winding.

another core, then the term $i_2 R_L$ in relation (7-10) should be replaced by a term due to the induced voltage. If other output windings are wound on the same core, additional terms in mmf should appear in relation (7-4).

The slope of the hysteresis loop in Fig. 7-1 is related to inductance. Since the sides of most rectangular loops are not exactly vertical, there is a small inductive effect during the major portion of the flux-reversal period. The inductive effect in conjunction with the effect of distributed capacitance in the windings can sustain a shock-excited oscillation. This oscillatory tendency can be reduced by proper circuit design. As inductance is proportional to the square of the number of turns, reducing the turns will reduce the inductance rapidly; it will also reduce the distributed capacitance. One approach is to reduce the number of turns until the resonant frequencies are above the circuit response frequencies and also to eliminate high-frequency components in driving pulses by slowing down the rise and fall time. In addition, proper spacing of windings can reduce leakage inductance and affect the coupling between separate windings.

7-2   Logic Operations on a Single Core

Input and Output Windings.   A single magnetic core with an input winding is shown in Fig. 7-5.   The input to the winding is either a pulse or no-pulse.
If a pulse is applied to the dotted terminal shown in circuit *a*, the core is magnetized in the counterclockwise direction.   This core state is designated the 0
state and the input winding called a *reset winding*.   If a pulse is applied to the
undotted terminal as shown in circuit *b*, the flux is in a clockwise direction.   This
core state is designated the 1 state and the input winding called a *set winding*.
For convenience, symbolic representations for these two cases are shown in Fig.
7-5*c* and *d*.   The core is represented by a circle, and a line with an arrow pointing to the circuit represents an input to the core.   The binary number 1 or 0
ahead of the arrow indicates whether the input winding is a set or a reset winding, respectively.

As shown in Table 5-2, when a pulse represents 1 and no-pulse represents 0,
this designation is called positive logic.   Since positive logic has been widely
used in magnetic-core logic circuits, it is presumed hereafter unless otherwise
stated.

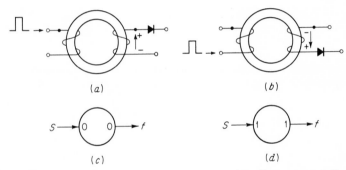

(a)   (b)

(c)   (d)

FIG. 7-6   Output reset and set windings.   (*a*) Output reset winding; (*b*) output set winding; (*c*) symbolic representation of output reset winding; (*d*) symbolic representation of output set winding.

Whether the original state of the core is 1 or 0, the core will be in the 0 or 1
state when a pulse is applied to a reset or a set winding, respectively.   If the
core is in the 1 state and a pulse is applied to a reset winding as shown in Fig.
7-6*a*, there is a flux reversal.   The core presents a relatively large impedance to
the input driver, and a relatively large voltage is generated at the output winding.   A similar but inverse output appears if the core is in the 0 state and a pulse
is applied to a set winding as shown in Fig. 7-6*b*.   Conversely, if the core is at
the 0 state and a pulse applied to a reset winding, there is no flux reversal and
a small voltage appears at the output.   These outputs are the voltage waveforms
shown in Fig. 7-2.

The core may have other input set or reset windings.   So that the output winding will permit current flow only when the core is switched to the 0 state, a diode
is provided at the output terminal, with its polarity connected as shown in Fig.
7-6*a*; such an output winding is called an *output reset winding*.   If the output
winding permits current flow only when the core is switched to the 1 state, the
diode is connected as shown in Fig. 7-6*b*; such an output winding is called an

output set winding. In either case, the associated input winding may be called the *shift winding.* The symbolic representations are shown in Fig. 7-6c and d. The line originating at the circuit represents the output terminal. The binary number 1 or 0 at the tail of the line and inside the circle represents the core state after the core is switched. It is noted that each pair of input and output windings must have the same binary symbol inside the circle.

Magnetic Cores with One Boolean Input. Figure 7-7 shows a core with three input windings and one output reset winding. Input windings R and S are reset windings. Winding A is a set winding, and its input represents a Boolean variable. The operation follows this sequence: The core is first reset by winding R at instant t_1; input A, whether it is 1 (pulse) or 0 (no-pulse), is then applied at instant t_2; the core is then reset by winding S at instant t_3. Instants t_1, t_2, and t_3 occur in time sequence separated by a time interval τ. If input A is 1, the reset by winding S produces a pulse output, as there is a flux reversal. If input A is 0, no output appears because no flux reversal has occurred. This operation is shown in the table in Fig. 7-7, where g and f represent the core state and the output voltage, respectively, and $+$ and $-$ represent a pulse or no-pulse, respectively. This sequential operation performs two functions: the storing of

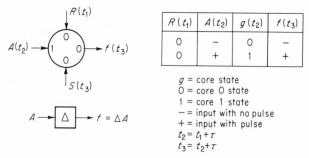

$R(t_1)$	$A(t_2)$	$g(t_2)$	$f(t_3)$
0	$-$	0	$-$
0	$+$	1	$+$

g = core state
0 = core 0 state
1 = core 1 state
$-$ = input with no pulse
$+$ = input with pulse
$t_2 = t_1 + \tau$
$t_3 = t_2 + \tau$

FIG. 7-7   A single core used as a 1-bit storage element or as a delay element.

the input information of the Boolean variable A by $R(t_1)$ and $A(t_2)$, and the reading out of the stored information by $S(t_3)$. Since the final output is identical to input A and occurs after a delay Δ (i.e., at time interval τ later), this is a delay operation, or

$$f = \Delta A \tag{7-13}$$

It should be pointed out that reset windings R and S may be combined and only reset winding S used.

If input winding S and output winding f are replaced by two set windings as shown in Fig. 7-8, the arrangement becomes a delayed logical-*not* circuit. The table of operation is shown in the figure. The contents of the tables in Figs. 7-7 and 7-8 are the same except in the last columns, owing to the difference in the output and shift windings. Symbolically, this operation is

$$f = \Delta \bar{A} \tag{7-14}$$

Windings A and S may be combined and only input winding A used.

Magnetic Cores with Two or More Boolean Inputs. Figure 7-9 shows a core with four input windings and one output reset winding. Input windings R and S are reset windings, and A and B are set windings. Windings A and B are the inputs and represent two Boolean variables. The operation follows the sequence: the core is reset by winding R at instant t_1; inputs A and B are applied at instant t_2; winding S resets the core to the 0 state at instant t_3. The table of operation is shown in Fig. 7-9. For positive logic, this is a delayed logical-*or* circuit,

$$f = \Delta(A + B) \qquad (7\text{-}15)$$

Again windings R and S can be combined into one. If the shift and output windings in Fig. 7-9 are both replaced by set windings, the resulting circuit is as

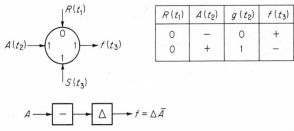

$R(t_1)$	$A(t_2)$	$g(t_2)$	$f(t_3)$
0	−	0	+
0	+	1	−

FIG. 7-8   A magnetic-core *not* circuit.

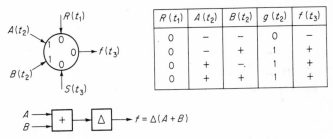

$R(t_1)$	$A(t_2)$	$B(t_2)$	$g(t_2)$	$f(t_3)$
0	−	−	0	−
0	−	+	1	+
0	+	−.	1	+
0	+	+	1	+

FIG. 7-9   A magnetic-core *or* circuit (positive logic).

shown in Fig. 7-10. For positive logic, this is a delayed logical-*nor* circuit, or

$$f = \Delta(\overline{A + B}) \qquad (7\text{-}16)$$

The function performed by winding S can be taken over by input windings A and B.

If input winding A in Fig. 7-9 is replaced by a reset winding (Fig. 7-11), positive logic designates this configuration as a delayed logical-*andnot-A* circuit (also known as an inhibit circuit), or

$$f = \Delta(\bar{A}B) \qquad (7\text{-}17)$$

Windings R and S can again be combined. If input winding A in Fig. 7-10 is replaced by a reset winding as in Fig. 7-12, then, for positive logic, this is a delayed *ornot-B* circuit, or

$$f = \Delta(A + \bar{B}) \qquad (7\text{-}18)$$

Winding S may again be combined with input winding B. The circuits in Figs. 7-11 and 7-12 are complementary.

The representation of the 1 and 0 states of the core in Fig. 7-5 has been arbitrarily chosen. If the clockwise and counterclockwise directions of the flux are now chosen to represent 0 and 1, respectively, the logic circuits of Figs. 7-7 to 7-12 have their 1's replaced by 0's and their 0's by 1's, as shown in Fig. 7-13. It

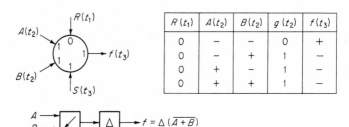

$R(t_1)$	$A(t_2)$	$B(t_2)$	$g(t_2)$	$f(t_3)$
0	—	—	0	+
0	—	+	1	—
0	+	—	1	—
0	+	+	1	—

$$f = \Delta\,(\overline{A + B})$$

FIG. 7-10   A magnetic-core *nor* circuit (positive logic).

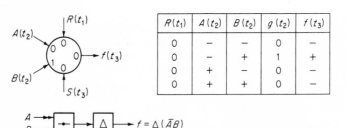

$R(t_1)$	$A(t_2)$	$B(t_2)$	$g(t_2)$	$f(t_3)$
0	—	—	0	—
0	—	+	1	+
0	+	—	0	—
0	+	+	0	—

$$f = \Delta\,(\bar{A}B)$$

FIG. 7-11   A magnetic-core *andnot-A* (or inhibitor) circuit (positive logic).

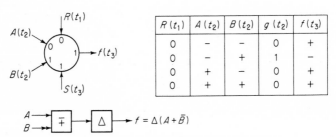

$R(t_1)$	$A(t_2)$	$B(t_2)$	$g(t_2)$	$f(t_3)$
0	—	—	0	+
0	—	+	1	—
0	+	—	0	+
0	+	+	0	+

$$f = \Delta\,(A + \bar{B})$$

FIG. 7-12   A magnetic core *ornot-B* circuit (positive logic).

can readily be verified that the six circuits of Fig. 7-13 perform the same logic operations as the circuits in Figs. 7-7 to 7-12.

Circuits for more than two Boolean variables can be similarly constructed. The practical limitations are considerations of noise as a result of the nonswitching operation, core size due to the required number of windings, driving currents, temperature effects, and operating speed.

7-3 Single-diode Transfer-loop Circuits

The transfer loop is a circuit that connects two or more cores. Since a magnetic-core circuit is bilateral, some means has to be provided in the transfer loop for controlling the information flow. The different types of transfer loops result in different magnetic-core logic circuits. Several transfer loops will now be described.

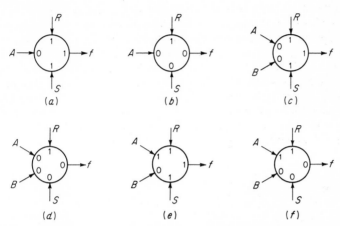

FIG. 7-13 Six magnetic-core symbolic circuits (positive logic) using clockwise and counterclockwise directions of flux to represent 0 and 1, respectively. (a) Delay circuit; (b) delayed *not* circuit; (c) delayed *or* circuit; (d) delayed *nor* circuit; (e) delayed *andnot-A* circuit; (f) delayed *ornot-B* circuit.

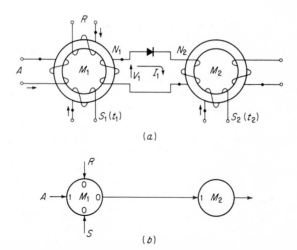

FIG. 7-14 Single-diode transfer loop. (a) Transfer loop; (b) symbolic representation.

The Single-diode Transfer Loop. This transfer loop [1] has a single diode in the loop. It is shown together with its symbolic representation in Fig. 7-14. The loop transfers information from core M_1 to core M_2. Assume that core M_2 is initially at 0 state. When core M_1 is at the 0 state, a pulse to the S_1 winding produces no output; and nothing happens to core M_2. This is a transfer of the 0 state of core M_1 to core M_2. If core M_1 is at the 1 state, a pulse to the S_1 winding produces a pulse with voltage V_1 at winding N_1. By a proper design of windings N_1 and N_2, current I_1 flowing through winding N_2 is sufficient to switch core M_2 into the 1 state. This is a transfer of the 1 state of core M_1 to core M_2. Shift pulses S_1 and S_2 are applied alternatively to cores M_1 and M_2.

One difficulty of the single-diode transfer loop is the reverse flow of information, as is illustrated in Fig. 7-15. Consider the case where core M_2 is in the 1 state. Application of a pulse to winding S_2 on core M_2 induces a voltage V_2 in its input winding N_2, and a current I_2 flows in the transfer loop in a direction tending to switch M_1 into the 1 state. This is an undesirable transfer of information and can be alleviated by a proper design of the loop. The number of turns N_2 is normally only one-third to one-fifth of N_1, and thus voltage V_2 will be only one-third to one-fifth of V_1. The reverse current I_2 can be designed so small as to be unable to switch core M_1. Another difficulty is the generation of an unwanted output pulse when the transmitting core such as the one shown in

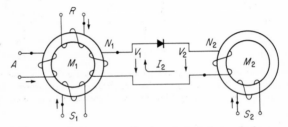

FIG. 7-15   Reverse current flow in a single-diode transfer loop.

Fig. 7-14 is reset by winding R. This is avoided by combining windings R and S into one.

The single-diode transfer loop can be branched out by connecting the input windings of the receiving cores in series with the transfer loop. An example is shown in Fig. 7-16. The number of permissible cores in series is limited by the possible reverse current flow.

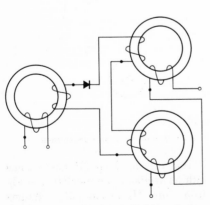

A Shift Register. A magnetic-core shift register is shown in Fig. 7-17. There are two sets of shift windings S_1 and S_2 in the series of four cores. Each set of windings links either the odd-numbered cores or the even-numbered cores. Shifting pulses are applied alternately to windings S_1 and S_2 in this manner; $S_1(t_2)$, $S_2(t_2)$, $S_1(t_3)$, $S_2(t_4)$, and so forth. The application of shift pulse $S_1(t_1)$ transfers binary information in cores M_1 and M_3 to cores M_2 and M_4, respectively,

FIG. 7-16   Branching of single-diode transfer loop.   leaving cores M_1 and M_3 in the 0 state. The application of shift pulse $S_2(t_2)$ transfers the binary information from core M_2 to M_3 and from core M_4 to outside of the shift register; this leaves core M_2 in the 0 state. With further application of shift pulses $S_1(t_3)$ and $S_2(t_4)$, all the cores will be in the 0 state.

Logic Circuits. A number of logic circuits using the single-diode transfer loop are illustrated in Fig. 7-18. Circuit a is the *andnot-A* circuit of Fig. 7-11 with its B input connected to a pulse source indicated by the symbol 1; this results in a delayed logical-*not* circuit. In circuit b, core M_1 is a delay, and both cores M_2 and M_3 are *andnot* circuits; this forms a delayed logical-*and* circuit. In circuit c, the *or* circuit cascades to the *not* circuit; this results in a delayed logical-*nor* circuit. In circuit d, both cores M_1 and M_2 are *not* circuits and cascade to the *or* circuit (core M_3); this arrangement is a delayed logical-*nand* circuit. In circuit e, both cores M_1 and M_2 are *andnot* circuits cascading to the *or* circuit (core M_3). The output of core M_3 gives a delayed logical exclusive-*or* operation. If M_3 is further cascaded to a *not* circuit (core M_4), the series becomes a de-

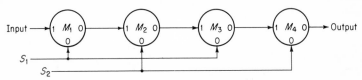

FIG. 7-17   A magnetic-core shift register.

layed logical-coincidence circuit. As apparent from the Fig. 7-18, the *not* circuit has one unit of delay, the coincidence circuit has three units of delay, and the other three circuits have two units of delay.

7-4   *Single-shift-line Transfer-loop Circuits*

In single-diode transfer-loop circuits, two shift lines are required to supply two sequences of shifting pulses. Information in each core is either shifted in or shifted out at the application of each shift pulse. The single-shift-line transfer loop permits both operations to be performed by one shift pulse.

Single-shift-line Transfer Loop. A single-shift-line transfer loop is a single-diode loop with a delay network between adjacent cores, as shown in Fig. 7-19a [12]. The delay network permits resetting all cores by one shift line, because the information in each core can be temporarily stored there and then transferred to the receiving core or cores. The symbolic representation of this transfer loop appears in Fig. 7-19b and can be further simplified into that shown in Fig. 7-19c, since there is only one shift line and the delay network has no logical significance. Furthermore, the output winding is a reset winding; hence, the 0's need not be indicated. The 1's and 0's representing input set and reset windings are replaced by a single and double arrowhead.

The delay network functions as a temporary storage between the transmitting and receiving cores. Such a network should be able to preserve the pulse shape and provide the required delay. Of the four delay networks in Fig. 7-20, circuit d may better preserve the pulse shape and reduce the rise and decay times.

The single-shift-line transfer loop suffers from two disadvantages—increased delay in a transfer and distortion of the signal. Since magnetic-core circuits utilize the threshold field in initiating core switching, the distorted signal reduces the margin of signal to noise for reliable operation.

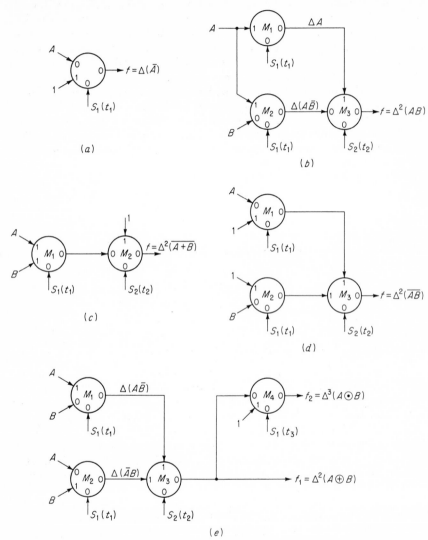

FIG. 7-18   Single-diode transfer-loop logic circuits.   (*a*) Delayed *not* circuit; (*b*) delayed *and* circuit; (*c*) delayed *nor* circuit; (*d*) delayed *nand* circuit; (*e*) delayed exclusive-*or* and coincidence circuit.

Logic Circuits.   Three basic logic circuits using the single-shift-line loop are the delay circuit, the delayed *or* circuit, and the delayed *andnot* circuit. Their simplified symbolic representations are shown in Fig. 7-21. The following paragraphs give examples of several magnetic-core logic circuits using the single-shift-line loop.

The first example to be considered is that of a half adder–subtractor, which performs the arithmetic operations of both a half adder and a half subtractor. The truth table for a single-bit half adder appeared in Table 5-4. Table 7-2 tabulates the functions of a single-bit half subtractor, where X and Y are, respectively, the minuend bit and the subtrahend bit. Note that the truth values for

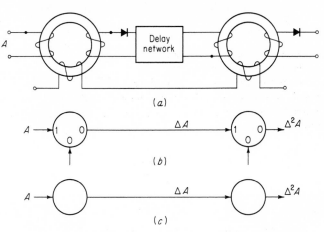

FIG. 7-19 Single-shift-line transfer loop and its symbolic representation.

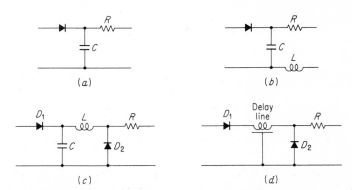

FIG. 7-20 Delay network for a single-shift-line transfer loop.

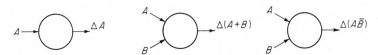

FIG. 7-21 Symbolic representation of three basic logic operations for the single-shift-line loop.

the sum (in Table 5-4) and the difference are the same. Boolean functions for the sum or difference S, the borrow B, and the carry C are

$$S = X \oplus Y$$
$$B = \overline{X}Y \qquad\qquad (7\text{-}19)$$
$$C = XY$$

Table 7-2   Truth Table for a Half Subtractor

X Y	D (difference)	B (borrow)
0 0	0	0
0 1	1	1
1 0	1	0
1 1	0	0

Table 7-3   Truth Table for a Full Subtractor

X	Y	B_i	D_2	B_o
0	0	0	0	0
0	0	1	1	0
0	1	0	1	1
0	1	1	0	0
1	0	0	1	1
1	0	1	0	0
1	1	0	0	1
1	1	1	1	1

where X is the augend or the minuend bit and Y the addend or the subtrahend bit.   As a prognosis from these relations, the half adder–subtractor will consist of the exclusive-*or*, the *and*, and the *andnot* circuits.   Because of inherent delays in magnetic-core circuits, the foregoing functions are expressed more realistically as

$$S = \Delta^2(X \oplus Y)$$
$$B = \Delta^2(\bar{X}Y)$$
$$C = \Delta^2(XY) = \Delta(W\bar{Z}) \qquad (7\text{-}20)$$
$$W = \Delta X$$
$$Z = \Delta(X\bar{Y})$$

The half adder–subtractor described by the above functions is shown in Fig. 7-22.

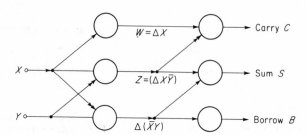

FIG. 7-22   A half adder–subtractor using single-shift-line transfer-loop circuit.

The second example is that of a full subtractor.   Similar to a full adder, a full subtractor has three inputs X, Y, and B_i, respectively the minuend bit, subtrahend bit, and input borrow bit.   It has two outputs D_2 and C_o, which are, respectively, the difference bit and the output borrow bit.   The block diagram is shown in Fig. 7-23*a*.   The operation of the full subtractor is shown in Table 7-3. The Boolean functions D_2 and B_o are

$$D_2 = \bar{X}\bar{Y}B_i + \bar{X}Y\bar{B}_i + X\bar{Y}\bar{B}_i + XYB_i$$
$$B_o = \bar{X}Y\bar{B}_i + X\bar{Y}B_i + XY\bar{B}_i + XYB_i \qquad (7\text{-}21)$$

These functions can be rewritten in the following form:

$$D_2 = X \oplus Y \oplus B_i$$
$$B_o = B_1 + B_2$$
$$B_1 = \bar{X}Y$$
$$B_2 = B_i(\overline{X \oplus Y}) \qquad (7\text{-}22)$$

The above equations suggest the use of two half subtractors and one *or* circuit; this arrangement is shown in the block diagram of Fig. 7-23*b*. Because of inherent delays in the magnetic-core circuits, the above equations are rewritten into the following functions

$$D_2 = \Delta^4(X \oplus Y \oplus B_i) = \Delta^2(D_1 \oplus \Delta^2 B_i)$$
$$D_1 = \Delta^2(X \oplus Y)$$
$$B_o = \Delta^2 B_1 + \Delta B_2 \qquad\qquad (7\text{-}23)$$
$$B_1 = \Delta^2(\overline{X}Y)$$
$$B_2 = \Delta[\overline{D}_1(\Delta^2 B_i)]$$

The full subtractor described by the above functions is shown in Fig. 7-24.

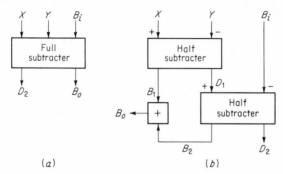

(a) (b)

FIG. 7-23 Block diagrams of a 1-bit full subtractor.

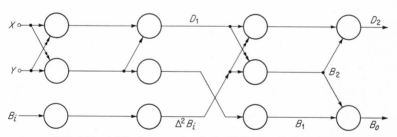

FIG. 7-24 A full subtractor using single-shift-line transfer-loop circuit.

Another circuit of interest transfers information having a relatively high bit rate to a shift register operating at a lower rate. High-rate 8-bit information is stored in a circulating register using the single-shift-line transfer loop shown in Fig. 7-25. The 8 bits in the circulating register are to be sequentially extracted and transferred to a shift register which shifts at a lower rate. An *and* circuit connects these two registers; one input of the *and* circuit connects to the circulating register and the other to a 1's generator. The output of the *and* circuit is connected to the input of the shift register. Information in the circulating register is circulated by pulses S_1, which occur at a high rate. The shift register and the 1's generator are operated by pulses S_2 at a lower rate. If pulse S_2 occurs every ninth pulse (which is the number of cores in the circulating register plus 1) of the pulses S_1, then the information in the circulating register is read out in sequence and shifted into the shift register at one-ninth the rate of S_1 pulses. If, instead, S_2 occurs every seventh S_1 pulse, then the information is read out in reverse order and at one-seventh the rate of S_1 pulses. Transfer ceases when the 1's generator stops.

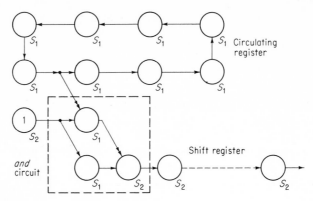

FIG. 7-25   Information transfer from a circulating register of a given rate to a shift register operating at a lower rate.

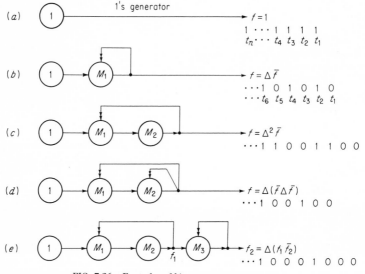

FIG. 7-26   Examples of binary sequence generators.

Generation of Binary Sequences.   Magnetic-core circuits are amenable to the generating of binary sequences and can be used as function generators in a digital computer. Several examples [16] are illustrated in Fig. 7-26.

Circuit a shows the symbolic representation of a 1's generator. The shift pulses occur in the time sequence t_1, t_2, etc., spaced at a time interval τ; the Boolean function of the output f is equal to unity.

In circuit b, the 1's generator is connected to an *andnot* circuit with its output fed back to the inhibiting input of the *andnot* circuit. The Boolean function of the output f is

$$f = \Delta(\bar{f}) \tag{7-24}$$

This function states that the output at a time interval later is the complement of the present output. It thus describes the generated binary sequence if the initial state of the core is given. Assume that the core is initially at the 0 state. The first output at t_1 is 0 because this is the initial state of the core. The second output at t_2 is the complement of the output at t_2, or 1. The sequence is a series of alternate 0's and 1's.

In circuit c, the Boolean function for the output f is

$$f = \Delta^2(\bar{f}) \tag{7-25}$$

which states that the output at a time interval of 2τ later is the complement of the present output. If the initial state of both cores is 0, the first two outputs at t_1 and t_2 are thus 0's and the third and fourth outputs at t_3 and t_4 are 1's. The sequence is a series of alternate double 0's and double 1's.

Circuit d incorporates two feedback loops; the Boolean function of the output f is

$$f = \Delta[\bar{f}(\Delta\bar{f})] = (\Delta\bar{f})(\Delta^2\bar{f}) \tag{7-26}$$

As stated, the final output is the logical product of the complement of the output at a time interval τ later and the complement of the output at a time 2τ later. The sequence is a series of alternate 3 bits of 100 ($t_3t_2t_1$).

Circuit e also embodies two feedback loops, but they are connected differently; the Boolean function of the output f is

$$f_2 = \Delta(f_1\bar{f}_2)$$

where

$$f_1 = \Delta^2\bar{f}_1$$

or

$$f_2 = (\Delta^3\bar{f}_1)(\Delta\bar{f}_2) \tag{7-27}$$

Function (7-27) states that the output is the logical product of the corresponding bits of the sequence formed by $\Delta^3\bar{f}_1$ and the sequence formed by $\Delta\bar{f}_2$. The former is the complement of the output f_1 at a time interval 3τ later, and the latter is the complement of the output f_2 at a time interval τ later. The sequence is a series of alternate four bits of 1000 ($t_4t_3t_2t_1$).

7-5 *Other Transfer Loops*

As mentioned, the single-diode transfer loop incurs two difficulties: reverse current flow in the loop when the receiving core is being reset, and the generation of an unwanted output pulse when the transmitting core is being reset, because two cores connected by the single-diode transfer loop are not completely isolated. The following transfer loops achieve isolation between cores by different schemes.

Split-winding Loop. A split-winding transfer loop is shown in Fig. 7-27 [28]. The winding on core M_2 has a center tap for the application of the shift current pulse. Information is transferred from core M_1 to M_2 only when shift current pulse S is applied. Consider the case where both cores are at the 0 state.

When the shift pulse is applied, branch current I_1 flows into the upper portion of the winding on core M_2 and branch current I_2 into the lower portion. Both portions of the winding on M_2 have $N_2/2$ turns. The net magnetizing force on core M_2 is zero. Winding N_1 on core M_1 offers very low impedance, as there is no flux reversal. The parallel paths between the points X and Y offer almost equal impedance, and the two branch currents are essentially equal; nothing happens to core M_2. This is a transfer of the 0 state from core M_1 to M_2.

Consider the case where core M_1 is in the 1 state and core M_2 in the 0 state. When the shift pulse is applied, branch current I_1 is much smaller than I_2 because the impedance of the winding with N_1 turns is larger than the other impedances in the transfer loop. The resulting effect is equivalent to a transfer current (equal to the difference of I_2 and I_1) flowing through the winding with N_2 turns on core M_2. The transfer current sets core M_2 into the 1 state; in the meantime, branch current I_1 resets core M_1 into the 0 state. This is a transfer of the 1 state from core M_1 to M_2.

In the absence of the shift pulse, the application of pulses to other input windings of either core does not cause any interaction between them because of the diodes D_1 and D_2. If, instead of parallel paths between points X and Y which

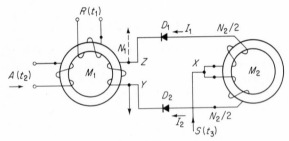

FIG. 7-27   Split-winding transfer loop.

will reset core M_1 to the 0 state after the transfer, parallel paths are used between points X and Z, indicated by the dashed line, this will set core M_1 to the 1 state. Thus, either the output reset or the set winding of core M_1 can be used.

Inhibit Transfer Loop.   With a slight modification, the split-winding loop becomes the inhibit transfer loop [28] shown in Fig. 7-28. It is so called because the transfer of information from core M_1 to M_3 occurs only when core M_1 is in the 1 state and core M_2 is in the 0 state. Consider the case where cores M_1 and M_2 are in the same state, either both 0 or both 1. When the shift current pulse is applied, branch currents I_1 and I_2 are nearly equal and core M_3 is left in its original state. Consider the case where core M_1 is in the 1 state and M_2 in the 0 state. When the shift current pulse is applied, branch current I_2 is larger than I_1 and core M_3 is set to the 1 state. Consider the case where core M_1 is in the 0 state and M_2 in the 1 state. When the shift pulse is applied, current I_1 is larger than I_2 and core M_3 is set to the 0 state. In the positive-logic designation, this is a delayed logical-*andnot-B* circuit (or inhibit circuit). The inhibit loop also offers the isolating property.

Gated-diode Transfer-loop Circuits.   Another loop configuration which has the isolating property is the gated-diode transfer loop [13] of Fig. 7-29.

The two diodes are connected to block current flow in either direction between the two cores, for isolation. Information is transferred when a shift current pulse S is applied in the manner shown. Core M_2 initially is reset to the 0 state. If core M_1 is in the 0 state, branch current I_1 is larger than I_2 because the impedance of output winding N_1 is designed to be lower than the input impedance of winding N_2. Under this condition, branch current I_2 is not large enough to cause flux

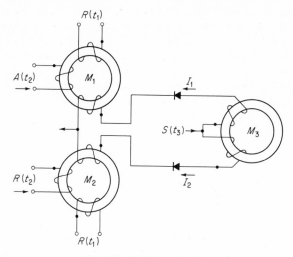

FIG. 7-28   Inhibit transfer loop.

reversal in core M_2. This is the transfer of the 0 state from core M_1 to M_2. If core M_1 is in the 1 state, the output impedance of winding N_1 is now larger than the input impedance of winding N_2 and branch current I_2 is larger than I_1. Under this condition, branch current I_2 is large enough to set core M_2 to the 1 state. This is the transfer of the 1 state from core M_1 to M_2. It is evident that winding N_2 will receive current whether core M_2 is switched or not.

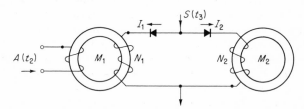

FIG. 7-29   Gated-diode transfer loop.

Diodeless Transfer Loop. The above-mentioned transfer loops all employ diodes. The inclusion of diodes may make the circuits less reliable. Russell [32] reported the use of a coupling core to replace the diode in the single-diode transfer loop, as shown in Fig. 7-30. This circuit requires three shift lines S_1, S_2, and S_3. Coupling cores C are reset to the 0 state by shift pulse S_3 after each shift pulse S_1 or S_2, which are applied alternately. When the coupling cores are in the 0 state, they present a low impedance in the forward transfer of information (as indicated by the loop current), as the diodes do. In this condition, when shift pulse S_1 is applied to the diodeless loop with core M_1 in the 0 state, no appreciable loop current occurs and core M_2 remains in its original 0 state. This is the transfer of the 0 state from core M_1 to M_2. If core M_1 is in the 1 state instead, shift pulse S_1 resets core M_1 to the 0 state. A large loop current occurs because of the low impedance of coupling core C_1, and core M_2 is thus set to the 1 state. This affects transfer of the 1 state from core M_1 to M_2. In the single-diode loop, when a pulse is applied to input A, a voltage is induced in the output winding of core M_1 but the loop current is blocked by the diode; the interaction in this direction is thus isolated. In the diodeless loop, when a similar pulse is applied, there is a reverse current. Because coupling core C_1 presents a large impedance under this condition, the loop current is not large enough to switch core M_2. However, coupling core C_1 is switched to the 1 state as the switching produces the high impedance to the reverse current flow. Thus, after each transfer, coupling core C_1 must be reset to the 0 state.

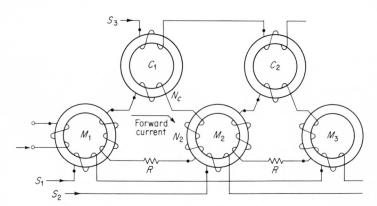

FIG. 7-30   A diodeless transfer-loop circuit.

Resetting of the coupling core to the 0 state does bring about a complication, because this resetting must not affect the state of cores M_1 and M_2. This resetting induces a voltage in its winding N_c, which causes a reverse current flow. This current does not affect the state of core M_1, because M_1 has been reset to the 0 state during the transfer. But it tends to change to the 0 state the core M_2, which must be prevented. If the loop can be designed so that this current is small, the change of state of core M_2 will be prevented. This is mainly achieved by using a resistor R in the loop. The value of the resistor in turn determines the minimum reset time for core C_1. If maximum operating speed is desired, the resistor should be made as large as possible. On the other hand, too large a resistor R also reduces the forward loop current. Therefore, there is a maximum value for the resistor above which the forward loop current will not be able to switch core M_2 to the 1 state. The proper choice of this resistance is a design problem which must take into consideration the core characteristics and the various windings. Replacement of the diode by the core is at the expense of a more severe design requirement, which in turn may limit the branching and cascading of succeeding cores. Also, the operating speed is limited by the requirement due to the coupling cores.

The use of coupling cores to replace diodes and the possible use of ferrite cores make magnetic-core logic circuits inexpensive and reliable. On the other hand, the operating frequency is limited to about 100 kc. Cores must have a prominent switching threshold characteristic, and current generators are necessary for the three-shift pulses.

7-6 *Magnetic-core–Transistor Logic Circuits*

The magnetic-core–transistor circuit [20] shown in Fig. 7-31*a* makes use of the magnetic core to store information and the transistor to drive succeeding stages. The core has the retangular hysteresis-loop characteristic shown in Fig. 7-31*b*. There are four windings: input set winding N_s, trigger reset winding N_t, collector reset winding N_c, and base winding N_b. The transistor is cut off, as its base and emitter are at the same potential.

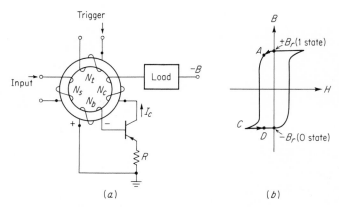

FIG. 7-31   A magnetic-core–transistor circuit.

Assume that the core is in the 1 state $(+B_r)$. If a small current pulse is applied to trigger winding N_t, a current flows in a direction toward point A around the knee of the B-H curve of Fig. 7-31*b*. The small change of flux during the rise time of the trigger pulse induces a voltage in the base winding N_b with the polarity shown in Fig. 7-31*a*. A negative voltage appears at the base of the transistor, causing collector current to flow; and the flow of collector current produces additional flux change in a direction toward point C of the B-H curve. This induces an increased negative voltage at the base of the transistor, which further increases the collector current. Once started, this process continues until the core is completely reset to its 0 state $(-B_r)$. The coupling by windings N_c and N_b provides a positive feedback. The gain of the feedback loop is nonlinear. If the core is in the 1 or 0 state, the permeability of the core material is low and the gain around the feedback loop is less than unity. If the core is in the process of switching, the permeability is high and the loop gain is well above unity. The output of the circuit is a large collector current pulse, which occurs during the switching.

Assume that the core is in the 0 state $(-B_r)$. If a small trigger pulse is applied to winding N_t, a current will flow in a direction toward point D on the B-H curve. Since that portion of the B-H curve is almost flat, there is little flux change, which in turn generates negligible output in the base winding. Regeneration through the positive-feedback loop would not take place. The circuit remains undisturbed by the trigger pulse as long as the core is in the 0 state.

Once the core is reset to the 0 state by the transistor, the core has to be set to the 1 state for any subsequent switching; this is accomplished by the input pulse. The input pulse will not turn on the transistor, because the voltage induced in winding N_b has the polarity opposite to that shown in Fig. 7-31a and drives the base to further cutoff. The standby power of this circuit is negligible, and only a small trigger current is required to initiate a small flux change in the core.

In the design of the circuit consideration should be given to the maximum output power, the relative independence of variation of transistor parameters, and the effect due to the minority carrier storage. The important circuit parameters for

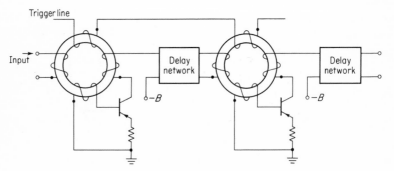

FIG. 7-32   Single-shift-line transfer loop for magnetic-core–transistor circuit.

the design are the gain, the α cutoff frequency of the transistor, and the collector load. The operating speed can reach as high as 300 kc.

Magnetic-core–transistor circuits can be cascaded by using the single-shift-line transfer loop (Fig. 7-32), which affords several advantages. First, the trigger pulse does not have to meet as severe a requirement in respect to its amplitude and duration as the ordinary shift pulse. Second, the power required for shift operations for a cascade of such basic circuits is distributed among the transistors, while in the previous single-shift-line circuits all power has to be supplied by the shift pulse. Third, isolation exists between two succeeding cores because the collector is normally cut off except when information is being transferred between the cores. This isolation property allows 10 or more branchings from the output of one basic circuit, while only three or four branches are practical in other transfer loops.

Logic circuits can be obtained by using the basic circuit in a manner similar to those using the single-shift-line transfer loop; hence they are not further discussed.

7-7   *Ferractor Magnetic-amplifier Logic Circuits*

Ferractor Magnetic Amplifier.   One type of magnetic-core–diode circuit has been developed under the trade name of Ferractor [31]. This amplifier (Fig. 7-33) consists of a magnetic core of rectangular-loop material with an input winding N_1, output winding N_2, and bias winding N_b. It is driven by shift current pulses shown in the figure. Each cycle of the shift current pulse is considered as two half cycles. The positive half cycle is the output half, during which the core is set to the 1 state. The negative half cycle is the input half, during which the core is reset to the 0 state if there is an input pulse. The amplitude of the shift pulse is so adjusted that it just switches the core from the residual magnetization $-B_r$ to $+B_r$.

Consider first the operation during the negative-input half cycle. Input diodes D_2 perform a logical-*or* operation (positive logic). Occurrence of an input pulse resets the core in the 0 state. If there is no input, the core remains in its original

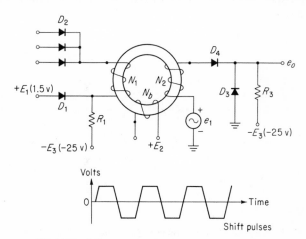

FIG. 7-33   A Ferractor complementing magnetic amplifier.

1 state. Voltage e_1 has a polarity ŏpposite to that shown in Fig. 7-33; no current flows in the output winding, because diode D_4 is back-biased. Next consider the operation during the positive-output half cycle. Voltage e_1 has a polarity like that shown in the figure. Diode D_4 conducts, and the core is set to the 1 state. If the core is switched from state 0 to 1, which means the occurrence of an input pulse during the previous half cycle, there is a small output. If the core is switched but remains at state 1, which means that no input pulse occurred during the previous half cycle, there is a substantial output. Therefore, the amplifier alone performs a logical-*not* operation. Together with input diodes D_2, for a positive-logic designation, the circuit performs a delayed logical-*nor* operation.

There are three design details in this circuit. First, it is desired to eliminate the small output signal which occurs when the core is switched but remains at state 1, because a complete suppression of this signal makes it possible to inter-connect a large number of these amplifiers without the danger of a small output growing into a full output. Suppression can be achieved by the current sink consisting of diode D_3, resistor R_3, and voltage source $-E_3$. The current flowing in R_3 is made just equal to this small current and is supplied through diode D_4 instead of D_3 during the half cycle when there is a small output. Second, it is desired to limit the amount of current which can be inductively transferred to the output circuit from the input circuit during the no-output half cycle of the preceding core. This is achieved by the constant-current circuit consisting of diode D_1, resistor R_1, and voltage supplies $+E_1$ and $-E_3$. The current in R_1 is set to be approximately equal to the magnetizing current of the core as seen from the input winding. This current limiting is also necessary because one amplifier may drive a number of others that have parallel input circuits. If one driven amplifier saturates before the others, it will short-circuit the source and prevent its paralleled amplifiers from switching the core. Third, to overcome the diode recovery time (the operating speed being thus increased), a bias winding is provided. The bias provides a constant current which flows in such direction and with such magnitude as to set the core to the 1 state when the input pulse is removed.

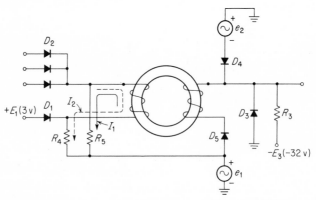

FIG. 7-34   A high-speed complementing magnetic amplifier (2- to 5-Mc Ferractor).

If the polarities of the input and the bias winding of Fig. 7-33 are reversed, the resulting circuit is a noncomplementing amplifier. The core is set to the 1 state instead of the 0 state of the previous circuit. The current in the bias winding flows in a direction to reset the core to the 0 state, to counteract the effect of diode recovery time. For positive logic, the noncomplementing amplifier is a delayed logical-*or* circuit.

   An Improved Ferractor Amplifier. The amplifier of Fig. 7-33 can be operated up to 660 kc. An improved version [23] shown in Fig. 7-34 can be operated up to 2.5 Mc. In this circuit, voltage sources e_1 and e_2 are sinusoidal. Again each cycle of e_1 consists of a positive and a negative half cycle. Consider the operation during the negative input cycle. Voltages e_1 and e_2 have polarities opposite to those shown in Fig. 7-34. If there is any input pulse, the core is reset to the 0 state by current I_2, which flows through the input winding and resistor R_4 and to source e_1. Sinusoidal voltage e_2, called the *blocking pulse*, has an amplitude of one half e_1. The positive blocking voltage e_2 is applied to the upper terminal of the output winding through diode D_4. In this manner, there is sufficient back voltage across diode D_5 to keep it open while an input pulse is switching the core from state 1 to 0. The lower terminal of the input winding is clamped to $+3V$ by E_1 and D_1, and the upper end of R_5 is clamped at ground potential through diodes D_2 and D_3 of the preceding core; this prevents a short circuit of the input winding by the input pulse. In the absence of an input, current I_1 flows from blocking source E_1 through the input winding and R_5 to source e_1 to overcome any reverse leakage through diode D_5 and to maintain the core in the 1 state.

Consider the operation during the positive output cycle. Both e_1 and e_2 have the polarities shown in Fig. 7-34. Diode D_4 is back-biased and the core set to the 1 state. If the core was at the 1 state already, there is a large output. If the core was at the 0 state, there is a small output. The current sink, consisting of R_3 and D_3, absorbs this small output current, and no output is produced. The input circuit is disconnected, since voltage at both input winding terminals is raised by e_1, and diodes D_1 and D_2 are both open. Therefore, the presence of the blocking pulse from the preceding core on the inputs of the core under discussion has no effect on the circuit.

For positive logic, this high-speed complementing amplifier is a logical-*nor* circuit; for negative logic, it is a logical-*nand* circuit. If the negative-logic designation is applied to the input signals of the amplifier and the positive-logic designation to the output signal, as shown in Table 7-4, this complementing amplifier becomes a logical-*and* circuit. Conversely, if the positive-logic designation is applied to the input signals and the negative-logic designation to the output signal, this complementing amplifier is a logical-*or* circuit.

7-8   Mirror Symbol

Mayer [8] has suggested a symbolic representation for magnetic core circuits, the mirror symbol, by means of which the flux state of the core and the direction of the induced voltage in the windings become more easily recognized.

The convention of set and reset windings for input and output has been shown in Figs. 7-5 and 7-6. The reset and set input windings are redrawn and shown in Figs. 7-35a and 7-36a; the corresponding mirror-symbol representations are respectively shown in Figs. 7-35b and 7-36b. In these figures, a rectangular bar instead of a ring represents the core. Binary states 0 and 1 of the core are designated, respectively, as the downward flux direction and the upward flux direction. The winding is represented by a short diagonal line making a $45°$ angle with the bar, indicating the two possible ways of winding on the core. This short line is referred to as the *mirror* because a current flowing from the left and im-

Table 7-4   *Mixed Positive- and Negative-logic Designation*

State	*and* operation		*or* operation	
	Input	Output	Input	Output
0	+ pulse	No-pulse	No-pulse	+ pulse
1	No-pulse	+ pulse	+ pulse	No-pulse

pinging on the mirror is reflected downward or upward as shown in Figs. 7-35*c* and 7-36*c*. This downward or upward direction is the flux direction. The horizontal line perpendicular to the bar and making an intersection with the mirror represents the input and output terminals of the winding. Unless specifically indicated otherwise, it is assumed that the current enters the winding at the left half of the horizontal line and leaves the winding at its right half. The slanted mirrors in Figs. 7-35 and 7-36 are designated as the reset and the set winding, respectively, because a current excites the core to the 0 or 1 state, respectively.

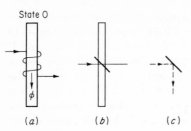

State 0

(a)   (b)   (c)

FIG. 7-35   Mirror symbol for a reset winding.

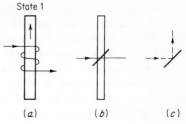

State 1

(a)   (b)   (c)

FIG. 7-36   Mirror symbol for a set winding.

Determination of the polarities of the induced voltages on the output reset and output set windings is shown in Figs. 7-37 and 7-38, respectively. In Fig. 7-37, the upper winding is the reset and the lower one the set; in Fig. 7-38, the upper winding is the set and the lower the reset. As shown in Fig. 7-37*c* when current flows from the left to the upper input winding, it impinges on the upper mirror at point *a*, is reflected downward, and continues to the end of the bar at point *b*, where it bounces back (indicating a flux reversal), impinges on the lower mirror at point *c*, and is reflected toward the right. The direction to the right is

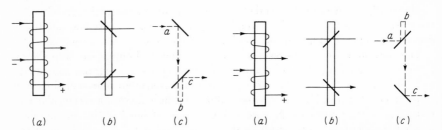

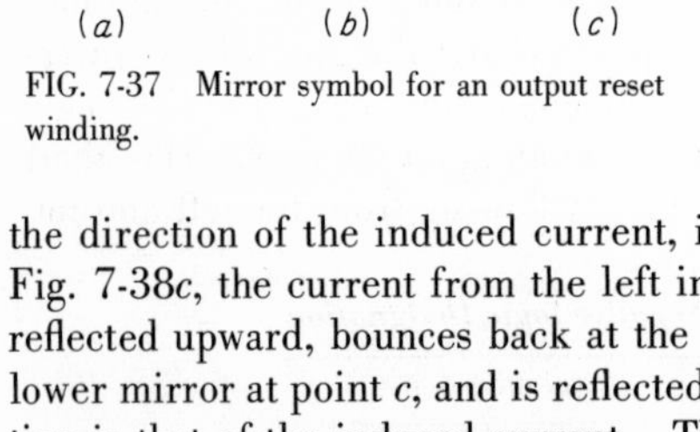

(a)   (b)   (c)

FIG. 7-37   Mirror symbol for an output reset winding.

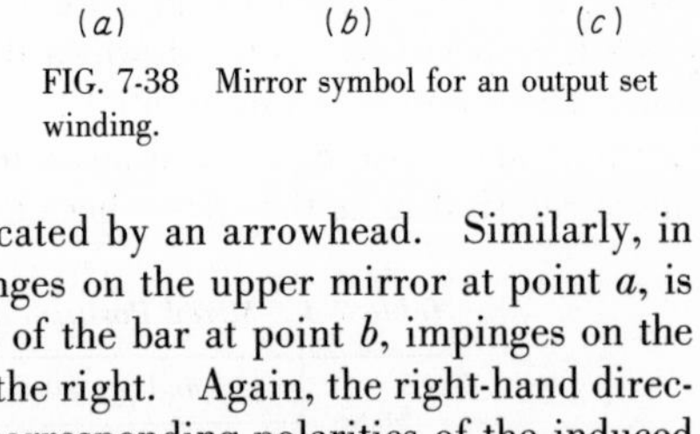

(a)   (b)   (c)

FIG. 7-38   Mirror symbol for an output set winding.

the direction of the induced current, indicated by an arrowhead. Similarly, in Fig. 7-38*c*, the current from the left impinges on the upper mirror at point *a*, is reflected upward, bounces back at the end of the bar at point *b*, impinges on the lower mirror at point *c*, and is reflected to the right. Again, the right-hand direction is that of the induced current. The corresponding polarities of the induced voltages are thus indicated by the arrowheads on the output windings. In short, the three steps in finding the induced voltages are: (1) The flux change due to the input current (or other causes) is found. (2) The current continues toward the bar end and bounces back. (3) It is reflected from all mirrors to give their respective positive voltages. This procedure gives a result which agrees with that obtained by applying Lenz's law.

It should be noted that the previously described output reset winding is actually a set winding itself and the output set winding a reset winding. Furthermore, if current comes from the right instead of the left, a reset winding becomes a set

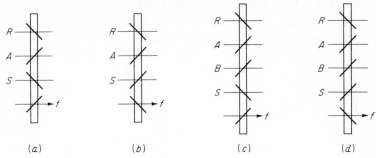

(a)   (b)   (c)   (d)

FIG. 7-39   Mirror-symbol representation of the circuits in Figs. 7-7 to 7-10. (a) Delay circuit; (b) *not* circuit; (c) *or* circuit; (d) *nor* circuit.

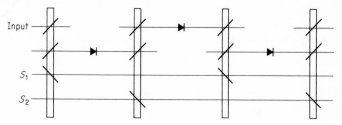

FIG. 7-40   A magnetic-core shift register using single-diode transfer loops.

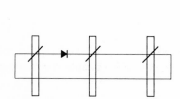

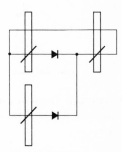

FIG. 7-41   Branching of single-diode transfer-loop circuit.

FIG. 7-42   A single-diode transfer-loop logical-*or* circuit.

winding and a set winding becomes a reset. However, by using the procedure for the mirror-symbol representation, the flux state of the core and the direction of the induced voltages of the windings can always be correctly determined.

A number of examples using the mirror symbols are shown in Figs. 7-39 to 7-44. Figure 7-39 shows the logical delay, logical-*not*, logical-*or*, and logical-*nor* circuits of Figs. 7-7 to 7-10. Figures 7-40 to 7-43 show the mirror-symbol representation of several single-diode transfer-loop circuits. These figures also include the diodes, and the transfer loops may be left open or drawn in closed loops if needed. Figure 7-44 shows the mirror-symbol representation of the shift register using the single-shift-line loop illustrated in Fig. 7-19.

7-9   *Synthesis of Magnetic-core Logic Circuits*

Boolean functions can be synthesized by using magnetic-core circuits. Circuit configurations developed by Karnaugh, Rosenfeld, and Andrews will now be described. The mirror symbols will be employed in the discussion.

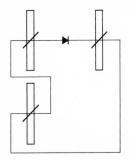

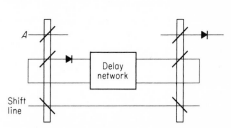

FIG. 7-43   A single-diode transfer-loop logical-*or* circuit.

FIG. 7-44   A magnetic-core circuit with single-shift-line transfer loop.

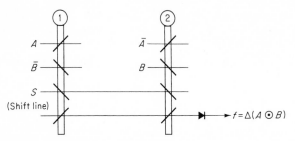

FIG. 7-45   Karnaugh magnetic-core coincidence circuit using type T output circuit.

Karnaugh Logical-and Magnetic-core Circuit. A Boolean function in the P form is a logical sum of logical-product terms. For example, the Boolean function

$$f(A,B) = AB + \overline{A}\overline{B} \qquad (7\text{-}28)$$

is a logical sum of the two product terms AB and $\overline{A}\overline{B}$. Since magnetic-core circuits are sequential in operation, the desired circuits can first perform the logical-*and* operation for several variables and then the logical-sum operation for the resulting products. Karnaugh-circuit [15] for a logical-*and* operation is achieved by the input windings. The logical-*and* circuits for the product terms in function (7-28) are shown in Fig. 7-45. In this figure, core 1 (indicated by the encircled 1) is for term AB; variables A and $\overline{B}$ are used as inputs to core 1, instead of A and B, because A is connected to a set winding and $\overline{B}$ to a reset winding. In operation, core 1 is initially reset to the 0 state. Core 1 is set to the 1 state only when a pulse appears at input A and no pulse at $\overline{B}$. This is the *andnot* circuit shown in Fig. 7-11 except that one input is $\overline{B}$ instead of B. The operation of core 2 is for term $\overline{A}B$ and is similar to that of core 1.

The choice of inputs in core 1 can be $\overline{A}$ for the reset winding and B for the set winding. When there are more than two input variables the choice is similar; in this case, there is only one set winding, the remainder being all reset windings. In short, the logical-*and* operation occurs only when the pulse is applied to the input set winding and at the same time there is no input to other input windings.

The above logical-*and* circuit requires a number of cores equal to the number of product terms in a given Boolean function in the P form. Furthermore, it requires close tolerance on the pulse timing and amplitude, because when pulses appear at both inputs A and $\overline{B}$ of core 1, these two pulses have to cancel each other for proper operation.

The logical-*not* circuit shown in Fig. 7-46 is similar to the above logical-*and* configuration; the set winding is connected to a clock and the reset winding to input A. In operation, the core is initially in the 0 state. When there is no input, the core is set to the 1 state by the clock. When there is a pulse input, it is canceled by the clock and the core remains in the 0 state.

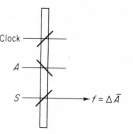

FIG. 7-46   Karnaugh magnetic-core logical-*not* circuit.

Karnaugh Logical-or Magnetic-core Circuit.

The above logical-*and* operation is performed at the input windings. Logical-*or* operation will be accomplished at the output windings; this utilizes the sequential nature of the magnetic-core circuit. For the two terms AB and $\overline{A}B$ in function (7-28), the logical-*or* operation is obtained by connecting the two output windings and a diode in series as shown in Fig. 7-45. This diode, similar to that in the single-diode transfer loop, is for the purpose of isolation. The circuit in Fig. 7-45 shows the coincidence operation of the two variables A and B and serves as an example of synthesizing a Boolean function in the P form.

Three methods are used to achieve logical-*or* operation. The logical-*or* scheme at the output winding in Fig. 7-45 is called type T by Karnaugh; in this type, the shift pulse winding and the output winding are separate. If the shift pulse winding is connected in series with the output winding, the arrangement is called type A. If the windings are connected in series aiding, it is called type AF; if in series opposing, type AB. These two types AF and AB for function (7-28) are shown in Figs. 7-47 and 7-48, respectively.

In Fig. 7-47, each of the two output set windings N_1 and N_2 is connected in series with a diode; they form two parallel paths f_1 and f_2 which are connected in series with the shift line. If either output winding has an induced voltage, the shift current flows through the path in series with that winding because the induced voltage aids in the current flow; a large current flows through the load. If neither core has been set to the 1 state, most of the shift current flows through the single-diode low-impedance path; a negligible current flows through the load. Thus, the output circuit performs a logical-*or* operation on terms AB and $\overline{A}\overline{B}$.

In Fig. 7-48, the two output reset windings N_1 and N_2 and the shift windings are connected in series. If either output winding has an induced voltage, the shift current does not flow through the serial output windings, because the induced voltage opposes the current flow; a large current flows into the load through

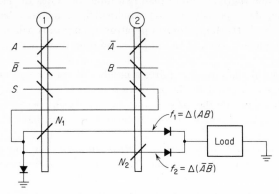

FIG. 7-47 Karnaugh magnetic-core coincidence circuit using type *AF* output circuit.

a diode. If neither core has been set to the 1 state, most of the shift current flows through the serial output windings to ground; a small current flows into the load. Thus, the output circuit performs a logical-*or* operation on terms AB and $\overline{A}\overline{B}$.

Rosenfeld Magnetic-core Logic Circuits. The Karnaugh type of mag-

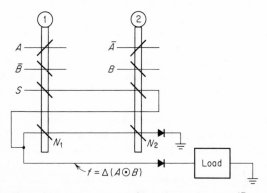

FIG. 7-48 Karnaugh magnetic-core coincidence circuit using type *AB* output circuit.

netic-core circuit requires the simultaneous occurrence of input pulses. Rosenfeld circuits [33] remove this requirement.

Rosenfeld's circuit for Boolean function (7-28) is shown in Fig. 7-49. Each core has one input set winding, and the state of the core represents the state of one variable. The two inputs are A and $\overline{B}$. The two output windings on each core form two parallel paths; each path represents a product term. Output path

f_1 represents term AB; output path f_2, term $\overline{A}\overline{B}$. The logical-*or* operation is performed by the two diodes; each diode is serially connected to one path.

The logical-*and* operation on the output windings will now be described. Consider output path f_1 of Fig. 7-49. Both cores are initially reset to the 0 state. When inputs are $\overline{A}$ and B, there is a pulse only at B input, which sets core 2 into the 1 state. The succeeding shift pulse induces a voltage in output winding N_3 in a direction opposing the shift current. Most of the shift current then flows through the single-diode path; a small current flows into the load. When the inputs are $\overline{A}$ and B, there is no pulse input. Both cores remain in the 0 state. Most of the succeeding shift current flows through the low-impedance single-diode path. When the inputs are A and $\overline{B}$, both input pulses occur. However, the induced voltages in their output windings N_1 and N_3 in the path f_1 cancel each other. Most of the shift current again flows into the single-diode path. When the inputs are A and B, only the input pulse A occurs and sets core 1 to the 1 state. The succeeding shift current pulse produces an induced voltage in the output winding N_1 in a direction which aids the shift current; a large current flows into the load. Thus, path f_1 performs a logical-*and* operation. Similar

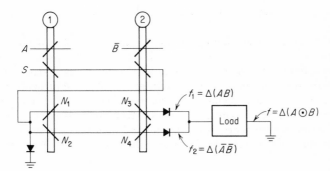

FIG. 7-49   Rosenfeld magnetic-core coincidence circuit.

operation occurs in output path f_2; only when the inputs are $\overline{A}$ and $\overline{B}$ is there a large current flowing into the load.

Note that two parallel output paths (excluding the single-diode path) do not conduct simultaneously; this is necessary to ensure proper switching operation of the core.

In summary, the Rosenfeld circuit uses input windings for storing the varibles. The logical-*and* operation is performed on the output windings, the logical-*or* operation by diodes. Both set and reset windings are used for the output windings; they are connected into a number of parallel paths equal to the number of product terms. The logical-*and* operation of a path occurs only when a pulse is applied to the input winding of the core whose output winding is the only set winding of the path.

Andrews Magnetic-core Logic Circuits. The Andrews circuit [25] makes use of the coincidence of half-amplitude currents in switching the core. The resulting circuit, called the *inhibit-wound core*, is shown in Fig. 7-50a. In this circuit, there are four windings—three input and one output. The upper two input windings are connected in series aiding and are referred to as the *shift* *winding.* The other input winding is for input A. The shift and input current pulses are shown in Fig. 7-50b. The shift pulse consists of two half cycles. During the positive half cycle, the positive pulse sets the core to the 1 state; during the negative half cycle, the negative pulse resets the core to the 0 state. The amplitudes of these positive and negative pulses are one-half the magnitude required to switch the core. Since ferrite cores with a square-loop characteristic are used, the half-amplitude current in one winding is not sufficient to switch the

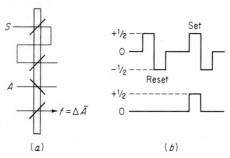

(a)   (b)

FIG. 7-50   Andrews magnetic-core logical-*not* circuit.

core. But with two input windings in series aiding, the half-amplitude shift current is sufficient to reset or set the core. The input current pulse is also of half amplitude and thus alone is insufficient to set the core to the 1 state. The input pulse occurs simultaneously with the setting half of the shift pulse, while the output pulse occurs simultaneously with the resetting half of the shift pulse.

The operation of the circuit is as follows: When there is no input pulse, the shift pulse first sets the core to the 1 state and then resets to the 0 state; this process produces an output pulse because of the flux reversal. When there is an

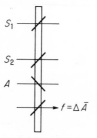

FIG. 7-51   Magnetic-core circuit using coincident-current shift pulse.

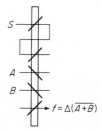

FIG. 7-52   Andrews magnetic-core logical-*nor* circuit.

input pulse, the shift pulse cannot set the core because of inhibition by the input pulse. The subsequent reset half of the shift pulse produces no pulse at the output. Thus, it is a logical-*not* circuit. It is advantageous to have the input pulse at half amplitude because the input does not have to overcome the large back voltage generated by the switching core.

The circuit in Fig. 7-51 is another logical-*not* circuit using the inhibiting principle. One of the two shift windings is shown activated by shift pulse S_1 and the other by control pulse S_2. In this way, the shift winding can be used for both shifting and control purpose.

If more than one input is provided in the circuit of Fig. 7-50 the resulting circuit (such as the one shown in Fig. 7-52), for positive logic, is a logical-*nor* circuit. In this circuit, if the complements of the inputs A and B ($\bar{A}$ and $\bar{B}$) are used instead, the logical *nor* of $\bar{A}$ and $\bar{B}$ becomes the logical *and* of A and B. This is the manner in which the product terms of a Boolean function are synthesized.

Similar to the Karnaugh-type T circuit, logical-*or* operation in the Andrews circuit is performed by the output windings, as shown in Fig. 7-53. In this circuit an output pulse occurs during the resetting half cycle if the input pulse A or B or both occur. For positive logic, this is a logical-*or* circuit.

As an example of synthesizing a Boolean function using the Andrews circuit, the circuit for function (7-28) is shown in Fig. 7-54. The input windings on the left core perform operation $\overline{AB}$; those on the right core, operation AB. The logical-*or* operation on product terms AB and $\overline{AB}$ is performed on the output windings.

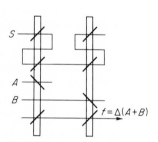

FIG. 7-53   Andrews magnetic-core logical-*or* circuit.

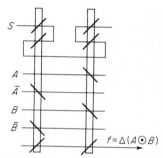

FIG. 7-54   Andrews magnetic-core coincidence circuit.

7-10   *Magnetic-rod Logic Circuits*

The magnetic-core logic circuits so far described are mostly limited to a switching rate of a few hundred kilocycles per second. A magnetic rod which makes use of a cylindrical thin film as a switching core can be operated at a faster rate.

Magnetic-rod Element. Figure 7-55 shows a magnetic-rod element: a glass-rod substrate 15 mils in diameter, chemically coated with a silver film and then electroplated with a thin film of magnetic alloy, 98 per cent iron and 2 per cent nickel. The magnetic film has a square-loop property and is about 3,000 Å in thickness. The magnetic alloy has a coercive force of 14 oersteds, a squareness ratio of 0.95, and a switching coefficient of 10^{-6} oersted-sec; the large coercive force makes possible a switching time of about 70 mμsec.

The rod of Fig. 7-55 was first developed for use in a magnetic-rod memory. Figure 7-56 shows an exploded view of a magnetic rod for logic circuits, called a *rod logic module*. As reported by Kaufman, Meier, and Rork [38], the rod is an electrical equivalent of a toroidal core. A rod logic module consists of a transposed sense winding to cancel air-coupled flux from clock and inhibit currents, plus multiple inhibit windings and a single clock winding overlying the sense windings. The rod itself is inserted into one leg of the sense winding. A typical rod module measures ⅛ by ¼ by ¼ in.

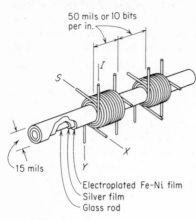

50 mils or 10 bits per in.

I

S

X

Y

15 mils

Electroplated Fe-Ni film
Silver film
Glass rod

FIG. 7-55   A magnetic-rod element.

Logic Circuits. The rod of Fig. 7-56 has been developed to replace the previously described inhibit-wound core of Andrew's circuits. Each rod logic module is a multiple-input logical-*nor* circuit (positive logic); this has been shown symbolically in Fig. 7-52. As described previously, the rod *nor* circuit makes use of the coincidence of half-amplitude currents in switching the rod, and the input pulse which acts as an inhibit pulse does not have to overcome the large back voltage otherwise generated during switching.

In rod circuits the clock is a sinusoidal current of 400 ma (rms), and the inhibit current is 200 ma; for a 10-turn winding, the output is about 300 mv. The use of sinusoidal clock pulses allows a greater tolerance in timing requirements for clock and inhibit currents. The rod can be operated at a rate of 2 Mc per sec. As many as 10 inhibit and sense windings can be connected in series, and up to 10 inhibit windings have been used on one rod. The power consumption of each rod module is about 0.1 watt. The output of a magnetic-rod logic circuit is directly coupled to a transistor amplifier for driving other logic circuits.

7-11   *Parametron Logic Circuits*

Parametric Subharmonic Oscillator.   The Parametron, developed by Goto of Japan [39], is a parametric phase-locked subharmonic oscillator (PLO). As described in Chap. 6, a PLO is a resonant circuit with a reactive element varying periodically at a pump frequency f_p; the resonant circuit products a parametric oscillation with a frequency f_o which is the second subharmonic of the pump frequency (or $f_p = 2f_o$). The parametric subharmonic oscillation has a remarkable property in that the oscillation has two stable phases which differ by 180°, as shown in Fig. 6-35. These two stable modes of oscillation represent the binary states; hence a PLO is a bistable storage element.

Under certain resonance conditions the parametric oscillation in a PLO can be easily self-started by a small initial oscillation; this is called *soft* oscillation. In this case the phase of the stable oscillation is guided by the phase of the small initial oscillation. Thus, a PLO has the properties of both memory and amplification. The parametric oscillation can be made non-self-starting; this is called *hard* oscillation. In this case, the circuit may have three stable states: the non-oscillating state, the oscillating state with a 0 phase, and the oscillating state with a 180° phase. In the hard-oscillation circuit the binary states can be represented by the presence or absence of an oscillation.

A parametric subharmonic oscillator may be regarded as a degenerative case of a parametric amplifier. In a parametric amplifier two resonant circuits which are tuned, respectively, to the signal frequency f_s and the idling frequency f_i are coupled regeneratively through a nonlinear reactor. A voltage at a pumping frequency f_p which satisfies the condition $f_p = f_i + f_s$ is applied to the nonlinear reactor. When the two resonant circuits for f_i and f_s are reduced into a single

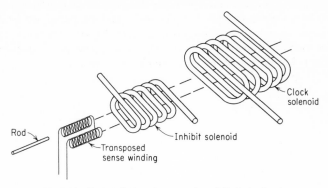

FIG. 7-56   Exploded view of a magnetic rod for logic circuits.

common circuit so that $f_i = f_s = f_o$, the condition becomes $f_p = 2f_o$, which is the condition for the parametric subharmonic oscillation.

The parametric oscillation is not a new phenomenon. Its application to the digital computer was independently conceived by both the late von Neumann and Goto of Japan at nearly the same time (1954). The Parametron has been used in several digital computers in Japan.

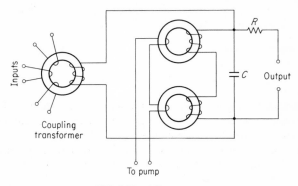

FIG. 7-57   A Parametron.

Parametron Circuit. A Parametron is shown in Fig. 7-57; it comprises a pair of ferrite cores with two windings on each, a resistor, a capacitor, and one coupling transformer. One winding on each core and the capacitor form a resonant circuit, which is tuned to the frequency f_o. The other windings are connected in series to the pump. The exciting current from the pump is the superposition of a d-c bias and an a-c current whose frequency f_p is equal to $2f_o$ and causes a periodic variation in the inductance of the resonant circuit at pump frequency f_p; the resonant circuit oscillates at the parametric frequency f_o. The circuit is connected to the other circuits by resistor R and the coupling transformer. The characteristics of some available Parametrons are shown in Table 7-5, where the coupling coefficient is defined as the ratio of the unit input voltage measured at the resonant circuit to the voltage of stationary oscillation.

The Parametron is a bilateral device, the direction of the information flow being controlled by a three-phase clock. The clock and the pump can be combined into one device which generates a pulse-modulated carrier, as illustrated in Fig. 7-58. Information transfer by the use of a three-phase pulse-modulated clock offers a parallel to the use of the tunnel-diode logic circuit.

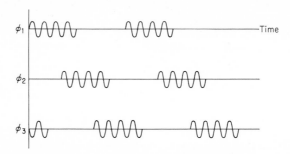

FIG. 7-58   A three-phase pulse-modulated clock.

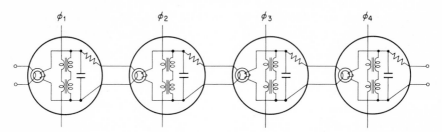

FIG. 7-59   A Parametron delay line.

Logic Circuits.   Figure 7-59 shows a delay line, a chain of Parametrons which are divided into three functional groups. The first group, consisting of the first and every fourth Parametron, is excited by clock phase ϕ_1. The second group, embracing the second and every fourth Parametron thereafter, and the third group, consisting of the third and every fourth Parametron thereafter, are

Table 7-5   Characteristics of Some Parametrons [39]

Characteristic	High-speed	Standard	Low-power
Pumping frequency............................	6 Mc	2 Mc	200 kc
Maximum clock frequency, kc................	140	25	2
Power per Parametron, mw..................	120	30	5
D-c bias, amp.............................	0.6	0.6	0.6
Fan-in....................................	3 or 5	3 or 5	3 or 5
Fan-out..................................	12	15	15
Coupling coefficient, db....................	−35	−40	−40

excited, respectively, by phases $\emptyset_2$ and $\emptyset_3$.   Overlapping of the three clock phases enables the oscillation of one stage to be started while the preceding stage is still oscillating.   The delay between two adjacent Parametrons is one-third the clock period.   The delay line in Fig. 7-59 is also a shift register.

Figure 7-60 shows a Parametron logic circuit.   The outputs of three Parametrons P_1, P_2, and P_3 are coupled to Parametron P_4; the coupling transformer forms the majority circuit (see Chaps. 3 and 6).   Briefly, if input C has a constant value of 1, then either input A or input B or both being 1 gives a majority decision of 1; and Parametron P_4 is switched into the 1 state.   The circuit becomes a logical-*or* circuit.   If circuit C has a constant value of 0, then both inputs A and B must be 1 to effect a majority decision of 1; and Parametron P_4 switches

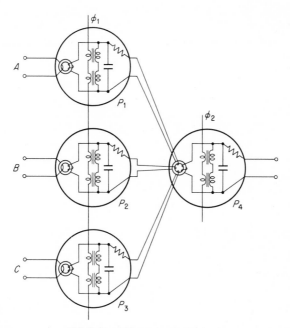

FIG. 7-60   A Parametron logic circuit.

to the 1 state.   This logic circuit becomes a logical-*and* circuit.   The constant signals are derived from the constant Parametrons or some voltage sources.

The logical-*not* operation can be simply obtained by reversing the polarity of the input terminals on the coupling transformer.

Because of the analog-addition nature of signals in a Parametron, the allowable number of inputs is limited to 3 or 5 in most cases.   Since each Parametron is an amplifier, the maximum allowable branching ranges from 10 to 20.   Thus, the Parametron has a limited fan-in but an adequately large fan-out capability.

The Parametron computer MUSASINO I [40], built in Japan, is a parallel machine with a word length of 40 bits and a fixed binary point.   The arithmetic and control unit employs about 4,400 Parametrons, in addition to 280 vacuum tubes for the pump.   The pump frequency is 2.4 Mc, and the repetition frequency of the three-phase clock is about 10 kc.

Problems

1. Establish tables of operation for the six single-core symbolic circuits of Fig. 7-13.

2. Draw schematic circuits for the single-diode transfer-loop logic circuits of Fig. 7-18.

3. Given Boolean equations for a serial adder,

$$S \text{ (sum)} = A \oplus B \oplus \Delta C_i$$
$$C_o(\text{output carry}) = AB + (A + B)C_i$$

where Δ is the delay operator, C_i the input carry, and A and B are the augend and addend bits, respectively, draw a magnetic-core symbolic circuit using the single-shift-line transfer loop.

4. Given the following functions,

(a) $f = \Delta(A\bar{f})$, where $A = \Delta(\bar{f})$ (b) $f = \Delta(A + \Delta^2 A)$, where $A = \Delta(\bar{f})$
(c) $f = \Delta(A \oplus f)$

draw magnetic-core sequence generators, and determine their binary sequences.

5. Synthesize magnetic-core logic circuits for the following Boolean functions by using Karnaugh circuits:

(a) $f = \bar{A}B + \bar{B}C + \bar{C}\bar{A}$ (b) $f(A,B,C,D) = P_2 + P_6 + P_9 + P_{13} + P_{15}$

6. Synthesize magnetic-core logic circuits for the following Boolean functions by using Rosenfeld circuits:

(a) $f = AB\bar{C} + A\bar{B}C + \bar{A}BC$ (b) $f(A,B,C,D) = P_3 + P_5 + P_8 + P_{11} + P_{14}$

7. Synthesize magnetic-core logic circuits for the following Boolean functions by using Andrews circuits:

(a) $f = ABC + B\bar{C}D + A\bar{B}D$
(b) $f = ABCD + A\bar{B}C\bar{D} + \bar{A}B\bar{C}D + \bar{A}BC\bar{D} + \bar{A}\bar{B}CD$
(c) $f(A,B,C,D) = P_1 + P_5 + P_7 + P_{10} + P_{12}$

References

1. Wang, An, and Way Dong Woo: Static Magnetic Storage and Delay Line, *J. Appl. Phys.*, vol. 21, pp. 49–54, January, 1950.

2. Wang, An: Magnetic Delay-line Storage, *Proc. IRE*, April, 1951, pp. 401–407.

3. Alden, J. M., M. Kincaid, and R. B. Hanna: Static Magnetic Memory, *Electronics*, January, 1951, pp. 108–111.

4. Wang, An: Static Magnetic Memory: Its Applications to Computers and Controlling Systems, *Proc. ACM*, 1952, pp. 207–212.

5. Ramey, R. A.: The Single-core Magnetic Amplifier as a Computer Element, *AIEE Communs. Electronics*, vol. 271, pp. 442–446, 1952.

6. Littman, M. F.: Ultrathin Tapes of Magnetic Alloys with Rectangular Hysteresis Loops, *Trans. AIEE*, vol. 71, pt. 1, pp. 220–223, 1952.

7. Sands, E. A.: Behavior of Rectangular Hysteresis Loop Magnetic Materials under Current Pulse Conditions, *Proc. IRE*, vol. 40, pp. 1246–1250, October, 1952.

8. Mayer, R. P.: The Mirror: A Proposed Simplified Symbol for Magnet Circuits, *MIT Digital Computer Lab. Eng. Note* E-472, Aug. 14, 1952.

9. Saunders, N. B.: Magnetic Binaries in the Logical Design of Information Handling Machines, *Proc. ACM*, May, 1952, pp. 223–229.

10. Wylen, J.: Pulse Response Characteristics of Rectangular Hysteresis Loop Ferromagnetic Materials, *Trans. AIEE*, vol. 72, pt. 1, pp. 648–656, 1953.

11. Sands, E. A.: An Analysis of Magnetic Shift Register Operation, *Proc. IRE*, August, 1953, pp. 993–999.

12. Kodis, R. D., S. Ruhman, and W. D. Woo: Magnetic Shift Register Using One Core per Bit, *IRE Conv. Record,* 1953, pp. 38–42.

13. Ferromagnetic Core Logical Circuitry and Its Application to Digital Computers, *Ballistic Research Labs. Mem. Rept.* 911, August, 1955.

14. Menyuk, N., and J. B. Goodenough: Magnetic Materials for Digital-computer Components: A Theory of Flux Reversal in Polycrystalline Ferromagnetics, *J. Appl. Phys.,* vol. 26, no. 1, pp. 8–18, January, 1955.

15. Karnaugh, M.: Pulse-switching Circuits Using Magnetic Cores, *Proc. IRE,* May, 1955, pp. 570–584.

16. Guterman, S., R. F. Kodis, and S. Ruhman: Logical and Control Functions Performed with Magnetic Cores, *Proc. IRE,* March, 1955, pp. 291–298.

17. Auerbach, I. L., and S. B. Disson: Magnetic Elements in Arithmetic and Control Circuits, *Elec. Eng.,* September, 1955, pp. 766–770.

18. Devenny, C. F., Jr., and L. G. Thompson: Ferromagnetic Core Characteristics for Computer Type Circuits, *Proc. Electronic Components Symposium,* May, 1955, pp. 15–17.

19. Brown, D. R., D. A. Buck, and N. Menyuk: A Comparison of Metals and Ferrites for High-speed Pulse Operations, *AIEE Communs. Electronics,* January, 1955, pp. 631–635.

20. Guterman, S. S., and W. M. Carey, Jr.: A Transistor–Magnetic Core Circuit: A New Device Applied to Digital Computing Techniques, *IRE Natl. Conv. Record,* 1955, pp. 84–94.

21. Report of a New Decision Element System, revised, Librascope Incorporated, Burbank Division, Jan. 9, 1956.

22. Evans, W. G., W. G. Hall, and R. I. Van Nice: Magnetic Logic Circuits for Industrial Control Systems, *AIEE Appl. Ind.,* July, 1956, pp. 166–171.

23. Torrey, R. D., and T. H. Bonn: A 2.5-megacycle Ferractor Accumulator, *Proc. Eastern Joint Computer Conf.,* 1956, pp. 50–53.

24. Scarrott, G. G., W. J. Harwood, and K. C. Johnson: The Design and Use of Logical Devices Using Saturable Magnetic Cores, *Proc. IEE (London),* vol. 103, pt. B, suppl. 2, pp. 302–312, April, 1956.

25. Andrews, L. J.: A Technique for Using Memory Cores as Logical Elements, *Proc. Joint Eastern Computer Conf.,* 1956, pp. 39–46.

26. Newhouse, V. L., and N. S. Prywes: High-speed Shift Registers Using One Core per Bit, *IRE Trans. on Electronic Computers,* September, 1956, pp. 114–120.

27. Hogue, E. W.: A Saturable-transformer Digital Amplifier with Diode Switching, *Proc. Eastern Joint Computer Conf.,* 1956, pp. 58–64.

28. Loev, D., W. Miehle, J. Paivinen, and J. Wyle: Magnetic Core Circuits for Digital Data Processing Systems, *Proc. IRE,* February, 1956, pp. 154–162.

29. Hunter, L. P., and E. W. Bauer: High Speed Coincident Flux Magnetic Storage Principles, *J. Appl. Phys.,* November, 1956, pp. 1257–1261.

30. Erb, D. R.: High Speed Magnetic Switches for Memory Matrices, *Proc. Electronic Components Symposium,* May, 1957, pp. 42–54.

31. Bonn, T. H.: Magnetic Computer, *Electronics,* August, 1957, pp. 156–160.

32. Russell, L. A.: Diodeless Magnetic Core Logical Circuits, *IRE Natl. Conv. Record,* 1957, pp. 106–114.

33. Rosenfeld, J. L.: Magnetic Core Pulse-switching Circuits for Standard Packages, *IRE Trans. on Electronic Computers,* September, 1958, pp. 223–228.

34. Morgan, W. L.: Bibliography of Digital Magnetic Circuits and Materials, *IRE Trans. on Electronic Computers,* June, 1959, pp. 148–158.

35. Karnaugh, M.: Magnetic Selectors, *Proc. Intern. Symposium on Theory of Switching,* 1959, pt. 2, pp. 186–191.

36. Dunham, B.: The Use of Multipurpose Logical Devices, *Proc. Intern. Symposium on Theory of Switching,* 1959, pt. 2, pp. 192–200.

37. Woo, W. D.: Magnetic-core Logic Circuits, *Proc. Intern. Symposium on Theory of Switching,* 1959, pt. 2, pp. 173–178.

38. Kaufman, B. A., D. A. Meier, and D. W. Rork: Megacycle Magnetic Rod Logic, *IRE Wescon Record*, pt. 4, pp. 27–31, 1959.

39. Goto, E.: The Parametron, A Digital Computing Element Which Utilizes Parametric Oscillation, *Proc. IRE*, August, 1959, pp. 1304–1316.

40. Muraga, S., and K. Takashima: The Parametron Digital Computer MUSASINO-I, *IRE Trans. on Electronic Computers*, September, 1959, pp. 308–316.

41. Meyerhoff, A. J. (senior ed.): "Digital Applications of Magnetic Devices," John Wiley & Sons, Inc., New York, 1960.

8

Magnetic Multiaperture-core Logic Circuits

A toroidal magnetic core has only one flux path. In a magnetic multiaperture core there are multiple flux paths, thus making possible a more complex logic circuit. This chapter describes magnetic logic circuits using multiaperture cores.

8-1   Flux-summation-core Logic Circuits

A Multiaperture Core.   A multiaperture core of ferrite, with a rectangular loop property, was reported by Lockhart [5] and is shown in Fig. 8-1.   There are six legs labeled a to f.   Legs a to c are input legs; legs d to f are output legs.   An input or an output winding is wound on each of the input or output legs; none of these windings is shown in the figure.   A flux path in the multiaperture core always links one input leg to one output leg; the dashed lines and arrows in Fig. 8-1 indicate possible flux paths.

If all flux paths are in a clockwise direction, as in Fig. 8-1, the flux pattern is taken to be the 0 state; all paths in a counterclockwise direction, as in Fig. 8-2c, represent the 1 state. The input, or set, windings switch the flux in their legs to a direction which is a *part* of a counterclockwise path.

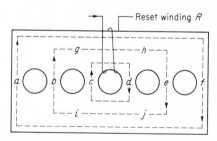

FIG. 8-1   A magnetic flux-summation core.

A pulse applied to reset winding R (Fig. 8-1) switches all flux paths to a clockwise direction, as shown in the figure; and the core is in the 0 state. During this resetting, voltages may be induced in output windings. The core is operated by applying the reset pulse and the input pulses alternately.

Flux Summation.   The six-leg core is operated according to the principle of flux summation. When a flux reversal occurs in one or more input legs, the flux in the first output leg d reverses; this is illustrated in Fig. 8-2a, where one pulse is applied to input winding A. When there are flux reversals in any two or more input legs, the fluxes in the first and second output legs d and e are reversed. Figure 8-2b illustrates the case where pulses are applied to input wind-

293

ings A and B. Flux reversal in all input legs means that a flux reversal is incurred in all three output legs, as shown in Fig. 8-2c. This technique is called *flux summation* because flux reversals in the output legs hinge on the sum of flux changes in the input legs. The flux reversal in the core follows a certain logic pattern which can be utilized to realize some logic operations.

To achieve the flux-summation operation, the core must fulfill certain geometrical requirements. First, the core must have an equal number of input and output legs, all having equal cross-sectional areas. These legs are joined in parallel by two legs gh and ij of the main body, indicated in Fig. 8-1. Second, the cross-sectional area of two legs gh and ij must be equal to or larger than the sum of the cross-sectional areas of all input legs (or output legs). Third, the three flux paths linking the first input leg a to one of the three output legs must show a well-defined difference in length. This means that the length of path $aghfjia$ is greater than the length of path $aghejia$, which in turn is greater than the length of path $agdia$. The differences in length of the three paths institute preferential flux reversals because these lengths cause an initial difference in reluctance to exist among the three paths and produce a flux reversal in the shorter or the shortest path. Similarly, this difference in length should be true for the three flux paths linking input leg b or c to any one of the three output legs.

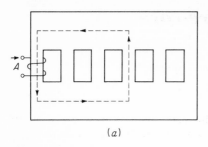

(a)

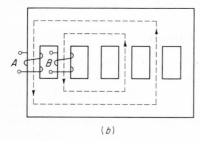

(b)

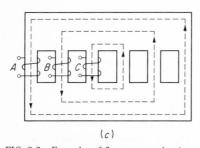

(c)

FIG. 8-2 Examples of flux patterns showing the principle of flux summation. (a) One input is applied; (b) two inputs are applied; (c) three inputs are applied.

Logic Circuits. Figure 8-3 shows a four-leg core with two input legs a and b and two output legs c and d. From the principle of flux summation, output leg c is switched and output f_1 produced when a pulse is applied to one or both input windings. Output leg d is switched and an output f_2 produced when pulses are applied to both input windings. No output leg is switched when no input is applied. This operation is shown in the table in the figure. For positive logic, output f_1 gives a delayed logical-*or* operation and f_2 a delayed logical-*and* operation.

If the two positive terminals of output f_1 and f_2 are connected, the other two terminals form an output f_3. Output f_3 is zero when both legs c and d are switched because outputs f_1 and f_2 cancel each other. There is an output f_3 when the pulse is applied to only one of the two inputs. For positive logic, this is a delayed exclusive-*or* circuit. In summary, these three outputs are

$$f_1 = \Delta(A + B)$$
$$f_2 = \Delta(AB) \qquad (8\text{-}1)$$
$$f_3 = \Delta(A \oplus B)$$

Figure 8-4 shows a six-leg core with three input legs a to c and three output legs d to f. From the flux-summation principle, output f_1 occurs whenever an input is applied to any one or more input windings; output f_2 occurs whenever inputs are applied to any two or more input windings, and output f_3 occurs when

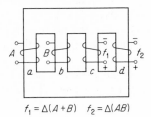

$f_1 = \Delta(A+B) \quad f_2 = \Delta(AB)$

Input pulse applied		Output leg switched	
Leg a	Leg b	Leg c	Leg d
−	+	−	−
−	+	+	−
+	−	+	−
+	+	+	+

FIG. 8-3   Logic operations on a four-leg core.

inputs are applied to all three input windings.   For positive logic, these three outputs are

$$f_1 = \Delta(A + B + C)$$
$$f_2 = \Delta(AB + BC + CA) \qquad (8\text{-}2)$$
$$f_3 = \Delta(ABC)$$

It is apparent that flux-summation core may readily implement symmetric Boolean function.

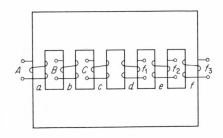

Input pulse applied			Output leg switched		
Leg a	Leg b	Leg c	Leg d	Leg e	Leg f
−	−	−	−	−	−
−	−	+	+	−	−
−	+	−	+	−	−
−	+	+	+	+	−
+	−	−	+	−	−
+	−	+	+	+	−
+	+	−	+	+	−
+	+	+	+	+	+

FIG. 8-4   Logic operations on a six-leg core.

Multipurpose Logic Circuits.   Circuits such as those of Figs. 8-3 and 8-4 are called *multipurpose logic circuits* [4] because they realize directly a number of simple Boolean functions.   Multipurpose circuits have the advantage of compactness and fewer wire connections.   On the other hand, the basic logic circuits, which are single-purpose circuits, are more flexible when more complex logic circuits are to be built.   It should be pointed out that the use of single-purpose or multipurpose logic circuits represents two different approaches which are heavily influenced by circuit feasibility, cost, and reliability.

Two additional multipurpose logic circuits will now be discussed. The first circuit is the single-bit full adder of Fig. 8-5. As was shown in Table 5-6, the sum S is 1 when any one input or all three inputs (but not two inputs) have the value 1. Examining the table in Fig. 8-4 reveals that the sum can be obtained by connecting outputs f_1 and f_2 in series subtracting and output f_3 in series adding. Also from Table 5-6, the output carry C_o is 1 whenever two or three inputs have the value 1. The carry is output f_2 of Fig. 8-4 because this output appears whenever there are two or three inputs.

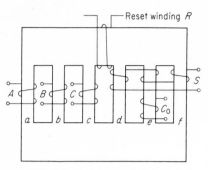

FIG. 8-5   A single-core full adder.

The second circuit is shown in Fig. 8-6. Input C is connected to a clock so that its value is always 1. Output f_1 is connected in the same manner as the sum output of the adder. Output f_2 is connected with the windings on legs d and e in series subtracting. For positive logic, f_1 is a delayed coincidence operation, and f_2 is a delayed *nor* operation.

8-2   Laddic Logic Circuits

The Laddic (derived from *ladder logic*), reported by Gianola and Crowley [8], is a ladderlike multiaperture structure illustrated in Fig. 8-7. It is made of ferrite material with a rectangular-loop property. In the magnetic structure there are 16 to 32 rungs per inch, and thus a large number of possible flux paths. By switching these flux paths, a Boolean function can be implemented.

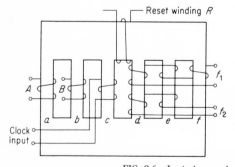

Input pulse applied		Output leg switched		
Leg a	Leg b	Leg d	Leg e	Leg f
−	−	+	−	−
−	+	+	+	−
+	−	+	+	−
+	+	+	+	+

$$f_1 = \Delta(A \odot B) \qquad f_2 = \Delta(\overline{A + B})$$

FIG. 8-6   Logical-*nor* and coincidence circuits.

Principle of Operation. The side rails and rungs of the Laddic are made equal in their minimum cross section so that all possible paths are flux-limited. Assume that the flux in the first rung is downward. When a reversal field is applied to the first rung, the switched flux is returned almost entirely through the closest path, rung 2, no matter how large the applied field. This flux pattern has been established by experiments. Furthermore, it has been found that if the ratio of rung spacing to side-rail spacing is 1 or 2, the ratio of the flux returned to the closest rung to the flux returned to the next closest rung is 21 or 83, respectively. Placing input windings on alternate rungs makes possible the control of flux paths and, in turn, the implementing of the Boolean function.

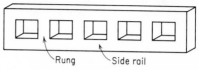

FIG. 8-7   The Laddic structure.

Logic Circuits.   Figure 8-8 shows a Laddic with a reset winding.   Applying a current pulse to the reset winding establishes a flux pattern of upward saturated flux in odd-numbered rungs and downward saturated flux in even-numbered rungs. The directions of these saturated fluxes are indicated by arrows.   This is the resetting process.

Consider the Laddic of Fig. 8-9*a*, which has been reset.   If a current pulse is

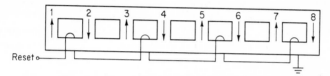

FIG. 8-8   Reset winding and flux pattern of the Laddic.

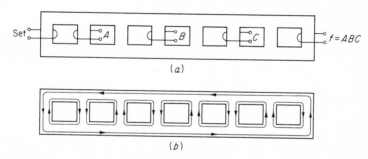

FIG. 8-9   A Laddic logical-*and* circuit.

applied to the set winding on rung 1, the flux in that rung is switched downward and the flux returns through the closest available path of rung 2.   However, if a current pulse is also being applied to winding *A* on rung 2 to hold the flux in that rung in its original downward direction, the flux cannot return through rung 2. Neither can the flux return through rungs 3, 5, and 7, because they have been saturated in the upward direction.   The closest available path is rung 4.   Furthermore, if current pulses are also being applied to windings *B* and *C* on rungs 4 and 6 to hold their respective fluxes in the original upward direction, the flux cannot return through those rungs.   The only available path is in rung 8.   The flux reverses in rung 8, and an output pulse is produced.   In short, a pulse is produced at the output when there are current pulses at input windings *A*, *B*, and *C*. For positive logic, this is a logical-*and* circuit.   Note that the output voltage corresponds to reversal of one-half the saturation flux in rung 8 because the other half of the flux in either of the two side rails is a portion of the flux paths around the holes, as shown in Fig. 8-9b. Also note that no input winding should be placed on odd-numbered rungs except the first rung, because these rungs serve only to maintain flux continuity.

If more than one input winding is placed on an even-numbered rung, as in the circuit of Fig. 8-10, application of a current pulse to either of these input windings holds the original flux direction. For positive logic, the Laddic in Fig. 8-10 is a logical-*or* circuit. The currents applied to input windings only prevent the flux from being switched in the rung; therefore, their magnitude needs to exceed only a minimum.

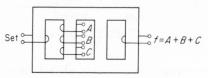

FIG. 8-10   A Laddic logical-*or* circuit.

The Laddic can also be wound to form the *or-and* circuit and the *and-or* circuit. Figure 8-11 shows an *or-and* circuit which merely adds input windings on even-numbered rungs (except the last rung) of the Laddic of Fig. 8-9a. Fig. 8-12 shows an *and-or* circuit wherein adjacent Laddics combine in a continuous sheet, with guard spaces in between. Each Laddic forms a product term, and the logical-*or* operation is performed by the output winding.

If more than one input winding is placed on even-numbered rungs (except the

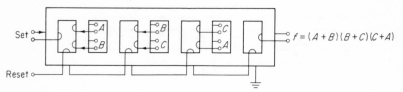

FIG. 8-11   A Laddic logical-*or-and* circuit.

last rung) of the Laddic of Fig. 8-12, the resulting circuit is an *or-and-or* circuit. Other forms of Boolean functions are possible; these are achieved by windings on side rails, by an output winding overlying more than one rung, or by using a more complicated ladder structure.

8-3   *Biax Logic Circuits*

Biax Logic Element.   The Biax, reported by Wanlass [9], is a two-aperture magnetic bar, as shown in Fig. 8-13. It is made of ferrite material with a square-loop property and a low coercive force. Two orthogonal holes intersect, as indicated in the figure, allowing wires to be threaded through them. There are four flux-constricting areas (shaded areas in the figure) at which flux interference occurs around the two holes.

A current pulse in set wire S sets up a flux around the lower hole (Fig. 8-13) but produces little flux enclosing the wires in the upper hole; this is the setting process of the element occurring at time t_1. Similarly, when a current pulse is applied to reset wire R in the upper hole, a flux is set up around the upper hole; this is the resetting process occurring at time t_2. Reset occurring after a setting process induces a pulse in output wire f because the pulse in reset wire R causes a flux change around a portion of the lower hole through two of the constricting areas.

Biax Logic Circuits. The Biax logic element in Fig. 8-13 is a logical-*not* circuit. If no pulse is applied to input *A* during the setting process, the subsequent resetting process induces a pulse in the output wire. However, an input pulse inhibits the setting process, and the subsequent resetting process produces little output. The principle of this logical-*not* operation is similar to that of the

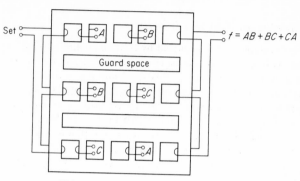

FIG. 8-12   A Laddic logical-*and-or* circuit.

Andrews inhibit-wound core shown in Fig. 7-61. In an inhibit-wound core, the inhibition occurs between the circular fluxes produced by current pulses. In a Biax element, the inhibition happens between the fluxes at the constricting areas.

Figure 8-14 shows a Biax logic element with two input wires *A* and *B*. Either or both inputs can inhibit the setting process. In positive logic, this is a delayed *nor* circuit and is similar to the Andrews circuit in Fig. 7-63. If complements

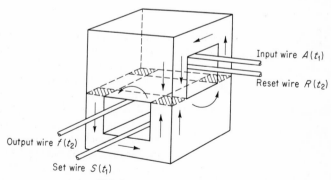

FIG. 8-13   A Biax logic element.

of the inputs ($\bar{A}$ and $\bar{B}$) are used instead, it becomes a logical-*and* circuit of *A* and *B*.

The logical-*or* operation is performed by connecting in series the output wire of more than one Biax logic element. Since each Biax logic element can be made to form a product term, the threading of the output wire through these logic elements results in an *and-or* circuit. The example of Fig. 8-15 (set and reset wires are not shown) implements the same Boolean function as does the Andrews circuit in Fig. 7-65. A transistor amplifier at the output terminal drives succeeding *and-or* circuits.

Reportedly the signal-to-noise ratio can be as high as $100:1$ with a single Biax logic element; this makes possible the threading of a large number of elements to form an *or* circuit. The Biax element is reported to be operable as fast as $\frac{1}{2}$ μsec per each *and-or* circuit.

8-4 Transfluxor Logic Circuits

In its first developed form, reported by Rajchman and Lo [1,2], the Transfluxor appeared as a two-aperture magnetic core (Fig. 8-16) and was so named because it operates by a controlled transfer of flux from one leg to the other in the magnetic core. This core is of ferrite material having a rectangular-loop property.

Two-aperture Transfluxor. The Transfluxor core contains two circular apertures of unequal diameter which result in distinct legs—1, 2, and 3. The cross-sectional areas of legs 1 and 2 are equal, and that of leg 3 equals or exceeds the sum of the areas of legs 1 and 2. There are four windings, N_1 to N_4. When a blocking, or reset, pulse is applied to reset winding N_3, a clockwise flux shown

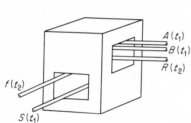

FIG. 8-14 A Biax logical-*nor* circuit.

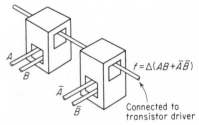

$$f = \Delta(AB + \bar{A}\bar{B})$$

Connected to transistor driver

FIG. 8-15 A Biax logical-*and-or* circuit.

in Fig. 8-17a flows and saturates legs 1 and 2; this is possible because of the larger size of leg 3. The flux in legs 2 and 3 remains saturated after termination of the input blocking pulse. The flux pattern in Fig. 8-17a is called the *blocked state*. When an unblocking, or set, pulse is applied to set winding N_4, a reversal of the flux in leg 2 and of a part of the flux in leg 3 occurs, as shown in Fig. 8-17b. This is achieved by having the magnitude of the unblocking, or set pulse being smaller than the blocking pulse. The result is that the magnetizing force in the nearer leg 2 is larger than the coercive force H_c but that the magnetizing force in the farther leg 1 is smaller than H_c. Leg 2 is saturated in a reverse direction (upward), but leg 1 is still saturated in the same downward direction. The flux pattern in Fig. 8-17b is called the *unblocked state*. The blocking and unblocking

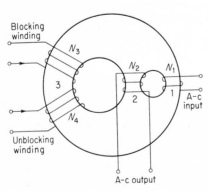

FIG. 8-16 A two-aperture Transfluxor.

states are the binary states of the core, representing, respectively, the 0 and 1 states.

Input winding N_1 connects to an a-c signal source. N_2 is an output winding in which an a-c signal is induced by the flux reversal in the material around the small aperture functioning as a transformer. This transformer operates differently at the two core states. Consider the case when the core is in the blocked state. The a-c source in N_1 produces an alternating magnetomotive force (mmf) along a path surrounding the smaller aperture shown by the shaded area in Fig. 8-17a. When the mmf is in a clockwise direction, it tends to increase the flux in leg 1 and to decrease the flux in leg 2. But the previous saturation of leg 1 permits no flux increase, in turn permitting no flux decrease in leg 2 because the magnetic flux is always in a closed path. When mmf is in a counterclockwise direction, a similar situation prevails. Therefore, the blocked state allows no flux reversal around the small aperture and thus no induced voltage in the output winding. Consider the case when the core is in the unblocked state. When the a-c source is applied to N_1, there can be a flux increase in one leg and a flux decrease in the other leg and the alternating flux induces a voltage in output winding N_2. Therefore, during the unblocked state, local flux reversal occurs around the small aperture, inducing a voltage in output winding N_2.

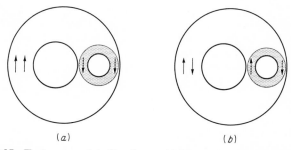

(a)   (b)

FIG. 8-17   The two states of the Transfluxor. (a) Blocked state; (b) unblocked state.

The above Transfluxor operation will now be summarized. First, in the blocked state, the fluxes in legs 1 and 2 are in the same direction; in the unblocked state, they are in the opposite direction. Second, in the blocked state, the flux around the small aperture is irreversible by the a-c source in winding N_1, and there is essentially no coupling between primary and secondary windings N_1 and N_2; in the unblocked state, there is a relatively large coupling between N_1 and N_2. Third, the generation of an a-c output depends on whether the core is in the unblocked or blocked state, all the while not disturbing the flux condition in leg 3. This can be regarded as a method of reading out the core state without destroying it and can be used to build a nondestructive read-out magnetic-core memory.

Logic Circuits.   Transfluxor logic circuits make use of multiaperture cores and a multiplicity of windings. A Transfluxor with five apertures [3] is shown in Fig. 8-18. There are four unblocking windings A to D; the input to each of these windings represents a Boolean variable. The two other windings are a-c input and a-c output. Operation relies on the condition that the output flux path around the central aperture through legs 1, 2, 3, and 4 can be blocked by any one or more of the four legs. This flux path is unblocked only when the directions of the flux in the four legs around the central aperture are the same. Thus, this core can be operated as a four-input logical-*and* circuit. However, there are two unblocked states due to the two possible clockwise and counterclockwise directions of the flux around the central aperture. One of the two states can be eliminated by using one of the four inputs as a reference.

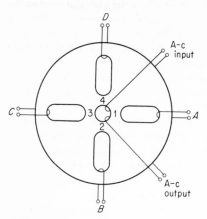

FIG. 8-18 A five-aperture Transfluxor as a logical-*and* circuit.

A Transfluxor with four apertures [3] is shown in Fig. 8-19. The blocked and unblocked states are shown in Fig. 8-20. If a pulse is applied to the blocking winding on leg 3, the core is blocked as two parallel flux paths 34263 and 38193 become saturated. This makes the flux in output flux path 15271 irreversible. The core is in the blocked state when the flux in legs 1 and 2 are saturated and are of the same polarity. If a pulse is applied to unblocking winding terminals, either A or B, the flux flow reverses in path 38193. This unblocks output flux path 15271, and the transformer function between primary and secondary windings N_1 and N_2 becomes possible. Since unblocking can be achieved by applying a pulse to either or both inputs, this is a logical-*or* circuit.

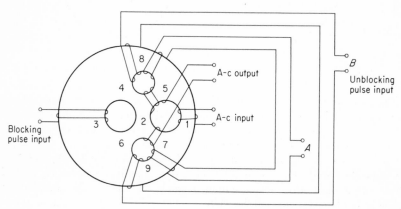

FIG. 8-19   A four-aperture Transfluxor as a logical-*or* circuit.

A Transfluxor with three apertures [3] is shown in Fig. 8-21. The output flux path consists of legs 1 and 2. When a pulse is applied to the blocking winding, the core flux state becomes that shown in Fig. 8-22a; the fluxes in legs 1 and 2 are in the same direction. No a-c output is produced. When pulses are applied to both unblocking windings A and B, the core flux state is that of Fig. 8-22b; the fluxes in legs 1 and 2 are again in the same direction. Again no a-c output is produced. Where a pulse is applied to input A (or B), the flux in leg 1 (or 2)

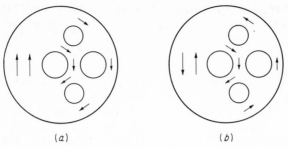

FIG. 8-20   The two states of the four-aperture Transfluxor.   (*a*) Blocked state; (*b*) unblocked state.

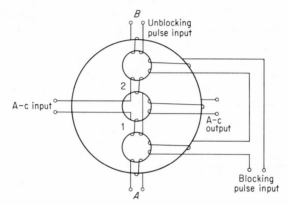

FIG. 8-21   A three-aperture Transfluxor as a logical-exclusive-*or* circuit.

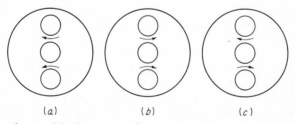

FIG. 8-22   Several states of the three-aperture Transfluxor.   (*a*) Blocking state; (*b*) blocking state; (*c*) unblocking state.

is reversed, as shown in Fig. 8-22*c*; the fluxes in legs 1 and 2 are in the opposite direction.   An a-c output is generated.   For positive logic, this is an exclusive-*or* operation.

8-5   MAD Logic Circuits

MAD, derived from *multiaperture device* and reported by Crane [6,7], stems from the two-aperture Transfluxor.   A MAD in its simplest form (Fig. 8-23) is a magnetic core with two additional small apertures, the input and output apertures; its transfer loop consists only of connecting wires.

Input and Output Apertures. There are two states in a MAD, the blocked and the unblocked states representing the 0 and 1 states, respectively; these two states, shown in Fig. 8-23, are similar to

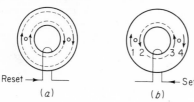

those of the Transfluxor of Fig. 8-17. In the blocked state, a reset pulse resets all flux in a clockwise direction. In an unblocked state, no more than half the circumferential flux is in a counterclockwise direction; this condition contributes to the isolation when MADs are connected together by wires, as will be seen. The unblocked flux pattern requires that a local flux reversal around either small

FIG. 8-23 Two states of the MAD elements. (a) Blocked, or 0, state; (b) unblocked, or 1, state.

aperture be possible; as shown in Fig. 8-23b, the fluxes in legs 1 and 2 or in legs 3 and 4 can be in a counterclockwise direction around either small aperture.

If a current I_T is applied to the winding at the output aperture, as shown in Fig. 8-24, the change of flux pattern in the MAD depends on its initial state. If the MAD is initially in the blocked state, no local flux around the output aperture can change, because the flux in leg 3 is already completely saturated in the down-

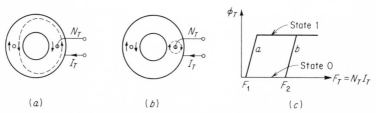

FIG. 8-24 Output aperture properties. (a) Set by an output-aperture current when the MAD was initially at 0 state; (b) local flux reversal by an output-aperture current when the MAD was initially at the 1 state; (c) flux and mmf relation.

ward direction. However, when the applied mmf F_T ($= N_T I_T$) is larger than setting threshold F_2 shown as curve b in Fig. 8-24c, the flux can change, but only around a path enclosing both the output and the central apertures, the dashed path in Fig. 8-24a. As F_T increases beyond F_2, the flux changes until leg 4 is completely switched. If the MAD is in the unblocked state initially, the applied mmf F_T needs to overcome a low threshold F_1 shown as curve a in Fig. 8-24c; a local flux reversal occurs in legs 3 and 4, as indicated by the dashed path in Fig. 8-24b. The flux pattern in legs 1 and 2, and thus the state of the MAD, remains unchanged.

If a current I_R is applied to the winding at the input aperture (Fig. 8-25), the change of the flux pattern in the MAD also depends on its initial state. But in the present application the MAD is always first reset to its 0 state. In this case the applied mmf F_R must be larger than the setting threshold F_2 before the flux pattern changes, as shown by the curve in Fig. 8-25b; and the flux can change only about a path along legs 1 and 3, the dashed path in Fig. 8-25a. If a negative set current $-I_R$ is subsequently applied, only a local flux reversal around the input aperture occurs, as shown in Fig. 8-25c, and the flux state around the output aperture is not affected. This isolation between the input and the output apertures is an important property.

Note that once the MAD is set into the 1 state, it is impossible to reset it from any small aperture winding; the reset winding around the central aperture has to be used.

Transfer Loop. A transfer loop may be constructed by connecting in parallel a transmitter winding of N_T turns of one MAD and a receiver winding of N_R turns of another MAD. The transfer loop is then connected in series with a shift-current-pulse source as shown in Fig. 8-26. This transfer loop admits three

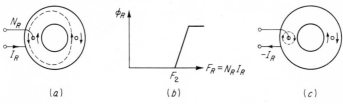

(a)   (b)   (c)

FIG. 8-25   Input aperture properties. (a) Set by an input-aperture current when the MAD was initially at the 0 state; (b) flux and mmf relation; (c) negative set by an input-aperture current when the MAD was initially at the 0 state.

possibilities, N_T being larger than, smaller than, or equal to N_R. The loop with N_T equal to N_R is called the *symmetric loop*; it has a bilateral shifting property and is the case to be described here. This transfer loop shows some similarity to the gated-diode transfer loop in Chap. 7.

The aim of the transfer loop is to transmit the state of the transmitting MAD to the receiving MAD when the shift current pulse I_A is applied. The receiving MAD is always in the 0 state initially.

Consider the case where the transmitting MAD is initially at the 0 state. Shift

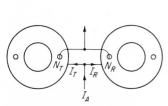

FIG. 8-26   A basic transfer loop.

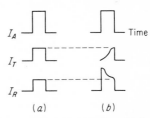

FIG. 8-27   Currents during a transfer. (a) 0 transfer; (b) 1 transfer.

current pulse I_A divides equally into the two branch currents I_T and I_R. The magnitude of the current $I_A/2$ is so chosen that its resulting mmf is equal to F_2; hence, there is no flux change in either MAD. This is the transfer of the 0 state of the transmitting MAD to the receiving MAD, and its current waveform is shown in Fig. 8-27a.

Consider the case where the transmitting MAD is initially in the 1 state. When shift current pulse I_A is applied, the transmitting MAD has a low threshold F_1; a local flux reversal occurs, as shown in Fig. 8-24b, and current I_T is small. However, the current I_R becomes large and overcomes setting threshold F_2; the receiving MAD is thus set to the 1 state, as shown in Fig. 8-25a. This is the transfer of the 1 state of the transmitting MAD to the receiving MAD, and its current waveform appears in Fig. 8-27b. Note that the transmitter read-out is nondestructive because there is only a local flux reversal.

A Shift Register. Cascading a chain of MADs (Fig. 8-28) results in a shift register. Its operation requires a four-phase clock. The MADs are divided into an odd-numbered group and an even-numbered group. Assume that the information is initially stored in the odd-numbered MADs and that the even-num-

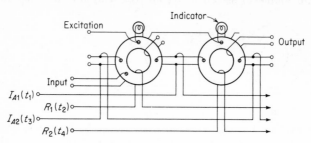

FIG. 8-28   A shift register using MADs.

bered MADs are all cleared. The operating cycle is (1) to shift the states in the odd-numbered to the even-numbered MADs at time t_1 by current $I_{A1}(t_1)$, (2) to reset the odd-numbered MADs into the 0 state at time t_2 by current $R_1(t_2)$, (3) to shift the states in the even-numbered to the odd-numbered MADs at time t_3 by current $I_{A2}(t_3)$, and then (4) to reset the even-numbered MADs to the 0 state at time t_4 by current $R_2(t_4)$

Figure 8-29 shows a MAD with a number of small apertures. The arrows in Fig. 8-29a show the flux pattern in the 0 state. Any aperture may be used either

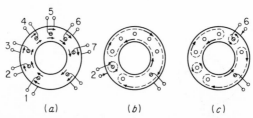

FIG. 8-29   A MAD with multiple small apertures. (*a*) Reset state flux pattern; (*b*) set at aperture 2; (*c*) output at aperture 6.

as an input or as an output. The MAD may be set to the 1 state from any input aperture such as input aperture 2 of Fig. 8-29b; and no signals are induced in any other windings. This is possible because of the condition that no more than half the circumferential flux around the central aperture is switched by any input winding; in this way, no flux changes in the leg linked by any other input winding. In Fig. 8-29c an output is taken at aperture 6. The use of these additional small apertures is exemplified in the shift register of Fig. 8-28. In this figure additional input and output apertures are indicated, and an indicator is added by connecting a suitable light and an exciting winding through another additional aperture. The amplitude of the exciting current must be limited to a value that merely alternates the flux locally about its aperture.

Logic Circuits. Logic circuits can be formed by properly connecting MADs. Figure 8-30*a* shows a two-input logical-*or* circuit. In this circuit, a wire is threaded through the two output apertures in the transmitting branch. If both MADs *A* and *B* are in the 0 state, no transmitter current is steered into the receiving branch and the receiving MAD remains in the 0 state. If MAD *A* or *B* (or both) is in the 1 state, most of the shift current flows into the receiving branch and the receiving MAD is set to the 1 state. Figure 8-30*b* shows a logical-*and* circuit having two transmitting branches. The transmitter current can be steered into the receiving branch only when both MADs *A* and *B* are in the 1 state. In this case the flux at their output apertures is locally reversible, and a large receiving current is available at the receiving branch to switch the receiving MAD into the 1 state.

The operation of the MAD is improved if it is shaped like the one shown in Fig. 8-31, which has substantially equal cross-sectional area everywhere. Logic circuits can also be formed by geometrically shaping the MAD; these will not be further described.

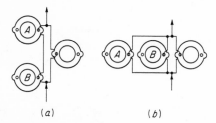

(a)   (b)

FIG. 8-30   MAD logic circuits.   (a) Logical-*or*; (b) logical-*and*.

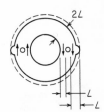

FIG. 8-31   A shaped MAD.

The great advantage of the MAD lies in its simple transfer loop, at the expense, however, of using a four-phase clock. At present, an information rate of about 250 kc is reported to be feasible.

References

1. Rajchman, J. A., and A. W. Lo: The Transfluxor: A Magnetic Gate with Stored Variable Setting, *RCA Rev.*, June, 1955, pp. 303–311.

2. Rajchman, J. A., and A. W. Lo: The Transfluxor, *Proc. IRE*, March, 1956, pp. 321–332.

3. Abbott, H. W., and J. J. Suran: Multihole Ferrite Core Configurations and Applications, *Proc. IRE*, August, 1957, pp. 1081–1093.

4. Dunham, B., and J. H. North: The Use of Multipurpose Logical Devices, *IBM Research Rept.* RC-9, Apr. 4, 1957.

5. Lockhart, N. F.: Logic by Ordered Flux Changes in Multipath Ferrite Cores, *IRE Natl. Conv. Record*, 1958, pp. 268–278.

6. Crane, H. D.: A Highspeed Logic System Using Magnetic Elements and Connecting Wire Only, *Proc. IRE*, January, 1959, pp. 63–73.

7. Bennion, D. R., and H. D. Crane: Design and Analysis of MAD Transfer Circuitry, *Proc. Western Joint Computer Conf.*, 1959, pp. 21–36.

8. Gianola, U. F., and T. H. Crowley: The Laddic: Magnetic Device for Performing Logic, *Bell System Tech. J.*, vol. 38, pp. 45–72, January, 1959.

9. Wanlass, C. L., and S. D. Wanlass: Biax High Speed Magnetic Computer Element, *Proc. Western Joint Computer Conf.*, 1959, pp. 40–54.

10. Morgan, W. L.: Transfluxor Design Considerations, *IRE Trans. on Electronic Devices*, March, 1961, pp. 155–162.

11. Vinal, A. W.: The Development of a Multiaperture Reluctance Switch, *Proc. Western Joint Computer Conf.*, 1961, pp. 443–474.

9

Switching Matrices

An important type of digital computer circuit, the switching matrix, is described in this chapter by means of the Boolean matrix function. Matrix circuits using diodes, magnetic cores, transistors, cryotrons, and other components are discussed. Both single-level and multiple-level matrices are described.

9-1 *Multiple-output Switching Circuits*

A multiple-output switching circuit may be described by a number of Boolean functions. Let us use the single-bit full adder as an example. The truth table has been shown in Table 5-6, from which two Boolean functions for sum S and output carry C_o are written as

$$S = \overline{X}\overline{Y}C_i + \overline{X}Y\overline{C_i} + X\overline{Y}\overline{C_i} + XYC_i \qquad (9\text{-}1)$$

$$C_o = \overline{X}YC_i + X\overline{Y}C_i + XY\overline{C_i} + XYC_i \qquad (9\text{-}2)$$

where X, Y, and C_i are the augend bit, addend bit, and input carry bit, respectively. These functions can be written in P terms,

$$S = P_1 + P_2 + P_4 + P_7 \qquad (9\text{-}3)$$

$$C_o = P_3 + P_5 + P_6 + P_7 \qquad (9\text{-}4)$$

They can also be written in terms of characteristic numbers.

$$S = (0 \times P_0) + (1 \times P_1) + (1 \times P_2) + (0 \times P_3) + (1 \times P_4) \\ + (0 \times P_5) + (0 \times P_6) + (1 \times P_7) \qquad (9\text{-}5)$$

$$C_o = (0 \times P_0) + (0 \times P_1) + (0 \times P_2) + (1 \times P_3) + (0 \times P_4) \\ + (1 \times P_5) + (1 \times P_6) + (1 \times P_7) \qquad (9\text{-}6)$$

These last two equations may further be translated into a Boolean matrix function as follows,

$$\begin{bmatrix} S \\ C_o \end{bmatrix} = \begin{bmatrix} 0 & 1 & 1 & 0 & 1 & 0 & 0 & 1 \\ 0 & 0 & 0 & 1 & 0 & 1 & 1 & 1 \end{bmatrix} \begin{bmatrix} P_0 \\ P_1 \\ P_2 \\ P_3 \\ P_4 \\ P_5 \\ P_6 \\ P_7 \end{bmatrix} \qquad (9\text{-}7)$$

or, in matrix notation,

$$[O] = [B] \cdot [P] \tag{9-8}$$

where $[O]$, $[B]$, and $[P]$ are the O matrix (or output matrix), the B matrix (or Boolean matrix), and the P matrix (or product-term matrix), respectively. Multiplication of the B matrix by P matrix follows the ordinary multiplication rule of matrix algebra. In other words, it is the sum of the products of one P term with a corresponding bit in the B matrix, in the manner shown in Eqs. (9-5) and (9-6). The above B matrix consists of two rows and eight columns; each row represents one output, and each column represents one P term. The 1's in row 01101001 represent terms P_1, P_2, P_4, and P_7, and those in row 00010111 represent the terms P_3, P_5, P_6, and P_7. The numbers in the two rows are thus the contents of the columns for the sum and the output carry in Table 5-6. In short, the above Boolean matrix is an array of characteristic numbers of Boolean functions (9-3) and (9-4).

Boolean functions for the above sum S and output carry C_o may be written in S terms as

$$S = S_0 S_3 S_5 S_6 \tag{9-9}$$
$$C = S_0 S_1 S_2 S_4 \tag{9-10}$$

These functions can also be written in terms of characteristic numbers,

$$S = (0 + S_0)(1 + S_1)(1 + S_2)(0 + S_3)(1 + S_4)(0 + S_5)(0 + S_6)(1 + S_7) \tag{9-11}$$

$$C_o = (0 + S_0)(0 + S_1)(0 + S_2)(1 + S_3)(0 + S_4)(1 + S_5)(1 + S_6)(1 + S_7) \tag{9-12}$$

Translated into a Boolean matrix form, these functions appear as follows,

$$\begin{bmatrix} S \\ C_o \end{bmatrix} = \begin{bmatrix} 0 & 1 & 1 & 0 & 1 & 0 & 0 & 1 \\ 0 & 0 & 0 & 1 & 0 & 1 & 1 & 1 \end{bmatrix} \begin{bmatrix} S_0 \\ S_1 \\ S_2 \\ S_3 \\ S_4 \\ S_5 \\ S_6 \\ S_7 \end{bmatrix} \tag{9-13}$$

or, in matrix notation,

$$[O] = [B][S] \tag{9-14}$$

where $[S]$ is the S matrix (or sum-term matrix). Multiplication of the B matrix by the S matrix does not follow the ordinary multiplication rule of matrix algebra. Instead, the multiplication is defined as shown in Eqs. (9-11) and (9-12): the product of the sums of one S term and the corresponding bit in the B matrix. Boolean matrix functions (9-7) and (9-13) are in canonical P and S forms, respectively, and the Boolean matrices in these two forms are identical. Thus, once the B matrix of the Boolean matrix function in canonical form is known for a multiple-output circuit, Boolean equations for all the outputs can readily be written in canonical P form or in canonical S form.

The foregoing Boolean equations (9-3) and (9-4) for the single-bit full adder express truth-table values for S and C_o equal to 1. If, instead, S and C_o are equal to 0, the complement expressions read

$$\bar{S} = P_0 + P_3 + P_5 + P_6 \tag{9-15}$$

$$\bar{C}_o = P_0 + P_1 + P_2 + P_4 \tag{9-16}$$

Similarly, these two complement functions translate into the following Boolean matrix function:

$$\begin{bmatrix} S \\ C_o \end{bmatrix} = \begin{bmatrix} 1 & 0 & 0 & 1 & 0 & 1 & 1 & 0 \\ 1 & 1 & 1 & 0 & 1 & 0 & 0 & 0 \end{bmatrix} \begin{bmatrix} P_0 \\ P_1 \\ P_2 \\ P_3 \\ P_4 \\ P_5 \\ P_6 \\ P_7 \end{bmatrix} \tag{9-17}$$

or, in matrix notation,

$$[\bar{O}] = [\bar{B}][P] \tag{9-18}$$

where $[\bar{O}]$ and $[\bar{B}]$ are the *complement output matrix* and the *complement B matrix*, respectively. Note that each bit in the $\bar{B}$ matrix is the 1's complement of the corresponding bit in the $\bar{B}$ matrix. Multiplication of the $\bar{B}$ matrix by the P matrix follows the ordinary multiplication rule of matrix algebra.

Boolean functions (9-9) and (9-10), are written from the truth table for S and C_o equal to 1. Conversely, S and C_o equal to 0 appear as the complement functions

$$\bar{S} = S_1 S_2 S_4 S_7 \tag{9-19}$$

$$\bar{C}_o = S_3 S_5 S_6 S_7 \tag{9-20}$$

These two equations may be written in the following matrix form,

$$\begin{bmatrix} S \\ \bar{C}_o \end{bmatrix} = \begin{bmatrix} 1 & 0 & 0 & 1 & 0 & 1 & 1 & 0 \\ 1 & 1 & 1 & 0 & 1 & 0 & 0 & 0 \end{bmatrix} \begin{bmatrix} S_0 \\ S_1 \\ S_2 \\ S_3 \\ S_4 \\ S_5 \\ S_6 \\ S_7 \end{bmatrix} \tag{9-21}$$

or, in matrix notation,

$$[\bar{O}] = [\bar{B}] \cdot [S] \tag{9-22}$$

Multiplication of the B matrix by the S matrix does not follow the ordinary multiplication rule of matrix algebra. The multiplication is defined as shown in Eqs. (9-11) and (9-12).

In summary, for a given truth table which describes a multiple-output switching circuit, the Boolean matrix and the complement Boolean matrix can be directly obtained. From the B matrix and the $\bar{B}$ matrix, four matrix functions for the multiple-output circuit such as (9-7), (9-13), (9-17), and (9-21) can be written. Boolean functions which describe the multiple-output circuit are readily obtained from the four matrix functions.

9-2   Switching Matrices

The switching matrix is a multiple-output switching circuit which realizes a Boolean matrix function. Logic structures of three special switching matrices are the rectangle, tree, and dual-tree matrices. Other switching matrices will be described later.

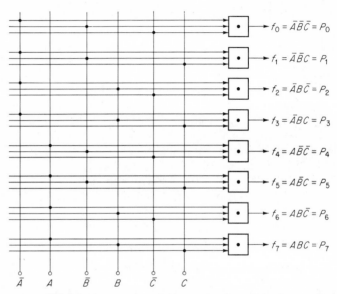

FIG. 9-1   A rectangular switching matrix using *and* circuits.

Rectangle Matrix. A rectangle switching matrix (using logical-*and* circuits) for three Boolean variables appears in Fig. 9-1 and involves three pairs of inputs and eight outputs. For each product term of three input variables, there is one, and only one, corresponding output. Boolean functions for the eight outputs are

$$\begin{aligned}
f_0 &= P_0 = \bar{A}\bar{B}\bar{C} \\
f_1 &= P_1 = \bar{A}\bar{B}C \\
f_2 &= P_2 = \bar{A}B\bar{C} \\
f_3 &= P_3 = \bar{A}BC \\
f_4 &= P_4 = A\bar{B}\bar{C} \\
f_5 &= P_5 = A\bar{B}C \\
f_6 &= P_6 = AB\bar{C} \\
f_7 &= P_7 = ABC
\end{aligned} \qquad (9\text{-}23)$$

The above Boolean functions equate with the following matrix function:

$$
\begin{bmatrix} f_0 \\ f_1 \\ f_2 \\ f_3 \\ f_4 \\ f_5 \\ f_6 \\ f_7 \end{bmatrix}
=
\begin{bmatrix}
1 & 0 & 0 & 0 & 0 & 0 & 0 & 0 \\
0 & 1 & 0 & 0 & 0 & 0 & 0 & 0 \\
0 & 0 & 1 & 0 & 0 & 0 & 0 & 0 \\
0 & 0 & 0 & 1 & 0 & 0 & 0 & 0 \\
0 & 0 & 0 & 0 & 1 & 0 & 0 & 0 \\
0 & 0 & 0 & 0 & 0 & 1 & 0 & 0 \\
0 & 0 & 0 & 0 & 0 & 0 & 1 & 0 \\
0 & 0 & 0 & 0 & 0 & 0 & 0 & 1
\end{bmatrix}
\begin{bmatrix} P_0 \\ P_1 \\ P_2 \\ P_3 \\ P_4 \\ P_5 \\ P_6 \\ P_7 \end{bmatrix}
\qquad (9\text{-}24)
$$

In this Boolean matrix a single 1 appears in each row, and all 1's lie on the diagonal of the matrix. No logical-*or* circuit is needed. This is the simplest form of the B matrix for a switching circuit with three pairs of inputs and eight outputs. For the case of four or more pairs of inputs, the pattern of 1's and 0's of the B matrix remains the same.

In Fig. 9-1, eight (or 2^n) three-input (or n) logical-*and* blocks are required. Both the normal and the complement of the three variables appear at the input of each *and* block. For n pairs of input variables, the required number of *and* inputs being $n2^n$ becomes very large for a large value of n.

A rectangle switching matrix for three Boolean variables using logical-*or* blocks is the same as that shown in Fig. 9-1 except that the *and* blocks are replaced by *or* blocks. In this case, for each S term of the three input variables, all outputs except one appear at output terminals. Boolean functions for the eight outputs are

$$
\begin{aligned}
f_0 &= S_0 = A + B + C \\
f_1 &= S_1 = A + B + \bar{C} \\
f_2 &= S_2 = A + \bar{B} + C \\
f_3 &= S_3 = A + \bar{B} + \bar{C} \\
f_4 &= S_4 = \bar{A} + B + C \\
f_5 &= S_5 = \bar{A} + B + \bar{C} \\
f_6 &= S_6 = \bar{A} + \bar{B} + C \\
f_7 &= S_7 = \bar{A} + \bar{B} + \bar{C}
\end{aligned}
\qquad (9\text{-}25)
$$

The above Boolean functions may be written into the following matrix function:

$$
\begin{bmatrix} f_0 \\ f_1 \\ f_2 \\ f_3 \\ f_4 \\ f_5 \\ f_6 \\ f_7 \end{bmatrix}
=
\begin{bmatrix}
1 & 0 & 0 & 0 & 0 & 0 & 0 & 0 \\
0 & 1 & 0 & 0 & 0 & 0 & 0 & 0 \\
0 & 0 & 1 & 0 & 0 & 0 & 0 & 0 \\
0 & 0 & 0 & 1 & 0 & 0 & 0 & 0 \\
0 & 0 & 0 & 0 & 1 & 0 & 0 & 0 \\
0 & 0 & 0 & 0 & 0 & 1 & 0 & 0 \\
0 & 0 & 0 & 0 & 0 & 0 & 1 & 0 \\
0 & 0 & 0 & 0 & 0 & 0 & 0 & 1
\end{bmatrix}
\begin{bmatrix} S_0 \\ S_1 \\ S_2 \\ S_3 \\ S_4 \\ S_5 \\ S_6 \\ S_7 \end{bmatrix}
\qquad (9\text{-}26)
$$

The above Boolean matrix is the same as (9-24) in that all 1's lie on the diagonal. The required number of *or* inputs is also $n2^n$.

Tree Matrix.† A tree (or pyramid) switching matrix using logical-*and* cir-

---

† Both the tree matrix and the dual-tree matrix are multiple-level matrices.

cuits for four Boolean variables is shown in Fig. 9-2. There are four pairs of inputs and 16 outputs. Boolean equations for the 16 outputs are

$$
\begin{aligned}
f_0 &= [(\bar{A}\bar{B})\bar{C}]\bar{D} & f_8 &= [(A\bar{B})\bar{C}]\bar{D} \\
f_1 &= [(\bar{A}\bar{B})\bar{C}]D & f_9 &= [(A\bar{B})\bar{C}]D \\
f_2 &= [(\bar{A}\bar{B})C]\bar{D} & f_{10} &= [(A\bar{B})C]\bar{D} \\
f_3 &= [(\bar{A}\bar{B})C]D & f_{11} &= [(A\bar{B})C]D \\
f_4 &= [(\bar{A}B)\bar{C}]\bar{D} & f_{12} &= [(AB)\bar{C}]\bar{D} \\
f_5 &= [(\bar{A}B)\bar{C}]D & f_{13} &= [(AB)\bar{C}]D \\
f_6 &= [(\bar{A}B)C]\bar{D} & f_{14} &= [(AB)C]\bar{D} \\
f_7 &= [(\bar{A}B)C]D & f_{15} &= [(AB)C]D
\end{aligned}
\tag{9-27}
$$

The above Boolean equations may be written into a matrix function. In this case, the Boolean matrix is multiple-level, indicated by the parentheses and brackets in the above equations. Multiple-level matrices will further be shown later.

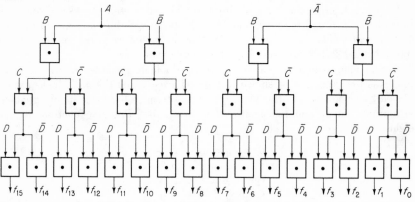

FIG. 9-2   A tree switching matrix using *and* circuits.

In the above functions (9-27), the parentheses and brackets indicate the manner of connecting the *and* blocks in Fig. 9-2. For n equal to 2, 2^3 *and* inputs are needed. For n equal to 3, $2^2 + 2^4$ *and* inputs are required. For n pairs of variables, the required number of *and* inputs N is

$$
N = \sum_{2}^{n} 2^{n+1}
\tag{9-28}
$$

Compared with the rectangular matrix, the tree matrix requires fewer *and* inputs because combinations of two variables share each input.

Boolean functions for a tree switching matrix using *or* blocks are similar to those of (9-27) but are expressed in S terms. The logic diagram will be the same as that of Fig. 9-2, except that all *and* blocks are replaced by *or* blocks.

Dual-tree Matrix.† Figure 9-3 shows a dual-tree switching matrix using *and* blocks for four Boolean variables. There are four pairs of inputs and 2^4 outputs. This configuration requires fewer *and* inputs than the rectangle or tree matrix.

---

† Both the tree matrix and the dual-tree matrix are multiple-level matrices.

Boolean equations for the 16 outputs are

$$
\begin{aligned}
f_0 &= (\bar{A}\bar{B})(\bar{C}\bar{D}) & f_8 &= (A\bar{B})(\bar{C}\bar{D}) \\
f_1 &= (\bar{A}\bar{B})(\bar{C}D) & f_9 &= (A\bar{B})(\bar{C}D) \\
f_2 &= (\bar{A}\bar{B})(C\bar{D}) & f_{10} &= (A\bar{B})(C\bar{D}) \\
f_3 &= (\bar{A}\bar{B})(CD) & f_{11} &= (A\bar{B})(\bar{C}D) \\
f_4 &= (\bar{A}B)(\bar{C}\bar{D}) & f_{12} &= (AB)(\bar{C}\bar{D}) \\
f_5 &= (\bar{A}B)(\bar{C}D) & f_{13} &= (AB)(\bar{C}\bar{D}) \\
f_6 &= (\bar{A}B)(C\bar{D}) & f_{14} &= (AB)(C\bar{D}) \\
f_7 &= (\bar{A}B)(CD) & f_{15} &= (AB)(CD)
\end{aligned}
\tag{9-29}
$$

The above functions may also be written into a Boolean matrix function; the Boolean matrix is also multiple-level. The parentheses in the above equations indicate the manner of connecting the *and* blocks of Fig. 9-3. In comparison

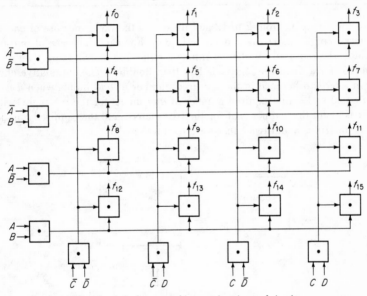

FIG. 9-3 A dual-tree switching matrix using *and* circuits.

with Eqs. (9-27), it is apparent that combinations of two variables are shared in a dual manner.

For a switching circuit with eight pairs of inputs and 256 outputs, a dual-tree matrix is shown in Fig. 9-4. The eight input variables are divided into two groups of four variables each. Each group is further divided into two groups of two variables each. In case n is not an even multiple of 4, the above steps can still be taken, except that the resulting configuration is not symmetrical.

Boolean equations for a dual-tree matrix using *or* blocks are similar to (9-29) but are expressed in S terms. The block diagram will be the same as that of Fig. 9-3, except that all *and* blocks are replaced by *or* blocks.

Comparison. The three types of switching matrices—rectangle, tree, and dual-tree—perform the same switching operations but require different numbers of *and* inputs (or *or* inputs). Table 9-1 compares the required *and* inputs (or *or*

Table 9-1   Comparison of Required and inputs (or or inputs)

Input pairs n	Outputs 2^n	Required *and* inputs (or *or* inputs)		
		Rectangle	Tree	Dual-tree
2	4	8	8	8
3	8	24	24	24
4	16	64	56	48
5	32	160	120	96
6	64	384	248	176
7	128	896	504	328
8	256	2,048	1,016	608
9	512	4,608	2,040	1,168
10	1,024	10,240	4,088	2,240
11	2,048	22,528	8,184	4,368
12	4,096	49,152	16,376	8,544

inputs) for n ranging from 2 to 12 and illustrates the rapid increase of *and* inputs for the rectangle matrix as n become large. For each increase of one pair of variables, the required number of inputs for the tree matrix more than doubles, while that for a dual-tree matrix is less than double. The cumulative effect results in a large difference in the required number of *and* inputs when n is large. For n equal to 12, the required number of *and* inputs for the rectangle switching matrix is about three times that for the tree matrix, and the required number for the tree matrix is about twice that for a dual-tree matrix.

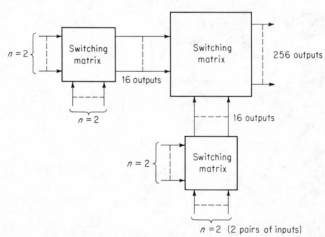

FIG. 9-4   A dual-tree matrix for eight pairs of inputs and 256 outputs.

Important in the selection of a particular switching matrix, the required number of *and* inputs (or *or* inputs) represents only one consideration. Another consideration is the number of levels that a signal has to go through from the input to the output. For the rectangle matrix, the signal passes through only one level. For the tree matrix, it goes through $n - 1$ levels. For the dual-tree matrix, it passes through one level for $n = 2$, two levels for $n = 3$ and 4, three levels for $n = 5$ to 8, and four levels for $n = 9$ to 16.

9-3 *Applications of Switching Matrices*

Figures 9-5 to 9-7 illustrate a number of applications in the use of switching matrices. A decoder is shown in Fig. 9-5a. There are n pairs of inputs and 2^n output terminals. As will be shown in Chap. 11, part of an instruction word of a digital computer is an operation code, which the decoder uses for identifying and initiating execution of the instruction. The output of the decoder can be less than 2^n terminals if it is so desired. A variation of the decoder matrix is a *translator,* or *radix converter,* which translates, for example, a binary-coded decimal digit into a corresponding decimal digit. In this case there are four pairs of inputs (assume a 4-bit code) and 10 output terminals to represent the 10 decimal digits. An encoder (or a coder) is shown in Fig. 9-5b. In an encoder there are 2^n input terminals and n pairs of output terminals. For instance, the 26 alphabetic letters can be coded by an encoder into the chosen 26 combinations of five Boolean variables.

Figure 9-6a shows a *selection matrix,* or a *many-one matrix.* In this matrix there are two groups of input terminals and one output terminal. One group,

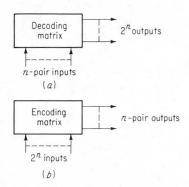

2^n outputs

n-pair inputs

(a)

n-pair outputs

2^n inputs

(b)

FIG. 9-5   Use of switching matrix as a decoder or an encoder.

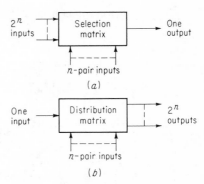

2^n inputs

Selection matrix

One output

n-pair inputs

(a)

One input

Distribution matrix

2^n outputs

n-pair inputs

(b)

FIG. 9-6   Use of switching matrix as a selector or a distributor.

consisting of 2^n input terminals, is connected to signal sources, and the other group, which consists of n pairs of input terminals, is actuated by a selected code. Only one signal source appears at the output at one time. For example, a serial word is read out from the reading head of a selected channel on a magnetic drum. In this case, the n pairs of inputs in Fig. 9-6a represent the channel address; the 2^n inputs come from the reading heads, and the output gives the read-out word. In reverse, a *distributor,* or *one-many matrix,* is shown in Fig. 9-6b. There are 2^n output terminals, one signal source, and n pairs of inputs. The signal is distributed to the selected output terminal by a given combination of the n pairs of inputs. For instance, a serial word from a signal source is distributed to the selected channel at which the head writes on the magnetic drum for storage.

If the n pairs of inputs of Fig. 9-5a are derived from a binary counter which counts a sequence of clock pulses, the resulting circuit is a *commutator,* as shown in Fig. 9-7. In a commutator, output terminals are selected one after the other, following the sequence of the states of the counter. For example, a commutator may be used to send pulses to various channels in a particular time sequence.

Matrices may also be used as sequence filters or sequence generators, as will be shown later.

9-4   *Diode Switching Matrices*

Diode networks are widely used as switching matrices, because of simplicity and high operating speed of the diode.   In this section the rectangle, tree, and dual-tree diode matrices are described, and in the subsequent two sections other diode matrices are shown.   In all these matrices logical-*and* and logical-*or* circuits are referred to the positive logic.

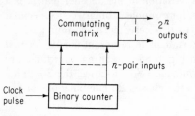

FIG. 9-7   Use of switching matrix as a commutator.

Rectangle, Tree, and Dual-tree Matrices.   A diode rectangle matrix with 16 outputs is shown in Fig. 9-8.   The four pairs of input terminals are energized by two voltage levels.   When a high voltage is applied to a terminal, the diodes connected to that terminal become back-biased; when a low voltage is applied,

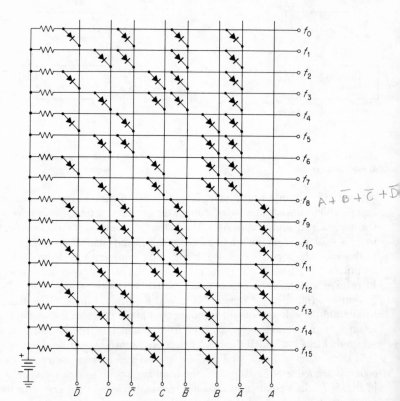

FIG. 9-8   A diode rectangle matrix with 16 outputs.

the diodes are forward-biased. If a high voltage is applied to terminals $\bar{A}$, $\bar{B}$, $\bar{C}$, and $\bar{D}$, a high voltage appears only at the output f_0. In other words, a high voltage level appears at the particular output where none of its four input *and* diodes is forward-biased. Because of the rectangular shape of the network, it is called a *rectangular diode matrix*. Each horizontal line gives one output, and each vertical line is connected to one of the input pair. Note the similarity between the diode rectangle matrix of Fig. 9-8 and the diagram of Fig. 9-1; all diodes form *and* circuits.

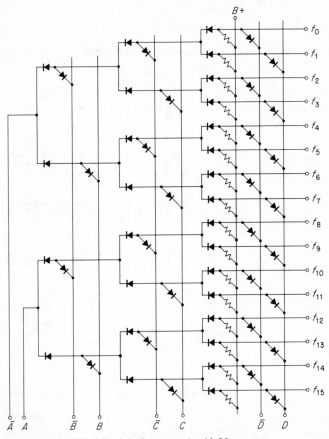

FIG. 9-9   A diode tree matrix with 16 outputs.

A diode tree matrix with 16 outputs is shown in Fig. 9-9. This is a multiple-output three-level logical-*and* circuit. These outputs are described by functions (9-27). Operation of the matrix is similar to the operation shown in Fig. 9-8. Because of the tree shape of the network, this is called a *tree diode matrix*. Similarity also exists between the tree matrix of Fig. 9-9 and the diagram of Fig. 9-2. Again, all diodes form *and* circuits.

A diode dual-tree matrix with 16 outputs is shown in Fig. 9-10. This is a multiple-output two-level logical-*and* circuit. The outputs are described by functions

(9-29).   Similar to the diagram of Fig. 9-3, a dual-tree matrix is formed by four intermediate input pairs using 16 *and* circuits.   The four intermediate input pairs are divided into two equal groups, and each group forms another diode matrix using four *and* circuits.   This dual-tree configuration employs fewer diodes and diode levels.

A Diode Selection Matrix.   A selection matrix is shown in Fig. 9-6a. Consider such a matrix with three pairs of inputs (A, B, and C).   Let the output be f and the eight signal inputs be $e_0, e_1, \cdots, e_7$.   Operation of the selection matrix can be described by the following Boolean equation,

$$f = e_0 P_0 + e_1 P_1 + e_2 P_2 + e_3 P_3 + e_4 P_4 + e_5 P_5 + e_6 P_6 + e_7 P_7 \quad (9\text{-}30)$$

where P_i are functions (9-23).   A rectangle diode selection matrix which imple-

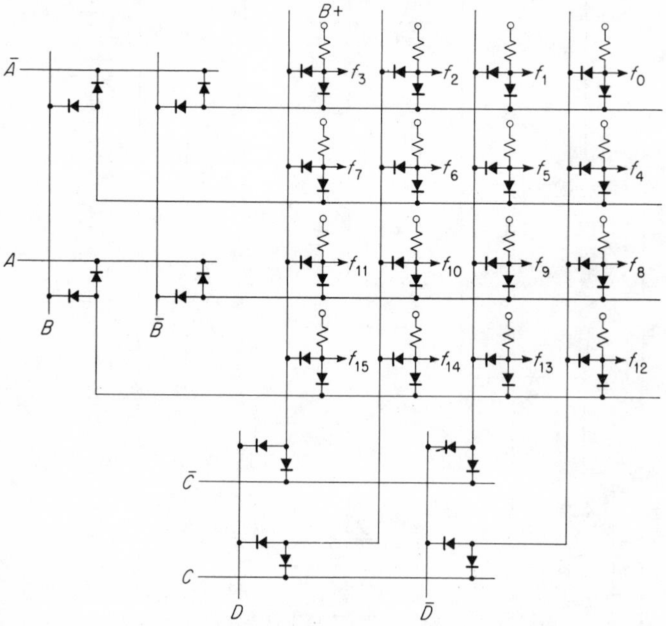

FIG. 9-10   A dual-tree diode matrix for 16 outputs.

ments the above function is shown in Fig. 9-11.   The *and*-circuit portion of the rectangle matrix is indicated there.   Note the two areas of functional importance. First, the eight input signals are applied to the open end of the eight resistors to achieve the logical-*and* operation.   Alternatively, we may use eight more diodes and eight more vertical lines to provide an additional *and* input to each of the eight horizontal lines.   Second, the *or* circuit is readily obtained by using an additional vertical line and eight additional diodes connected in the manner shown in Fig. 9-11.   The output f is taken from the ungrounded terminal of resistor R.

Equivalent Circuit of the Diode Matrix.   Performance of the diode matrix depends on diode characteristics and circuit parameters.   Consider a rectangle diode matrix with three pairs of inputs.   The equivalent circuit of this matrix is shown in Fig. 9-12.   This equivalent circuit assumes that the diode resistance is R_f when forward-biased and R_b when back-biased. The supply voltage is V, and the resistance connected to the voltage supply is R. As a further assumption, the two voltage levels applied to the input terminals are voltage V and ground potential. In Fig. 9-12, the voltages are applied to the input terminals so that only the output f_0 is at the high voltage level. The equivalent

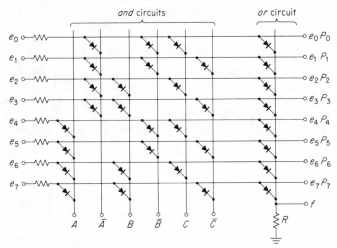

FIG. 9-11   An eight-input rectangle diode selection matrix.

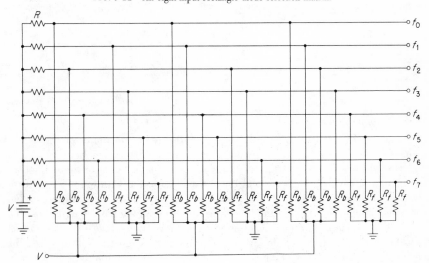

FIG. 9-12   Equivalent circuit of a rectangle diode matrix with eight outputs.

circuit of Fig. 9-12 is shown in Fig. 9-13. In this figure the output terminals f_1 to f_7 are all tied together, as they are at the same voltage level. If the rectangle matrix in Fig. 9-12 is for n pairs of inputs and 2^n outputs, the equivalent circuit is as shown in Fig. 9-14. This circuit adds a load resistance R_L. Examining this equivalent circuit reveals that the ratio of diode backward resistance to forward resistance should be large so that the nonselected terminal is near ground potential. Resistance R_L should be large in comparison with R or R_b/n so that the output can maintain the desired output voltage level. If proper values of R, V, and R_L are chosen, the performance of the above diode matrix does not deteriorate significantly when n becomes large. However, if the applied voltage level to the input terminals becomes insufficient to back-bias the input diodes, the output voltage drops rapidly as n increases.

9-5   Synthesis of Diode Switching Matrices

The previous diode selection matrix is an example showing the synthesis of one Boolean equation. The synthesis of a switching matrix (i.e., a set of Boolean equations) will now be illustrated by a number of examples. Again, the following logic circuits are referred to the positive logic.

A Full-adder Switching Matrix. Boolean equations for the single-bit full adder are Eqs. (9-1) and (9-2). A diode matrix implementing these two equations

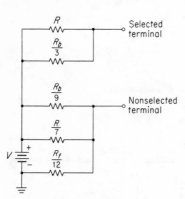

FIG. 9-13   Equivalent circuit of Fig. 9-12.

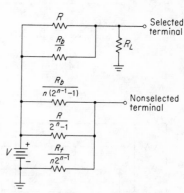

FIG. 9-14   Equivalent circuit of a rectangle diode matrix with 2^n outputs.

is shown in Fig. 9-15. The left portion of the rectangle diode matrix is the *and* circuit. There are only seven horizontal lines because Eqs. (9-1) and (9-2) need only seven P terms (of the eight possible P terms of three Boolean variables). Two additional vertical lines, each connected with four diodes, form the two *or* circuits for outputs S and C_o. An item of additional interest is that the arrangement of diodes in the two *or* circuits follows the pattern of 1's and 0's in the Boolean matrix for the full adder given in matrix function (9-7). This means that there is an *or*-circuit diode for each 1 in the matrix function but no diode for each 0. If there are more than two rows in the matrix function, each added row requires only one more vertical line together with associated diodes to form the *or* circuit. The simplicity of using the diode matrix in synthesizing a Boolean matrix is apparent.

The diode matrix for the full adder of Fig. 9-15 is called the *and-or matrix*. It is synthesized from Eqs. (9-1) and (9-2), which are of canonical P form. If synthesized from Eqs. (9-9) and (9-10), which are of canonical S form, the resulting diode matrix for the full adder is as shown in Fig. 9-16. This is an *or-and matrix.* Again the arrangement of diodes in the two *or* circuits follows the pattern of 1's and 0's in the Boolean matrix (9-13) for the full adder. Although the number of diodes in the matrices in Figs. 9-15 and 9-16 happens to be the same, usually one form may have more diodes than the other.

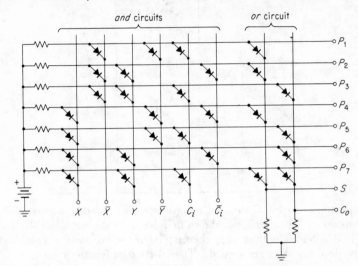

FIG. 9-15 A single-bit full adder using an *and-or* diode matrix.

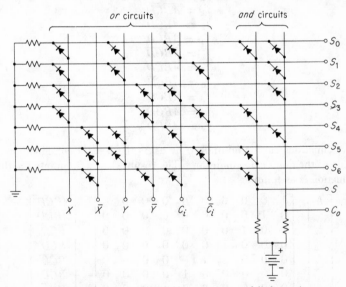

FIG. 9-16 A single-bit full adder using an *or-and* diode matrix.

A Translator Switching Matrix. The foregoing examples illustrated synthesis of Boolean equations in canonical P form and canonical S form. Such synthesis also applies to elementary P-form (or elementary S-form) equations. This is exemplified by a translator switching matrix.

Table 9-2   Truth Table for 8-4-2-1 Coded Decimal Digit

A	B	C	D	Decimal digit	Function
0	0	0	0	0	f_0
0	0	0	1	1	f_1
0	0	1	0	2	f_2
0	0	1	1	3	f_3
0	1	0	0	4	f_4
0	1	0	1	5	f_5
0	1	1	0	6	f_6
0	1	1	1	7	f_7
1	0	0	0	8	f_8
1	0	0	1	9	f_9
1	0	1	0		
1	0	1	1		
1	1	0	0		
1	1	0	1	not used	
1	1	1	0		
1	1	1	1		

(The heading spans: 8-4-2-1 coded digit over A B C D)

The operation of a translator which converts a binary-coded decimal digit into its corresponding decimal digit is shown in Table 9-2. In this table, the decimal digit is in 8-4-2-1 code; thus, only the first 10 of the 16 possible combinations of four Boolean variables are needed. The 10 Boolean functions are

$$f_0 = \bar{A}\bar{B}\bar{C}\bar{D}$$
$$f_1 = \bar{A}\bar{B}\bar{C}D$$
$$f_2 = \bar{A}\bar{B}C\bar{D}$$
$$f_3 = \bar{A}\bar{B}CD$$
$$f_4 = \bar{A}B\bar{C}\bar{D}$$
$$f_5 = \bar{A}B\bar{C}D$$
$$f_6 = \bar{A}BC\bar{D}$$
$$f_7 = \bar{A}BCD$$
$$f_8 = A\bar{B}\bar{C}\bar{D}$$
$$f_9 = A\bar{B}\bar{C}D$$

(9-31)

The above functions can be minimized by using the last six combinations in the above table as the don't care condition. The result when written into the Boolean matrix function is as follows:

$$
\begin{bmatrix} f_0 \\ f_1 \\ f_2 \\ f_3 \\ f_4 \\ f_5 \\ f_6 \\ f_7 \\ f_8 \\ f_9 \end{bmatrix} =
\begin{bmatrix}
1 & 0 & 0 & 0 & 0 & 0 & 0 & 0 & 0 & 0 \\
0 & 1 & 0 & 0 & 0 & 0 & 0 & 0 & 0 & 0 \\
0 & 0 & 1 & 0 & 0 & 0 & 0 & 0 & 0 & 0 \\
0 & 0 & 0 & 1 & 0 & 0 & 0 & 0 & 0 & 0 \\
0 & 0 & 0 & 0 & 1 & 0 & 0 & 0 & 0 & 0 \\
0 & 0 & 0 & 0 & 0 & 1 & 0 & 0 & 0 & 0 \\
0 & 0 & 0 & 0 & 0 & 0 & 1 & 0 & 0 & 0 \\
0 & 0 & 0 & 0 & 0 & 0 & 0 & 1 & 0 & 0 \\
0 & 0 & 0 & 0 & 0 & 0 & 0 & 0 & 1 & 0 \\
0 & 0 & 0 & 0 & 0 & 0 & 0 & 0 & 0 & 1
\end{bmatrix}
\begin{bmatrix} \bar{A}\bar{B}\bar{C}\bar{D} \\ \bar{A}\bar{B}\bar{C}D \\ \bar{B}C\bar{D} \\ \bar{B}CD \\ B\bar{C}\bar{D} \\ B\bar{C}D \\ BC\bar{D} \\ BCD \\ A\bar{D} \\ AD \end{bmatrix}
$$

(9-32)

The above matrix function is in the elementary P form. A translator diode matrix is shown in Fig. 9-17. The 30 diodes in this matrix represent a saving of 10 diodes, achieved by expressing the matrix function in elementary form instead of canonical form.

A Comparator Switching Matrix. The switching matrix for the translator is an example using the matrix function in elementary form. This can be extended to a matrix function in nonelementary form by using a multiple-level diode matrix.

A comparator, chosen as an example, is a multiple-output switching circuit which compares two binary numbers. It gives an output signal (say, 1) when these two numbers are identical. Figure 9-18a shows an application of the comparator. In this figure the recorded magnetic states on three tracks of a magnetic drum represent the addresses of words recorded at corresponding positions of the other tracks of the drum. These recorded magnetic states are being read as the drum rotates. The read-out pulses are temporarily stored in the B register. The address of the word to be selected is stored in the A register. When the contents in registers

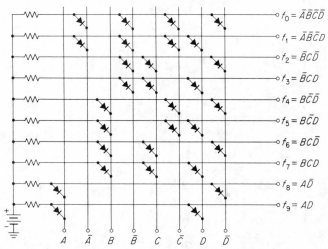

FIG. 9-17   A translator matrix (binary-coded decimal digit to decimal digit) using a switching matrix in an elementary form.

A and B are identical at a certain instant, the contents in register B indicate the location at the correct address. The comparator issues a signal so that the word on the other tracks, now at the correct address, is immediately read out.

The operation of the comparator is described by the following Boolean functions:

$$f = f_1 f_2 f_3 \tag{9-33}$$

$$f_1 = \bar{A}_1 \bar{B}_1 + A_1 B_1 \tag{9-34}$$

$$f_2 = \bar{A}_2 \bar{B}_2 + A_2 B_2 \tag{9-35}$$

$$f_3 = \bar{A}_3 \bar{B}_3 + A_3 B_3 \tag{9-36}$$

Functions f_1, f_2, and f_3, respectively, become 1 when the first, second, and third pair of corresponding bits of the two registers are equal, and function f becomes 1 when f_1, f_2, and f_3 are all 1. The above four functions can be written into a

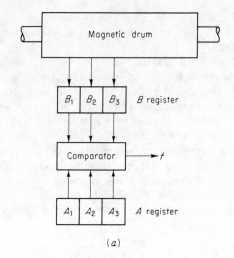

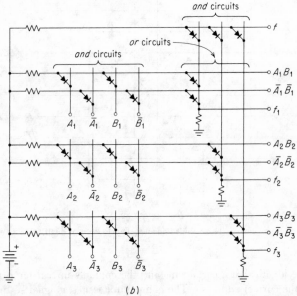

FIG. 9-18   A comparator using an *and-or-and* switching matrix.   (*a*) An application of the comparator; (*b*) diode matrix for a comparator.

Boolean matrix function in nonelementary form.

$$[f] = [1][f_1 f_2 f_3]$$

$$\begin{bmatrix} f_1 \\ f_2 \\ f_3 \end{bmatrix} = \begin{bmatrix} 1 & 1 & 0 & 0 & 0 & 0 \\ 0 & 0 & 1 & 1 & 0 & 0 \\ 0 & 0 & 0 & 0 & 1 & 1 \end{bmatrix} \begin{bmatrix} \bar{A}_1 \bar{B}_1 \\ A_1 B_1 \\ \bar{A}_2 \bar{B}_2 \\ A_2 B_2 \\ \bar{A}_3 \bar{B}_3 \\ A_3 B_3 \end{bmatrix} \qquad (9\text{-}37)$$

This function can be realized by the diode matrix of Fig. 9-18b. This is an *and-or-and* matrix which employs 21 diodes. If the above function is expanded into canonical P form, the corresponding diode rectangular matrix requires 56 diodes.

A Squaring Matrix. A squaring matrix is another example of a multiple-level switching matrix. This matrix gives an output which is numerically the square of the input. Consider a matrix having a 4-bit input and thus giving an 8-bit output. The operation of the squaring matrix is shown in Table 9-3. In this table, A_1 to A_4 are the 4 input bits and B_1 to B_8 are the 8 output bits. Both input and output are expressed in binary numbers. From this table, eight output functions can be written. These functions when minimized are

$$\begin{aligned}
B_1 &= A_1\\
B_2 &= 0\\
B_3 &= \bar{A}_1 A_2\\
B_4 &= A_1(A_2\bar{A}_3 + \bar{A}_2 A_3)\\
B_5 &= A_1(A_3\bar{A}_4 + \bar{A}_3 A_4) + \bar{A}_2 A_3(\bar{A}_4 + \bar{A}_1 A_4)\\
B_6 &= A_2(A_3\bar{A}_4 + \bar{A}_3 A_4) + A_1 A_3 A_4\\
B_7 &= A_4(\bar{A}_3 + A_2 A_3)\\
B_8 &= A_3 A_4
\end{aligned} \tag{9-38}$$

The above functions can be written as a Boolean matrix function in a nonelementary form which actually consists of two matrix functions both of which are in elementary form,

$$\begin{bmatrix} C_1\\ C_2\\ C_3\\ C_4 \end{bmatrix} = \begin{bmatrix} 0&0&0&0&0&0&1&1\\ 0&0&0&0&1&1&0&0\\ 0&0&1&1&0&0&0&0\\ 1&1&0&0&0&0&0&0 \end{bmatrix} \begin{bmatrix} A_2\bar{A}_3\\ \bar{A}_2 A_3\\ A_3\bar{A}_4\\ \bar{A}_3 A_4\\ \bar{A}_4\\ \bar{A}_1 A_4\\ \bar{A}_3\\ A_2 A_3 \end{bmatrix} \tag{9-39}$$

$$\begin{bmatrix} B_1\\ B_2\\ B_3\\ B_4\\ B_5\\ B_6\\ B_7\\ B_8 \end{bmatrix} = \begin{bmatrix} 1&0&0&0&0&0&0&0&0\\ 0&0&0&0&0&0&0&0&0\\ 0&1&0&0&0&0&0&0&0\\ 0&0&1&0&0&0&0&0&0\\ 0&0&0&1&1&0&0&0&0\\ 0&0&0&0&0&1&1&0&0\\ 0&0&0&0&0&0&0&1&0\\ 0&0&0&0&0&0&0&0&1 \end{bmatrix} \begin{bmatrix} A_1\\ \bar{A}_1 A_2\\ A_1 C_4\\ A_1 C_3\\ \bar{A}_2 A_3 C_2\\ A_2 C_3\\ A_1 A_3 A_4\\ A_4 C_1\\ A_3 C_4 \end{bmatrix} \tag{9-40}$$

These two matrix functions can be realized by the multiple-level diode matrix shown in Fig. 9-19. It is an *and-or-and-or* switching matrix, using 49 diodes. If, instead of a multiple-level matrix, an *and-or* matrix is used by expanding functions (9-39) and (9-40) into one matrix function in elementary P form, the required number of diodes is 52. The savings in diodes in this case are not substantial.

Like multiple-level diode logic circuits, the multiple-level diode matrix requires

Table 9-3   Truth Table of a 4-bit Squaring Matrix

A_4	A_3	A_2	A_1	B_8	B_7	B_6	B_5	B_4	B_3	B_2	B_1
0	0	0	0	0	0	0	0	0	0	0	0
0	0	0	1	0	0	0	0	0	0	0	1
0	0	1	0	0	0	0	0	0	1	0	0
0	0	1	1	0	0	0	0	1	0	0	1
0	1	0	0	0	0	0	1	0	0	0	0
0	1	0	1	0	0	0	1	1	0	0	1
0	1	1	0	0	0	1	0	0	1	0	0
0	1	1	1	0	0	1	1	0	0	0	1
1	0	0	0	0	1	0	0	0	0	0	0
1	0	0	1	0	1	0	1	0	0	0	1
1	0	1	0	0	1	1	0	0	1	0	0
1	0	1	1	0	1	1	1	1	0	0	1
1	1	0	0	1	0	0	1	0	0	0	0
1	1	0	1	1	0	1	0	1	0	0	1
1	1	1	0	1	1	0	0	0	1	0	0
1	1	1	1	1	1	1	0	0	0	0	1

the use of amplifiers between switching matrices. These amplifiers have not been shown in Figs. 9-18 and 9-19.

9-6 *Binary Sequence Generators*

As mentioned in Chap. 3, a binary sequence is a time sequence of 1's and 0's. The time interval between two adjacent bits is called *bit time* or *digit time*.

A binary-coded decimal number may be represented by one or more binary sequences. For instance, consider the decimal number 159. For the 8-4-2-1 code, it becomes 0001, 0101, 1001. Four possible ways of representing this number are shown in Fig. 9-20. In Fig. 9-20a, all digits and bits appear in one binary sequence; this is the serial-digit serial-bit representation. If the digits occur serially while the bits occur in parallel as shown in Fig. 9-20b, this is the serial-digit parallel-bit representation. When the digits are arranged in parallel and the bits serially as shown in Fig. 9-20c, this is the parallel-digit serial-bit representation. In Fig. 9-20d all digits and bits appear in parallel; this is the parallel-digit parallel-bit representation. In a decimal computer which sequence is chosen depends on considerations such as computing speed, number of components and circuits, etc.

Binary Sequence Generator. The switching matrix may be regarded as a sequence filter or a sequence generator to the input of which many possible sets of binary sequences can be applied. For each set, the outputs produce another set of binary sequences. The switching matrix is then processing or filtering the input sequence in a certain manner and may be called a *binary sequence filter*, as it is analogous to the filter for analog signals. The previously described switching matrices for the full adder, the translator, and the squarer are all sequence filters. If only a chosen set of binary sequences is applied to the inputs of a switching matrix, the sequences from the outputs are another known set of sequences. The switching matrix is then generating a set of sequences and may be called a *binary sequence generator*.

Instead of using a switching matrix, a binary sequence generator may use storing circuits such as the shift register and the counter. The magnetic-core sequence generators described in Chap. 7 are examples of this. Thus, switching matrices when fed a known set of binary sequences may serve as storing circuits for applications where the stored information is known in advance. To illustrate this important property of the switching matrix, two sequence generators will now be described.

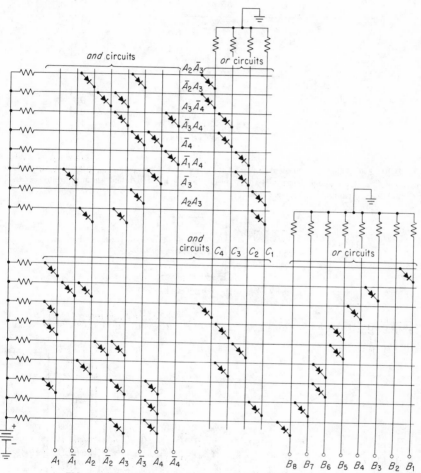

FIG. 9-19 A squaring matrix using an *and-or-and-or* switching matrix.

A Constant Generator. A binary sequence generator is shown in Fig. 9-21. In this figure, a binary counter counts the clock pulse. For each counter state, the switching matrix produces a binary-coded decimal-digit output. As the binary counter counts, a serial-digit parallel-bit decimal number is generated. The matrix described here generates the constant π. The operation of the matrix is described by Table 9-4. In this table the output of the binary counter is represented by the letters A, B, C, and D and the output of the matrix by the letters W, X, Y, and Z. Both outputs are expressed in binary numbers. Thus, the contents of the columns under W, X, Y, and Z in Table 9·4 represent the decimal number 3141592653589793, the decimal point being assumed located between the first two most significant digits. The four output functions can be written from

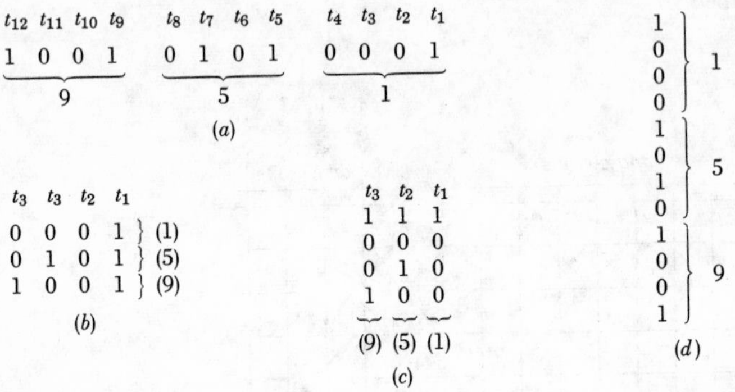

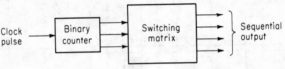

FIG. 9·20   Four sequential representations of a binary-coded decimal number. (*a*) Serial-digit serial-bit representation; (*b*) serial-digit parallel-bit representation; (*c*) parallel-digit serial-bit representation; (*d*) parallel-digit parallel-bit representation.

Clock pulse → Binary counter → Switching matrix → Sequential output

FIG. 9·21   A binary sequence generator.

Table 9·4. If these functions are minimized, the resulting Boolean matrix function is

$$
\begin{bmatrix} W \\ X \\ Y \\ Z \end{bmatrix} = \begin{bmatrix} 0 & 0 & 0 & 0 & 0 & 0 & 0 & 0 & 0 & 1 & 0 & 0 & 0 & 0 & 1 & 1 \\ 0 & 0 & 0 & 0 & 0 & 0 & 0 & 1 & 1 & 0 & 0 & 1 & 1 & 1 & 0 & 0 \\ 0 & 0 & 0 & 0 & 1 & 1 & 1 & 0 & 0 & 0 & 1 & 0 & 0 & 0 & 0 & 0 \\ 1 & 1 & 1 & 1 & 0 & 0 & 0 & 0 & 0 & 0 & 0 & 0 & 0 & 0 & 0 & 0 \end{bmatrix} \begin{bmatrix} \bar{C} \\ AB \\ A\bar{D} \\ \bar{A}\bar{B}D \\ \bar{A}BC \\ ABD \\ A\bar{C}D \\ \bar{B}C\bar{D} \\ A\bar{B}\bar{D} \\ AB\bar{D} \\ \bar{A}B\bar{C}D \\ \bar{A}B\bar{C}\bar{D} \\ \bar{A}BCD \\ A\bar{B}\bar{C}D \\ \bar{A}\bar{B}C\bar{D} \\ \bar{A}\bar{B}CD \end{bmatrix} \quad (9·41)
$$

This matrix function is in elementary P form. A diode-matrix constant-π gen-

Table 9-4   Truth Table for Constant-π Generator

A	B	C	D	W	X	Y	Z
0	0	0	0	0	0	1	1
0	0	0	1	0	0	0	1
0	0	1	0	0	1	0	0
0	0	1	1	0	0	0	1
0	1	0	0	0	1	0	1
0	1	0	1	1	0	0	1
0	1	1	0	0	0	1	0
0	1	1	1	0	1	1	0
1	0	0	0	0	1	0	1
1	0	0	1	0	0	1	1
1	0	1	0	0	1	0	1
1	0	1	1	1	0	0	0
1	1	0	0	1	0	0	1
1	1	0	1	0	1	1	1
1	1	1	0	1	0	0	1
1	1	1	1	0	0	1	1

erator is shown in Fig. 9-22. It is an *and-or* matrix. There are only 66 diodes in the matrix, in comparison with 92 diodes if not minimized. The pattern of 1's and 0's in Boolean matrix (9-41) corresponds to diodes and no diodes in the *or* circuits of the switching matrix of Fig. 9-22.

A Character Generator. Figure 9-23a shows an array of squares, 5 by 7, each square representing a light. Characters are displayed by the array when the proper lights of the array are turned on. The lights in one row are turned on simultaneously, and each row is turned on in turn by five parallel binary sequences each 7 bits long. For simplicity, assume that only the four letters F, G, H, and I are generated.

The composition of these four letters and the designation of each sequence are shown in Fig. 9-23a. The shaded squares in each letter signify the lights that should be turned on to display that letter. When the composition of these four letters is examined, one finds that the four letters can be composed by selecting those seven row elements shown in Fig. 7-23b and designated by small letters q_1 to q_7. The configuration of the character generator is shown in the diagram of Fig. 9-24. The four letters F through I are represented by a 2-bit code. The code of the selected letter to be displayed is stored in the 2-bit register and is decoded by a switching matrix. The y coordinate, y_1 to y_7, is generated by a commutator, which consists of a 3-bit counter counting the clock pulse at a desired rate and a y-coordinate switching matrix. The letter-selection matrix selects the set of seven outputs of the matrix from the four possible sets (for four letters) according to the selected output from the decoder. The four possible sets are represented by the letters y_{fj}, y_{gj}, y_{hj}, and y_{ij} (where j is for 1 to 7), for the letters F, G, H, and I, respectively. Specifically, the letter-selection matrix performs the selection described by the following Boolean functions:

$$\begin{aligned} y_{fj} &= Fy_j \\ y_{gj} &= Gy_j \\ y_{hj} &= Hy_j \\ y_{ij} &= Iy_j \end{aligned} \quad \text{for } j = 1, \ldots, 7 \qquad (9\text{-}42)$$

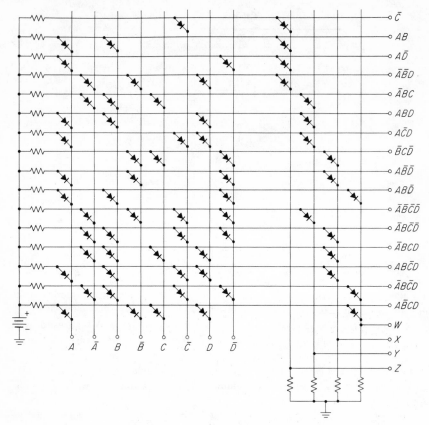

FIG. 9-22   Constant-π generator using an *and-or* matrix in an elementary form.

The letter-composition matrix of Fig. 9-24 selects the proper sequential composition of the letter elements q_i. For example, for the letter F, the required sequential composition is the letter elements q_1, q_2, q_2, q_3, q_2, q_2, and q_2, occurring, respectively, at the sequential coordinates y_{f1}, y_{f2}, y_{f3}, y_{f4}, y_{f5}, y_{f6}, and y_{f7}. Therefore, the letter-composition matrix performs the functions described by the following Boolean functions:

$$q_1 = y_{f1} + y_{g1} + y_{g7} + y_{h4}$$
$$q_2 = y_{f2} + y_{f3} + y_{f5} + y_{f6} + y_{f7} + y_{g3}$$
$$q_3 = y_{f4}$$
$$q_4 = y_{g2} + y_{g6} + y_{g7} + y_{h1} + y_{h2} + y_{h3} + y_{h5} + y_{h6} + y_{h7} \qquad (9\text{-}43)$$
$$q_5 = y_{g4}$$
$$q_6 = y_{i2} + y_{i3} + y_{i4} + y_{i5} + y_{i6}$$
$$q_7 = y_{i1} + y_{i7}$$

Finally, a letter-element matrix generates the required letter elements. The outputs of the letter-element matrix are the required five 7-bit binary sequences, which are described by the following Boolean functions:

$$x_1 = q_1 + q_2 + q_3 + q_4 + q_5$$
$$x_2 = q_1 + q_3 + q_7$$
$$x_3 = q_1 + q_3 + q_6 + q_7 \qquad (9\text{-}44)$$
$$x_4 = q_1 + q_5 + q_7$$
$$x_5 = q_1 + q_4 + q_5$$

The Boolean functions (9-42) to (9-44) may all be written into Boolean matrix functions. For example, the Boolean matrix function for (9-44) is

$$
\begin{bmatrix} x_1 \\ x_2 \\ x_3 \\ x_4 \\ x_5 \end{bmatrix}
=
\begin{bmatrix}
1 & 1 & 1 & 1 & 1 & 0 & 0 \\
1 & 0 & 1 & 0 & 0 & 0 & 1 \\
1 & 0 & 1 & 0 & 0 & 1 & 1 \\
1 & 0 & 0 & 0 & 1 & 0 & 1 \\
1 & 0 & 0 & 1 & 1 & 0 & 0
\end{bmatrix}
\begin{bmatrix} q_1 \\ q_2 \\ q_3 \\ q_4 \\ q_5 \\ q_6 \\ q_7 \end{bmatrix}
\qquad (9\text{-}45)
$$

The decoder and y-coordinate matrices are similar to the diode matrix of Fig. 9-8. The letter-selection matrix composed of *and* circuits is shown in Fig. 9-25.

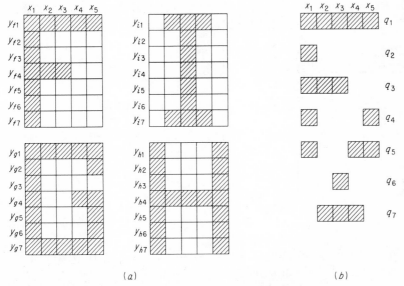

(a) (b)

FIG. 9-23 Format or letter symbols. (a) Composition of letter symbols; (b) letter elements.

The letter-element matrix and the letter-composition matrix, both composed of *or* circuits, are shown in Fig. 9-26. The arrangement of the diodes in the letter-element matrix follows the pattern of 1's and 0's in the matrix function (9-45).

9-7 Simplification of Boolean Matrix Function

Characteristics of a Boolean Matrix. It has been shown thus far that a multiple-output switching circuit can be expressed as a matrix function in canonical form, in elementary form, or in nonelementary form. The characteristics of a Boolean matrix in these forms are now summarized (the following logical-*and* circuits and logical-*or* circuits refer to positive logic).

1. Each row of the matrix represents one Boolean function or one output of the switching matrix. The number of rows in the matrix cannot be reduced unless one row consists of all 0's or two rows or more are identical.

2. Each column of the matrix represents one product term (or one sum term). The number of columns is reducible and should be reduced whenever possible.

3. If a row in the matrix consists of all 0's, this row and its corresponding output variable can be removed from the matrix function. For example, the output variable B_2 and the 0's in the second row in matrix function (9-40) can be removed.

4. If a column in the matrix consists of all 0's, the corresponding term in the matrix function can be eliminated.

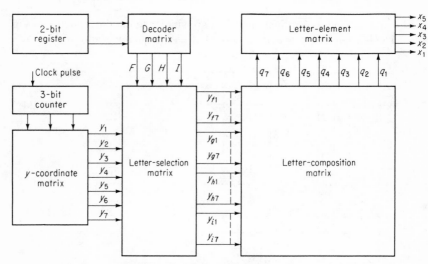

FIG. 9-24   Block diagram of a character generator.

5. If there is only one 1 in every row, the switching matrix consists of only *and* circuits (or *or* circuits), as illustrated by matrix functions (9-24) and (9-26).

6. If there is more than one 1 in at least one row, the switching matrix is an *and-or* matrix when the matrix function is in *P* form and is an *or-and* matrix when the matrix function is in *S* form. This is illustrated by the full-adder matrices in Figs. 9-15 and 9-16.

7. When an output of a Boolean matrix function is a variable of the product term (or sum term) of another Boolean matrix function, the combined switching matrix has two or more levels.

Simplification of a Boolean Matrix Function. Simplifying a Boolean matrix function results in a simpler switching matrix. However, a satisfactory method is lacking for minimizing a matrix function systematically. A general approach is to reduce the redundancy in each Boolean function, to share some

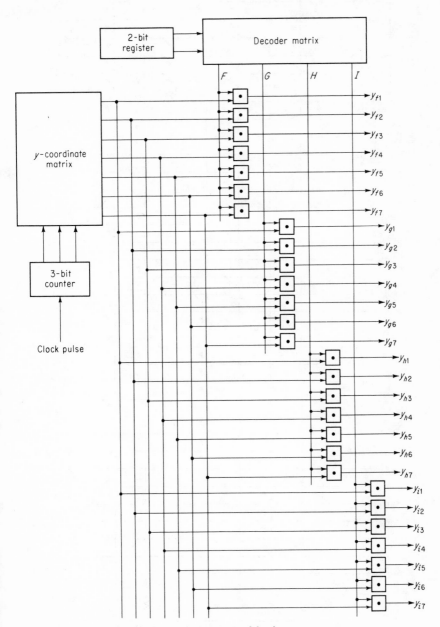

FIG. 9-25 Letter-selection matrix of the character generator.

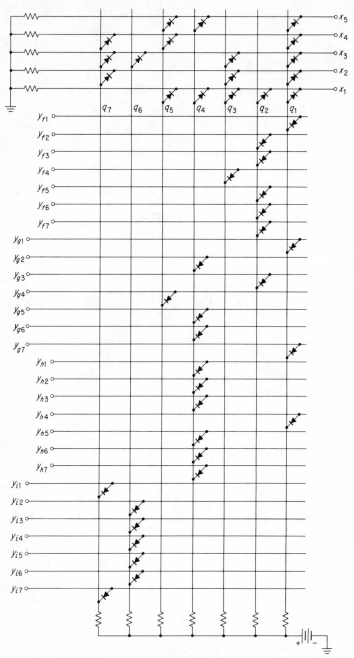

FIG. 9-26   Letter-element matrix and letter-composition matrix of the character generator.

product terms (or sum terms), and to add some redundant terms if this addition results in a simpler matrix function.   Some general rules that may be helpful in simplifying a Boolean matrix are:

1. Each Boolean function is minimized by methods described in Chap. 4. During minimization of these functions, don't care conditions should be used. Minimization of complement functions should also be worked out and those minimized functions which give a simpler matrix chosen.

2. If there is more than one 1 in a column of a Boolean matrix, the corresponding term can be shared.   This possibility can be enhanced by choosing the proper one of several minimized functions (if they occur) when each function is being minimized.   In some cases, the use of nearly minimized functions may give an over-all simpler matrix.

3. If the given matrix function is in canonical form but cannot be minimized and if there are more 1's than 0's in the matrix, the complement Boolean matrix gives a simpler matrix.

4. Simplification can be achieved by expressing the matrix function in non-elementary form; this requires the use of more-than-two-level matrices.

9-8   *Magnetic-core Switching Matrices*

Magnetic-core logic circuits, described in Chap. 7, can be used to form switching matrices.   A magnetic-core switching matrix sometimes serves as a multiple-position-switch device to select a desired word from a magnetic-core memory. In this application, the switching matrix also supplies a current to the magnetic-core memory, and thus it performs the dual functions of word selection and current drive.   When a magnetic-core switching matrix is used for a magnetic-core memory, it is often called a *matrix switch.*

Coincident-current Matrix Switch.   A magnetic-core matrix switch usually employs a metal-ribbon core with a rectangular hysteresis-loop characteristic, as the metal ribbon core gives a larger flux reversal than does a ferrite core of the same size.   Referring to Fig. 7-1, if the core state is at the point $-B_r$, the application of a current pulse $I_m/2$ (equivalent to a magnetizing force of $H_m/2$) does not change the core state.   The current $I_m/2$ is called the *half-select current.*   If a pulse with a full-select current I_m is applied, the core state is changed to B_r. The coincident-current matrix switch utilizes this amplitude-discrimination property of the core.

Figure 9-27 shows a two-row by three-column coincident-current matrix switch. There are three windings on each core—an x winding, a y winding, and an output winding.   All x windings and all y windings are respectively connected in series with one terminal grounded.   The output winding is to be connected to the memory proper of a magnetic-core memory.   If the state of core C_{12} is to be changed, a half-select current is applied to both lines x_1 and y_2.   The core is switching at coincidence of two half-select currents.   Because a large flux reversal occurs in the switched core, a current pulse appears at the terminals of the output winding of that core.   The core performs both functions of selecting an output terminal and supplying a current pulse.

Before the matrix switch is ready for another selection, the state of the switched core should be changed back to $-B_r$. There are two methods for doing this. Assume that core C_{12} has been selected and switched at the time t_1. At a later time t_2, a negative half-select current is applied to both lines x_1 and y_2. In this manner, core C_{12} is switched back to its initial state $-B_r$, and the matrix switch is ready for the next selection. This method takes a longer time to accomplish the switching cycle than the second method.

The second method makes use of a *biased core,* a core with a bias winding (not shown in Fig. 9-27). All cores are initially biased to $-H_m$. The half-select current now has an amplitude of I_m. The core is again switched by coincidence of two half-select currents, but it is automatically switched back at completion of the half-select current pulses. The faster selection of a biased core is at the expense of a constant-bias current.

In both methods a positive and a negative current pulse are produced. This is advantageous when a magnetic-core memory is selected by a magnetic-core matrix switch, because the sequential positive and negative pulses from the matrix

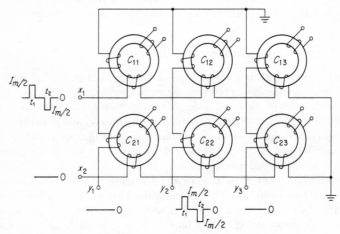

FIG. 9-27   A coincident-current magnetic-core matrix switch.

switch serve the need for a positive pulse during the earlier reading portion and for a negative pulse during the later writing portion of the memory cycle.

For n x inputs and m y inputs in the above matrix switch there are mn outputs for selecting mn words of a magnetic-core memory. Each input is driven by a driver; thus, $n + m$ drivers are needed for selecting mn words. If such a matrix switch is not used, mn drivers (one for each word of the memory) may be required. Therefore, the use of the coincident-current matrix switch (or the following anticoincident-current matrix switch) reduces the number of expensive drivers for a magnetic core memory.

Anticoincident-current Matrix Switch. The amplitude of the half-select current in a coincident-current matrix switch requires a close tolerance. This requirement makes a large matrix switch difficult to build. The anticoincident-current matrix switch lessens this requirement.

Figure 9-28 shows a two-row by three-column anticoincident-current matrix switch [5]. The windings and their connections are similar to the coincident-current matrix switch in Fig. 9-27; the difference lies largely in the applied current pulses. All cores are initially at state $-B_r$. If core C_{12} is to be switched, lines x_1 and y_2 are selected. A positive current pulse of amplitude I_m is applied to line x_1 and negative current pulses with an equal amplitude I_m applied to lines y_1 and y_3. No current is applied to lines x_2 and y_2 at this instant t_2. With these current pulses, only core C_{12} is switched to state $+B_r$; cores C_{11} and C_{13} are inhibited, and other cores remain at state $-B_r$. The switching of core C_{12} produces a desired current pulse. To return the switched core C_{12} to its initial state $-B_r$ for the next selection, a negative current pulse with an amplitude I_m at a later time t_2 is applied to line y_2. Since all other cores are at the state $-B_r$, this negative current pulses changes only the state of core C_{12} to $-B_r$.

In the anticoincident-current matrix switch, the positive driving current can be varied to obtain a desired waveform as long as the inhibiting current is always equal to or larger than the driving current. As a consequence, the current-pulse

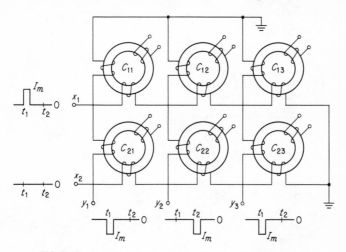

FIG. 9-28 An anticoincident-current magnetic-core matrix switch.

requirement is less critical—one advantage of using an anticoincident-current matrix switch.

There is another advantage—increased output. The magnetic-core memory requires a large current from the matrix switch. If a coincident-current matrix switch is used, the output current from the matrix switch is limited by the usable amplitude of the half-select current $I_m/2$. If an anticoincident-current matrix switch is used, a larger output current is possible by using a driving current larger than the current I_m, provided that the inhibit current is equally increased.

The current required by a magnetic-core memory for the read and write operations varies with the information stored in the memory. If either a coincident-current or an anticoincident-current matrix switch is used for the memory word selection, the shape and width of the output current from the matrix switch are affected by the varying load. Some means must be employed for regulating or stabilizing the output current of the matrix switch.

A Triangle Switching Matrix. An interesting matrix which also makes use of the coincident-current principle is shown in Fig. 9-29. It is a triangle switching matrix, first reported by Wilkes, Renwick, and Wheeler [19]. In this matrix switch, there are 10 cores, which are controlled by five input lines x_1 to x_5. The application of the half-select current $I_m/2$ to any two of the five input lines results in the switching of one core. For example, if the half-select current is applied to input lines x_1 and x_3, core C is switched and a pulse appears at the output terminals of that core. The configuration in Fig. 9-29 can be extended to a larger matrix. In comparison with the matrix switch in Fig. 9-27 or 9-28, the triangle matrix switch requires fewer input lines, and thus fewer drivers. However, it suffers from the disadvantage that each driver drives a different number of cores. Since the number of windings which can be driven by a driver is the

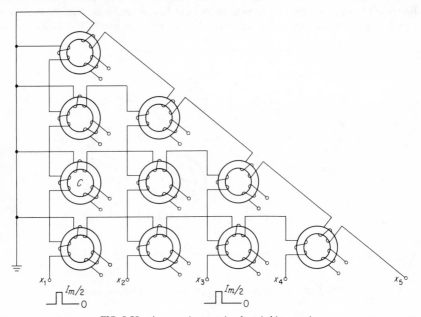

FIG. 9-29   A magnetic-core triangle switching matrix.

factor that ultimately determines the maximum size of a matrix, the advantage of a triangle matrix switch is limited to a small matrix.

Olsen Switching Matrix. An eight-position magnetic-core switching matrix reported by Olsen [3] is shown in Fig. 9-30. It consists of 2^n magnetic cores for n pairs of inputs. There are three types of windings on each core: bias winding, driving winding, and output winding. Each input line connects four bias windings in series in the manner shown in Fig. 9-30. The eight driving windings on eight cores are connected in series and driven by a driver. Each output winding provides an output terminal. The bias currents drive all but the selected core into saturation. The driving pulse then delivers power only through the core which has not been biased. For example, with the biased condition indicated in the figure, the selected core is the first one, and the driving pulse delivers a current pulse at the output f_0. Note the similarity between the magnetic-core matrix in Fig. 9-30 and the diode matrix in Fig. 9-8.

Rajchman Switching Matrix. A magnetic-core matrix somewhat similar to Olsen's matrix has been reported by Rajchman [4]. An eight-position Rajchman matrix is shown in Fig. 9-31. There are four types of windings on each core: restore winding, reset winding, set winding, and output winding. There are k turns on each set winding, $2k$ turns on each reset winding, and $3k$ turns on each restore winding. The number of turns on the output windings is determined by the load requirement. Initially, all cores are in reset condition (core at $-B_r$ state). For every combination of three input pairs, only one core is selected. The selected core has all three set windings excited and delivers an output pulse. The other unselected cores have both set and reset windings

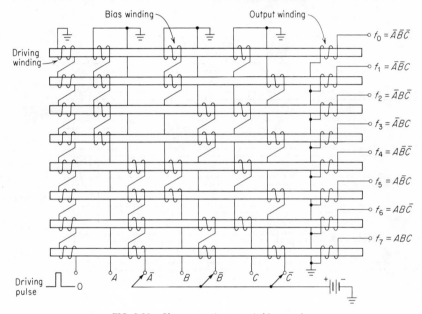

FIG. 9-30   Olsen magnetic-core switching matrix.

excited; the summation of mmf on each unselected core is either zero or a force causing the core to remain in the reset condition. This is the basis for choosing a different number of turns on the reset and set windings. After each selection, the restore winding will drive all cores to their initial reset condition. For this reason, the restore winding needs a number of turns three times that of each set winding.

This matrix has two advantages. First, when the required load current is heavy, large currents have to be supplied to the set windings of the selected core. The increase of these currents also compensates for the larger required currents in the reset winding of the unselected core. In this manner, the power delivered by the matrix may be varied. Second, the power delivered at the output is equally shared by all set windings on the selected core.

By comparison, Olsen's matrix requires fewer windings on each core, while Rajchman's matrix has the advantage of load sharing. Both matrices depend on the fact that it is possible to drive the unselected cores to an arbitrarily large excitation along the near-horizontal portion of the hysteresis loop.

Constantine Switching Matrix. In the above two matrices, the biases on the unselected cores vary during the selections. Since the portion of the hysteresis loop along the residual flux density is not exactly constant, noise pulses are generated at the outputs of the unselected cores.

A magnetic-core switching matrix which reduces noise output but retains the load-sharing property has been reported by Constantine [20]. Consider a 16-position Rajchman matrix with four input pairs. If the number of turns of the set and reset control windings are all equal and if only 4 cores with outputs $\overline{A}\overline{B}\overline{C}\overline{D}$, $\overline{A}B\overline{C}\overline{D}$, $\overline{A}\overline{B}C\overline{D}$, and $\overline{A}B C\overline{D}$ are kept and the other 12 cores are discarded, the re-

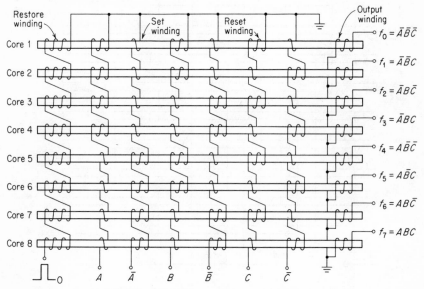

FIG. 9-31   Rajchman magnetic-core switching matrix.

sulting 4-core circuit becomes Constantine's four-position matrix switch. This switch is a portion of the matrix shown in Fig. 9-32; this portion consists of the first 4 cores and no restore windings. In this four-position switch, the number of turns on set and reset windings on each core is equal.

For any one of the four permissible combinations of the four input pairs, only one core is selected. This selected core has all its four set control windings excited and thus generates an output pulse. The unselected cores have an equal number of excited set and reset windings; thus, the net mmf is zero. In other words, Constantine has utilized only the 4 cores and rejected the other 12 cores that result in an unbalanced mmf when unselected. Since the net mmf is zero when the cores are not selected, the noise pulses at their outputs become practically zero. At the same time, the load-sharing property is still retained.

The above reduction of the noise level is achieved at the expense of more circuitry. If we allow one of the unselected cores to have a larger noise output, then four other cores (with outputs $ABCD$, $A\overline{B}C\overline{D}$, $AB\overline{C}\overline{D}$, and $\overline{A}B\overline{C}D$) can also be used, provided that a restore winding is added on each core. This is shown in Fig. 9-32. In this configuration, all unselected cores except one have zero net mmf. This unselected core has a larger noise output because there is a net mmf whose magnitude is equal but opposite to that in the selected core. For example, if the input terminals $\overline{A}$, $\overline{B}$, $\overline{C}$, and $\overline{D}$ are excited, the first core is selected because all its set windings are excited, and a pulse appears at its output terminal. The fifth core, which is not selected, has all its reset windings excited; thus, a larger noise pulse appears at its output. All other unselected cores have two set and two reset windings excited; this results in a zero net mmf in these cores.

In the first matrix, the input winding pattern realizes 2^{n-1} outputs with 2^n inputs

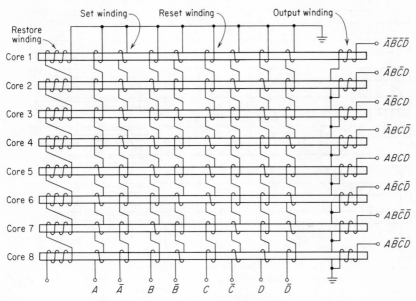

FIG. 9-32   Constantine magnetic-core switching matrix.

(for example, when n is equal to 3, there are eight inputs and four outputs) if all unselected cores have zero mmf. In this second switch, the inputs are grouped in 2^{n-1} complementary pairs. Marcus [21] has shown that, if the inputs are not grouped in pairs but are treated independently, a matrix switch with $2^n - 1$ outputs for 2^n inputs can be realized. By treating inputs independently, there are more possible input combinations. The principle is still retained of utilizing only those input combinations which result in zero excitation for unselected cores.

Transfluxor Switching Matrix. The two-aperture Transfluxor was first developed by Rajchman and Lo and is described in Chap. 8. As shown in Fig. 8-17, the Transfluxor has two states, blocked and unblocked. These two states are established, respectively, by applying a current pulse to the blocking (reset) winding and the unblocking (set) winding. When the Transfluxor is in the blocked state, no a-c voltage appears at the output terminal. When it is in the unblocked state, an a-c voltage is induced in the output windings. Thus, the Transfluxor gates an a-c signal on and off by the application of suitable control pulses.

Transfluxors can be used to form the switching matrix shown in Fig. 9-33. In this figure, the rectangular hole in each bar represents the small aperture in the Transfluxor. The arrangement of the blocking, or reset, windings is similar to the bias windings of Olsen's matrix of Fig. 9-30. When a given combination of three blocking pulses together with the unblocking pulse is applied, all Transfluxors are blocked (reset) except one, which is unblocked (set). An a-c voltage is induced in the output winding of this selected Transfluxor. The Transfluxor matrix of Fig. 9-33 can also distribute a modulated signal to the selected channel.

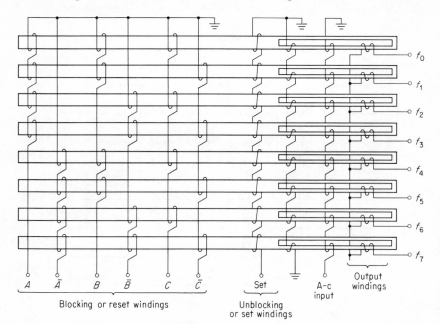

FIG. 9-33 A Transfluxor switching matrix.

The simultaneous application of blocking pulses and unblocking pulse performs the selection, because the unblocking pulse has insufficient amplitude to overcome the blocking effect of even a single one of these blocking currents and therefore sets only the selected Transfluxor. There is no danger of oversetting by the unblocking pulse, because the unblocking winding is wound on the common leg between the large and small apertures. The selected Transfluxor remains set until a different combination of three blocking pulses is applied. At that time, a new Transfluxor is set, and the previously selected one is automatically blocked.

9-9 Synthesis of Magnetic-core Switching Matrices

The synthesis of magnetic-core logic circuits for a single Boolean function has been given in Chap. 7, which also described magnetic-core circuits by Karnaugh,

Rosenfeld, and Andrews. Briefly, the logical-*and* operation in Karnaugh's circuit is achieved by the input windings through the inhibiting operation of the core. The logical-*or* operation is performed sequentially in the output winding which provided three types of *or* circuit, type *T*, type *AF*, and type *AB*. Rosenfeld's circuits alleviate the requirement of Karnaugh's circuits that input pulses have to be applied simultaneously. In his circuits, input windings are used only for storing the input variables. The logical-*and* operation is performed by the output windings and the logical-*or* operation by the diodes. Andrews' circuit makes use of "inhibit-wound cores," in which inputs act as inhibitory signals; both the shift pulse and the input pulse are half-select currents. This utilization not only requires less power from the inputs but also performs quite adequately with a single-wire input winding on the ferrite core.

Synthesis of the magnetic-core switching matrix can make use of these circuits.

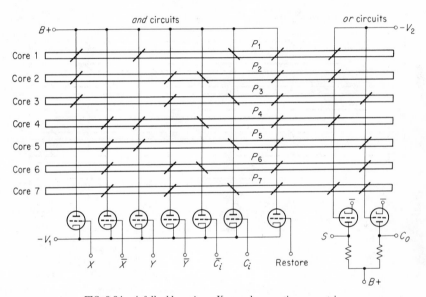

FIG. 9-34 A full adder using a Karnaugh magnetic-core matrix.

Because a large number of cores and windings is usually needed in a switching matrix, the mirror symbols described in Chap. 7 are used here. In the synthesis of the following switching matrices, the full adder is chosen as the example. These matrices, however, can be similarly applied to other multiple-output circuits.

Karnaugh Magnetic-core Switching Matrix. The first matrix configuration makes use of Karnaugh's circuit shown in Fig. 7-56. The full adder using Karnaugh's magnetic-core switching matrix is shown in Fig. 9-34. There are seven cores for the seven product terms in functions (9-1) and (9-2). On each core there are two input reset windings and one input set winding—in addition to one restore winding for the reset purpose and one or two output windings. As described in Chap. 7, the core is set when a pulse is applied to the input set winding and none is applied to the input reset windings. Apply a positive pulse to inputs X, Y, and C_i. Core 6 receives no excitation; cores 3 and 5 have zero set mmf;

and cores 1, 2, and 4 are again reset. The state of all these six cores remains unchanged at the reset condition. However, core 7 becomes set; this is the selected core and represents the selected product term. The setting of core 7 produces a pulse at its output windings. The output windings of these seven cores are connected to perform a logical-*or* operation according to functions (9-1) and (9-2). Connections for the *or* operation reflect the type T circuit of Fig. 7-56. For the application of a pulse to inputs X, Y, and C_i, a pulse appears at both sum and output carry terminals. When the operation is completed, a pulse is applied to the restore windings to reset the cores to their initial condition. A similar operation occurs with other combinations of the three inputs. The matrix of Fig. 9-34 is an *and-or* magnetic-core switching matrix and is similar to the diode matrix of Fig. 9-15.

Olsen Magnetic-core Switching Matrix.   The second matrix configuration

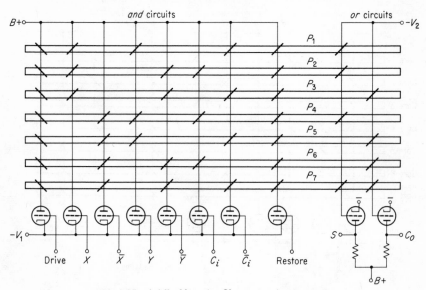

FIG. 9-35   A full adder using Olsen magnetic-core matrix.

utilizes Olsen's matrix to perform the logical-*and* operation and Karnaugh's type T circuit for the logical-*or* operation. The magnetic-core switching matrix for the full adder is shown in Fig. 9-35. The seven product terms of the full adder are generated as in Olsen's matrix, shown in Fig. 9-30, except that restore windings are also provided. Output windings representing proper product terms are connected in series to form two outputs for the sum and output carry (S and C_o); these connections are identical to those of Karnaugh's circuit of Fig. 9-34. After completion of one operation, the restore windings reset the cores to their initial condition. The magnetic-core matrix of Fig. 9-35 is an *and-or* matrix and is also similar to the *and-or* diode matrix of Fig. 9-15. Apparently, the full-adder matrix of Fig. 9-35 can also use Rajchman's matrix (Fig. 9-31) instead.

Andrews Magnetic-core Switching Matrix.   The third matrix configuration makes use of Andrews' magnetic-core circuit shown in Fig. 7-63. Andrews' full-adder switching matrix shown in Fig. 9-36 necessitates two shift windings and three input windings on each core in addition to one or two output windings. The shift and input windings are of an equal number of turns, and both are excited by half-select current pulses. The shift current pulse has both a positive portion and a negative portion, as shown in Fig. 9-36, while the input current pulse has only a positive portion and occurs simultaneously with the positive portion of the shift current pulse. In operation, the cores are initially at the reset condition. At the application of the positive set portion of the driving pulse, those cores whose inputs are simultaneously excited by a half-select current are too inhibited to be set. For example, inputs X, Y, and C_i in Fig. 9-36 are excited by the half-select current; the first six cores are prevented from being set, and only the last core is set. When the negative portion of the shift pulse is applied, a large flux change occurs only in the last core and a pulse appears at the output windings of that core. This generates the desired product term P_7 or

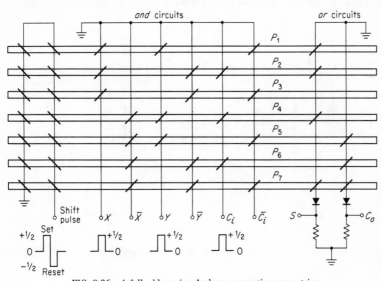

FIG. 9-36 A full adder using Andrews magnetic-core matrix.

XYC_i. The outputs of the matrix are formed by connecting the proper output windings in series according to functions (9-1) and (9-2). The above output pulse then appears at both outputs S and C_o. All cores are in a reset condition after completion of a set-reset cycle.

In comparison with the full-adder matrix of Fig. 9-35, the driving and reset windings of the matrix of Fig. 9-35 are combined into one set of shift windings in Andrews' matrix. The arrangement of input windings in these two matrices are identical, but their operations are different. The output windings in these two matrices are arranged in the same manner, and their operations are also alike. Andrews reported the use of small ferrite cores with a single wire for each input; this results in an inexpensive matrix. It is noted that, if the magnetic rod described in Chap. 7 is used to form Andrews' matrix, the operating speed can be greatly increased.

9-10   *Magnetic-core Current-steering Matrices*

Current steering in magnetic circuits reported by Rajchman and Crane [15] provides another matrix configuration. A steered matrix switch can readily perform the functions of selecting the word of and supplying the current to a magnetic-core memory. Current steering can be achieved either by core-diode combinations or by Transfluxors.

Principle of Current Steering. A core-diode steering circuit is shown in Fig. 9-37*a*, illustrating two steering cores. On each core there are a preset winding, an interrogate winding, and a drive winding. Rajchman and Crane reported the use of square-loop ferrite cores as the steering cores, with an outside diameter of 0.35 in., an inside diameter of 0.22 in., and a thickness of 0.12 in. The preset, interrogate, and drive windings were of 4, 2, and 7 turns, respectively. These windings are connected in the manner shown in Fig. 9-37*a*. If a current pulse is applied to terminal *A* of the preset winding, cores 1 and 2 are, respectively,

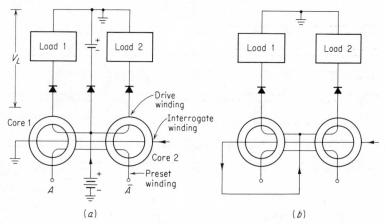

FIG. 9-37   Core-diode current-steering circuits. (*a*) Direct steering circuit; (*b*) complementary steering circuit.

set and reset. A subsequent pulse to the interrogate windings resets both cores. The drive windings are connected to a current source; the drive current flows through the dummy branch, which is the middle branch of Fig. 9-37*a*, and no current flows in the two load branches.

In operation, one of the two steering cores is set: assume core 1. When a current pulse is applied to the interrogate windings, there is little flux change in core 2. But a large flux change occurs in core 1, and the induced voltage in its drive winding is large enough in the direction to cause a current pulse to flow through load branch 1. Thus a current is steered through the selected load branch. Similarly, the current can be steered through load branch 2 if core 2 has been initially set. This principle can also be applied to more than two load branches.

To steer the driving current through the load, the induced voltage in the drive winding should be large enough. This requires that the net mmf, which is the difference between the mmfs due to the interrogate and drive currents,

$N_i I_i - N_d I_d$ (where N_i and N_d are the number of turns of the interrogate and the drive winding, respectively, and I_i and I_d are the interrogate and the drive current, respectively) should be larger than some minimum determined by the size and coercivity of the core. The excess over this minimum determines the speed of switching and hence the induced voltage. The voltage must exceed the voltage appearing across the load V_L to keep all other diodes nonconducting.

The dummy branch can be eliminated if the drive current is supplied and terminated at the same time as the interrogate current. This suggests one current source for both drive and interrogate windings. This arrangement is shown in Fig. 9-37b.

The current-steered circuit of Fig. 9-37a is an example of *direct steering*, as the current is steered to load 1 if core 1 is initially set. If the current is steered to load 2 when core 1 is initially set, this is called *complementary steering* (Fig. 9-37b). The difference between the direct and complementary steering circuits lies in the polarities of the drive windings. With two load branches, the complementary steering circuit requires the same total drive and interrogate power as the direct steering circuit and is preferable because fewer total turns are required on the steering cores. With n load branches, the selected steering core in a direct steering circuit is switched over, while $n - 1$ unselected cores are merely driven further into reset saturation. In a complementary circuit with n load branches, all steering cores except the selected one switch over. In comparison, the interrogate source in a complementary steering circuit needs less current than that for a direct steering circuit, since the drive current does not produce a counter mmf in the cores it is resetting; but the interrogate source must generally deliver more voltage, since it resets $n - 1$ cores rather than a single core.

If separate interrogate and drive current sources are used, as shown in Fig. 9-37a, there is the advantage that the drive current pulse during steering may be of any desired shape as long as it is within the limit of the duration and amplitude of the interrogate current. For example, the drive current can be modulated, and its modulation will appear in the selected load during steering.

Current-steered Magnetic-core Matrix Switch. A magnetic-core matrix switch using the current-steering principle is shown in Fig. 9-38. There are three complementary steering circuits of Fig. 9-37b. The magnetic-core matrix portion is similar to Karnaugh's matrix, shown in Fig. 9-34, and thus replaces the loads of Fig. 9-37b. In operation, the switching cores are initially at the reset condition. If a current pulse is applied to inputs A, B, and C, steering cores 1, 3, and 5 are set and the other three steering cores are reset. When a current pulse is applied to the interrogate windings, it resets cores 1, 3, and 5. Induced voltages are generated at the output windings of steering cores 1, 3, and 5 in such a direction that currents are steered through the branches connected to steering cores, 2, 4, and 6 (owing to the complementary nature of the circuit). In this manner, only the last switching core (i.e., the core with output f_7) is set (as explained in connection with Karnaugh's matrix), and all other switching cores remain at the reset condition. A pulse appears at terminals f_7 of the output winding of the last switching core. When the operation is completed, a pulse is applied to restore windings to reset the switching cores to their initial condition. Similar selection can be made for any other combination of the three inputs.

The current-steered matrix switch gives the advantage that only a single drive source is required other than the source for the restore windings. When there are four or more input pairs, the restore windings and their source can be eliminated. In this case, the switching cores can reset themselves automatically if the interrogate current is of sufficient duration to divide equally in all branches after being steered. This is due to the situation that, on each switching core, the net mmf is in the reset direction and is larger than that due to the interrogate current during the steering.

Not only the current for the switching cores of the matrix but also the output current from the matrix can be steered. Such a matrix switch is shown in Fig. 9-39. In this double steering circuit the interrogate current interrogates the steering cores as the first-round steering, sets and thereby interrogates the switch-

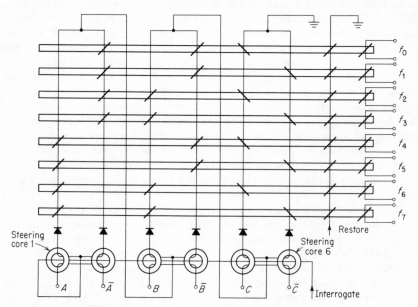

FIG. 9-38   A current-steered magnetic-core matrix switch.

ing cores for the second-round steering, and finally drives the selected output. In Fig. 9-39, eight additional diodes are required.

Transfluxors can also be used for the current-steered matrix switch, where the steering operation is based on the spurious unblocking mode of the Transfluxor. The Transfluxor current-steered matrix will not be further described except to mention the advantage it possesses of using no diodes; however, the steering is not as perfect as that with diodes.

9-11   Transistor Switching Matrices

Transistor logic circuits can be used to form switching matrices, but a significant difference exists between a transistor matrix and a diode matrix. In a diode matrix the logic circuits are either *and* circuits or *or* circuits, while in a transistor matrix the logic circuits are either *nand* or *nor* circuits. As a result, the terms (product or sum terms) represented by the output terminals in a transistor matrix are different from the corresponding output terminals in a similar diode matrix. These transistor matrices are *nor* matrices or *nand* matrices. Several examples which employ negative-logic designation will now be discussed.

RC-coupled Transistor Switching Matrix. An *RC*-coupled transistor rectangle switching matrix with two pairs of inputs and four outputs is shown in Fig. 9-40. This matrix is composed of four *p-n-p* inverter *nor* circuits (negative logic), shown in Fig. 5-31. In operation, consider the case where a negative potential (representing 1) is applied to inputs *A* and *B*; this means that ground potential is applied to inputs $\bar{A}$ and $\bar{B}$. When inputs $\bar{A}$ and $\bar{B}$ are at ground potential, terminal P_3 (representing the term *AB*) is the only terminal at a negative potential. Switching operation is similar to that with other combinations of inputs or with a larger matrix.

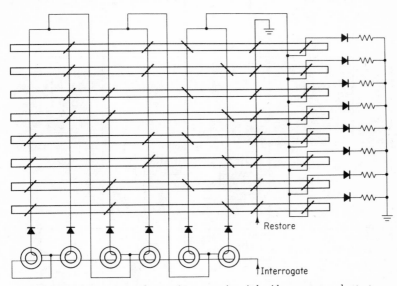

FIG. 9-39   A current-steered magnetic-core matrix switch with current-steered outputs.

Transistor-Resistor Switching Matrix. A transistor-resistor rectangle switching matrix with three pairs of inputs and eight outputs is shown in Fig. 9-41. This matrix is composed of eight three-input transistor-resistor *nor* circuits, shown in Fig. 5-51, and appears to be a matrix of resistors. Its operation is similar to the above *RC*-coupled transistor rectangle matrix.

Another transistor-resistor switching matrix is shown in Fig. 9-42. The *p-n-p* transistor forms the *nor* circuit shown in Fig. 5-51, and the *n-p-n* transistor forms the *nand* circuit appearing in Fig. 5-52. The matrix is connected into a dual tree (unsymmetrical) as in Fig. 9-3 by using *nor* circuits as one level and *nand* circuits as another level.

In operation the *p-n-p* transistor in a *nor* circuit is cut off and the output collector voltage is negative (representing 1) when both input voltages are at ground potential (representing 0). The *n-p-n* transistor in the *nand* circuit is cut off and the output voltage is at ground potential when both inputs are at a negative potential. Consider the case where terminal P_7 (representing the term ABC) is to be selected. Negative voltage is applied to inputs A, B, and C, and ground potential is applied to inputs $\overline{A}$, $\overline{B}$, and $\overline{C}$. The *n-p-n* transistor with inputs B and C is cut off, with its output at ground potential. The *p-n-p* transistor with this output as its input and with input $\overline{A}$ is the only *p-n-p* transistor that is cut off; this is the *p-n-p* transistor with terminal P_7 at a negative potential. Operations are similar if other terminals are selected.

It is possible to form a dual-tree matrix with only *nor* circuits (or only *nand*

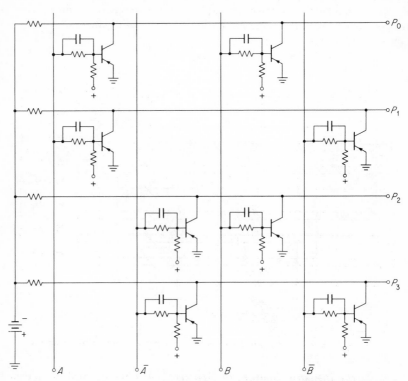

FIG. 9-40   An *RC*-coupled transistor rectangle matrix (negative logic).

circuits) instead of both *nor* and *nand* circuits. In such a case, the number of transistors required will be larger, however.

Direct-coupled Transistor Switching Matrix. A rectangle switching matrix using direct-coupled transistor logic circuits is shown in Fig. 9-43 and comprises three pairs of inputs and eight outputs. The matrix is composed of eight three-input *nor* circuits (see Fig. 5-57). The operation of this matrix is similar to the *RC*-coupled transistor rectangle switching matrix of Fig. 9-40.

A direct-coupled transistor tree matrix similar to that shown in Fig. 9-2 is shown in Fig. 9-44. This matrix configuration is similar to the direct-coupled transistor logic circuit of Fig. 5-60; however, its operation more nearly resembles the *nand* circuit of Fig. 5-58.   Consider the case where a negative potential (representing 1) is applied to inputs A, B, and C.   The transistors with these inputs are turned into conduction, and these three transistors form the only closed path between the voltage source $-V_{cc}$ and ground.   Terminal f_7 is the only terminal at ground potential; therefore, the output at terminal f_7 represents the term $\overline{ABC}$ or $\bar{A} + \bar{B} + \bar{C}$.   Operations for selecting other terminals are similar.

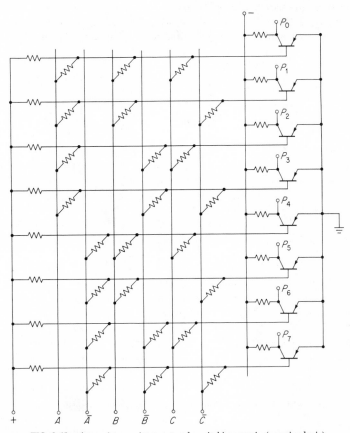

FIG. 9-41   A transistor-resistor rectangle switching matrix (negative logic).

9-12   *Other Switching Matrices*

A Diode-Transformer Matrix.   A diode-transformer matrix that was used in a diode-capacitor memory is shown in Fig. 9-45.   Three horizontal x lines and three vertical y lines allow nine paths to be formed between pairs of x and y lines by a serial connection of a diode and the primary winding of a transformer. The terminals of the secondary windings of the transformers are the outputs. Multiple outputs at each terminal are possible; two outputs at each terminal are shown in Fig. 9-45.   When a path is selected, a current enters one of the x lines, flows through the selected path at the junction, and leaves at one of the y lines. All other paths are either open at one terminal or open at both terminals.

As shown in Fig. 9-45, all x and y lines are normally at -10 volts and $+10$ volts, respectively; thus, all diodes are back-biased, and all paths are open. If the path from line x_1 to line y_2 is to be selected, a pulse of $+10$ volts is applied to line x_1 and a pulse of -10 volts is applied to line y_2. The diode for this path becomes forward-biased; a current flows through the primary winding of the selected transformer, and a pulse appears at its secondary winding as the output.

A Transistor-Transformer Matrix.   A transistor-transformer matrix is shown in Fig. 9-46. There are three horizontal x lines and three pairs of vertical y lines; each pair is connected to the normal and complement outputs of a

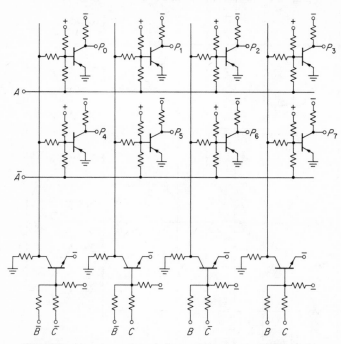

FIG. 9-42   A transistor-resistor dual-tree switching matrix (negative logic).

flipflop.   Assume that 1 is normally at ground potential.   When a negative pulse is applied to line x_2, the bases of the transistors connected to line x_2 are at a negative potential.   If flipflop Y_2 is in state 1, its normal output is at a negative potential and its complement output is at ground potential; the transistor in the center of the matrix conducts, and a pulse appears at the output terminal.   It is also possible to produce a pulse output at other transistors along line x_2 if their corresponding flipflops are in state 1.   Therefore, this matrix of Fig. 9-46 is capable of producing more than one output.

If the transistors in the matrix of Fig. 9-46 are symmetrical in that the emitter and collector are interchangeable, the current can flow in either direction.   Then it is possible to have either a positive pulse or a negative pulse (depending on the state of the flipflops) on all transistors along line x_2 when a negative current pulse is applied to line x_2.

Cryotron Switching Matrix. An eight-position switching matrix using cryotrons and reported by Buck [11] is shown in Fig. 9-47. There are eight gate wires and three control coils on each gate. The gate is normally in a supercon-

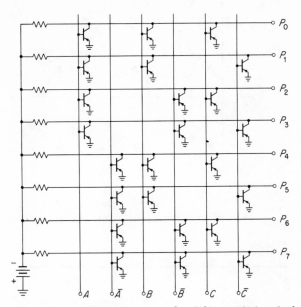

FIG. 9-43 A direct-coupled transistor rectangle switching matrix (negative logic).

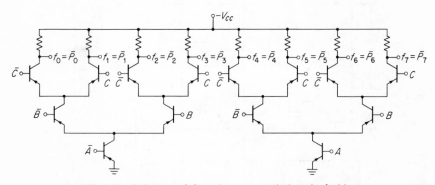

FIG. 9-44 A direct-coupled transistor tree matrix (negative logic).

ductive state. When a current is applied to the coil to produce a magnetic field, the gate is changed from the superconductive state to the normal conducting state. The arrangement of control coils on these gates is similar to the magnetic-core matrix switch of Fig. 9-30, except that the direction of magnetic field in the gate has no effect on the control of the gate.

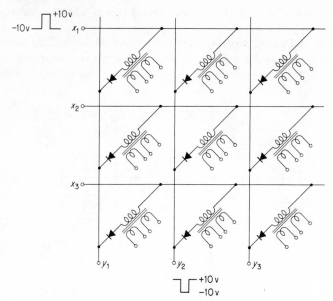

FIG. 9-45   A diode-transformer switching matrix.

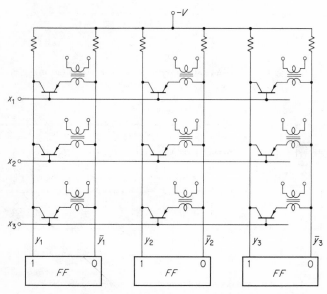

FIG. 9-46   A transistor-transformer switching matrix.

For any combination of the three inputs being applied with a control current, all gate wires except one are changed to the normal conducting state. This gate wire in the superconductive state is the selected path, and a current flows through it. The paths f_i of Fig. 9-47 represent the product terms shown in functions (9-23).

A Glow-lamp Switching Matrix. When a high enough voltage is applied across the two terminals of a glow lamp, the gas in the lamp ionizes and glows and the lamp becomes a conducting path. A four-output glow-lamp rectangle matrix is shown in Fig. 9-48. This matrix configuration is similar to the diode matrix of Fig. 9-8 with the diodes replaced by glow lamps.

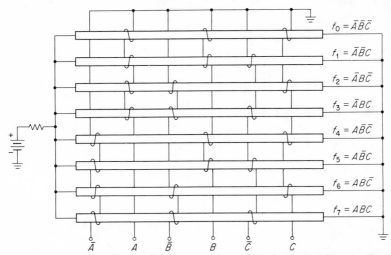

FIG. 9-47   An eight-position cryotron switching matrix.

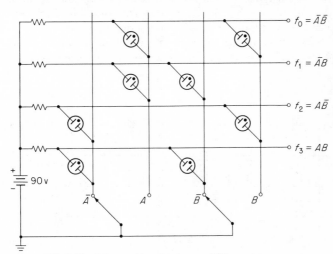

FIG. 9-48   A four-position glow-lamp switching matrix.

When inputs A and B are grounded as shown in Fig. 9-48, all horizontal lines except the first one are connected through one or more conducting glow lamps to ground; only the output terminal f_0 is then at a high voltage. For neon glow lamp NE-2, the terminal f_0 is at 90 volts, while other terminals are at about 67 volts. Operations are similar if other combinations of inputs are grounded. The glow-lamp matrix has an advantage in that the matrix operation is visible to the operator.

Electroluminescent-Photoconductor Switching Matrices.   The EL-PC logic circuit of Fig. 6-43 can be extended into a logical-*and* switching matrix shown in Fig. 9-49.   This EL-PC matrix is for two input variables A and B; there are four possible light outputs for the four possible product terms P_0 to P_3.   Note

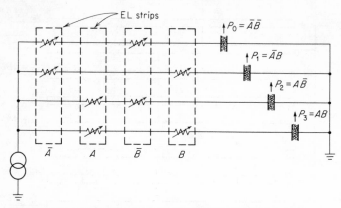

FIG. 9-49   An EL-PC switching *and* matrix for two Boolean variables.

that the EL elements of the matrix are made into EL strips which are the output EL elements of other EL-PC logic circuits.   The EL-PC logic circuit of Fig. 6-44 can be extended into a switching logical-*or* matrix, shown in Fig. 9-50.   The four light outputs represent the four possible sum terms S_0 to S_3.

Figure 9-51 is a switching *and-or* matrix which makes use of both circuits of Figs. 6-44 and 6-45.   The dots in the matrix show *or* connections.

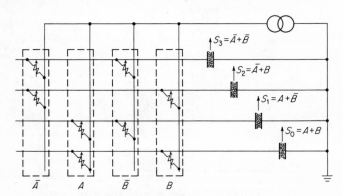

FIG. 9-50   An EL-PC switching *or* matrix for two Boolean variables.

In the above three switching matrices, the PC elements are arranged into an array in which some elements are present while others are not.   If PC elements are all caused to be present in the array for the purpose of simpler fabrication (they are thin layers on a substrate), the presence or absence of each element can be achieved by using a mask (made of opaque paper or foil) between the EC strip and the PC matrix; the presence or absence of a hole at each PC location determines inclusion or exclusion of the PC element. The use of a mask also promotes flexibility: the function of the matrix can be changed by merely changing the mask.

A Self-organizing Logic Network. Figure 9-52 shows a *universal fixed logic network* which, if extended into a much more complicated form, can be a digital computer. In this figure, the *and-or* matrix is similar to that of Fig. 9-51. The registers are made of EL-PC flipflops as shown in Fig. 6-49 or 6-50. The amplifiers are EL-PC amplifiers, shown in Fig. 6-42 or 6-43, with the addition of

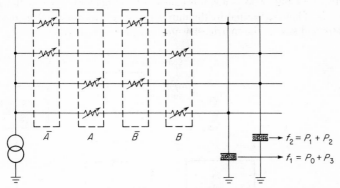

FIG. 9-51   An EL-PC switching *and-or* matrix for two outputs.

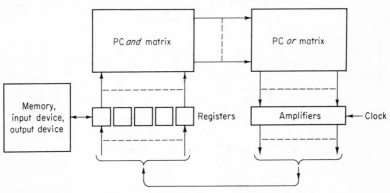

FIG. 9-52   An EL-PC universal logic network.

a clocking scheme. The memory, input device, and output device are connected to one or more registers. The logic network processes the information in the memory or from the input device according to the instructions stored in the memory and presents the result to the output device.

The above logic network is fixed; therefore, the capability of the logic network is limited. However, the logic function of a photoconductor (or photodiode or phototransistor) network can be altered by changing the illumination on the PC elements. A network with such a capability is called a *self-organizing logic network*. The EL-PC network has the potential of low fabrication cost.

The PC elements in the *or* matrix of Fig. 9-52 can be made alterable by using an alterable PC *or* matrix. An alterable PC *or* matrix can be the PC matrix of Fig. 9-50, where EL strips are made into an array of EL dots. The illumination on each PC element of the *or* matrix by the array of EL dots can be altered. This alterable *or* matrix is now used to replace the dot connections of the *and-or* matrix of Fig. 9-52. When this is done, the resulting network together with a pattern generator is shown in Fig. 9-53. The alteration is actuated by the outputs of the amplifiers, which in turn cause the pattern generator to actuate a different pattern of EL luminescing dots on the control plate. Thus, the functioning of the logic network of Fig. 9-53 is a self-organizing logic network. The self-organizing capability is of course limited by the number of logic circuits (such as the number of registers and size of the matrices) which constitute the network.

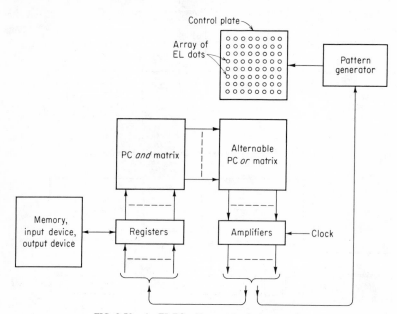

FIG. 9-53   An EL-PC self-organizing logic network.

Problems

1. Given two Boolean functions of a multiple-output circuit,

$$f_1(A,B,C) = P_0 + P_1 + P_2$$
$$f_2(A,B,C) = P_3 + P_4 + P_5$$

write the two canonical forms of the matrix function and also those of the complement matrix function.

2. Repeat Prob. 1 for the following set of Boolean functions:

$$f_1(A,B,C) = P_0 + P_7$$
$$f_2(A,B,C) = P_3 + P_4$$
$$f_3(A,B,C) = P_3 + P_5 + P_6$$
$$f_4(A,B,C) = P_0 + P_3 + P_5 + P_6$$
$$f_5(A,B,C) = P_1 + P_2 + P_6 + P_7$$
$$f_6(A,B,C) = P_0 + P_3 + P_4 + P_5$$
$$f_7(A,B,C) = P_1 + P_2 + P_4 + P_5 + P_7$$

3. Repeat Prob. 1 for the following set of Boolean functions:

$$f_1(A,B,C,D) = P_0 + P_7 + P_8 + P_{15}$$
$$f_2(A,B,C,D) = P_0 + P_3 + P_{12} + P_{15}$$
$$f_3(A,B,C,D) = P_0 + P_{15}$$

4. Construct the block diagram of a rectangular matrix with four pairs of inputs and 16 product terms as outputs:

(a) By using *nor* blocks only (b) By using *nand* blocks only
(c) By using *andnot* blocks only (d) By using *ornot* blocks only

5. Repeat Prob. 4 if the 16 outputs are sum terms.
6. Repeat Probs. 4 and 5 for a tree matrix.
7. Repeat Probs. 4 and 5 for a dual-tree matrix.
8. Tabulate and compare the total number of inputs of *nor* blocks, *nand* blocks, *andnot* blocks, and *ornot* blocks for the rectangle, the tree, and the dual-tree matrices of Probs. 4 to 7.
9. Construct the *and-or* and *or-and* diode matrices for the matrix functions of Prob. 1.
10. Repeat Prob. 9 for the matrix function of Prob. 2.
11. Repeat Prob. 9 for the matrix function of Prob. 3.
12. Draw the comparator matrix of Fig. 9-18 by using an *and-or* diode matrix in the elementary form.
13. Draw the squaring matrix of Fig. 9-19 by using an *and-or* diode matrix in the elementary form.
14. Minimize the number of diodes in the diode matrix for the matrix function of Prob. 2.
15. Repeat Prob. 12 for the matrix function of Prob. 3.
16. A squaring diode matrix has a 5-bit input and a 10-bit output:

(a) Establish the truth table.
(b) Write out the matrix function.
(c) Simplify the above matrix function into two-level matrix functions in the elementary form.
(d) Draw the schematic of the diode matrix.

17. Construct a diode matrix for the generation of constant 2.71828182845 (constant *e*). Minimize the required number of diodes.
18. Construct the magnetic-core switching matrix for the matrix function of Prob. 1:

(a) By using Karnaugh's matrix
(b) By using Olsen's matrix
(c) By using Andrews' matrix

19. Repeat Prob. 18 for the matrix function of Prob. 2.
20. Repeat Prob. 18 for the matrix function of Prob. 3.

References

1. Brown, D. R., and N. Rochester: Rectifier Networks for Multiposition Switching, *Proc. IRE*, February, 1949, pp. 139–147.

2. Staff of Harvard Computation Laboratory: "Synthesis of Electronic Computing and Control Circuits," vol. 27, Harvard University Press, Cambridge, Mass., 1951.

3. Olsen, K. H.: A Magnetic-matrix Switch and Its Incorporation into a Coincident-current Memory, *MIT Lincoln Lab. Rept.* R-211, June 6, 1952.

4. Rajchman, J. A.: Static Magnetic Matrix Memory and Switching Circuits, *RCA Rev.*, June, 1952, pp. 183–201.

5. Olsen, K. H.: A Linear Selection Magnetic memory Using an Anticoincident Current Switch, *MIT Digital Computer Lab. Memo.* M-2110, May 8, 1953.

6. Rajchman, J. A.: A Myriabit Magnetic-core Matrix Memory, *Proc. IRE*, October, 1953, pp. 1407–1421.

7. Richards, R. K.: "Arithmetic Operations in Digital Computers," D. Van Nostrand Company, Inc., Princeton, N. J., 1955.

8. Computer Development (SEAC and DYSEAC) at the National Bureau of Standards, *NBS Circ.* 551, Jan. 25, 1955.

9. Karnaugh, M.: Pulse Switching Circuits Using Magnetic Cores, *Proc. IRE*, May, 1955, pp. 570–583.

10. Merwin, R. E.: The IBM 705 EDPM Memory System, *IRE Trans. on Electronic Computers*, December, 1956, pp. 219–223.

11. Buck, D. A.: The Cryotron: A Superconductive Computer Component, *Proc. IRE*, April, 1956, pp. 482–493.

12. Cavalieri, A. L., Jr.: What's inside Transac—I, *Electronic Design*, July 1, 1956, pp. 22–25.

13. Cavalieri, A. L., Jr.: What's inside Transac—II, *Electronic Design*, July 15, 1956. pp. 30–33.

14. Andrews, L. J.: A Technique for Using Memory Cores as Logical Elements, *Proc. Eastern Joint Computer Conf.*, 1956, pp. 39–46.

15. Rajchman, J. A., and H. D. Crane: Current Steering in Magnetic Circuits, *IRE Trans. on Electronic Computers*, March, 1957, pp. 21–30.

16. Renwidk, W.: A Magnetic-core Matrix Store with Direct Selection Using a Magnetic-core Switch Matrix, *Proc. IEE (London)*, pt. B, suppls. 5–7, vol. 104, pp. 436–444, 1957.

17. Ridler, D. S., and R. Grimmond: The Magnetic Cell, *Proc. IEE (London)*, pt. B. suppls. 5–7, vol. 104, pp. 445–457, 1957.

18. Rajchman, J. A.: Magnetic Switching, *Proc. Western Joint Computer Conf.*, May 6–8, 1958, pp. 107–116.

19. Wilkes, W. V., W. Renwick, and D. J. Wheeler: The Design of the Control Unit of an Electronic Digital Computer, *Proc. IEE (London)*, pt. B, March, 1958, pp. 121–128.

20. Constantine, G.: A Load-sharing Matrix Switch, *IBM J. Research Develop.*, July, 1958, pp. 204–211.

21. Marcus, M. P.: Doubling the Efficiency of the Load-sharing Matrix Switch, *IBM J. Research Develop.*, April, 1959, pp. 195–196.

22. Maley, G. A., and J. Earle: Synthesizing Multiple-output Switching Networks, a paper presented at the Seventh Symposium on Computers and Data Processing, July 28–29, 1960, Estes Park, Colo.

10

Digital Computer Elements

This chapter describes the logic of basic digital computer elements—basic elements that include adders, subtractors, complementers, shift registers, counters, and accumulators. The important concept of information transfer is presented—the basis of digital operation. This chapter also discusses the problem of propagation of carry or borrow in an accumulator and various methods for handling that problem and shows the generation of control (or command) signals in a digital computer.

10-1 Binary Adders and Subtractors

Single-bit Adders and Subtractors. Previous chapters have mentioned some binary adders and subtractors. There are six single-bit binary adders and subtractors which are basic computing elements: half adder (HA), half subtractor (HS), half adder–subtractor (HAS), full adder (FA), full subtractor (FS), and full adder–subtractor (FAS). The symbolic representation of these adders and subtractors is given in Fig. 10-1. The first three are two-input elements; the last three are three-input elements. Each of these six elements has two outputs. The adder–subtractors have two additional command (or control) inputs. For these inputs and outputs the following nomenclature is used:

X = augend or minuend
Y = addend or subtrahend
Z = sum or difference
W_i = input carry or input borrow
W_o = output carry or output borrow
P_1 = add command signal
$\overline{P}_1$ = subtract command signal

Boolean functions for the sum (or difference) and the carry (or borrow) for these adders and subtractors are given in Table 10-1. A single letter Z represents either a sum or a difference, and the letters W_o and W_i represent either a carry or a borrow. As shown in Table 10-1, Boolean functions Z for the sum and difference of the two-input elements are the same, and those for three-input elements are also alike. Boolean functions W_o for the half adder and half subtractor are the same except that X appears for the adder and $\overline{X}$ for the sub-

Table 10-1 *Boolean Functions Z and W_o*

Circuit	Sum or difference	Output carry or output borrow
HA	$Z = X \oplus Y$	$W_o = XY$
HS	$Z = X \oplus Y$	$W_o = \bar{X}Y$
HAS	$Z = X \oplus Y$	$W_o = (P_1 \odot X)Y$
FA	$Z = X \oplus Y \oplus W_i$	$W_o = XY + XW_i + YW_i$
FS	$Z = X \oplus Y \oplus W_i$	$W_o \doteq \bar{X}Y + \bar{X}W_i + YW_i$
FAS	$Z = X \oplus Y \oplus W_i$	$W_o = (P_1 \odot X)Y + (P_1 \odot X)W_i + YW_i$

tractor; this is also true of Boolean functions W_o for the full adder and full subtractor. Boolean function W_o for the half adder–subtractor is merely the function W_o for the half adder or W_o for the half subtractor, depending on the command signal P_1; this is also true of the Boolean function W_o for the full adder–subtractor.

Serial Adder and Subtractor. An adder for adding two binary numbers or a subtractor for subtracting one binary number from the other can be operated either in series or in parallel. If a flipflop W (or a delay) connects the carry output

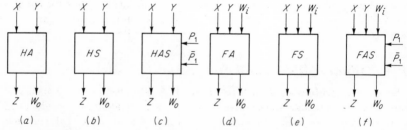

FIG. 10-1 Symbolic representation of two-input and three-input adders and subtractors. (a) Half adder; (b) half subtractor; (c) half adder–subtractor; (d) full adder; (e) full subtractor; (f) full adder–subtractor.

to the carry input of a full adder as in Fig. 10-2a, the resulting circuit is a serial adder. Similar connections to a full subtractor or a full adder–subtractor results in a serial subtractor or a serial adder–subtractor. These circuits are shown in Fig. 10-2b and c.

When two binary sequences, one representing an addend and the other an augend, are applied to inputs X and Y of a serial adder (Fig. 10-2a), a binary sequence representing the sum appears at the output Z. This is possible because flipflop W delays the carry one digit time of the binary sequence, and that delayed carry serves as an input carry at the next digit time. This situation also holds for either a serial subtractor or a serial adder–subtractor.

The delay in the output carry bit of a serial adder or subtractor by one digit time is equivalent to multiplying the output carry by 2. Therefore, the binary sequence, representing an addend, an augend, a minuend, or a subtrahend, must have its least significant bit appearing at the earliest digit time.

Parallel Adder and Subtractor. When the output carry terminal of each full adder in a row of full adders, as shown in Fig. 10-3, is connected to the input carry terminal of the full adder at its left, the resulting circuit is a parallel adder.

If such output-to-input connections were to join full subtractors or full adder–subtractors, the resulting circuit would constitute a parallel subtractor or a parallel adder–subtractor. The dashed line in Fig. 10-3 connects output W_5 to input W_0, illustrating a simple way to incorporate the end-around carry.

A parallel adder summing two n-bit numbers requires n full adders (the adder for the least significant bit can be a half adder), but only one full adder is needed if the two numbers are added serially. On the other hand, a parallel adder completes the addition in one digit time plus the time for propagating the possible carry, while addition in a serial adder requires n digit times. Therefore, the

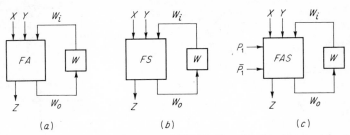

FIG. 10-2   Serial binary adders and subtractors.   (*a*) Serial adder; (*b*) serial subtractor; (*c*) serial adder–subtractor.

parallel adder has the advantage of speed of operation, and the serial adder the advantage of fewer circuits. An intermediate solution is a serial-parallel addition. For example, consider the addition of two 24-bit binary numbers. One can add every 2 adjacent bits in parallel and perform 12 additions serially in 12 digit times. Or one can add every 3, 4, or 6 bits in parallel and perform 8, 6, or 4 additions serially in 8, 6, or 4 digit times. This discussion is equally applicable to a parallel subtractor or a parallel adder–subtractor.

As an added note, when a subtraction is performed serially by addition of the

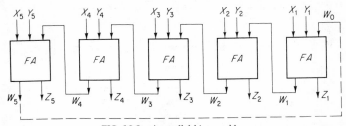

FIG. 10-3   A parallel binary adder.

1's complement, the end-around carry is not available when the two least significant bits are being added unless the output of the adder and the carry from the most significant bit are both stored and returned to the adder for a second adding operation.

10-2   Binary Complementers

A binary complementer converts an input binary number to its complement as an output. If the output is the 1's complement of the input number, the complementer is a 1's complementer; if the output is the 2's complement, it is a 2's complementer. A complementer can be made to receive either a parallel or a serial input. Several complementers will now be described.

1's Complementers. Two 1's complementers are shown in Fig. 10-4, where P and $\bar{P}$ are control signals, respectively, for a true and a 1's complement output. Figure 10-4a shows a serial complementer where a binary sequence representing

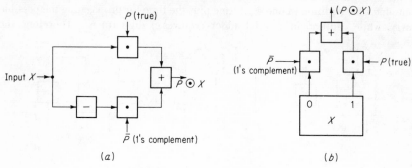

FIG. 10-4   Two 1's complementers.

a binary number appears at input X. This circuit can also be used as a parallel complementer, but such usage requires circuits equal to the number of bits of the binary number. Figure 10-4b shows a parallel complementer where the two outputs of flipflop X are shown as the two inputs. There should be as many of these circuits as there are bits in the binary number. This circuit may also be used as a serial complementer, requiring only one such circuit; the state of the

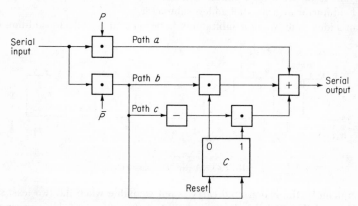

FIG. 10-5   A serial 2's complementer for unsigned binary number.

flipflop changes at each digit time to generate a binary sequence representing the binary number.

2's Complementers. Figure 10-5 shows a serial complementer for an unsigned binary number where P and $\bar{P}$ are control signals, respectively, for a true and a 2's complement output. As shown in Chap. 1, one algorithm for obtaining a 2's complement of an unsigned binary number requires that the least significant nonzero bit and all zeros to its right (i.e., toward the least significant end) be unchanged and that each of the other bits be complemented with respect to 1. As an example, consider a serial input number 110100. This number is a time sequence of pulses (representing 1) or no-pulses (representing 0). If P is 1, then path a of Fig. 10-5 is closed and the sequence passes through the complementer without change. If $\bar{P}$ is 1, path b but not path c is closed because the complementing flipflop C is initially reset to the 0 state.

The first nonzero bit arrives, passes through path b, but changes the state of flipflop C from 0 to 1; path b now becomes open and path c closed. Any subsequent bit of the number now passes through path c and is complemented with respect to 1.

Figure 10-6 shows a serial complementer for a signed binary number; the right portion is the same as that in Fig. 10-5. Assume that the sign bit of the incoming binary sequence leads the serial number and that the sign flipflop S is initially reset to the 0 state, closing path a. When the leading sign bit arrives at the input,

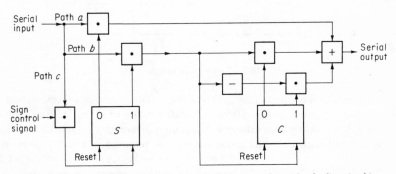

FIG. 10-6   A serial 2's complementer for signed binary number with a leading sign bit.

it passes through path a and is unchanged at the output. In the meantime, a sign control signal closes path c. If the sign bit is 0 (positive number), flipflop S remains in the 0 state and the succeeding number bits again pass through path a and appear at the output. If the sign bit is 1 (negative number), flipflop S is set to the 1 state. Path a becomes open and path b closed. As the succeeding number bits pass through path b, they are complemented in the manner described for an unsigned binary number.

The parallel 2's complementer in Fig. 10-7 consists of n 1's complementers, an n-bit parallel adder, and a carry flipflop C, where n is the quantity of number bits of the incoming parallel number. The sign bit passes through without any change. The algorithm for 2's complementation here is first to perform the 1's complement and then add 1 at the least significant bit. The addition of 1 at the least significant bit is achieved by initially setting flipflop C to the 1 state. Since this operation is an addition with one number being 0, each adder in the parallel adder degenerates into a half adder.

10-3   Shift Registers

A *register* in a digital computer is a storage circuit, usually for a machine word. Since a machine word consists of a number of bits, and since a flipflop is a binary storage element, a number of flipflops form a register. The symbolic representation of a register is given in Fig. 10-8; each square represents a flipflop. Letter A designates register A, and letter A_i designates the ith flipflop. The input and output lines have been omitted for the sake of clarity.

A *shift register* can shift its contents either to the right or to the left or both, depending on the particular design. Interconnecting circuits are thus needed

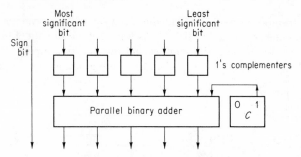

FIG. 10-7   A parallel 2's complementer.

between adjacent flipflops to effect the shifting. The symbolic representation of a shift register is given in Fig. 10-9a. A shift register of n bits shifting 1 bit at a time requires n shifting operations to insert an n-bit serial word into or to extract it from the shift register. Additional circuits are required in a shift register if a word is also to be inserted or extracted in parallel. Such a register can convert a serial word into a parallel word, as shown in Fig. 10-9b, or a parallel word into a serial word, as in Fig. 10-9c.

A_1	A_2	A_3				A_n

FIG. 10-8   Symbolic representation of a register.

Connect the output at one end of a shift register to the input at the other end, and the register becomes a *circulating register*. This is symbolically shown in Fig. 10-9d.

Logic Equations of the Shift Register.   A shift register requires a temporary storage between two adjacent flipflops; so the state of one flipflop stage being changed is stored and used as the input to the subsequent flipflop stage. Two methods are usually employed; one method uses a delay network shown in Fig. 10-10, and the other uses an additional flipflop B_n shown in Fig. 10-11. The delay is usually implemented as an input or an output network of the flipflop.

In Fig. 10-10 the flipflops are of the RS-input type, the capital letter designating the output, as A_n or its complement $\bar{A}_n$. The inputs are designated by small letters, as a_{nr} and a_{ns}, which represent, respectively, the reset and set inputs of the nth flipflop stage. Letter p represents the clock pulse for carrying out the shift. There are two types of logic equations concerning storing circuits such as shift registers, counters, and others. The first type describes the states of the register and is called the *state equation,* which was discussed in Chap. 3. The states of each flipflop of the shift register are described in Table 10-2, from which the state equation of the shift register can be written as

$$A_n(\tau) = A_{n-1}p \tag{10-1}$$

This equation means that the state of the nth flipflop following a time interval τ is the state of the $(n - 1)$st flipflop. The second type of logic equation prescribes

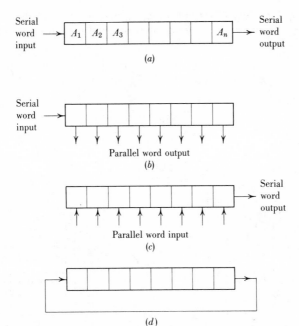

FIG. 10-9 Symbolic representation of shift registers. (*a*) Shift register; (*b*) conversion of a serial word into a parallel word; (*c*) conversion of parallel word into a serial word; (*d*) circulating register.

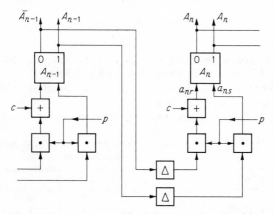

FIG. 10-10 Logic diagram of a shift-register stage using delays.

flipflop input connections; this logic expression is called the *input equation*. The truth values of the reset and set inputs of the nth flipflop are shown in Table 10-3, where 1 and 0 in the columns for inputs a_{nr} and a_{ns} represent, respectively, a triggering pulse and no-pulse. From Table 10-3, the input equations of the flipflops of the shift register appear as

$$a_{nr} = \bar{A}_{n-1}p$$
$$a_{ns} = A_{n-1}p \tag{10-2}$$

These flipflop input equations mean that flipflop A_n is set to the 0 or 1 state if flipflop A_{n-1} is at the 0 or 1 state, respectively, and the setting occurs coincident

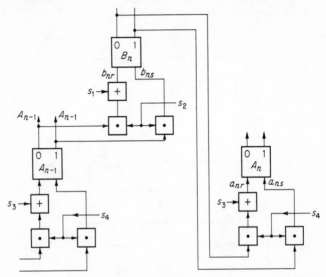

FIG. 10-11   Logic diagram of a shift-register stage using a temporary register.

with clock pulse p. It is often desired that the contents of a shift register be cleared by a clearing pulse c. In this case, input equations (10-2) become

$$a_{nr} = \bar{A}_{n-1}p + c$$
$$a_{ns} = A_{n-1}p \tag{10-3}$$

Input equations (10-3) prescribe the manner of connecting the inputs of the flipflops of the shift register as diagrammed in Fig. 10-10.

Note that the state equation is a logic difference equation, whereas the input equation is a logic algebraic equation.

Figure 10-11 depicts the nth stage of a shift register A which incorporates a

Table 10-2   Truth   Table for Shift Register

p	$A_{n-1}(t)$	$A_n(t + \tau)$
1	0	0
1	1	1

Table 10-3   Truth   Table for Input Equation of Shift Register

p	$A_{n-1}(t)$	$A_n(t + \tau)$	a_{nr}	a_{ns}
1	0	0	1	0
1	1	1	0	1

temporary register B.   Operation requires a sequence of four control signals $s_1(t_1)$, $s_2(t_2)$, $s_3(t_3)$, and $s_4(t_4)$.   The first signal s_1 clears register B.   Signal s_2 transfers information from register A to B; signal s_3 clears register A; and finally signal s_4 transfers the information from register B back to A.   During the transfer initiated by s_4, the shifting of the information in register A is accomplished.

Logic Diagram.   A logic diagram is a symbolic representation of logic elements and the manner in which these elements are connected.   The block diagrams so far described in this chapter are logic diagrams.   Since input equations designate the inputs of logic elements and describe the interconnections, the logic diagram and the input equations are logically equivalent.   One advantage of using logic diagrams is that logically insignificant circuits such as amplifiers, level restorers, and the like can be readily incorporated.   On the other hand, representation by input equations is concise.

10-4   Counters

Counting, an important operation in a digital computer, is achieved by a circuit which takes note of the number of input pulses and stores the result.   If a counter adds each arriving input pulse, it is known as a *forward counter*, or *up counter*.   If a counter can be set initially to a certain number and each input pulse

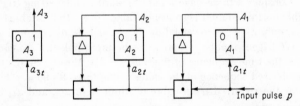

FIG. 10-12   Logic diagram of a modulo-2^3 binary forward counter using trigger flipflops.

subtracts from that number, it is known as a *reverse counter*, or *down counter*.   If a counter is provided with two input terminals so that it adds for pulses arriving at one input and subtracts for pulses arriving at the other input, it is known as a *reversible counter*, an *up-down counter*, or a *bilateral counter*.

Counters may also be classified according to the manner in which they store the number of counts.   If the stored number is a binary number, the counter is a *binary counter*; if the stored number is a decimal number, the counter is a decimal counter.   A decimal counter usually consists of a number of decimal-digit counters.   If the decimal digit is stored in a binary code, the counter is a *binary-coded decimal digit counter*.   If the decimal digit has to be stored decimally, the a ring counter is used.   In a ring counter there are N distinct states, each of which can be sensed from a distinct output line.   Thus, a *ring counter* with N states is a digit counter for radix N.   Ring counters are practical for a small value of the radix N.   Counters can also be designed to express the count in a special sequence of binary numbers.   Such a counter may appear in a digital computer as a program counter (or an operation counter), a word-time counter, or a digit-time counter.

Logic Equations of Binary Counters.   A binary counter is formed by cascading flipflops with the proper logic circuits.   Figures 10-12 to 10-14 show the logic diagrams of three versions of a three-stage binary forward counter. In each version three flipflops are used, but they differ in the interconnection of the logic circuits. These counters are also called *modulo-2³ counters* because the maximum capacity is eight counts (including no count); they cannot distinguish counts which differ by an integral multiple of 8.

The logic design of a counter may proceed by first preparing a truth table. The table shows not only the relations among the succeeding states of the flipflops but

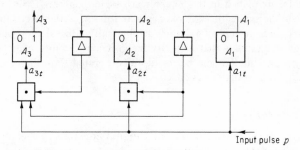

FIG. 10-13   Logic diagram of a modulo-2³ binary forward counter using trigger flipflops.

also the required input states (of the flipflop) which cause the *changes* of these flip-flop states. Consider a three-stage binary forward counter using trigger flipflops. The truth table for this counter is shown in Table 10-4. In this table the three flip-flops and their outputs are represented by A_3, A_2, and A_1; a_{3t}, a_{2t}, and a_{1t} represent their respective trigger inputs; p represents the input pulses to be counted; t_0, t_1, etc., represent the time sequence of the pulses. The three columns for the three A's show the desired sequence of the states of the three flipflops. The last three columns show the required truth value of inputs a_{3t}, a_{2t}, and a_{1t} to cause the

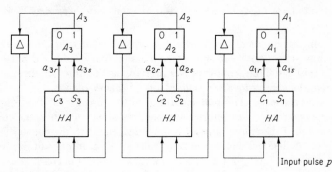

FIG. 10-14   Logic diagram of a modulo-2³ counter using half adders and *RS* flipflops.

change of the counter state. In these three columns, the 0's signify that no-pulse at the flipflop input is required, while the 1's signify that a triggering pulse occurs at the flipflop input. These 0's and 1's are obtained from the *changes* of the flip-flop states in the three columns for the three A's. For instance, when the state of the counter is changed from 000 to 001, the states of A_3 and A_2 do not change; thus the value of a_{3t} and a_{2t} are both 0 in the first row of the columns under a_{3t} and a_{2t}. But the state of A_1 changes from 0 to 1; thus the value of a_{1t} is 1 in the first row of the last column. The other values in the last three columns are similarly obtained. Note that at t_8 the counter state is 000, which is the same as that at t_0; the counter then cycles again.

The *input equations* for the three flipflops can readily be written from Table 10-4,

$$a_{1t} = p$$
$$a_{2t} = A_1 p \qquad (10\text{-}4)$$
$$a_{3t} = A_2 A_1 p$$

The above input equations can be reexpressed as

$$a_{1t} = p$$
$$a_{2t} = A_1 a_{1t} \qquad (10\text{-}5)$$
$$a_{3t} = A_2 a_{2t}$$

The binary counter prescribed by input equations (10-5) is shown in Fig. 10-12. Two delays have been added in this figure to indicate that the inputs to the *and* gates from the flipflops are the flipflop states before they are changed.   If the

Table 10-4   Truth Table for Three-stage Binary Forward Counter Using Trigger Flipflops

Time	p	A_3	A_2	A_1	a_{3t}	a_{2t}	a_{1t}
t_0	1	0	0	0	0	0	1
t_1	1	0	0	1	0	1	1
t_2	1	0	1	0	0	0	1
t_3	1	0	1	1	1	1	1
t_4	1	1	0	0	0	0	1
t_5	1	1	0	1	0	1	1
t_6	1	1	1	0	0	0	1
t_7	1	1	1	1	1	1	1
t_8	1	0	0	0			

flipflops possess sufficient delay, these added delays are not needed.   The counting speed of this counter is limited by the maximum repetition rate of flipflop A_1.

The binary counter prescribed by input equations (10-4) is shown in Fig. 10-13. This counter has an advantage which can be explained as follows: If a binary counter such as one shown in Fig. 10-12 has many stages (say, six), the change of state from 011111 to 100000 requires the signal to go through many *and* gates (five *and* gates for six stages); the counting speed of the counter may thus be limited by the carry-propagation time through the cascade of the *and* gates. Such a long carry propagation does not exist in the counter of Fig. 10-13.   However, multiple-input *and* gates are required; if the number of stages becomes large, the circuits become excessive.

When the inputs in Eqs. (10-4) are substituted into state equation (3-90), we have

$$A_1(\tau) = A_1 \oplus p$$
$$A_2(\tau) = A_2 \oplus A_1 p \qquad (10\text{-}6)$$
$$A_3(\tau) = A_3 \oplus A_2 A_1 p$$

374   Digital Computer Design Fundamentals

These are the *state equations* of the counter which describe the states of the three flipflops.

Instead of trigger flipflops, *RS* flipflops may be used for binary counting. Table 10-5 lists conditions for a three-stage forward binary counter using *RS* flipflops. In this table, a_{3r}, a_{2r}, and a_{1r}, represent the reset inputs in the three flipflops and a_{3s}, a_{2s}, and a_{1s} the set inputs. The columns for the time sequence and the incoming pulses are omitted. The 0's and 1's in the last six columns are again obtained from the *changes* of the flipflop states in the first three columns; they differ, however, from those in Table 10-4. In Table 10-5 the 1's in the reset input columns (the fourth, sixth, and eight columns) signify the change of state of a flipflop from 1 to 0, while the 0's signify all other changes (from 0 to 0, 1 to 0, and 0 to 1). The 1's in the set input columns (the fifth, seventh, and last columns) signify the change of the state of a flipflop from 0 to 1, while 0's signify all other changes (from 0 to 0, 1 to 1, and 1 to 0). For instance, when the state of the counter changes from 000 to 001, the states of A_3 and A_2 do not change; thus, the values of a_{3r}, a_{3s}, a_{2r}, and a_{2s} are all 0 in the first row of the fourth, fifth, sixth, and seventh columns. But the state of A_1 is required

Table 10-5   Truth Table for a Three-stage Binary Forward Counter Using *RS* **Flipflop**

A_3	A_2	A_1	a_{3r}	a_{3s}	a_{2r}	a_{2s}	a_{1r}	a_{1s}
0	0	0	0	0	0	0	0	1
0	0	1	0	0	0	1	1	0
0	1	0	0	0	0	0	0	1
0	1	1	0	1	1	0	1	0
1	0	0	0	0	0	0	0	1
1	0	1	0	0	0	1	1	0
1	1	0	0	0	0	0	0	1
1	1	1	1	0	1	0	1	0
0	0	0	0	0	0	0	0	1

to change from 0 to 1; the value of a_{1r} is 0, while the values of a_{1s} is 1 in the first row of the last two columns. The values of the other reset and set inputs in the last six columns are similarly obtained.

The input equations for the three flipflops are written from Table 10-5 and are shown below:

$$
\begin{aligned}
a_{1s} &= \bar{A}_1 p \\
a_{2s} &= \bar{A}_2 A_1 p = \bar{A}_2 a_{1r} \\
a_{3s} &= \bar{A}_3 A_2 A_1 p = \bar{A}_3 a_{2r} \\
a_{1r} &= A_1 p \\
a_{2r} &= A_2 A_1 p = A_2 a_{1r} \\
a_{3r} &= A_3 A_2 A_1 p = A_3 a_{2r}
\end{aligned}
\tag{10-7}
$$

The inputs of the three flipflops can be connected according to these six input equations. If they are substituted into state equation (3-99), we have after simplification state equations (10-6). This should be the case, as these two counters perform the same counting function.

To the first three equations of (10-7), the terms $A_1 \bar{p}$, $A_2 \bar{a}_{1r}$, and $A_3 \bar{a}_{2r}$ can be added, respectively. The logical addition of the term $A_1 \bar{p}$ to the first equation does not affect this equation, because the value of a_{1s} is equal to 1 when A_1 is 1 (irrespective of p being 1 or 0) and makes the flipflop A_1 remain in the 1 state. Similarly the logical addition of the terms $A_2\bar{a}_{1r}$ and $A_3\bar{a}_{2r}$ to the respective equations does not affect these equations. When these redundant terms are added, the above six equations become

$$a_{1s} = A_1 \oplus p \qquad a_{1r} = A_1 p$$
$$a_{2s} = A_2 \oplus a_{1r} \qquad a_{2r} = A_2 a_{1r} \qquad (10\text{-}8)$$
$$a_{3s} = A_3 \oplus a_{2r} \qquad a_{3r} = A_3 a_{2r}$$

Recall that the sum output and carry output of a half adder are, respectively, the logical-exclusive-*or* operation and logical-*and* operation of its two inputs. Thus, a_{1s} and a_{1r} are, respectively, the sum and carry output of a half adder whose inputs are A_1 and p. Similarly, a_{2s} and a_{2r} as well as a_{3s} and a_{3r} are also outputs of half adders. The binary counter using half adders as prescribed by input equations (10-8) is shown in Fig. 10-14.

State Diagram. The state diagram of a counter (or a storing circuit in general) shows the time sequence of its states. Figure 10-15 portrays the states of the foregoing three-stage binary forward counter. In this diagram each circle

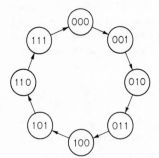

FIG. 10-15   State diagram of a modulo-2^3 binary forward counter.

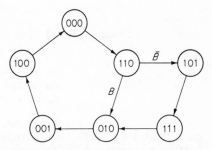

FIG. 10-16   State diagram of a special-sequence counter.

represents one state; the binary number in the circle signifies that state, and the arrows indicate the sequence of the states as they change. In this simplest case a state diagram appears almost trivial. However, it becomes important in a complicated sequential circuit.

Figure 10-16 shows the state diagram of a binary counter. There are two branches at the output of state 110; the choice between them depends on a control signal's being B or its complement $\bar{B}$ as indicated in the diagram. By application of the control signal, the sequence of the counter states can be altered. Such a special sequenced counter can be used as an operation counter in a computer.

The logic design of this counter resembles the designs already described. Since there are seven states, three flipflops are needed. A truth table for the state diagram in Fig. 10-16 can be prepared as shown in Table 10-6. The 0's and 1's in the columns for the inputs are obtained in the manner previously described. The input equations are

$$a_{1t} = (\bar{A}_3 A_2 \bar{A}_1 + \bar{A}_3 \bar{A}_2 A_1 + \bar{B} A_3 A_2 \bar{A}_1 + A_3 A_2 A_1)\,p$$
$$a_{2t} = (\bar{A}_3 A_2 \bar{A}_1 + \bar{A}_3 \bar{A}_2 A_1 + \bar{B} A_3 A_2 \bar{A}_1 + A_3 \bar{A}_2 A_1)\,p \qquad (10\text{-}9)$$
$$a_{3t} = (\bar{A}_3 \bar{A}_2 A_1 + A_3 \bar{A}_2 \bar{A}_1 + \bar{A}_3 \bar{A}_2 \bar{A}_1 + A_3 A_2 A_1 + B A_3 A_2 \bar{A}_1)\,p$$

Since state 011 does not exist, term $\bar{A}_3 A_2 A_1$ (and thus also terms $B\bar{A}_3 A_2 A_1$ and $\bar{B}\bar{A}_3 A_2 A_1$ can be utilized to simplify the above equations.

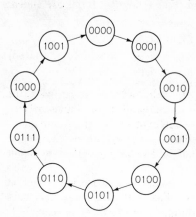

FIG. 10-17   State diagram of an 8-4-2-1-coded decimal-digit counter.

These input equations indicate how the inputs of the three flipflops are connected. For a design such as that described, the step of preparing the truth table can be omitted and input equations written directly from the state diagram, once such a procedure becomes familiar.

Decimal-digit Counters. A decimal-digit counter, or a decade counter, requires 10 states, the obtaining of which can be achieved by utilizing 10 of the 16 states of a four-stage binary counter. The counting sequence can be designed to follow any desired sequence. Following a binary-coded sequence identifies a binary-coded decimal digit counter. The state diagram of such a counter using the 8-4-2-1 code is shown in Fig. 10-17. The input equations can be written directly from this diagram. After simplification they are

$$
\begin{aligned}
a_{1t} &= p \\
a_{2t} &= A_1 \bar{A}_4 p \\
a_{3t} &= A_1 A_2 p \\
a_{4t} &= A_1 (A_4 + A_2 A_3) p
\end{aligned}
\qquad (10\text{-}10)
$$

Simplification of these input equations has involved employing the nonexisting states 1010, 1011, 1100, 1101, 1110, and 1111.

Ring Counters. Instead of using 10 of the 16 states of a four-stage binary counter, a digit counter of radix N can be formed by cascading N flipflops connected with the proper logic circuits in the form of a ring. The logic diagram of a four-stage ring counter is shown in Fig. 10-18; it is a special circulating register, all bits of the circulating word being 0 except that one bit is 1. The state of the ring counter is indicated by the flipflop whose state is 1, as shown in Table 10-7. From this table can be derived the input equations for the four flipflops,

$$
\begin{aligned}
a_{1r} &= a_{2s} = A_1 p \\
a_{2r} &= a_{3s} = A_2 p \\
a_{3r} &= a_{4s} = A_3 p \\
a_{4r} &= a_{1s} = A_4 p
\end{aligned}
\qquad (10\text{-}11)
$$

These equations describe the input connections shown in Fig. 10-18. In this figure the circulation and information (a word) occurs in a counterclockwise direction. When these input equations are substituted in Eq. (3-99), we have the state equations

$$
\begin{aligned}
A_1(\tau) &= A_1 \bar{p} + A_2 p = A_2 p \\
A_2(\tau) &= A_2 \bar{p} + A_3 p = A_3 p \\
A_3(\tau) &= A_3 \bar{p} + A_4 p = A_4 p \\
A_4(\tau) &= A_4 \bar{p} + A_1 p = A_1 p
\end{aligned}
\qquad (10\text{-}12)
$$

Table 10-6   Truth   Table of Special Sequence Counter

A_3	A_2	A_1	B	a_{3t}	a_{2t}	a_{1t}
0	1	0		0	1	1
0	0	1		1	0	1
1	0	0		1	0	0
0	0	0		1	1	0
1	1	0	1	1	0	0
1	1	0	0	0	1	1
1	0	1		0	1	0
1	1	1		1	0	1
0	1	0		0	1	1

Terms $A_1 \bar{p}$, $A_2 \bar{p}$, $A_3 \bar{p}$, and $A_4 \bar{p}$ are redundant in the above state equations. When they are removed, the result agrees with the state equation of the shift register

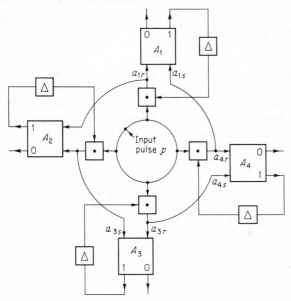

FIG. 10-18   Logic diagram of a four-stage ring counter.

except that the latter is not circulating. In the ring counter, the shifting of the last stage (such as flipflop A_4) to the first stage (flipflop A_1) may be done by a separate control signal if required. Because N flipflops are required for a ring of N states, a ring counter with a large value of N is not practical. However, N pairs of output lines are available for the N states without any additional switching

Table 10-7   Truth Table of Four-stage Ring Counter

A_4	A_3	A_2	A_1	a_{4r}	a_{4s}	a_{3r}	a_{3s}	a_{2r}	a_{2s}	a_{1r}	a_{1s}
0	0	0	1	0	0	0	0	0	1	1	0
0	0	1	0	0	0	0	1	1	0	0	0
0	1	0	0	0	1	1	0	0	0	0	0
1	0	0	0	1	0	0	0	0	0	0	1
0	0	0	1								

circuits. This is not so if a binary-coded counter is used as a decimal-digit counter, as a binary-coded counter requires additional decoding networks to translate the 4-bit codes to separate output lines.

10-5   Information Transfer

The information stored in a register is a word.   By information transfer, we mean the transfer of the word from one register to another or multiple transfers from one or more registers to one or more other registers.   The change of state in a shift register or in a counter amounts to an information transfer, except that it occurs within one register.

The importance of an information transfer rests, not merely on the transfer itself, but also on the possibility of performing logic operations on the word during the transfer.   The word transfer in a shift register is a degenerate case, as no logic operation is performed other than shifting.   In a counter, logic operations are performed to change its state.   *The information transfer among various registers is the basic approach by which computing, data processing, decision making, and the like are accomplished.*

Symbolic Method.   The digital computer performs its arithmetic, logic, and other operations during the transfer of words (which are initially stored in the memory unit) to the various registers in a certain sequential manner.   It is most desirable to develop a technique by means of which these transfers and the operations during the transfers can be precisely described.

The symbolic method is one which attempts to describe precisely the process of information transfer.   This method was first reported by Reed and others [4,12].   A required transfer occurring at a specified state of the computer is first expressed in a *symbolic statement*.   The logic equations and/or the logic diagrams can then be obtained from the symbolic statements.

Before describing the symbolic method, the symbols are first defined and are shown in Table 10-8.   (Additional symbols will be given when needed.)   In this

Table 10-8   Symbols for Symbolic Method

Symbols	Description of symbol
Capital letter	Capital letter denotes register
Subscript i	Subscript i denotes ith bit of register
Parentheses ( )	Parentheses denote contents of register
Double-line arrow $\Rightarrow$ . .	Double-line arrow denotes transfer of word from one to another register
Brackets [ ]	Brackets denote a portion of register the contents of which has a functional dependence on register
Colon :	Colon (following a Boolean variable) denotes the occurrence of subsequent statement (or statements) when the variable has the value 1
Single-line arrow $\rightarrow$ . . .	Single-line arrow, or simply arrow, denotes a sequence of states
Plus + ...	This symbol has two meanings: (1) a logical-*or* operation when used among Boolean variables, and (2) an arithmetic addition when used between numbers
Minus −	This symbol denotes an arithmetic subtraction

table the capital letter denotes the register. For example, A denotes register A; subscript i denotes its ith bit: A_i means the ith bit of register A. In this case A_i is a Boolean variable. These two representations are not new, as they have been earlier described.

Parentheses denote the contents of a register. Thus, (A) signifies the contents of register A, and (A_i) means the contents of the ith bit of register A. This symbol may also denote the complement of the contents; thus, $(\bar{A})$ denotes the complement of the contents of register A. Parentheses may also denote a combined register. For example, (A,B) means the contents of registers A and B, which are placed in tandem and used as one register. The double-line arrow denotes the transfer of a word from one register to another. Thus,

$$(A) \Rightarrow B \tag{10-13}$$

means that the contents of register A are transferred to register B. And

$$0 \Rightarrow A \tag{10-14}$$

means that zeros are transferred to register A. Others are the shift-left operation (index i increases toward the most significant bit),

$$(A_i) \Rightarrow A_{i+1} \tag{10-15}$$

the shift-right operation,

$$(A_i) \Rightarrow A_{i-1} \tag{10-16}$$

the extract operation, which is the logical-*and* operation of the corresponding bits,

$$(A_i) \cdot (B_i) \Rightarrow A_i \tag{10-17}$$

and the merge operation, which is the logical-*or* operation of the corresponding bits,

$$(A_i) + (B_i) \Rightarrow A_i \tag{10-18}$$

Brackets denote a portion of a register the contents of which have a functional dependence on the register. Thus, $\text{Sn}[A]$ and $\text{Nm}[A]$ mean, respectively, the sign part and the number part of register A. The colon following a Boolean variable (which represents a state or a command signal) denotes the occurrence of subsequent statement (or statements) when the value of the variable is 1; thus,

$$P_i: 0 \Rightarrow A \tag{10-19}$$

means that, when the value of P_i is 1, the statement that zeros go to register A occurs. The single-line arrow, or simply the arrow, denotes a sequence of states; thus,

$$P_1 \rightarrow P_2 \rightarrow P_3 \tag{10-20}$$

means that state P_3 follows state P_2, which follows state P_1.

The plus sign has two meanings. First, it means a logical-*or* operation when used among Boolean variables. For instance, $A + B$ means the logical-*or* operation on Boolean variables A and B. Second, it means an arithmetic addition. For example, $(A) + (B)$ means the arithmetic sum of the contents of registers A and B. If there is a possibility of confusion, the word *add* is used for addition instead of the plus sign. The minus sign denotes an arithmetic subtraction.

*Table 10-9   Truth Table
for Word Transfer*

p	A_i	B_i	b_{it}
1	0	0	0
1	0	1	1
1	1	0	1
1	1	1	0

Thus, $(A) - (B)$ means that the contents of register B are subtracted from the contents of register A.

The symbolic method is the application of these symbols to describe information transfer. A simple information transfer will now be worked out as an illustration. It is required to transfer a 3-bit word in register A to register B; the transfer occurs at state P_1, a control (or command) signal which will be provided by the control unit in the computer. The registers consist of trigger flipflops.

The above information transfer condenses to a concise symbolic statement by using the symbols in Table 10-8,

$$P_1: (A) \Longrightarrow B \tag{10-21}$$

From this symbolic statement Table 10-9 is prepared. In this table the clock pulse p initiates the transfer. Input equations for the flipflops of the B register can be written from Table 10-9.

$$b_{it} = (A_i \oplus B_i)P_1 p \qquad \text{for } i = 1, 2, 3 \tag{10-22}$$

The equation shows that an exclusive-*or* operation is required for a simple transfer if register B consists of trigger flipflops. The logic diagram which describes the interconnections of these two registers is shown in Fig. 10-19.

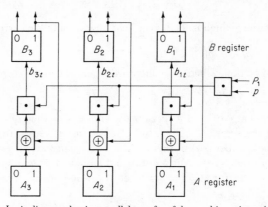

FIG. 10-19   Logic diagram showing parallel transfer of the word in register A to register B.

Parallel Transfer of Information. Information transfer from one register to the other can be performed either in parallel or in series. The previous example was one of a parallel transfer. As an additional example, consider the arithmetic addition of two 3-bit binary numbers. Assume that the augend and the addend are stored, respectively, in registers A and B and that the sum after addition is to be stored in register Q. The addition operation occurs at computer state P_1. RS flipflops are used. This transfer can be expressed by the following symbolic statement:

$$P_1: (A) + (B) \Longrightarrow Q \tag{10-23}$$

From this symbolic statement, the input equations for register Q are

$$q_{is} = S_i P_1 p \qquad \text{for } i = 1, 2, 3 \qquad (10\text{-}24)$$

Recall that the ith sum and carry bits S_i and C_i in Table 5-6 are, after expansion,

$$
\begin{aligned}
S_i &= (\overline{A}_i \overline{B}_i C_{i-1} + \overline{A}_i B_i \overline{C}_{i-1} + A_i \overline{B}_i \overline{C}_{i-1} + A_i B_i C_{i-1}) P_1 p \qquad i = 1, 2, 3 \\
C_i &= (\overline{A}_i B_i C_{i-1} + A_i \overline{B}_i C_{i-1} + A_i B_i \overline{C}_{i-1} + A_i B_i C_{i-1}) P_1 p \qquad i = 1, 2, 3 \\
C_o &= 0
\end{aligned}
$$
$$(10\text{-}25)$$

The logic diagram for these equations appears as Fig. 10-20, wherein the full adder performs the operations inside parentheses of the functions. When state P_1 occurs, the clock pulse p initiates the transfer and the addition occurs during the transfer.

Serial Transfer of Information. Instead of parallel transfer, the information can be transferred in a serial manner. Consider the arithmetic addition of two 5-bit binary numbers which are stored in the two shift registers A and B (Fig.

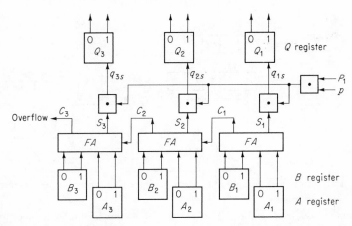

FIG. 10-20   Logic diagram showing binary addition of two 3-bit numbers by parallel transfer.

10-21). Addition occurs at state P_1. In serial addition 2 corresponding bits of the two numbers are added at a time as these two numbers are being shifted out of the shift register by clock pulses p_1 to p_5.

The transfer can be expressed in the following symbolic statements.

$$
\begin{aligned}
P_1 p_i : (B_i) &\Longrightarrow B_{i-1} \\
0 &\Longrightarrow B_5 \\
(A_i) &\Longrightarrow A_{i-1} \qquad \text{for } i = 1, \ldots, 5 \qquad (10\text{-}26) \\
S_i &\Longrightarrow A_5 \\
C_{i+1} &\Longrightarrow \Delta C_i
\end{aligned}
$$

where S_i and C_i are described by functions (10-25). The first three symbolic statements describe the shift-right operation of registers A and B. The last two statements describe the connection of the carry bit and the storing of the sum bit in flipflop A_5. The logic diagram for this serial binary adder is shown in Fig. 10-21. The carry output of the full adder is delayed and fed back to the carry input of the full adder; in this manner, the carry is added to the correct digit of the number. Note that the least significant bits of the two binary numbers are initially in locations A_1 and B_1 and are added first.

The symbolic statement can express either a parallel or a serial information transfer. It can also express synchronous or asynchronous operation; in the latter case, a starting signal and a completion signal are specified.

Logic-equation and Logic-diagram Methods [13]. Logic design of a digital computer calls for a sequential visualization of the information flow in time among various spatial registers. There are two widely used methods—the logic-equation method and the logic-diagram method. Historically, the logic-diagram method was first adopted; later the logic-equation method was developed and accepted.

The logic-diagram method has the advantages of providing a spatial visualization of the interconnection of logic circuits and of being easily understood without the

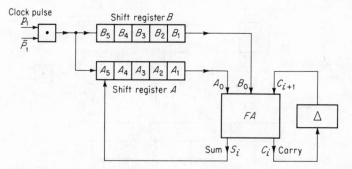

FIG. 10-21 Logic diagram showing binary addition of two 5-bit numbers by serial transfer.

background of Boolean algebra. Furthermore, it is more adaptable to incorporating those elements which are logically insignificant, such as emitter followers, pulse amplifiers, etc. On the other hand, the logic-equation approach has the advantage of giving a precise and concise description of the computer operation. It is more adaptable to simulation on a digital computer for checking the design, preparing the wiring tabulation, and the like. Thus, these two approaches complement each other. It is desirable to be familiar with both.

It should be pointed out that the symbolic method is adaptable to either the logic-equation or the logic-diagram approach, because the symbolic statements merely state the operations to be performed under given computer states. By either method it is possible to describe the exact manner in which the operations are carried out.

10-6 Binary Accumulators

A binary accumulator consists of a register which stores a binary number and upon receiving another binary number adds the second number to (or subtracts it from) the first number and then stores the sum (or the difference) in the register. The logic diagram in Fig. 10-20 is a binary accumulator (though not practical) if the Q register is discarded and the sum is stored in the A register.

Serial Accumulator. An accumulator is designed for either serial or parallel operation. The logic diagram of a serial binary accumulator is shown in Fig. 10-22. It consists of a serial adder for performing addition and a shift register for storing the augend before addition or the sum after addition. Sub-

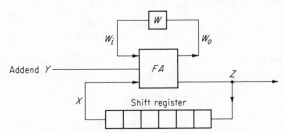

FIG. 10-22   Logic diagram of a serial binary accumulator.

traction can be performed by addition of the 2's complement of the number. Subtraction by adding the 1's complement of the number is not preferred, because a second addition is required for adding the end-around carry and this increases the addition time. If the serial adder of Fig. 10-22 is replaced by a serial subtractor or a serial adder–subtractor, the accumulator can perform subtraction or both addition and subtraction.

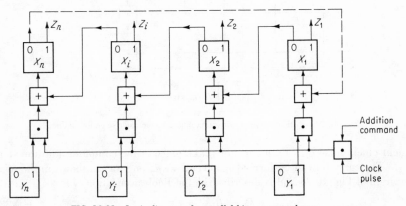

FIG. 10-23   Logic diagram of a parallel binary accumulator.

Parallel Accumulator. The logic diagram of a simple parallel binary accumulator is shown in Fig. 10-23. Each flipflop in the accumulator functions as a modulo-2 counter. The augend is initially stored in these counters. During addition, each counter counts parallel incoming pulses representing the addend bit or the carry bit and generates a carry pulse to the next significant bit when the counter changes its state from 1 to 0. The dashed line in the diagram shows a possible connection for an end-around carry if needed.

Symbolic Design of Binary Accumulators.   Logic design of a parallel binary accumulator for addition will now be described as an additional example of the symbolic method.   Since every stage is the same (except perhaps the first and the last stages), we consider only the ith stage.   The adding operation in the parallel accumulator can be divided into two steps, the first of which adds the augend bit A_i and the addend bit B_i; the second step adds the resulting sum bit and carry bit from the next lower significant bit stage.   The symbolic statements follow for these two steps:

$$P_1p_1:\ B_i(\bar{A}_i) + \bar{B}_i(A_i) \Rightarrow A_i$$
$$P_1p_2:\ C_{i-1}(\bar{A}_i) + \bar{C}_{i-1}(A_i) \Rightarrow A_i \tag{10-27}$$

In these statements the addition of the A_i bit and B_i bit occurs at clock pulse p_1; addition of the resulting sum bit A_i and carry bit C_{i-1} occurs at the subse-

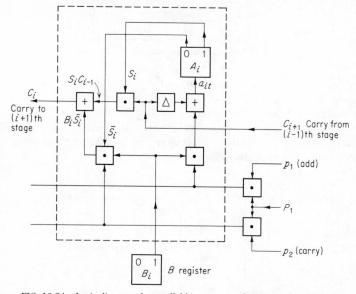

FIG. 10-24   Logic diagram of a parallel-binary-accumulator stage for addition.

quent clock pulse p_2.   Both additions take place at the computer addition state P_1.   The carry bit can be formed in several ways; one way is shown in the logic diagram of Fig. 10-24 and is described by the Boolean function

$$C_i = B_i\bar{S}_i + C_{i-1}S_i \tag{10-28}$$

where S_i and $\bar{S}_i$ are, respectively, the 1's and 0's output of the flipflop A_i after the occurrence of clock pulse p_1.   The added delay ensures that the change of the state of the flipflop A_i occurs after the carry addition is completed.

The above function shows that there are two possibilities for obtaining a carry bit, $B_i\bar{S}_i$ and $C_{i-1}S_i$.   However, they do not occur at the same time, because one term involves S while the other term involves $\bar{S}$.   Carry bit $B_i\bar{S}_i$ occurs when both A_i and B_i are 1; but the complement of S_i is used because the addition of the carry bit occurs at the subsequent clock pulse p_2.   At that time, there is a carry if the sum bit is 0. The arrangement of the carry shown in Fig. 10-24 has the advantage that the carry generated in one stage needs to propagate only one succeeding stage. Furthermore, the additions of the carries of all stages are performed during clock pulse p_2; this is possible because of the mutually exclusive nature of the above-mentioned two possible carry bits $B_i\bar{S}_i$ and $C_{i-1}S_i$.

An accumulator can also be designed to perform subtraction. The operation for a single-bit full subtractor has been shown in Table 10-1. Recall that the sum of a full adder is the same as the difference of a full subtractor, but the carry of a full adder and the borrow of a full subtractor are different. Symbolic statements (10-27) for the sum bit still hold for a subtracting accumulator, except that the addition state P_1 is to be replaced by the state for subtraction P_2. We thus have

$$P_2 p_1: \quad B_i(\bar{A}_i) + \bar{B}_i(A_i) \Rightarrow A_i$$
$$P_2 p_2: \quad R_{i-1}(\bar{A}_i) + R_{i-1}(A_i) \Rightarrow A_i \tag{10-29}$$

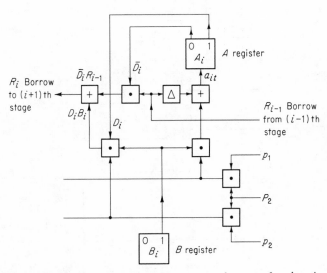

FIG. 10-25   Logic diagram of a parallel-binary-accumulator stage for subtraction.

where R_i is the ith borrow bit, which can be formed like the carry bit of function (10-28). Thus, we have the borrow bit

$$R_i = D_i B_i + \bar{D}_i B_{i-1} \tag{10-30}$$

where D_i is the ith difference bit. The logic diagram for the ith stage of the subtracting accumulator is shown in Fig. 10-25.

A parallel binary accumulator for both addition and subtraction can now be formed. Examining the diagrams in Fig. 10-24 and 10-25 reveals a difference only in the connection at the output lines of flipflop A_i. An accumulator for both addition and subtraction can be formed by using four additional logical-*and* circuits and two additional logical-*or* circuits as shown in Fig. 10-26. When the state is P_1, the accumulator is that of Fig. 10-24; when the state is P_2, the accumulator is that of Fig. 10-25.

10-7   Propagation of Carry or Borrow

The Problem of Carry or Borrow Propagation. In a parallel addition of two binary numbers, the problem arises of carry or borrow propagation. If in the parallel binary adder of Fig. 10-3 the binary number 0001 is added to the number 1111, a carry is produced in the least-significant-bit adder. This carry causes another carry to be generated from the next-significant-bit adder. This process continues until a carry is generated from the most-significant-bit adder. In the parallel binary accumulator of Fig. 10-23 the addition of the above two numbers causes a similar carry propagation. In either case the time of propagation increases with the increase of the number of bits, and the addition is not completed until the carry propagation is completed. Similar propagation of bor-

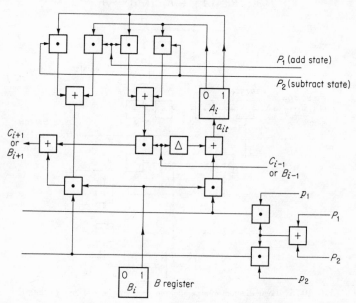

FIG. 10-26   Logic diagram of a parallel-binary-accumulator stage for both addition and subtraction.

row occurs in a parallel subtraction. In short, there is a problem of carry (or borrow) propagation which is due to the creation of one carry (or borrow) by another.

The use of a parallel adding circuit (instead of a serial one) attempts to reduce addition time. If the time of carry propagation is significant, the addition time of a parallel adding circuit is limited by the time for the carry propagation. Therefore, the propagation time in a parallel circuit must be reduced.

Nature of Carry or Borrow. Addition of two binary bits incurs four possibilities, $0 + 0$, $0 + 1$, $1 + 0$, and $1 + 1$; a carry is generated when both bits are 1. Once generated, the carry is propagated when it continuously encounters a stage which has at least one bit (either augend or addend) which is 1; the carry is not further propagated when both bits of a stage are 0. In the case of subtraction, a borrow is produced when a bit 1 is subtracted from a bit 0. The borrow when generated is propagated when both bits are 0 or 1 or when a bit 1 is subtracted from a bit 0 and is not propagated any further when a bit 0 is subtracted from a bit 1. The above nature of carry can be described by the carry function,

$$W_o = XY + X\overline{Y}W_i + \overline{X}YW_i \tag{10-31}$$

Term XY is regarded as the carry generation, while the other two terms are the carry propagation. Similarly, in the borrow function,

$$W_o = \overline{X}Y + \overline{X}\overline{Y}W_i + XYW_i \tag{10-32}$$

term $\overline{X}Y$ is regarded as the borrow generation, and the other two terms are the borrow propagation. It should be noticed that in the addition of 2 bits the carry generation and carry propagation can be regarded as not occurring simultaneously. This can be shown by

$$XY(X\overline{Y}W_i + \overline{X}YW_i) = 0 \tag{10-33}$$

Since both augend and addend (or minuend and subtrahend) are known prior to an addition (or a subtraction) in a parallel operation, this fact is most often utilized in reducing the propagation time. As the propagation of carry and that of borrow are similar, only the former will now be discussed.

Gated Carry. Propagation of a carry through adder stages one after another as in Fig. 10-3 or similarly through flipflop stages as in Fig. 10-23 is slow and thus undesirable. One widely used method, called *gated carry*, propagates the carry without passing through the adder or flipflop stages in succession, i.e., propagates the carry through a series of gates. One logic diagram utilizing this method is shown in Fig. 10-27; the uppermost solid line in this figure, passing through a series of *and* gates and *or* gates, is the carry propagation line. The *and* gates on this line propagate the carry, while the *and* gates connecting the 0 outputs of the flipflops to the carry line are for inserting generated carries.

In operation, the add control pulse p_1 is applied in the presence of P_1, the addition state signal. This results in the addition of 2 corresponding bits and the insertion of the generated carries to the carry line along which the carries are propagating. Then the carry control pulse p_2 is applied, causing the carry to enter each stage so that the sum in the accumulator becomes correct. Maximum propagation time for n stages approaches the sum of the time spent during passage through each *and*-gate–*or*-gate pair. The gated carry configuration requires a relatively small number of components and gives a reasonably short propagation time.

Stored Carry. In the parallel binary accumulator of Fig. 10-27 the *and* gate for inserting the generated carry requires a signal from the addend during the carry propagation. If this is not available during the propagation, the above-mentioned *and* gate can be replaced by a flipflop for temporarily storing the carry. The carry still propagates along the carry line without passing through the stages in succession. This method is called *stored carry*, and the logic diagram is shown in Fig. 10-28. The carry flipflops should initially be reset to the 0 state.

Average-length Carry. The carry in the previous example of adding two numbers such as 1111 and 0001 is an extreme case. Burkes, Goldstine, and von

Neumann [1] have shown that in the parallel addition of two 40-bit binary numbers the average carry length is only 4.6 stages.

Gilchrist, Pomerene, and Wong [7] utilized this average property in designing a rapid parallel binary adder. The principle is shown in the logic diagram of Fig. 10-29. There are two carry lines, one for a carry of 1 and the other for a

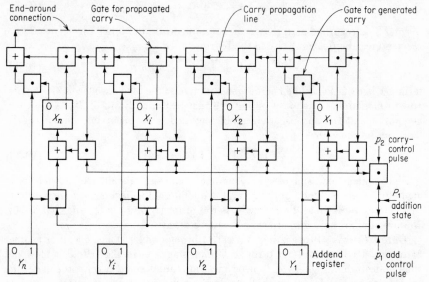

FIG. 10-27   Logic diagram of a parallel binary accumulator with gated carry.

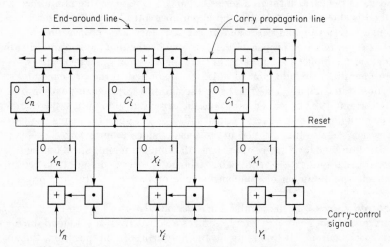

FIG. 10-28   Logic diagram of a parallel binary accumulator with stored carry.

carry of 0. The *and* gates along the upper carry line are for propagating carries of 1; the *or* gates along the same line are for inserting carries of 1. Similarly, the *and* gates along the lower carry line propagate carries of 0, and the *or* gates along the same line insert carries of 0. In each stage there will be only one signal, either in the upper or in the lower line, and its presence will be sensed by the *or* gates across these two lines. The carry-completion *and* gate will produce a signal when the carry or no-carry signal completes the propagation through each stage. Figure 10-30 is the logic diagram showing the detail of one stage. At the start of an addition, the two carry lines are disabled by using parallel inhibition on the lines

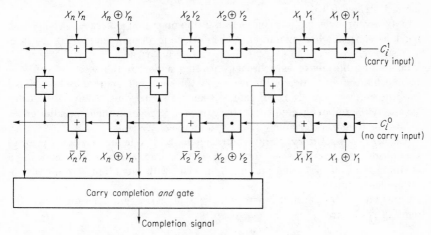

FIG. 10-29 Logic diagram showing the principle of average-sequence carry.

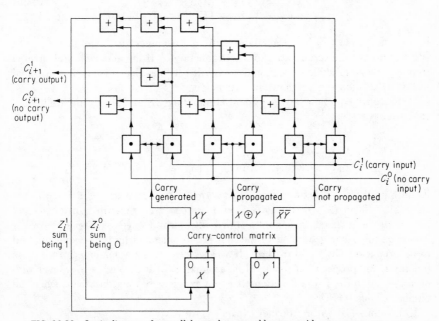

FIG. 10-30 Logic diagram of a parallel asynchronous adder stage with average-sequence carry.

or by operating on the serial gates. The carry propagation is started by enabling the carry lines (not shown in the figure) and enabling the zero carry input C_1^0 at the least significant bit. Carry and no-carry sequences then arise from the zero carry input C_1^0 and from the stages whose two bits are either both 0 or both 1.

By performing many additions of two 40-bit random numbers, it was found that the average maximum carry length is 5.6 stages; thus, the average carry propagation time is only about one-eighth of the maximum carry propagation time. The total computing time is the sum of the carry propagation time and the addition time. In the 40-bit parallel adder developed, computing time is 0.36 (the sum of 0.21 and 0.15) μsec.

In an asychronous circuit, completion of the operation generates a completion signal to start another operation. The foregoing design, employing average-carry sequence logic, is an asynchronous parallel binary adder.

In starting the above asynchronous parallel adder, if the zero carry $C_1{}^0$ is enabled but the *and* gates of the two carry lines are not, there may be a signal from the carry-completion *and* gate. If such a signal does occur, it indicates that the two numbers are equal. Thus, the above asynchronous parallel adder can also be used to determine whether two numbers are equal.

Simultaneous Carry.   Since both augend and addend are known prior to an addition in a parallel operation, a brute-force method uses logic circuits in obtaining the carry for each bit simultaneously with the adding circuits in obtaining the sum.

Consider a 3-bit parallel binary adder. The carry functions for the 3 bits, from Eq. 10-31, are

$$
\begin{aligned}
W_1 &= X_1 Y_1 \\
W_2 &= X_2 Y_2 + (X_2 \oplus Y_2) W_1 \\
W_3 &= X_3 Y_3 + (X_3 \oplus Y_3) W_2
\end{aligned}
\tag{10-34}
$$

In these functions W_3 is not available until W_2 becomes available, nor W_2 until W_1, because of the serial nature of these functions. If the adder is implemented from the above functions, the resulting circuit becomes that previously illustrated in Fig. 10-3; the carry propagation time is long.

If the above equations are rewritten, eliminating W_1 and W_2 on the right-hand side, we have

$$
\begin{aligned}
W_1 &= X_1 Y_1 \\
W_2 &= X_2 Y_2 + (X_2 \oplus Y_2) X_1 Y_1 \\
W_3 &= X_3 Y_3 + (X_3 \oplus Y_3) X_2 Y_2 + (X_3 \oplus Y_3)(X_2 \oplus Y_2) X_1 Y_1
\end{aligned}
\tag{10-35}
$$

Examining the W_3 function reveals that term $X_3 Y_3$ is the carry generated in the third bit. Term $(X_3 \oplus Y_3) X_2 Y_2$ would be the carry generated in the second bit, to be propagated through the third bit; term $(X_3 \oplus Y_3)(X_2 \oplus Y_2) X_1 Y_1$ would be the carry generated in the first bit, propagated by the second bit, and to be propagated by the third bit. If a carry circuit is implemented from these functions, the propagation time will be as small as that through a four-level *and-or-and-or* circuit. These functions become excessively long, however, when the number of bits increases.

If functions (10-35) are further expanded, we have

$$
\begin{aligned}
W_1 &= X_1 Y_1 \\
W_2 &= X_2 Y_2 + X_1 Y_1 X_2 \overline{Y}_2 + X_1 Y_1 \overline{X}_2 Y_2 \\
W_3 &= X_3 Y_3 + X_2 Y_2 X_3 \overline{Y}_3 + X_1 Y_1 X_2 \overline{Y}_2 X_3 \overline{Y}_3 + X_1 Y_1 \overline{X}_2 Y_2 X_3 \overline{Y}_3 \\
&\quad + X_2 Y_2 \overline{X}_3 Y_3 + X_1 Y_1 X_2 \overline{Y}_2 \overline{X}_3 Y_3 + X_1 Y_1 \overline{X}_2 Y_2 \overline{X}_3 Y_3
\end{aligned}
\tag{10-36}
$$

If a carry circuit is implemented from the above functions, it is called *simultaneous carry;* the propagation time will be as small as that through a two-level *and-or* circuit.   Unfortunately, these functions become much too long to be practical when the number of bits lies in the practical range of 20 to 60 bits.   The simultaneous carry can also be implemented in a parallel binary accumulator.

Some applications may warrant implementing the simultaneous carry only partially.   In this case the number of bits is divided into groups; simultaneous carry circuits are incorporated only within the group.   For example, for the addition

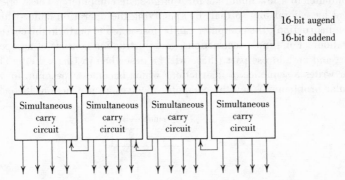

FIG. 10-31   A configuration showing simultaneous carry circuits.

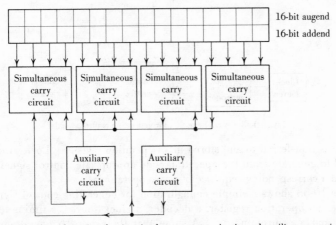

FIG. 10-32   A configuration showing simultaneous carry circuits and auxiliary carry circuits.

of two 16-bit numbers, four simultaneous carry circuits are provided as shown in Fig. 10-31.   This reduces the propagation time considerably; yet the required number of components may become reasonable.   Weinberger and Smith [8] have reported the use of simultaneous carry circuits and auxiliary carry circuits to reduce the carry propagation time of a parallel binary adder; the principle is shown in Fig. 10-32.   The auxiliary carry circuits essentially apply repeatedly the principle of simultaneous carry to the carries from the simultaneous carry circuits.   In the adder reported by Weinberger and Smith, two levels of auxiliary carry circuits are employed to accommodate 53 bits.

10-8   *Generation of Control Signals*

A digital computer operates in discrete steps, and a micro-operation is performed during each step. Examples of micro-operations are shift, count, transfer, add, clear, and complement. A sequence of micro-operations which is formed for a particular purpose is called an *operation*. A digital computer is designed to perform a number of operations ranging from several operations for a small computer to a few hundreds for a large-scale computer. These operations are coded by several bits so that, by specifying the operation code (which is a part of an instruction), the computer can be instructed to perform the corresponding operation. For simple instructions, each instruction consists of an operation-code part and an address part (these will be described in Chap. 11). The programmer writes a sequence of instructions which becomes a program for solving a particular problem. When the computer receives an instruction, its operation-

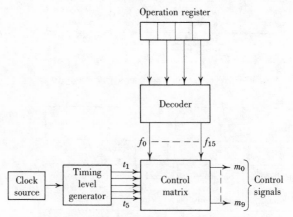

FIG. 10-33   A configuration for generating control signals.

code part is transferred to and stored in an operation register. Logic circuits are required to generate from the operation code appropriate control signals which command a corresponding sequence of micro-operations.

Figure 10-33 shows a simple configuration for generating control signals. It comprises an operation register, a decoder, a clock source, a timing-level distributor, and a control matrix. Assume that there are 16 operations in the computer and that these operations, designated as f_i, where i is 0 to 15, are coded by a 4-bit operation code. Assume that there are 10 micro-operations (from which 16 sequences of micro-operations are formed for the 16 operations) and that the control signals for these micro-operations are designated as m_j, where j is 0 to 9. The purpose is, for each operation code in the operation register, to generate a corresponding sequence of micro-operation control signals.

When the operation-code part of an instruction is stored in the operation register, the decoder having 16 output lines (one for each of the 16 operation codes) actuates 1 and only 1 output line. In the meantime, timing levels are generated from a clock source by the timing-level generator. Assume that there are 5 output lines from the timing-level generator and that the levels on these lines, designated as t_k, where k is 1 to 5, are shown in Fig. 10-34; these levels form a time sequence which is called a *basic timing cycle*. The number of levels in a basic cycle is usually chosen to execute one instruction (i.e., to control one sequence of micro-operations). For certain instructions such as multiplication and division, however, more than one basic cycle is employed, and an additional counter (not shown in Fig. 10-33) is provided to count the required number of cycles.

The inputs to the control matrix are the 16 output lines f_i from the decoder and the 5 output lines t_k from the timing-level generator. The matrix has 10 output lines, and the level on each of these lines controls a specific micro-operation; these levels are represented by the previously shown letters m_j. Each micro-operation is actuated by the combination of a control signal and a clock pulse. The function performed by the control matrix is shown, as an example, by the following set of logic equations,

$$m_0 = (f_3t_1 + f_7t_3 + f_9t_4)p$$
$$m_1 = (f_8t_1 + f_4t_2 + f_6t_3 + f_{12}t_5)p$$
$$\dotfill$$
$$m_9 = (f_{11}t_2 + f_7t_3 + f_{15}t_5)p$$

(10-37)

where p represents the clock pulse. The first equation means that micro-opera-

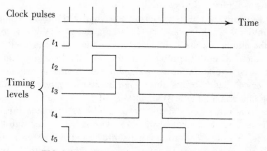

FIG. 10-34   Clock pulses and timing levels.

tion m_0 is controlled by operation code f_3 at timing level t_1, or by operation code f_7 at timing level t_3, or by operation code f_9 at timing level t_4; the micro-operation takes place at the occurrence of clock pulse p. Similarly, other micro-operations are controlled by other combinations of operation codes and timing levels. For the above set of logic equations, it is apparent that the control matrix is essentially an *and-or* switching matrix.

For a large-scale computer, the basic cycle may consist of several phases or several minor cycles to accommodate a large number of operations. Another simple configuration for generating control signals is described in Chap. 11.

Problems

1. A single-digit adder for adding three binary digits simultaneously has 3 input bits, 2 input carry bits, 1 output sum bit, and 2 output carry bits. Find the Boolean functions for the adder, and draw the logic diagram.

2. Draw the logic diagram of a parallel binary adder for adding three 4-bit numbers by using the adder to Prob. 1 and the gated-through carry propagation.

3. Prepare a truth table for the inputs to flipflops B_n and A_n of the shift register of Fig. 10-11. Write equations for inputs b_{nr}, b_{ns}, a_{nr}, and a_{ns}, and draw the logic diagram.

4. Design a three-state reverse binary counter using trigger flipflops. Prepare a truth table for the inputs to the three flipflops, obtain the input equations, and draw the logic diagram.

5. Design a three-stage reversible binary counter using RS flipflops. Prepare a truth table for inputs to the three flipflops, write the input equations, and draw the logic diagram.

6. From the input equations of Probs. 4 and 5, obtain their respective state equations, and draw their state diagrams.

7. Design an excess-3-coded decimal-digit counter using trigger flipflops. Both the input equations and the logic diagram are required.

8. Two 4-bit registers A and B are given. A binary number is initially stored in register A and 0's in register B. The number in register A is transferred in parallel to register B. During the transfer:

(a) The number is arranged into a reverse order.

(b) The number is translated into an excess-3-coded decimal digit.

Give the symbolic statements for the transfer, the input equations, and the logic diagram.

9. Two 4-bit binary numbers are stored in registers A and B. The number in register A is transferred to register B; at the same time the number in register B is transferred to register A. Obtain the symbolic statements and input equations, and draw the logic diagrams for the following two cases:

(a) The transfer is performed serially.

(b) The transfer is performed in parallel.

10. A binary sequence of pulses (a pulse and no-pulse represent, respectively, 1 and 0) is being shifted into a 4-bit shift register. It is required to establish a configuration determining whether the number in the shift register is odd or even after each pulse is shifted in. Use the symbolic method. Both the input equations and the logic diagram are required.

11. Formulate a configuration for a serial subtractor similar to that shown in Fig. 10-21. The binary number consists of 5 bits plus a sign bit and is represented in the signed-magnitude form, the sign bit leading the least significant bit.

12. Four-bit numbers are being shifted in parallel into a register during each successive clock pulse. It is desired to determine whether the number shifted into the register during the clock pulse p_i is larger or smaller than that shifted into the register during the clock pulse p_{i+1}. Formulate a configuration. Use the symbolic method. Both the input equations and the logic diagram are required.

13. Find the Boolean functions for the simultaneous carry when two 4-bit numbers are added. Draw the logic diagram.

14. Draw the logic diagram of a parallel decimal adder for four decimal digits, using the gated carry propagation. Assume that the decimal digit is in (a) 8-4-2-1 code, (b) excess-3 code, and (c) 2-4-2-1 code.

15. Find the input equations for the flipflops in a serial decimal adder when the decimal digit is in (a) excess-3 code and (b) 8-4-2-1 code.

16. Given the single-error-correcting code described in Chap. 2, establish a configuration for automatic correcting of a single error, and find the Boolean equations.

References

1. Burks, A. W., H. H. Goldstine, and J. von Neumann: Preliminary Discussion of the Logical Design of an Electronic Computing Instrument, *Inst. Advanced Study*, vol. 1, pt. 1, June 28, 1946.

2. Nelson, E. C.: Algebraic Theory for Use in Digital Computer Design, *IRE Trans. on Electronic Computers*, November, 1952, pp. 12–21.

3. Reed, I. S.: Symbolic Synthesis of Digital Computers, *Proc. ACM*, Sept. 8–10, 1952, Toronto.

4. Reed, I. S.: Symbolic Design of Digital Computers, *MIT Lincoln Lab. Tech. Mem.* 23, January, 1953.

5. Brown, R. M.: Some Notes on Logical Binary Counters, *IRE Trans. on Electronic Computers*, June, 1955, pp. 67–69.

6. Richards, R. K.: "Arithmetic Operations in Digital Computers," D. Van Nostrand Company, Inc., Princeton, N. J., 1955.

7. Gilchrist, B., J. H. Promerente, and S. Y. Wong: Fast Carry Logic for Digital Computers, *IRE Trans. on Electronic Computers*, December, 1955, pp. 133–136.

8. Weinberger, A., and J. L. Smith: A One-microsecond Adder Using One-megacycle Circuitry, *IRE Trans. on Electronic Computers*, June, 1956, pp. 65–73.

9. Golay, M. J. E.: The Logic of Bidirectional Binary Counters, *IRE Trans. on Electronic Computers*, March, 1957, pp. 1–4.

10. Arant, G. W.: A Time-sequential Tabular Analysis of Flipflop Logical Operation, *IRE Trans. on Electronic Computers*, June, 1957, pp. 72–74.

11. Phister, M., Jr.: "Logical Design of Digital Computers," John Wiley & Sons, Inc., New York, 1958.

12. Dinneen, G. P., I. S. Reed, and I. L. Below: The Logical Design of CG 24, *Proc. Eastern Joint Computer Conf.*, 1958, pp. 91–94.

13. Hesse, V. L.: The Advantages of Logical Equation Techniques in Design Digital Computers, *Proc. Western Joint Computer Conf.*, May, 1958, pp. 186–188.

14. Smith, C. V. L.: "Electronic Digital Computers," McGraw-Hill Book Company, Inc., New York, 1959.

11

Logic Design of a Simple Digital Computer

Previous chapters have described logic circuits for information switching and storing, as well as the algebraic method for describing the behavior of these circuits. We now present the logic design of a simple digital computer. The computer on which the discussion is based was devised by Jeffrey and Reed [4].

11-1 Computer Design

A digital computer operates with information, numerical or otherwise, represented in digital form. From a logic designer's viewpoint, a digital computer can be ideally described as an aggregate of two-valued memory devices (such as flipflops) functionally connected by logic networks. The states of these memory devices undergo discrete changes at certain instants of time. Their initial states are set up by programming. The *programming* of a problem for a digital computer is the preparation of a sequence of instructions by which the given problem is solved by the computer. To achieve this task, the programming includes problem analysis, preparation of a flow chart, and coding of instructions.

The design of a digital computer may be divided into three phases: system design, logic design, and circuit design. In the first phase requirements of the given problem are interpreted and computer specifications formulated with due consideration to cost, size, reliability, maintainability, operating environment, and other factors. This task includes the establishment of design objectives, design philosophy, required operations (arithmetic, logic, and others), speed of operation, error-checking provisions, and special features (such as index registers, program interrupt, and others) for more efficient use of the machine. It may include selection of the type of logic circuits, the type of memory and its capacity, and the kind and quantity of input-output devices. The second phase establishes word format, computer configuration, and machine instructions; the phase ends with a set of logic equations or a set of detailed logic diagrams. The third phase carries out the actual design of logic circuits, memory, and input-output devices. Because these three phases interrelate, they are considered concurrently.

Logic design of a digital computer may again be divided into three phases: functional design, symbolic design, and detail design. In phase 1, word format is first established. Registers, counters, matrices, adders, and other elements are selected; they are organized with the chosen memory and input-output devices to carry out a particular set of machine instructions. In the second phase the program control sequence is established and the machine instructions are expressed into symbolic statements. A detailed study of the sequential operations of the machine instructions is advisable during this phase to ascertain the symbolic design. In the third phase a set of logic equations or a set of logic diagrams which prescribes the detailed operations of the computer is worked out. In our logic design of a simple digital computer, logic equations will be worked out completely; logic diagrams will be shown in sufficient detail so that the complete diagram can be worked out by the reader.

11-2   System Design

The computer to be designed in this chapter will illustrate in detail the logic design of a general-purpose stored-program digital computer. To implement this, a reasonable first step is to outline the machine specifications.

For the present purpose the digital computer should be simple enough so that it can be described within the bounds of a chapter. But it should not be trivial: the configuration should be sufficiently complicated to illustrate the salient features. It should be a stored-program computer, capable of performing several simple operations. The operations should include addition, subtraction, shifting of a number 1 bit to the right and to the left, and unconditional and conditional transfers. The computer should be synchronous, binary, and parallel; this gives simplicity in subsequent descriptions.

As a further specification, crystal diodes are to be used for switching circuits and transistors for storing circuits. The transistor flipflops are of a single-input type and can be loaded with multiple-level diode logic circuits; they also have sufficient delay so that no additional delay is needed. The memory shall constitute an array of 64 by 9 transistor flipflops.

For convenience, other items, which are summarized in Table 11-16, will be specified during the functional-design phase.

11-3   Functional-design Phase

The first phase of logic design is functional design. In this phase the word format is first selected. The computer configuration is formulated by choosing the registers, matrices, memory, and input-output devices. Machine instructions are established. Sequential operation of the computer will be briefly described.

Word Format. A *word* (or a machine word) in a computer is an ordered set of digits which is processed as a unit in the computer. Word format is the word structure when the word is used as a number or as an instruction.

For convenience in designing our hypothetical computer, word length should be short and fixed. As will be seen, the short word length allows only a small number of machine instructions and a small number of memory addresses. Word length is chosen to be 9 bits. Let word X be represented as

$$X = x_0 x_1 x_2 x_3 x_4 x_5 x_6 x_7 x_8$$

where x_0, x_1, etc., are the 9 bits of the word.

A word is treated by the arithmetic unit as a number; in this case the word format is called the *number format*. The number is specified to be binary and fractional with negative numbers in 2's-complement representation. The binary point lies between bits x_0 and x_1, x_0 being the sign bit. This representation of signed binary numbers has been given in Chap. 1.

Since the actual value of the above signed binary number lies in the range $-1 \leq X < 1$, such a computer is called a *binary fractional computer*. This does not really restrict the computation, because a number outside this range can be represented in the computer by multiplying it by 2^n, with an appropriate value of n. The multiplication of 2^n is merely a shifting operation. Since the binary point is fixed, the computer is a *fixed-point computer*. This is different from a *floating-point computer*, which is capable of performing floating-point arithmetic.

The program control unit treats a word as an instruction. The *instruction format* consists of two parts (or two fields), the operation-code part and the address part. The instruction format of the simple computer is

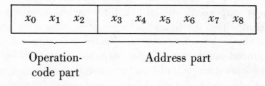

x_0 $\quad$ x_1 $\quad$ x_2	x_3 $\quad$ x_4 $\quad$ x_5 $\quad$ x_6 $\quad$ x_7 $\quad$ x_8
Operation- code part	Address part

Having only one address, this format is known as a *single-address format*. The 3-bit operation-code part is the binary code of a machine operation; for example, it designates an information transfer, an arithmetic operation, or a logic operation. The 6-bit address part is the address number to locate a word in the memory; this memory word is called an *operand*. The foregoing instruction format indicates that an operation (specified by the operation-code part) is to be performed to the operand located in the memory specified by the address part. The 6-bit address allows 64 addresses, or 64 memory words. Some instructions do not involve an operand; in this case, the corresponding address part may also be used as the operation-code part if needed. Thus, for a 3-bit operation code, more than eight instructions are possible, as will be shown subsequently.

Computer Configuration. The configuration of the computer is shown in Fig. 11-1. To be a stored-program computer, the computer must store both numbers and instructions. This introduces the *memory unit* (designated as M registers); its capacity has been specified to be 64 words of 9 bits each. As shown in Fig. 11-2, these flipflops are denoted M_{ji}, where j is the jth word and i is the ith bit. Each word location in the memory is assigned an address; the selection of the address is performed by *memory-address register C*. Register C consists of six flipflops, whose notation is also shown in Fig. 11-2. An address decoder is connected between register C and the memory. Because the computer is to perform arithmetic operations, that function introduces an *arithmetic unit*. This simple computer limits arithmetic operations to addition and subtraction. An accumulator (designated as register A) is sufficient for this purpose. Register A consists of 9 bits so as to store a whole word; the notation for the nine flipflops is shown in Fig. 11-2. When an instruction is taken out of the memory, it is temporarily stored in a register for subsequent execution. This register is commonly called the *instruction register* (designated as register R). Since register R has to store a whole word, it consists of 9 bits. As shown in Fig. 11-2, the 3 bits R_0 to R_2 store the operation-code part; and the 6 bits R_3 to R_8 store the address part of the instruction word.

The need of sequential control introduces the *program control unit*. Our simple computer employs an *operation counter* (designated as register F), which consists of 4 bits, as shown in Fig. 11-2. The 3 bits F_2 to F_4 are the instruction part. The operation counter counts the clock pulses and provides control signals by using an operation decoder. A *clock-pulse generator* creates a string of timing (clock) pulses separated by time intervals τ. The clock pulse triggers the flipflops and synchronizes operation of the computer. Another clock-pulse generator (not shown in Fig. 11-1) may be provided to generate a single clock pulse. This generator is under the control of the operator; in this way, the

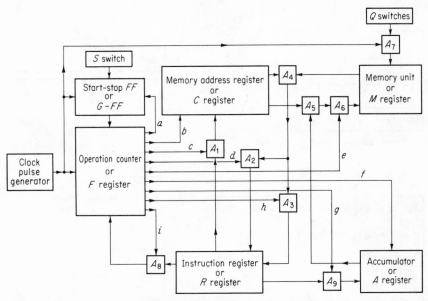

FIG. 11-1   Configuration of a simple digital computer.

operation of the computer can be observed, step by step, for testing purposes. Also as a part of the control, a flipflop G provides start or stop operation of the computer. The triggering of the start-stop flipflop G is accessible externally to the computer by *switch S*. Simple *switches Q* as input devices insert the instruction and data into the memory, and the simple *neon lights* (not shown in Fig. 11-1) are chosen as the output device to present the result. Both switches Q and the neon lights are connected to each bit of the memory. The neon lights are also connected to each bit of the registers as a means of observing the operation of the computer during testing. Switches S and Q normally remain in the neutral position, making only momentary-on or momentary-off contact.

Machine Instructions.   We shall now formulate a set of instructions that the machine should be capable of performing.   The formulated set of instructions should be sufficiently adequate (and sufficiently versatile, for a more sophisticated computer) so that, for a given problem to be solved by the computer, a list of instructions can be prepared from the formulated set, this list together with any pertinent data furnishing a program for the given problem. This list of instructions

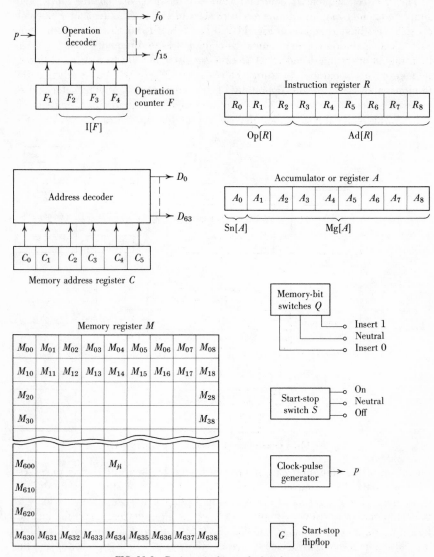

FIG. 11-2   Registers in the simple digital computer.

is coded before being fed into the computer so that the instructions become intelligible to it.

As specified in the system-design phase, the machine should be capable of performing the arithmetic operations of addition and subtraction, the two 1-bit shift operations, and the two transfer-of-control operations. The details of these six instructions are given in Table 11-1; the registers therein are those of Fig. 11-2. The unconditional- and the conditional-transfer instructions are commonly referred to as the *jump* and the *jump-on-sign* instruction, respectively. To perform these six instructions, three additional instructions are necessary: the store instruction, which stores a number from the accumulator into the memory, the clearing-accumulator instruction, and the stop instruction. Since the machine is not to perform any operation in connection with the input and output devices, no instruction for such operations is provided. The machine instructions total nine.

The code numbers for the nine instructions are assigned and shown in Table 11-1. The quantity *uvwxyz* indicates any one of the 64 possible address numbers. Furthermore, the operations of the last four instructions do not involve any memory reference (i.e., no operand is needed); this means that the address part of the code number would have no meaning. On the other hand, there are nine instructions, which is more than the 3-bit operation code can distinguish. Therefore, the last four instructions employ a portion of the address code as a part of the operation code. In doing so, more code numbers become available than are actually needed. The final choices are those in Table 11-1.

Sequential Operation of the Computer. Sequential operation of the computer in carrying out machine instructions will now be briefly described. With reference to the configuration in Fig. 11-1, the coded instructions which form a program are first inserted into the memory by switches Q through gate A_7. The operator then turns switch S momentarily on, and the machine starts to function.

Table 11-1   Machine Instructions

Code	Instruction	Description of instruction
000*uvwxyz*	Addition	Take number from memory at address *uvwxyz*, and put it in R register; add contents of R register to contents of A register, and leave result in A register
001*uvwxyz*	Subtraction	Take number from memory at address *uvwxyz*, and put it in R register; subtract contents of R register from contents of A register, and leave result in A register
010*uvwxyz*	Conditional transfer (jump-on-sign)	If $A_0 = 1$† (sign of A is negative), take next instruction from memory at address *uvwxyz*; if $A_0 = 0$ (sign of A is positive), take next instruction in sequence
011*uvwxyz*	Store	Store contents in A register into memory located at address *uvwxyz*
100*uvwxyz*	Unconditional transfer (jump)	Take next instruction from memory located at address *uvwxyz*
1011000*yz*	Shift right	Shift contents of A register 1 bit to right
1010100*yz*	Shift left	Shift contents of A register 1 bit to left
1010010*yz*	Clear accumulator	Clear A register by substituting zeros into A register
1010001*yz*	Stop	Stop machine‡ and return address in C register to its first address 000000

† The leftmost bit of the A register.

‡ Machine is stopped at the end of an execution cycle, as will be shown.

The states of all registers are changed under the command of control signals from the operation counter. These changes occur at the instant when clock pulses occur. When the machine first begins to operate, the contents of register C is 000000; therefore, the first memory word is the first instruction. Control signal h transfers this instruction from memory unit to register R via gates A_3 and A_4. The operation-code part of the instruction now at register R is next transferred to register F via gate A_8 under control signal i, while control signal c transfers the address part via gate A_1 to register C. The operation code in register F is now decoded and new commands generated for executing the instruction. For arithmetic operations, control signal d transfers through gates A_2 and A_4 a number from the memory to register R, and control signal g actuates gate A_9 for a specified arithmetic operation to be performed on the number in register R and the number initially in register A. For shift and clear-accumulator operations, control signal f is sent to the accumulator. The transfer-of-control operations are carried out under control signal b or h. Control signal e actuates gate A_6 to store the number in the accumulator into the memory at the address in register C through gate A_5. The last instruction of the program in the memory is usually the stop instruction. The operation counter sends control signal a to flipflop G, and the machine stops.

11-4   *Symbolic-design Phase*

In this phase the program control sequence is established, and machine operations are expressed in symbolic statements. Symbolic design results in the state-

Table 11-2   *Symbols for Symbolic Design of Computer*

Symbol	Description of symbol
( )	Parentheses denote contents of a register. Thus (R) means contents of R register; (R_i) means contents of ith bit of register
[ ]	Square brackets denote a portion of a register, the contents of which has a functional dependence on a register. Thus I $[F]$ means instruction part of F register. Op $[R]$ means operation part of R register. Ad $[R]$ means address part of R register. Sn $[A]$ and Mg $[A]$ mean sign and magnitude parts of A register (see Fig. 11-2)
$M<C>$	This symbol denotes location of a memory word addressed by C register
$(M<C>)$	This symbol denotes contents of a memory word location addressed by C register
$\Rightarrow$	Double-line arrow denotes transfer of a word from one register to another. Thus $(A) \Rightarrow R$ means that contents of A register is transfered to R register. $(A) \Rightarrow M<C>$ means contents of A register is transferred to memory location addressed by C register. $(A_{i-1}) \Rightarrow A_i$ means that value of $(i-1)$st bit of A register is transferred to its ith bit. $0 \Rightarrow C$ means that zeros are transferred to C register
$+$	This symbol has two meanings: (1) It means a logical-*or* operation when used among Boolean variables. (2) It means an arithmetic addition when used between pairs of parentheses in this chapter. Thus, $(A) + (R)$ means the arithmetic sum of contents of A register and R register
$-$	This symbol denotes an arithmetic subtraction. Thus, $(A) - (R)$ means the arithmetic difference between contents of A register and R register
:	Colon following a variable (representing the state or the command) denotes the occurrence of the subsequent statement (or statements) when the value of the variable is 1. Thus, $f_{15}: 0 \Rightarrow C$ means that, when value of f_{15} is 1, zeros go to C register
$\rightarrow$	Arrow denotes a sequence of operations from one state to another. Thus, $f_4 \rightarrow f_{10}$ means that state f_{10} follows state f_4

operation diagram of Fig. 11-6, which shows the states and operations of the computer.

Symbolic Statements of Machine Instructions. The symbolic method, as described in Chap. 10, expresses the process of information transfer precisely by symbolic statements. The symbols in Table 10-8 are augmented and listed in Table 11-2. This table introduces the double caret $<\ >$, denoting the address of a memory word. The reader is advised to become familiar with these symbols before reading further. The examples in the table cover most types of symbolic statements that will be encountered in this chapter.

The description of instructions in Table 11-1 is now expressed in terms of the symbols in Table 11-2. The resulting symbolic statements (or symbolic operations) are shown in Table 11-3; their explanation follows.

The addition instruction in Table 11-1 is carried out in two operations. The first operation is "Take number from memory at address *uvwxyz*, and put it in R register," or symbolically

$$(M<C>) \Rightarrow R$$

where C refers to memory address *uvwxyz*. The second operation is "Add contents of R register to contents of A register, and leave result in A register," or symbolically

$$(R) + (A) \Rightarrow A$$

These two symbolic statements of the addition instruction are shown in Table 11-3. Two similar symbolic statements for the subtraction instruction are also shown in the table. The store instruction is "Store contents of A register into memory located at address *uvwxyz*," or

$$(A) \Rightarrow M<C>$$

Table 11-3　Symbolic Statements of Instructions

Instruction	Required operations	Auxiliary operations
Addition (000*uvwxyz*)............	$(M<C>) \Rightarrow R$ $(R) + (A) \Rightarrow A$	$(Ad\,[R]) \Rightarrow C$ $(C) + 1 \Rightarrow C$
Subtraction (001*uvwxyz*).........	$(M<C>) \Rightarrow R$ $(A) - (R) \Rightarrow A$	Same as above
Conditional transfer (010*uvwxyz*)....	None None	Same as above if $A_0 = 0$ None if $A_0 = 1$
Store (011*uvwxyz*)...............	$(A) \Rightarrow M<C>$	$(Ad\,[R]) \Rightarrow C$ $(C) + 1 \Rightarrow C$
Unconditional transfer (100*uvwxyz*)..	None	None
Shift right (1011000*yz*)...........	$(A_{i-1}) \Rightarrow A_i \quad i = 1, \ldots, 8$ $(A_0) \Rightarrow A_0$	$(Ad\,[R]) \Rightarrow C$ $(C) + 1 \Rightarrow C$
Shift left (1010100*yz*)...........	$(A_{i+1}) \Rightarrow A_i \quad i = 0, \ldots, 7$ $(A_0) \Rightarrow A_8$	Same as above
Clear accumulator (1010010*yz*).....	$0 \Rightarrow A$	Same as above
Stop (1010001*yz*)...............	$0 \Rightarrow G; \quad 0 \Rightarrow C; \quad 1 \Rightarrow F$	None
Start command (manual)	$1 \Rightarrow G$	None
Insert-word command (manual)......	$(Q_{ji}) \Rightarrow M_{ji}$	None

where C again refers to memory address $uvwxyz$. The shift-right instruction is "Shift contents of A register 1 bit to right," or symbolically

$$(A_{i-1}) \Rightarrow A_i \qquad \text{where } i = 1, \ldots, 8$$
and
$$(A_0) \quad \Rightarrow A_0$$

The second of the above symbolic statements follows the shift algorithm (Chap. 1) and requires the leftmost bit of the A register to retain its original value. The shift-left instruction is "Shift contents of A register 1 bit to left," or symbolically

$$(A_{i+1}) \Rightarrow A_i \qquad \text{where } i = 0, \ldots, 7$$
and
$$(A_0) \quad \Rightarrow A_8$$

This shift-left operation moves the leftmost bit of A register in an end-around manner to become the rightmost bit, thus making a circulating register of register A. The clear-accumulator instruction is "Clear A register by substituting zeros into A register," or symbolically

$$0 \Rightarrow A$$

The stop instruction is "Stop machine, and return address in C register to its first address 000000," or symbolically

$$0 \Rightarrow G \qquad \text{and} \qquad 0 \Rightarrow C$$

The operations to start the computation and to insert the words (coded instructions and data) into the memory are not listed in Table 11-1, as they are manual operations. Symbolically, they are

$$1 \Rightarrow G \qquad \text{and} \qquad (Q_{ji}) \Rightarrow M_{ji}$$

The first statement means to turn on the G flipflop, while the second one means to insert the contents of switch Q_{ji} into the memory bit M_{ji}. The statements for the two transfer instructions, for the operation $(1 \Rightarrow \text{F})$, and for the auxiliary operations (in Table 11-3) will be explained shortly.

Instruction and Execution Cycles. Both the instructions and the data which form a program for the purpose of solving a given problem are initially stored in the memory. The programmer writes these instructions into a sequence according to the order of memory addresses at which these instructions are stored. In this simple computer the first instruction of the program is designed to be located at address 000000.

The digital computer is to execute the sequence of instructions in the program stored in the memory. The computer operates on an internal sequence, executing each instruction (which can be any one of the nine instructions in Table 11-1) as called for, one after another, from the program. The operations to execute the nine instructions (and two manual commands) shown in Table 11-3 are augmented by operations in the last column in Table 11-3 to form an internal sequence. The internal sequence alternates between an instruction cycle and an execution cycle. During the instruction cycle the proper instruction is taken from the memory, and the computer is set ready for the subsequent execution. The execution cycle carries out the instruction and readies the computer for the next instruction cycle. The operations for both instruction and execution cycles are shown in Fig. 11-3. Note the alternate nature of these two cycles in the figure.

There are four operations during the instruction cycle, as shown in Fig. 11-4a by the four symbolic statements. The first is the *fetch-instruction operation:* a word is taken from the memory as located in memory-address register C (000000 for the first instruction) and transferred to register R; or symbolically

$$(M<C>) \Rightarrow R$$

The memory address during the fetch-instruction operation is an *instruction address.* The second and third operations (which occur simultaneously) are transfer operations which transfer the operation-code part of register R, Op $[R]$, to the instruction part of register F, I $[F]$, and the address part of register R, Ad $[R]$, to register C; or symbolically

$$\text{Op } [R] \Rightarrow \text{I } [F]$$
$$\text{Ad } [R] \Rightarrow C$$

The address part in register R at this time is an *operand address,* which is not

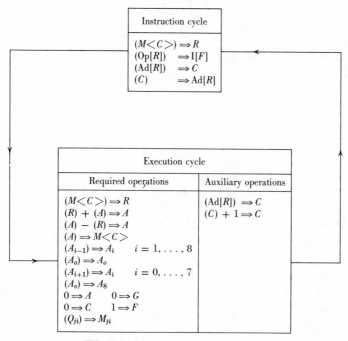

FIG. 11-3   Instruction and execution cycles.

the above-mentioned instruction address. After the transfers the operation-code part causes the operation decoder to generate command signals, initiating operations to carry out the instruction; and the operand address is now in register C. Normally, this completes the instruction cycle. In this simple computer, however, a fourth operation transfers the instruction address in register C to the address part of register R,

$$(C) \Rightarrow \text{Ad } [R]$$

The reason for requiring this operation is that, when the address part of register R (operand address) is transferred to register C, the instruction address in register C (000000 for the first instruction) would be lost. This present instruction address has to be stored somewhere because the next instruction address is obtained by adding 1 to the present instruction address. Since the address part

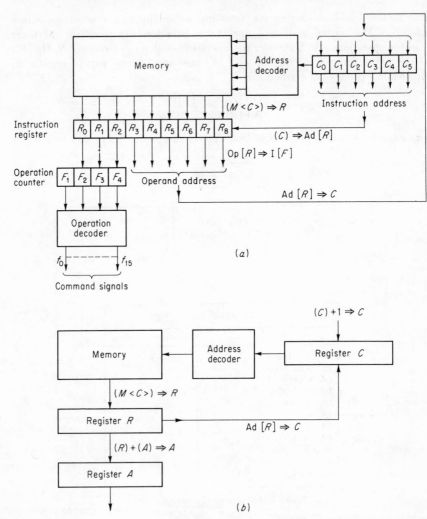

FIG. 11-4. Operations during instruction and execution cycles. (*a*) Four operations during instruction cycle; (*b*) four operations during execution cycle for an addition instruction.

of register R has been transferred to register C and thus has no further use at this time, the present instruction address is transferred to the address part of register R for temporary storage. In other words, the present instruction address in register C is transferred to the address part of register R; at the same time, the operand address at the address part of register R is transferred to register C. These two simultaneous transfers are possible because of our earlier assumption: that the transistor flipflops have sufficient delay to permit our doing so.

In an ordinary stored-program digital computer a separate instruction counter stores the present instruction address, and an add-1 operation after each instruction obtains the next instruction address. This case does not need the transfer of the present instruction address in register C to the address part of register R. In this simple computer, this counter is saved.

The operations during the instruction cycle are the same, but those during the execution cycle depend on the operation code of the instruction. As an illustration, consider the execution cycle of an addition instruction. There are four operations, as shown in Fig. 11-4b by the four symbolic statements. The execution cycle for an addition instruction begins by taking the operand word from the memory as located by the operand address in register C. The operand word is transferred to instruction register R, which is utilized at this moment as a temporary storage, or symbolically

$$(M{<}C{>}) \Rightarrow R$$

During the above *fetch-operand operation* the present instruction address in the address part of register R is transferred back to register C,

$$\text{Ad } [R] \Rightarrow C$$

This latter is the *address-return operation*, as the present instruction address is returned to the memory-address register. The operand now in register R is actuated by the command signal from the operation decoder and added to the contents in register A (which is an accumulator); symbolically

$$(R) + (A) \Rightarrow A$$

The last, an *add*-1 *operation*, increases by 1 the contents of register C (now holding the present instruction address), which now becomes the address for the next instruction; symbolically

$$(C) + 1 \Rightarrow C$$

This completes the execution cycle. The next instruction is ready to be taken out of the memory by the fetch-instruction operation of the succeeding instruction cycle, as the next instruction address is now in register C.

In case of an unconditional-transfer instruction the return-address operation is not required, because the operand address in register C is the next instruction address. In case of a conditional-transfer instruction, the sequence proceeds as for unconditional transfer if the condition is fulfilled ($A_0 = 1$); if the condition is not fulfilled ($A_0 = 0$), the address-return operation is performed so that the normal sequence can take place. The internal sequence for other instructions will be shown later more precisely by a state-operation diagram.

Thus, the auxiliary operations listed in Table 11-3 have all been explained except the *insert*-1 *operation* ($1 \Rightarrow F$), which will be described later.

State Diagram. The program control unit of the simple computer consists of the operation counter and its associated decoder, as shown in Fig. 11-2. The states of the counter represent the states of the computer; thus, the sequence of the states of the counter controls the sequential operation of the computer. Our aim is to design the counter so that the counter will produce a multiple-path sequence for commanding the operations shown in Fig. 11-3. The state diagram of the operation counter to be designed is given in Fig. 11-5.

Since there are 9 instructions, at least 9 states are required; this calls for a minimum of four flipflops F_1 to F_4, as shown in Fig. 11-2. Flipflops F_2 to F_4 are designated as the instruction part of register F (or I [F]); they are to store the 3-bit operation-code part of instruction register R. For a four-stage counter there are 16 possible states; these states are denoted by f_i in Table 11-4 (the subscript i represents the corresponding binary number of the 4 bits). Each state

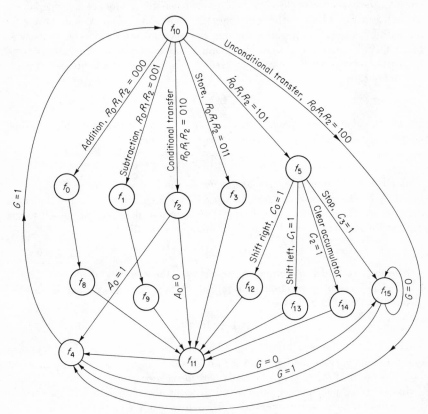

FIG. 11-5 State diagram of the simple digital computer.

represents 1 command signal; the designation of these 16 command signals is also given in Table 11-4. Only 14 states are needed, states f_6 and f_7 not being used. The 14 states are drawn into a state diagram shown in Fig. 11-5. States f_4 and f_{10} are those for the instruction cycle; the remaining states are those for the execution cycle. Since there are 9 instructions, there are 9 possible paths from states f_{10} to f_4; during each execution cycle, the counter sequence takes one of these 9 paths. When the computer is executing a program, it is merely cycling various paths of the state diagram according to the programmed instructions.

The above designation of the 14 command signals from the 16 possible states

Table 11-4   States of Operation Counter

Operation counter				State	Command signal
F_1	F_2	F_3	F_4		
0	0	0	0	f_0	Addition command
0	0	0	1	f_1	Subtraction command
0	0	1	0	f_2	Conditional-transfer command
0	0	1	1	f_3	Store command
0	1	0	0	f_4	Instruction-cycle command†
0	1	0	1	f_5	Command for $f_{12}, f_{13}, f_{14}, f_{15}$
0	1	1	0	f_6	Not used
0	1	1	1	f_7	Not used
1	0	0	0	f_8	Addition-operation command
1	0	0	1	f_9	Subtraction-operation command
1	0	1	0	f_{10}	Instruction-cycle command
1	0	1	1	f_{11}	Add-1-operation command
1	1	0	0	f_{12}	Shift-right command
1	1	0	1	f_{13}	Shift-left command
1	1	1	0	f_{14}	Clear-accumulator command
1	1	1	1	f_{15}	Stop command

† Also unconditional-transfer command.

of the counter is not entirely arbitrary. Advantages of certain logic simplicity are taken. For instance, states f_0, f_1, f_2, f_3, f_4, and f_5 are designated for the instruction commands, and states f_6 and f_7 are discarded. This choice gives the value of F_1 bit equal to 0 for all instruction commands and a simpler counter logic. It should be mentioned that a minimum number of states does not necessarily mean an over-all minimization of circuitry.

When the state diagram of Fig. 11-5 is being established, the operations in Fig. 11-3 (or Table 11-3) are allocated under each state. The result is the state-operation diagram of Fig. 11-6, showing the states as well as the operations under each state. A satisfactory allocation of these operations in Fig. 11-6 requires a simultaneous study of Figs. 11-3 and 11-5.

In Fig. 11-6 the fetch-instruction operation during the instruction cycle occurs at state f_4, and the other three operations at state f_{10}. The internal sequence branches at the end of the instruction cycle, depending on the contents of flipflops R_0 to R_2. There are six branches, one each for the addition, subtraction, conditional-transfer, unconditional-transfer, and store commands, plus the remaining branch (when $R_0R_1R_2$ is 101), which has four subbranches, one each for the shift-left, shift-right, clear-accumulator, and stop commands. The address-return operation occurs during states f_0, f_1, f_2, f_3, and f_5 and is not needed for the unconditional-transfer instruction. A zero is inserted into flipflop G at state f_5 if C_3 is 1. The add-1 operation occurs during state f_{11}. The fetch-operand operation happens at states f_0 and f_1. The addition and subtraction operations occur at states f_8 and f_9, respectively.

At state f_{15} for the stop command, 0's are inserted into register C, and 1's are inserted into register F. The operation counter continues counting the clock pulse, but its state remains at f_{15} because of the insert-1 operation $(1 \Rightarrow F)$. Therefore, the operation of the computer under the stop command actually does not stop; only the sequencing of computer states does.

When switch S is turned momentarily to the off position, flipflop G is changed to the 0 state; the computer continues to execute the current instruction until the operation counter reaches state f_4. At this time, the operation counter will switch to state f_{15} and will stay at this state. When the sequencing has been halted, it can be restarted by turning switch S momentarily to the on position. When this happens, flipflop G is changed to the 1 state and the operation counter is then switched to state f_4. Since the contents of register C have been changed into 000000, the computer begins at the instruction in the first memory word.

11-5   A Tabular Study of Sequential Operations

The states and the symbolic operations of Fig. 11-6 prescribe the sequential operation of the computer. It is desirable at this time to make a tabular study of the sequential operations of the nine machine instructions to ascertain that the diagram, Fig. 11-6, is in order.

To observe the sequential operation, a program using the nine instructions is given in Table 11-5. This program consists of 10 instruction words and 2 data words; it is initially fed into the computer by switches. The 9 memory words at addresses 000000 to 000110 and 001000 to 001001 are the 9 instructions in Table 11-1. The memory words at addresses 111000 and 111001 are the stored minuend and subtrahend for use during subtraction. The memory word at address 111111 is an alternative instruction in the conditional-transfer instruction. A brief description of each memory word is given in Table 11-5.

The tabular study utilizes a form shown in Table 11-6. The instructions appear in the first column. Symbols $\emptyset_1$ and $\emptyset_2$ in the second column represent the instruction cycle and execution cycle, respectively, and symbol $\emptyset_0$ indicates the period during which initial operations occur. Clock pulses p_i in the third column indicate the time sequence. The states of registers are shown in the fourth to the eighth columns. The description of the operations which occur during each clock-pulse period is stated symbolically in the last column. Each row shows the operations occurring during one clock-pulse period. Thus, Table 11-6 shows

Table 11-5   Program Illustrating Operations of the Nine Instructions

Memory address	Word initially stored in memory	Description of stored word
000000	101,001000	Clear accumulator
000001	000,111000	Add number in address 111000 to A register
000010	001,111001	Subtract number in address 111001 from that in A register
000011	011,001010	Store number in A register to memory at address 001010
000100	101,100000	Shift A register 1 bit to right
000101	101,010000	Shift A register 1 bit to left
000110	100,001000	Unconditional transfer of control to instruction at address 001000
001000	010,111111	Conditional transfer of control to the instruction at address 111111 if number in A register is negative. If it is positive, take next instruction in sequence
001001	101,000100	Stop machine
111000	011,111110	Minuend
111001	001,101110	Subtrahend
111111	100,000000	Unconditional transfer of control to instruction at address 000000

the sequence of the states of the registers in executing the programmed instructions in Table 11-5.

The sequential operations in Table 11-6 will now be explained in detail. Initially, the contents of registers C and F are, respectively, 000000 and 1111;

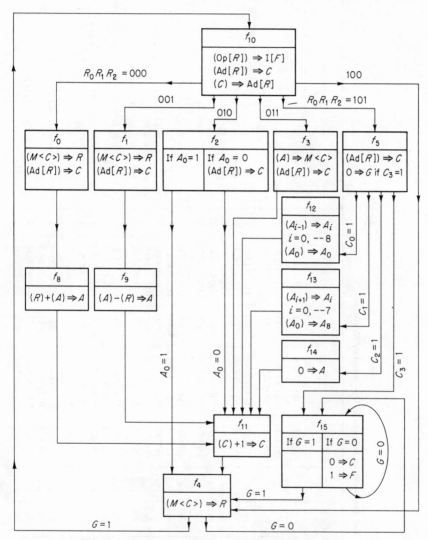

FIG. 11-6 State-operation diagram of the simple digital computer.

this situation occurs when the G flipflop is changed to the 0 state. Assume that the initial contents of registers R and A are, respectively, 000,000000 and 111,111111. During pulse period p_1, switch S is turned on; flipflop G changes to the 1 state. During p_2 the counter state is being changed from f_{15} (1111) to f_4 (0100). This completes the initial turning-on operations.

Table 11-6   Tabular Study of Sequential Operation of Registers

Instruction	Cycle	Clock pulse	Register					Symbolic description
			C	R	F	A	G	
			000000	000,000000	1111	111,111111	0	Initial states
	ϕ_0	p_1	000000	000,000000	1111	111,111111	1	S switch on, $1 \Rightarrow G$
	ϕ_0	p_2	000000	000,000000	0100	111,111111	1	$f_{15} \to f_4$
Clear accumulator	ϕ_1	p_3	000000	101,001000	1010	111,111111	1	$(M<C>) \Rightarrow R, f_4 \to f_{10}\ (G = 1)$
	ϕ_1	p_4	001000	101,000000	0101	111,111111	1	$f_{10} \to f_5\dagger$
	ϕ_2	p_5	000000	101,000000	1110	111,111111	1	$(\mathrm{Ad}\ [R]) \Rightarrow C, f_5 \to f_{14}\ (C_2 = 1)$
	ϕ_2	p_6	000000	101,000000	1011	000,000000	1	$0 \Rightarrow A, f_{14} \to f_{11}$
	ϕ_2	p_7	000001	101,000000	0100	000,000000	1	$(C) + 1 \Rightarrow C, f_{11} \to f_4$
Addition	ϕ_1	p_8	000001	000,111000	1010	000,000000	1	$(M<C>) \Rightarrow R, f_4 \to f_{10}\ (G = 1)$
	ϕ_1	p_9	111000	000,000001	0000	000,000000	1	$f_{10} \to f_0\dagger$
	ϕ_2	p_{10}	000001	011,111110	1000	000,000000	1	$(M<C>) \Rightarrow R, (\mathrm{Ad}\ [R]) \Rightarrow C, f_0 \to f_8$
	ϕ_2	p_{11}	000001	011,111110	1011	011,111110	1	$(R) + (A) \Rightarrow A, f_8 \to f_{11}$
	ϕ_2	p_{12}	000010	011,111110	0100	011,111110	1	$(C) + 1 \Rightarrow C, f_{11} \to f_4$
Subtraction	ϕ_1	p_{13}	000010	001,111001	1010	011,111110	1	$(M<C>) \Rightarrow R, f_4 \to f_{10}\ (G = 1)$
	ϕ_1	p_{14}	111001	001,000010	0001	011,111110	1	$f_{10} \to f_1\dagger$
	ϕ_2	p_{15}	000010	001,101110	1001	011,111110	1	$(M<C>) \Rightarrow R, (\mathrm{Ad}\ [R]) \Rightarrow C, f_1 \to f_9$
	ϕ_2	p_{16}	000010	001,101110	1011	010,010000	1	$(A) - (R) \Rightarrow A, f_9 \to f_{11}$
	ϕ_2	p_{17}	000011	001,101110	0100	010,010000	1	$(C) + 1 \Rightarrow C, f_{11} \to f_4$
Store	ϕ_1	p_{18}	000011	011,001010	1010	010,010000	1	$(M<C>) \Rightarrow R, f_4 \to f_{10}\ (G = 1)$
	ϕ_1	p_{19}	001010	011,000011	0011	010,010000	1	$f_{10} \to f_3\dagger$
	ϕ_2	p_{20}	000011	011,000011	1011	010,010000	1	$(A) \Rightarrow M, (\mathrm{Ad}\ [R]) \Rightarrow C, f_3 \to f_{11}$
	ϕ_2	p_{21}	000100	011,000011	0100	010,010000	1	$(C) + 1 \Rightarrow C, f_{11} \to f_4$

	φ	p						
Shift right	ϕ_1	p_{22}	000100	101,100000	1010	010,010000	1	$(M\!<\!C\!>) \Rightarrow R, f_4 \to f_{10}\ (G = 1)$
	ϕ_1	p_{23}	100000	101,000100	0101	010,010000	1	$f_{10} \to f_5$†
	ϕ_2	p_{24}	000100	101,000100	1100	010,010000	1	$(\text{Ad }[R]) \Rightarrow C, f_5 \to f_{12}\ (C_0 = 1)$
	ϕ_2	p_{25}	000100	101,000100	1011	001,001000	1	$(A_{i-1}) \Rightarrow A_i, (A_0) \Rightarrow A_0, f_{12} \to f_{11}$
	ϕ_2	p_{26}	000101	101,000100	0100	001,001000	1	$(C) + 1 \Rightarrow C, f_{11} \to f_4$
Shift left	ϕ_1	p_{27}	000101	101,010000	1010	001,001000	1	$(M\!<\!C\!>) \Rightarrow R, f_4 \to f_{10}\ (G = 1)$
	ϕ_1	p_{28}	010000	101,000101	0101	001,001000	1	$f_{10} \to f_5$†
	ϕ_2	p_{29}	000101	101,000101	1101	001,001000	1	$(\text{Ad }[R]) \Rightarrow C, f_5 \to f_{13}, (C_1 = 1)$
	ϕ_2	p_{30}	000101	101,000101	1011	010,010000	1	$(A_{i+1}) \Rightarrow A_i, (A_0) \Rightarrow A_8, f_{13} \to f_{11}$
	ϕ_2	p_{31}	000110	101,000101	0100	010,010000	1	$(C) + 1 \Rightarrow C, f_{11} \to f_4$
Unconditional transfer	ϕ_1	p_{32}	000110	100,001000	1010	010,010000	1	$(M\!<\!C\!>) \Rightarrow R, f_4 \to f_{10}\ (G = 1)$
	ϕ_1	p_{33}	001000	100,000110	0100	010,010000	1	$f_{10} \to f_4$†
Conditional transfer	ϕ_1	p_{34}	001000	010,111111	1010	010,010000	1	$(M\!<\!C\!>) \Rightarrow R, f_4 \to f_{10}\ (G = 1)$
	ϕ_1	p_{35}	111111	010,001000	0010	010,010000	1	$f_{10} \to f_2$†
	ϕ_2	p_{36}	001000	010,001000	1011	010,010000	1	$(\text{Ad }[R]) \Rightarrow C, f_2 \to f_{11}\ (A_0 = 0)$
	ϕ_2	p_{37}	001001	010,001000	0100	010,010000	1	$(C) + 1 \Rightarrow C, f_{11} \to f_4$
Stop	ϕ_1	p_{38}	001001	101,000100	1010	010,010000	1	$(M\!<\!C\!>) \Rightarrow R, f_4 \to f_{10}\ (G = 1)$
	ϕ_1	p_{39}	000100	101,001001	0101	010,010000	1	$f_{10} \to f_5$†
	ϕ_2	p_{40}	001001	101,001001	1111	010,010000	0	$(\text{Ad }[R]) \Rightarrow C, f_5 \to f_{15}\ (C_3 = 1), 0 \Rightarrow G\ (C_3 = 1)$
	ϕ_2	p_{41}	000000	101,001001	1111	010,010000	0	$0 \Rightarrow C, 1 \Rightarrow F$
	ϕ_0	p_{42}	000000	101,001001	1111	010,010000	1	S switched on, $1 \Rightarrow G$
	ϕ_0	p_{43}	000000	101,001001	0100	010,010000	1	$f_{15} \to f_4$

† Three operations during the state f_{10}: $(\text{Op }[R]) \Rightarrow 1\ [F], (\text{Ad }[R]) \Rightarrow C, (C) \Rightarrow \text{Ad }[R]$.

The first instruction cycle begins at p_3 and lasts two pulse periods p_3 and p_4. The first instruction address is 000000. The contents of the memory at this address are the first instruction (101,001000); this is transferred to register R. In the meantime, state f_4 changes to state f_{10} (1010). During p_4 the operation-code part and address part of the instruction now in register R transfer, respectively, to the instruction part of register F and to register C, the original contents of register C (000000) being transferred to the address part of the register R for temporary storage. At the end of pulse period p_4 the contents of the C register are 001000 (the operand address); those of the R register are 101,000000, and the counter state is f_5 (0101). The execution cycle begins at pulse period p_5 at state f_5. It covers three pulse periods p_5, p_6, and p_7. During p_5, state f_5 is being changed to state f_{14}, since the state of flipflop C_2 is 1. This is the operation code of the clear-accumulator instruction. It is a necessary step so that subsequent arithmetic operation can be correctly performed in the accumulator. Also during p_5 the original instruction address 000000 (which has been temporarily stored in the address part of the R register) is returned to the C register. During p_6, zeros are inserted into the A register, and the state changes from f_{14} to f_{11}. The add-1 operation is performed during p_7, and state f_{11} is changed to f_4. At the end of pulse period p_7 the contents of the C register is 000001 (next instruction address), and the execution of the first instruction is accomplished.

The second instruction cycle covers pulse periods p_8 and p_9, during which the same operations as those during p_3 and p_4 are performed. At the end of pulse period p_9 the contents of the C register, R register, and F register are, respectively, 111000, 000,000001, and 0000. These states call for an addition operation taking the number at memory address 111000 (where 011,111110 is stored, as shown in Table 11-5) and adding it to the contents of the A register (which is 000,000000). During p_{10} the number 011,111110 is taken out of the memory and stored temporarily in the R register. Also the address-return operation is performed, and the state is being changed from f_0 to f_8. The actual addition of the contents in the R register to that in the A register is performed during p_{11}. During p_{12} the add-1 operation is again performed, and the state is being changed from f_{11} to f_4. At the end of pulse period p_{12} the contents of the C register is 000010, and execution of the second instruction has been accomplished. This addition and the previous clear-accumulator instructions are actually a way to read a number from the memory into the accumulator. The operations carrying out the next instruction of subtraction are similar to those of addition. This instruction occupies pulse periods p_{13} to p_{17}. At the end of p_{17} the contents of the C register are 000011, and the execution of the third instruction is completed.

The next store instruction covers pulse periods p_{18} to p_{21}. Transfer of the number (010,010000) in register A to the memory at the address (001010) in register C occurs during pulse period p_{20}, while the number in register A remains unchanged.

The next two instructions shift the contents of the A register 1 bit to the right and then 1 bit to the left; they cover pulse periods p_{22} to p_{30}. At the end of the shift-right instruction (p_{26}) the contents of the A register are 001,001000. At the end of the shift-left instruction (p_{30}) the contents of the A register are 010,010000.

The subsequent instruction for unconditional transfer of control covers pulse periods p_{32} and p_{33}, during which the instruction cycle performs its operations. At the end of p_{33}, the contents of the C register are 001000 instead of 000111; no subsequent address-return operation is performed, as this is required in other instructions. Therefore, the normal sequence is broken; and the next instruction is located in the memory at address 001000 (where the number 010,111111 is stored, as shown in Table 11-5).

The subsequent instruction for conditional transfer covers pulse periods p_{34} to p_{37}. At the end of p_{35} the contents of the C register, R register, F register, and A register are, respectively, 111111, 010,001000, 0010, and 010,010000. These states call for a conditional transfer of control, depending on the state of A_0. Since the state of A_0 is 0 at this pulse period, the computer takes the normal sequence. This means that the next instruction is in the memory at address 001001. If state A_0 was 1 at the end of p_{35}, the normal sequence is broken; and the next instruction is located at memory address 111111 as shown in the C register during p_{35}. This can happen if we change our program in Table 11-5 to perform the shift-left operation ahead of the shift-right operation.

The last instruction, stopping the computation, covers pulse periods p_{38} to p_{41}. During p_{40} zero is inserted into flipflop G. During p_{41}, 0's are substituted into the C register and 1's into the F register—the initial states in Table 11-6. The operations during p_{42} and p_{43} are the same as those during p_1 and p_2 if the computation is to be repeated.

The state diagram of Fig. 11-6 has been verified operable. With such a study, errors in the symbolic design can be corrected.

11-6 Detail-design Phase

In this phase logic equations are derived from the symbolic statements of Fig. 11-6. These logic equations prescribe the switching operations of all registers shown in Fig. 11-2. They are the input equations of the flipflops of these registers. We proceed to establish the input equations for the F register, A register, C register, R register, M register, and G flipflop. Logic diagrams for these registers will be drawn or illustrated.

Operation Counter. In the operation counter there are four flipflops F_1, F_2, F_3, and F_4. The counter is required to perform the counting sequence as shown in Fig. 11-5 and to change its contents to 1111 when G is 0.

The technique of designing a counter has been described in Chap. 10. In Fig. 11-5 the state of flipflop F_1 changes when state f_4 (0100) changes to f_{10} (1010), because F_1 is 0 in 0100 and F_1 becomes 1 in 1010. When state f_{10} (1010) changes to f_0 (0000), if $R_0R_1R_2$ is 000, the state of F_1 is again changed. In short, the state of F_1 changes when one of the following six conditions occurs:

$$f_{10}\bar{R}_0\bar{R}_1\bar{R}_2 + f_{10}\bar{R}_0\bar{R}_1R_2 + f_{10}\bar{R}_0R_1\bar{R}_2 + f_{10}\bar{R}_0R_1R_2 + f_{10}R_0\bar{R}_1R_2$$
$$+ f_{10}R_0\bar{R}_1\bar{R}_2 + (f_{10}R_0R_1\bar{R}_2 + f_{10}R_0R_1R_2) = f_{10}$$

The two terms in the parentheses are don't care terms (see Table 11-4); they are added for simplification. Other conditions for changing the state of F_1 can be similarly found, and the flipflop input equation of F_1 is

$$f_{1t} = [f_4 + f_{10} + f_0 + f_1 + f_2\bar{A}_0 + f_3 + f_5(C_0 + C_1 + C_2 + C_3) \\ + f_{11} + f_{15}G]p \quad (11\text{-}1)$$

where p is the clock pulse which triggers the flipflops. The input equations for F_2, F_3, and F_4 are similarly determined and are shown below:

$$f_{2t} = (f_4G + f_{10}R_0 + f_2A_0 + f_{11} + f_{12} + f_{13} + f_{14})\,p \qquad (11\text{-}2)$$

$$f_{3t} = [f_4 + f_{10}\overline{R}_1 + f_2A_0 + f_5(C_2 + C_3) + f_8 + f_9 + f_{11} + f_{12} \\ + f_{13} + f_{15}G]\,p \qquad (11\text{-}3)$$

$$f_{4t} = [f_4\overline{G} + f_{10}R_2 + f_2\overline{A}_0 + f_5(C_0 + C_2) + f_8 + f_{11} + f_{12} \\ + f_{14} + f_{15}G]\,p \qquad (11\text{-}4)$$

The state-operation diagram of Fig. 11-6 calls for the operation $(1 \Rightarrow F)$ when G is 0 at state f_{15}. This symbolic operation is shown in Table 11-7. The input equations from Table 11-7 are

$$f_{it} = \overline{F}_i\overline{G}f_{15}p \qquad \text{where } i = 1, \ldots, 4 \qquad (11\text{-}5)$$

Since f_{15} is $F_1F_2F_3F_4$, $\overline{F}_i f_{15}$ in Eq. (11-5) is always 0 and therefore is not needed. Input equations (11-1) to (11-4) are those for the F register.

In the above input equations, each f_i is a logical product of F_j, as shown in Table 11-4. These and subsequent logic equations can thus be simplified, but the identity of each term may be lost unless, of course, the simplification is apparent. For this reason, simplification or minimization of logic equations will not be pursued.

Logic diagram for the operation counter by using Eqs. (11-1) to (11-4) is shown in Fig. 11-7. Note that the number of dots on the input line to the *and* block or *or* block denotes the number of connected *and* inputs or *or* inputs.

Accumulator. As shown in the state-operation diagram of Fig. 11-6, the accumulator is called upon to perform the following operations at the specified states:

Table 11-7

F_i	$F_i(\tau)$	f_{it}
0	1	1
1	1	0

f_8: $(R) + (A) \Rightarrow A$

f_9: $(A) - (R) \Rightarrow A$

f_{12}: $(A_0) \Rightarrow A_0 \qquad (A_{i-1}) \Rightarrow A_i \qquad i = 1, \ldots, 8$

f_{13}: $(A_0 \Rightarrow A_8) \qquad (A_{i+1}) \Rightarrow A_i \qquad i = 0, \ldots, 7$

f_{14}: $0 \Rightarrow A$

For the addition operation occurring at state f_8, A_i and R_i are, respectively, the ith bit of augend and addend. K_i is the carry to the ith bit from the $(i + 1)$st bit, as shown in Fig. 11-8. The addition operation is shown in Table 11-8. The input equations, from Table 11-8, are

$$a_{it} = (R_i \oplus K_i)\,f_8p \qquad \text{where } i = 0, \ldots, 8 \qquad (11\text{-}6)$$

and the carry equations are

$$K_{i-1} = (R_iK_i + R_iA_i + A_iK_i)\,f_8p \qquad \text{where } i = 1, \ldots, 8 \qquad (11\text{-}7)$$

$$K_8 = 0$$

For the subtraction operation occurring at state f_9, A_i and R_i are, respectively, the ith bit of minuend and subtrahend. The input and carry equations are the same as (11-6) and (11-7) except that R_i is replaced by its complement R_i and K_8 is replaced by 1 owing to the replacing of the contents of register $\overline{R}$ by its 2's complement. The input and carry equations are

$$a_{it} = (R_i \odot K_i)f_9p \qquad\qquad \text{where } i = 0, \ldots, 8 \quad (11\text{-}8)$$
$$K_{i-1} = (\bar{R}_iK_i + \bar{R}_iA_i + A_iK_i)f_9p \qquad \text{where } i = 1, \ldots, 8$$
$$K_8 = f_9p \qquad\qquad\qquad\qquad\qquad\qquad\qquad (11\text{-}9)$$

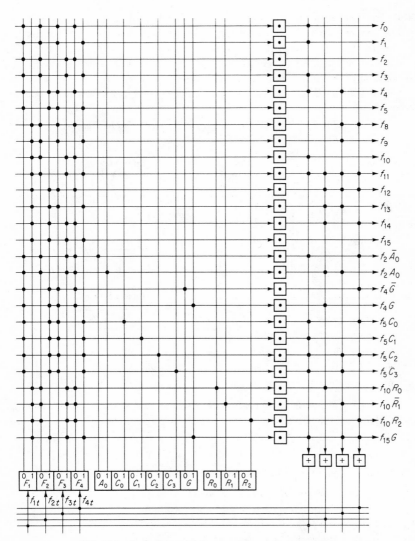

FIG. 11-7   Logic diagram of the operation counter and decoder.

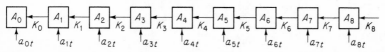

FIG. 11-8   Carry notation for the nine flipflops of the accumulator.

The shift-right operation occurs at state f_{12}. It shifts the contents of the accumulator 1 bit to the right, the state of the A_0 bit remaining unchanged. Table 11-9 is the truth table for this shift-right operation. The input equations from this table are

$$a_{it} = (A_{i-1} \oplus A_i) f_{12} p \qquad \text{where } i = 1, \ldots, 8 \qquad (11\text{-}10)$$

Note that there is no a_{0t} equation because the state of flipflop A_0 is not changed.

The shift-left operation occurs at state f_{13}. It shifts the accumulator contents 1 bit to the left, the state of the A_8 bit being replaced by that of the A_0 bit. This is the circulatory shift-left operation, which can be used to inspect the individual bit of a word in the accumulator. The shift-left operation is the same as that given in Table 11-9, except that A_{i-1} is replaced by A_{i+1}. The input equations are

$$a_{it} = (A_i \oplus A_{i+1}) f_{13} p \qquad \text{where } i = 0, \ldots, 7 \qquad (11\text{-}11)$$
$$a_{8t} = (A_0 \oplus A_8) f_{13} p$$

Table 11-8

A_i	R_i	K_i	K_{i-1}	$A_i(\tau)$	a_{it}
0	0	0	0	0	0
0	0	1	0	1	1
0	1	0	0	1	1
0	1	1	1	0	0
1	0	0	0	1	0
1	0	1	1	0	1
1	1	0	1	0	1
1	1	1	1	1	0

Table 11-9

A_{i-1}	A_i	$A_i(\tau)$	a_{it}
0	0	0	0
0	1	0	1
1	0	1	1
1	1	1	0

Table 11-10

A_i	$A_i(\tau)$	a_{it}
0	0	0
1	0	1

Table 11-11

R_{i+3}	C_i	$C_i(\tau)$	c_{it}
0	0	0	0
0	1	0	1
1	0	1	1
1	1	1	0

The clearing-accumulator operation occurs at state f_{14} and inserts 0's into the accumulator. Table 11-10 shows this operation. The input equations from this table are

$$a_{it} = A_i f_{14} p \qquad \text{where } i = 0, \ldots, 8 \qquad (11\text{-}12)$$

Accumulator input equations finally evolve in the following form:

$$a_{it} = (R_i \oplus K_i) f_8 p + (R_i \odot K_i) f_9 p + (A_{i-1} \oplus A_i) f_{12} p$$
$$\qquad + (A_i \oplus A_{i+1}) f_{13} p + A_i f_{14} p \qquad \text{where } i = 1, \ldots, 7$$
$$a_{0t} = (R_0 \oplus K_0) f_8 p + (R_0 \odot K_0) f_9 p + (A_0 \oplus A_1) f_{13} p + A_0 f_{14} p \qquad (11\text{-}13)$$
$$a_{8t} = (R_8 \oplus K_8) f_8 p + (R_8 \odot K_8) f_9 p + (A_7 \oplus A_8) f_{12} p$$
$$\qquad\qquad\qquad + (A_0 \oplus A_8) f_{13} p + A_8 f_{14} p$$
$$K_{i-1} = (R_i K_i + R_i A_i + A_i K_i) f_8 p + (\overline{R}_i K_i + \overline{R}_i A_i + A_i K_i) f_9 p$$
$$\qquad\qquad\qquad \text{where } i = 1, \ldots, 8 \qquad (11\text{-}14)$$
$$K_8 = f_9 p$$

A logic diagram for the ith stage of the accumulator is shown in Fig. 11-9.

Memory-address Register.   In the state-operation diagram of Fig. 11-6, register C is required to perform the following operations at the specified states:

$$f_{10}, f_0, f_1, f_2\bar{A}_0, f_3, f_5: \text{(Ad } [R]) \Rightarrow C$$
$$f_{11}: (C) + 1 \Rightarrow C$$
$$f_{15}\bar{G}: 0 \Rightarrow C$$

The first operation is the return-address operation; its truth table appears as Table 11-11.   The input equations from this table are

$$c_{it} = (R_{i+3} \oplus C_i)gp \tag{11-15}$$

where $i = 0, \ldots , 5$
$$g = f_{10} + f_0 + f_1 + f_2\bar{A}_0 + f_3 + f_5$$

The add-1 operation occurs at state f_{11}.   In this operation, register C acts as a binary counter.   The logic design of such a counter has been described in Chap. 10.   The input equations can be similarly obtained and are listed here:

$$\begin{aligned}
c_{5t} &= f_{11}p \\
c_{4t} &= C_5 f_{11}p = C_5 c_{5t} \\
c_{3t} &= C_4 c_5 f_{11}p = C_4 c_{4t} \\
c_{2t} &= C_3 C_4 C_5 f_{11}p = C_3 c_{3t} \\
c_{1t} &= C_2 C_3 C_4 C_5 f_{11}p = C_2 c_{2t} \\
c_{0t} &= C_1 C_2 C_3 C_4 C_5 f_{11}p = C_1 c_{1t}
\end{aligned} \tag{11-16}$$

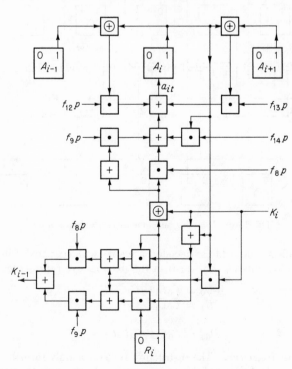

FIG. 11-9   Logic diagram of an accumulator stage.

The third operation, to insert 0's into register C, occurs at state $f_{15}\overline{G}$. The operation is the same as that given in Table 11-10. The input equations are

$$c_{it} = C_i f_{15}\overline{G}p \qquad \text{where } i = 0, \ldots, 5 \qquad (11\text{-}17)$$

The final form of the input equations for memory-address registers is

$$
\begin{aligned}
c_{0t} &= C_1 C_2 C_3 C_4 C_5 f_{11}p + (R_3 \oplus C_0)gp + C_0 f_{15}\overline{G}p \\
c_{1t} &= C_2 C_3 C_4 C_5 f_{11}p + (R_4 \oplus C_1)gp + C_1 f_{15}\overline{G}p \\
c_{2t} &= C_3 C_4 C_5 f_{11}p + (R_5 \oplus C_2)gp + C_2 f_{15}\overline{G}p \\
c_{3t} &= C_4 C_5 f_{11}p + (R_6 \oplus C_3)gp + C_3 f_{15}\overline{G}p \\
c_{4t} &= C_5 f_{11}p + (R_7 \oplus C_4)gp + C_4 f_{15}\overline{G}p \\
c_{5t} &= f_{11}p + (R_8 \oplus C_5)gp + C_5 f_{15}\overline{G}p
\end{aligned}
\qquad (11\text{-}18)
$$

where $g = f_{10} + f_0 + f_1 + f_2 \overline{A}_0 + f_3 + f_5$.

A logic diagram for the memory-address register is shown in Fig. 11-10. This

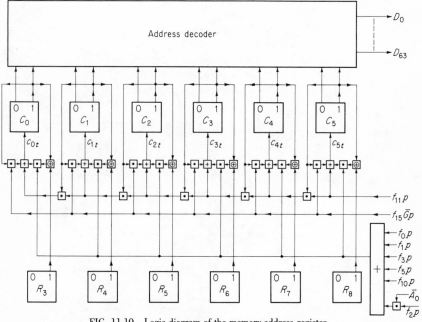

FIG. 11-10   Logic diagram of the memory-address register.

figure also indicates the address decoder, a matrix with six pairs of inputs and 64 outputs. The outputs D_j (*j*th word) of the decoder are represented as follows:

$$
\begin{aligned}
D_0 &= \overline{C}_0 \overline{C}_1 \overline{C}_2 \overline{C}_3 \overline{C}_4 \overline{C}_5 \\
D_1 &= \overline{C}_0 \overline{C}_1 \overline{C}_2 \overline{C}_3 \overline{C}_4 C_5 \\
&\cdots\cdots\cdots\cdots\cdots \\
D_{63} &= C_0 C_1 C_2 C_3 C_4 C_5
\end{aligned}
\qquad (11\text{-}19)
$$

Instruction Register.   The instruction register mainly furnishes temporary storage for a word taken out of the memory unit. As shown in the state-operation diagram of Fig. 11-6, it is required to perform two operations at the specified states,

$$f_{10}: (C) \Rightarrow \text{Ad } [R]$$
$$f_0, f_1, \text{ or } f_4: (M < C >) \Rightarrow R$$

The first operation, to transfer the contents of the C register to the address part of the R register, is shown in Table 11-12. The input equations from this table are

$$r_{it} = (C_{i-3} \oplus R_i) f_{10} p \qquad \text{where } i = 3, \ldots, 8 \qquad (11\text{-}20)$$

The second operation takes a word out of the memory at the address stored in the C register and puts it in the R register. It has been shown that the address in the C register is designated as D_j, where j denotes the jth word. As illustrated in Fig. 11-2, there are 576 bits in the memory register for storing 64 words, each of which (designated by symbol M_{ji}) represents the contents of the ith bit of the jth word. The operation transferring the contents of the M_{ji} bit of the memory unit to the jth bit of the R reg-

Table 11-12

C_{i-3}	R_i	$R_i(\tau)$	r_{it}
0	0	0	0
0	1	0	1
1	0	1	1
1	1	1	0

register equates with that shown in Table 11-12, except that C_{i-3} is replaced by M_{ji}. The input equations are

$$r_{it} = (\overline{M}_{ji} R_i + M_{ji} \overline{R}_i)(f_0 + f_1 + f_4) p$$

The above equation is not complete, because it performs only the transfer of the contents of the M_{ji} bit. The selection by the memory address D_j has not been included. If the ith bit of the jth word in the memory is selected under address command D_j (which can be any of the 64 address commands) M_{ji} and $\overline{M}_{ji}$ should be, respectively, replaced by the following functions:

$$\sum_{j=0}^{63} M_{ji} D_j = M_{0i} D_0 + \cdots + M_{63i} D_{63}$$

$$\sum_{j=0}^{63} \overline{M}_{ji} D_j = \overline{M}_{0i} D_0 + \cdots + \overline{M}_{63i} D_{63}$$
(11-21)

Thus, the input equations are

$$r_{it} = \left\{ \overline{R}_i \left(\sum_{j=0}^{63} M_{ji} D_j \right) + R_i \sum_{j=0}^{63} \overline{M}_{ji} D_j \right\} (f_0 + f_1 + f_4) p \qquad (11\text{-}22)$$

where $i = 0, \ldots, 8$.

The final form of the input equations for the instruction register is

$$r_{it} = \left\{ \overline{R}_i \left(\sum_{j=0}^{63} M_{ji} D_j \right) + R_i \left(\sum_{j=0}^{63} \overline{M}_{ji} D_j \right) \right\} (f_0 + f_1 + f_4) p \qquad \text{for } i = 0, \ldots, 2$$

$$(11\text{-}23)$$

$$r_{it} = \left\{ \overline{R}_i \left(\sum_{j=0}^{63} M_{ji} D_j \right) + R_i \left(\sum_{j=0}^{63} \overline{M}_{ji} D_j \right) \right\} (f_0 + f_1 + f_4) p + (C_{i-3} \oplus R_i) f_{10} p$$

$$\text{for } i = 3, \ldots, 8$$

where D_j is given by Eq. (11-19).   A logic diagram for the ith stage of the R register is shown in Fig. 11-11.

   Memory Unit.   The memory unit is an array of 576 flipflops, shown in Fig. 11-2.   It is required to perform two operations,

$$f_3: (A) \Rightarrow M < C >$$
$$\text{Manual: } (Q_{ji}) \Rightarrow M_{ji}$$

The first operation is to store the contents of the accumulator into the memory located by the address D_j under the state f_3 or

$$f_3 D_j: (A_i) \Rightarrow M_{ji} \qquad \text{where } i = 0, \ldots, 8$$

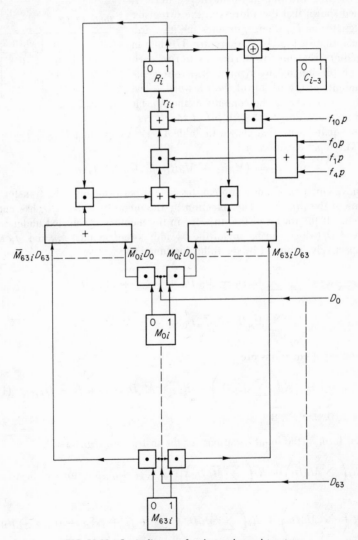

FIG. 11-11   Logic diagram of an instruction-register stage.

This operation is described in Table 11-13; the input equations have the form

$$m_{jit} = (A_i \oplus M_{ji}) f_3 D_j p$$

where
$$i = 0, \ldots, 8 \qquad (11\text{-}24)$$
$$j = 0, \ldots, 63$$

The second operation is to insert words into the memory register by means of Q switches. If Q_{ji} denotes the switch connected to the memory bit M_{ji}, this operation is the same as that described in Table 11-13, except that A_i is replaced by Q_{ji}. Thus, the input equations are

$$m_{jit} = (Q_{ji} \oplus M_{ji}) p$$

where
$$i = 0, \ldots, 8 \qquad (11\text{-}25)$$
$$j = 0, \ldots, 63$$

The final form of the input equations for the memory unit is

$$m_{ji} = (A_i \oplus M_{ji}) f_3 D_j p + (Q_{ji} \oplus M_{ji}) p$$

where
$$i = 0, \ldots, 8 \qquad (11\text{-}26)$$
$$j = 0, \ldots, 63$$

An abridged logic diagram for the memory registers appears in Fig. 11-12.

Start-Stop Flipflop. Starting and stopping of the computer are controlled by the G flipflop, which is activated by the S switch, a direct operator control. The two following operations are required:

$$f_5 C_3 : 0 \Rightarrow G$$
$$\text{Manual: } (S) \Rightarrow G$$

The first operation, which changes the G flipflop to the 0 state at state f_5 when C_3 is 1, is the same as that given in Table 11-10, except that A_i is replaced by G. Thus, the input equation is

$$g_t = G f_5 C_3 p \qquad (11\text{-}27)$$

The second operation turns on or off the S switch for starting or stopping the machine. The input equation is similar to Eq. (11-25), or

$$g_t = (S \oplus G) p \qquad (11\text{-}28)$$

The final form of the input equation for the start-stop flipflop is

$$g_t = G f_5 C_3 p + (S \oplus G) p \qquad (11\text{-}29)$$

The diagram for the G flipflop and S switch is shown in Fig. 11-13.

11-7   Complete Computer

The input equations for all registers of the computer have now been established. They are listed in Table 11-14 for convenient reference. Although these equations precisely prescribe the logic operations of the computer, yet they have not been minimized.

Table 11-13

A_i	M_{ji}	$M_{ji}(\tau)$	m_{jit}
0	0	0	0
0	1	0	1
1	0	1	1
1	1	1	0

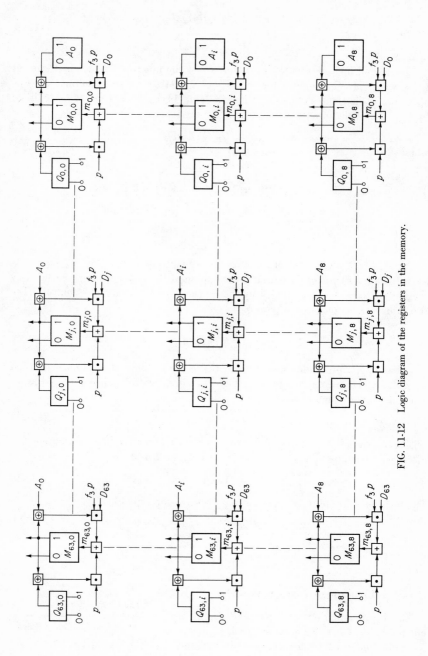

FIG. 11-12 Logic diagram of the registers in the memory.

Table 11-14   List of Input Equations

Operation counter

$$f_{1t} = [f_4 + f_{10} + f_0 + f_1 + f_2\bar{A}_0 + f_3 + f_5(C_0 + C_1 + C_2 + C_3) + f_{11} + f_{15}G]p$$
$$f_{2t} = (f_4G + f_{10}R_0 + f_2A_0 + f_{11} + f_{12} + f_{13} + f_{14})p$$
$$f_{3t} = [f_4 + f_{10}\bar{R}_1 + f_2A_0 + f_5(C_2 + C_3) + f_8 + f_9 + f_{11} + f_{12} + f_{13} + f_{15}G]p$$
$$f_{4t} = [f_4\bar{G} + f_{10}R_2 + f_2\bar{A}_0 + f_5(C_0 + C_2) + f_8 + f_{11} + f_{12} + f_{14} + f_{15}G]p$$

Accumulator

$$a_{it} = (R_i \oplus K_i)f_8p + (R_i \odot K_i)f_9p + (A_i \oplus A_{i-1})f_{12}p + (A_i \oplus A_{i+1})f_{13}p + A_if_{14}p$$
$$\text{for } i = 1, \ldots, 7$$
$$a_{0t} = (R_0 \oplus K_0)f_8p + (R_0 \odot K_0)f_9p + (A_0 \oplus A_1)f_{13}p + A_0f_{14}p$$
$$a_{8t} = (R_8 \oplus K_8)f_8p + (R_8 \odot K_8)f_9p + (A_7 \oplus A_8)f_{12}p + (A_0 \oplus A_8)f_{13}p + A_8f_{14}p$$
$$K_{i-1} = (R_iK_i + R_iA_i + A_iK_i)f_8p + (\bar{R}_iK_i + \bar{R}_iA_i + A_iK_i)f_9p \quad \text{for } i = 1, \ldots, 8;$$
$$K_8 = f_9p$$

Memory-address register

$$c_{0t} = C_1C_2C_3C_4C_5f_{11}p + (R_3 \oplus C_0)gp + C_0f_{15}\bar{G}p$$
$$c_{1t} = C_2C_3C_4C_5f_{11}p + (R_4 \oplus C_1)gp + C_1f_{15}\bar{G}p$$
$$c_{2t} = C_3C_4C_5f_{11}p + (R_5 \oplus C_2)gp + C_2f_{15}\bar{G}p$$
$$c_{3t} = C_4C_5f_{11}p + (R_6 \oplus C_3)gp + C_3f_{15}\bar{G}p$$
$$c_{4t} = C_5f_{11}p + (R_7 \oplus C_4)gp + C_4f_{15}\bar{G}p$$
$$c_{5t} = f_{11}p + (R_8 \oplus C_5)gp + C_5f_{15}\bar{G}p \quad \text{where } g = f_{10} + f_0 + f_1 + f_2\bar{A}_0 + f_3 + f_5$$

Instruction register

$$r_{it} = \left\{ \bar{R}_i \left(\sum_{j=0}^{63} M_{ji}D_j \right) + R_i \left(\sum_{j=0}^{63} \bar{M}_{ji}D_j \right) \right\} (f_0 + f_1 + f_4)p \quad \text{for } i = 0, \ldots, 2$$

$$r_{it} = \left\{ \bar{R}_i \left(\sum_{j=0}^{63} M_{ji}D_j \right) + R_j \left(\sum_{j=0}^{63} \bar{M}_{ji}D_j \right) \right\} (f_0 + f_1 + f_4)p + (C_{i-3} \oplus R_i)f_{10}p$$
$$\text{for } i = 3, \ldots, 8$$

Memory registers

$$m_{jit} = (A_i \oplus M_{ji})f_3D_jp + (Q_{ji} \oplus M_{ji})p \quad \text{for } i = 0, \ldots, 8; j = 0, \ldots, 63$$

Start-stop flipflop

$$g_t = Gf_5C_3p + (S \oplus G)p$$

The configuration of the simple digital computer of Fig. 11-1 is augmented with symbolic operations for each register and is shown in Fig. 11-14. This diagram can be expanded into a more detailed logic diagram by making use of the diagrams in Figs. 11-7 to 11-13.

The operation procedure for the computer is as follows:

1. Turn on the power supply for warming up. If the start-stop flipflop happens to be in the 1 state during this time, the computer will function in an abnormal or irregular manner.

2. Hold or lock switch S in the off position. This sets the start-stop flipflop to the 0 state, the operation counter to 1111, and the memory-address register to 000000. Insert the program into the memory unit by means of the Q switches.

3. Release switch S to the neutral position. Push it to the on position momentarily. This sets the start-stop flipflop to the 1 state. The machine proceeds to execute the program. The first instruction is located at memory address 000000.

4. The program should end with a stop instruction. This holds the contents of all registers except registers G, F, and C (G to 0, F to 1111, and C to 000000).

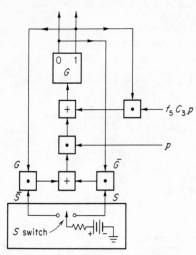

FIG. 11-13   Logic diagram of G flipflop and S switch.

A new program may now be read into the memory, and the computer may be restarted by pushing switch S to the on position momentarily.

5. Read-out of computed results is from neon lights attached to the memory flipflops (not shown in previous figures).

The operating time of the nine instructions can be found from Table 11-6 in terms of clock periods. The results are shown in Table 11-15. None of the nine instructions exceeds five clock periods. The actual operating time depends on the clock rate. If we had chosen a clock period of 1 μsec, the time per instruction would vary between 2 and 5 μsec. To perform an addition (or a subtraction) requires one clear-accumulator instruction and two addition instructions; this takes 15 μsec.† Only 5 μsec is required for either a shift-right or a shift-left operation.

The number of components in the computer is a matter of some interest. The number of flipflops, switches, and neon lights can be readily tallied. Logical-*and*, logical-*or*, and logical-*not* circuits are counted in terms of number of inputs. It has been found that our simple computer requires about 10,000 *and* inputs, 5,000 *or* inputs, 9 *not* inputs, 605 flipflops, 577 switches, and 605 neon lights. The surprisingly large number of components is traceable to the memory unit. The memory unit takes about 70 per cent of all *and* inputs, 70 per cent of all *or* inputs, and more than 90 per cent of all flipflops, switches, and neon lights, even though the memory capacity is regarded as very small. Furthermore, about 92

Table 11-15   *Operating Time of Nine Instructions*

Instruction	Required clock periods		
	Instruction cycle	Execution cycle	Total
Addition................	2	3	5
Subtraction.............	2	3	5
Shift right..............	2	3	5
Shift left...............	2	3	5
Unconditional transfer.....	2	0	2
Conditional transfer.......	2	2	4
Clear accumulator.........	2	3	5
Store..................	2	2	4
Stop...................	2	2	4

† Commercial computers often consider the time taken in carrying out an addition instruction as the addition time.

per cent of the *and* inputs and 95 per cent of the *or* inputs in the R register are logic circuits associated with the memory. The comparatively large number of *and* inputs in the C register is due to a decoder, which is also related to the number of words in the memory. This decoder is usually considered as a part of the memory unit. We can readily conclude that the memory unit and its associated circuits involve the largest portion of the electronics of the computer. Thus, a transistor memory in the form described here is not practical at all. For computers of today which do not use a transistor memory, the memory is still a major portion of the computer.

In the foregoing design neither simplification nor minimization of the logic

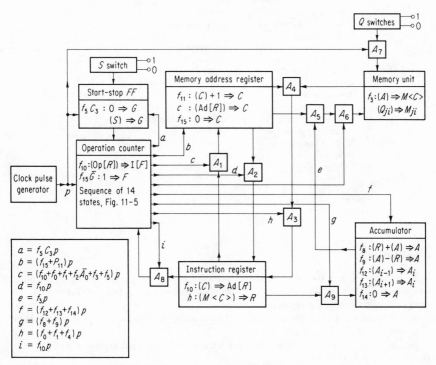

FIG. 11-14   Operations of the simple digital computer.

circuits has been attempted. This demonstrates the necessity of circuit minmization with any large-scale digital computer. Another factor which contributes to the number of logic circuits is the use of parallel operation. Thus, if the cost of the computer outweighs its speed of operation, serial operation should be adopted. The number of switches and neon lights can be greatly reduced if a selection circuit which allows only one word to be inserted or displayed at a time is provided.

Characteristics of the simple computer are summarized in Table 11-16. These characteristics and the instruction list (Table 11-1) give a concise description of the performance of the computer.

Table 11-16   Computer Characteristics

Application..............	General purpose and educational
Sequence control:	
Control...............	Stored program
Timing...............	Synchronous
Operation.............	Parallel
Instruction type........	Single address
Available instructions.....	Nine
Word structure:	
Number base..........	Binary
Word length...........	9 binary digits (including sign digit)
Number range..........	$-1 \leq N \leq (1 - 2^{-8})$
Instruction per word.....	One
Binary point...........	Fixed
Negative number.......	2's complement
Arithmetic unit:	
Clock rate.............	1,000,000 cps
Addition or subtraction...	15 μsec
Shift right or shift left....	5 μsec
Construction...........	Transistors and crystal diodes
Memory unit:	
Storage medium........	Transistor flipflops
Capacity..............	576 bits or 64 words
Random access time......	1 μsec
Terminal equipment:	
Input device...........	Key switches
Output device..........	Neon lights

Problems

1. In Table 11-5, if the fifth and sixth instructions are interchanged so that the shift-left instruction is ahead of the shift-right instruction, revise the contents of Table 11-6 for sequential operations of the registers accordingly.

2. Draw the complete logic diagram of the computer in adequate detail, using the logic diagrams of Figs. 11-7 to 11-13.

3. The input equations in Table 11-14 are written for single-input flipflops. Rewrite these equations for *RS* flipflops.

4. If states f_6 and f_7 in Table 11-4 are used for input and output instructions, respectively, construct a new state diagram (like that of Fig. 11-6), and modify the symbolic operations if necessary.

5. Simplify the following Boolean equations:

(*a*) Input equations (11-1)to (11-4) for the operation counter

(*b*) Input equations (11-13) and (11-14) for the accumulator

(*c*) Input equations (11-18) for the memory-address register

6. An instruction counter is provided to perform the add-1 operation $(C) + 1 \Rightarrow C$ and to eliminate the operation $(C) \Rightarrow \text{Ad } [R]$ during the instruction cycle and the operation $(\text{Ad } [R]) \Rightarrow C$ during execution cycle. Revise the input equations in Table 11-14.

7. The state diagram of Fig. 11-5 is not unique.

(*a*) Select a different arrangement for the 14 states, and construct a new diagram.

(*b*) Write a complete set of input equations for the new diagram.

References

1. Burks, A. W., H. H. Goldstine, and J. von Neumann: Preliminary Discussion of the Logical Design of an Electronic Computing Instrument, *Inst. Advanced Study Rept.*, vol. 1, pt. 1, 1946.

2. West, C. F., and J. E. Deturk: A Digital Computer for Scientific Applications, *Proc. IRE*, vol. 36, no. 12, 1948, pp. 1452–1460.

3. Van der Poel, W. L.: A Simple Electronic Digital Computer, *Appl. Sci. Research*, vol. 2, pt. B, 1951, pp. 367–400.

4. Jeffery, R. C., and I. S. Reed: Design of a Digital Computer by Boolean Algebra, *MIT Digital Computer Lab. Eng. Note* E-462, May 20, 1952.

5. Wilkes, M. V., and Stringer, J. B.: Micro-programming and the Design of Control Circuits in an Electronic Digital Computer, *Proc. Cambridge Phil. Soc.*, vol. 49, pt. 2, pp. 230–238, 1953.

6. Reed, I. S.: Symbolic Design of Digital Computers, *MIT Lincoln Lab. Tech. Mem. 23*, 1953.

7. Burks, A. W., and J. B. Wright: Theory of Logical Nets, *Proc. IRE*, vol. 41, 1953, pp. 1357–1365.

8. "Symposium on Automatic Programming for Digital Computers," PB11607, U.S. Department of Commerce, Office of Technical Service, May, 1954.

9. Richards, R. K.: "Arithmetic Operations for Digital Computers," D. Van Nostrand Company, Inc., Princeton, N. J., 1955.

10. Burks, A. W., and I. M. Copi: The Logical Design of an Idealized General-purpose Computer, *J. Franklin Inst.*, pt. I, March, 1956, 299–314, pt. II, April, 1956, pp. 421–436.

11. Frankel, S. P.: The Logical Design of a Simple General Purpose Computer, *IRE Trans. on Electronic Computers*, vol. EC-6, no. 1, March, 1957, pp. 5-14.

12. Dinnen, G. P., I. L. Lebow, and I. S. Reed: Logical Design of CG 24, *Proc. Eastern Joint Computer Conf.*, 1958, pp. 91–94.

13. Mercer, R. J.: Micro-programming, *J. ACM*, April, 1957, pp. 157–171.

14. Burks, A. W., and H. Wang: The Logic of Automata, *J. ACM*, pt. I, April, 1957, pp. 193–218, pt. II, July, 1957, pp. 279–297.

15. McCraken D. D.: "Digital Computer Programming," John Wiley & Sons, Inc., New York, 1957.

16. Phister, M.: "Logical Design of Digital Computers," John Wiley & Sons, Inc., New York, 1958.

12

Arithmetic and Control Units

In Chap. 11, a simple arithmetic and control unit was described for a stored-program digital computer. This chapter describes arithmetic and control units in more detail. The first four sections discuss arithmetic units, including a floating-point arithmetic unit, while the remaining four sections describe control units. Whenever symbolic statements are made, the symbols in Tables 10-8 and 11-2 are used unless otherwise stated.

12-1 A Parallel Binary Arithmetic Unit

An arithmetic unit is usually capable of performing (among other operations) addition, subtraction, multiplication, division, and sometimes extraction of the square root; and for parallel operation it often employs three registers, as shown

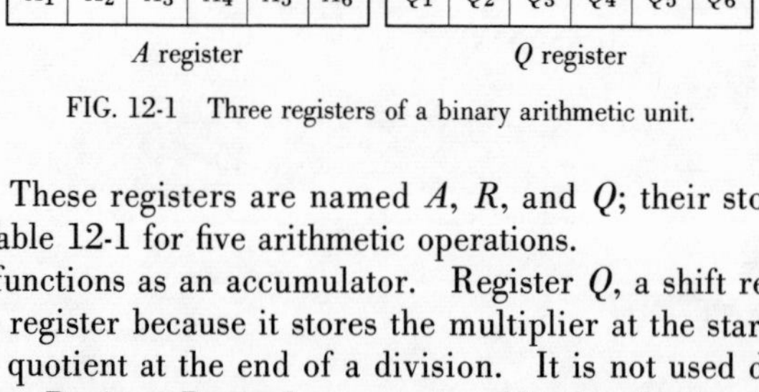

2^0	2^{-1}	2^{-2}	2^{-3}	2^{-4}	2^{-5}
R_1	R_2	R_3	R_4	R_5	R_5

R register

2^0	2^{-1}	2^{-2}	2^{-3}	2^{-4}	2^{-5}	2^0	2^{-1}	2^{-2}	2^{-3}	2^{-4}	2^{-5}
A_1	A_2	A_3	A_4	A_5	A_6	Q_1	Q_2	Q_3	Q_4	Q_5	Q_6

A register   Q register

FIG. 12-1   Three registers of a binary arithmetic unit.

in Fig. 12-1. These registers are named A, R, and Q; their storage functions are shown in Table 12-1 for five arithmetic operations.

Register A functions as an accumulator. Register Q, a shift register, is often called the MQ register because it stores the multiplier at the start of a multiplication and the quotient at the end of a division. It is not used during addition and subtraction. Register R merely stores the addend, subtrahend, multiplicand, divisor, or root extractor.

In the subsequent description, the algorithms developed in Chap. 1 are applied. For convenience, each word is assumed to consist of 5 number bits plus a sign bit, and the number bits are fractional. Capital letters with subscripts 1 to 6 denote the six flipflops in the registers of Fig. 12-1. R_6, A_6, and Q_6 are the least sig-

Table 12-1   *Functions of Registers during Arithmetic Operations*

Operation	R register	A register		Q register	
		At start	At end	At start	At end
Addition.............	Addend	Augend	Sum	Unused	Unused
Subtraction...........	Subtrahend	Minuend	Difference	Unused	Unused
Multiplication.........	Multiplicand	Zeros	Product (most significant half)	Multiplier	Product (least significant half)
Division.............	Divisor	Dividend	Remainder	Zeros	Quotient
Extraction of square root........	Root extractor	Radicand	Remainder	Zeros	Quotient or root

nificant bits; R_1, A_1, and Q_1, the sign bits. In operation, the first operand (such as the augend, minuend, dividend, or radicand) is initially transferred to the

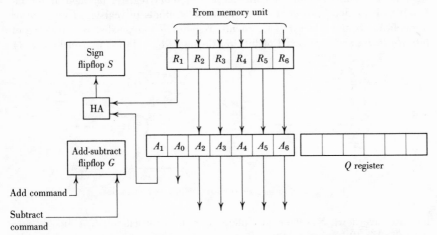

FIG. 12-2   A parallel binary arithmetic unit in addition and subtraction configuration with numbers in signed-magnitude representation.

accumulator by first clearing the accumulator and then adding this operand to the zero contents in the accumulator. To load the multiplier into the Q register for multiplication, a loading operation is required. Loading of the addend, subtrahend, multiplicand, or divisor into the R register is usually included as a part of the execution of an arithmetic instruction.

Addition and Subtraction. The configuration of an arithmetic unit varies to a certain extent with the chosen representation of numbers. A binary addition and subtraction configuration for numbers in signed-magnitude representation is shown in Fig. 12-2. There are two registers R and A (the latter is an accumulator) in addition to a half adder (HA), a sign flipflop S, and an add-subtract flipflop G to indicate the add-subtract command (assume that add and subtract commands are represented by G equal to 0 and 1, respectively), and an overflow bit A_0. The overflow bit stores the carry coming from bit A_2. The algorithm for addition and subtraction was given in Table 1-11.

Initially, the augend is stored in register A, and the addend is taken from the memory and stored in register R. Sign bits R_1 and A_1 are compared by the half adder and the result is stored in flipflop S. By combination of the contents in flipflops S and G, an addition or a subtraction is determined. The number bits in register R are added to those in register A if sign bits R_1 and A_1 are the same in the case of an add command or if they are different in the case of a subtract command. The number bits in register R are subtracted from those in register A if sign bits R_1 and A_1 are different in the case of an add command or if they are the same in the case of a subtract command. The sign bit of the sum or difference is stored in A_1, and its value remains the same as originally in A_1 except in the case when a borrow occurs in A_0 during subtraction. In this latter case, the sign bit of the sum or difference is again stored in A_1, but its value should be the complement of that originally in A_1; the magnitude in register A, which is now in 2's-complement form, should be converted into its true form.

The above addition and subtraction operations are now expressed in symbolic statements. This calls for the contents in a memory register (addend or subtrahend) to be added to or subtracted from the contents in register A (augend or minuend). In the following statements, register R is regarded as consisting of bits R_2 to R_6 and register A of bits A_2 through A_6. A_0 is the overflow bit (1

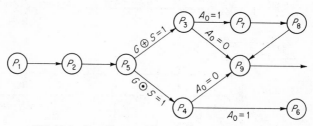

FIG. 12-3   State diagram of binary addition and subtraction.

indicates overflow); S is the sign flipflop (1 indicates negative); G is the add-subtract flipflop (0 indicates add). P_i represents counter states or control signals. (M) denotes the contents of the memory. The state diagram is shown in Fig. 12-3; the symbolic statements are as follows:

$$P_1: (M) \Rightarrow R$$
$$P_2: (R_1) + (A_1) \Rightarrow S$$
$$P_3 \text{ or } P_8: (A) - (R) \Rightarrow A$$
$$P_4: (A) + (R) \Rightarrow A$$
$$P_5: \text{No operation}$$
$$P_6: \text{Turn on overflow indicator}$$
$$P_7: (\bar{A}_1) \Rightarrow A_1 \qquad (A) \Rightarrow R \qquad 0 \Rightarrow A$$
$$P_9: \text{Addition or subtraction completed}$$

(12-1)

Logic equations can now be derived from these symbolic statements. However, they are not derived here, as such a step has been well illustrated in Chap. 11.

Multiplication. A binary multiplication configuration is shown in Fig. 12-4 for numbers in signed-magnitude representation. There are three registers R, A, and Q. Register A is an accumulator. Registers A and Q (except the A_1 bit) are combined into one shift register capable of shifting the combined contents to the right. Flipflop A_0 is for temporarily storing the possible carry during multiplication. The signs of the multiplicand and the multiplier are stored in R_1 and Q_1, respectively. The sign of the product is determined by the half adder. Counter C tallies the number of additions. The direct-multiplication method is chosen, its algorithm being shown in Table 1-17.

Initially, the multiplier has been stored in register Q. The multiplicand is taken from the memory and stored in register R, register A is set to zero, and counter C is set to number 5 (for 5 number bits). The multiplication (see Fig. 1-2) begins by examining Q_6, the least significant bit of the multiplier. If it is 1, the number in register R is added to that in register A; if it is 0, no addition is performed. The number in counter C is reduced by 1. The contents of the combined register are shifted to the right 1 bit. The shifting should follow the algorithm of Table 1-9. After the shift, the original contents in Q_6 contain the second least significant bit of the multiplier, and its value again determines an addi-

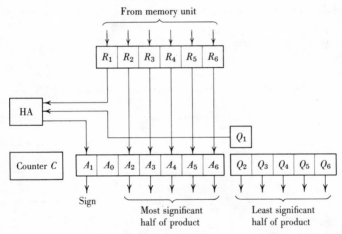

FIG. 12-4 A parallel arithmetic unit in multiplication configuration with numbers in signed-magnitude representation.

tion or no addition. This process continues until all number bits of the multiplier are shifted out of register Q. At this time, the counter shows a number of 0. The sign bit is then inserted into A_1. The product is available in A_2 to A_6 (the most significant half of the product) and in Q_2 through Q_6 (the least significant half).

The remaining problem is round-off. The multiplication can be instructed either with round-off or without. For the latter case, no additional operation is done. For the former case, the round-off can be performed in two ways, as described in Chap. 1. One way is to replace the A_6 bit by 1, regardless of whether that bit was originally 1 or 0. The other way is to add 1 to the Q_2 bit (the most significant bit of the least significant half of the product) and then to add the carry or carries which this may induce; and only the most significant half of the product is kept.

The above multiplication is now expressed in symbolic statements. This calls for the multiplication of the contents in register Q (multiplier) by the contents in a memory register (multiplicand). In the following, AQ signifies the combined register consisting of A_0, A_2 to A_6, and Q_2 to Q_6, which are denoted by AQ_0 to AQ_{10}. (M) denotes the contents of the memory. P_i represents counter states or control signals. The state diagram is shown in Fig. 12-5; the symbolic statements are as follows:

$$
\begin{aligned}
&P_1: (M) \Rightarrow R \qquad 0 \Rightarrow A \qquad 5 \Rightarrow C \\
&P_2: (R) + (A) \Rightarrow A \quad \text{if } Q_6 = 1 \\
&\quad \text{No operation if } Q_6 = 0 \\
&\quad (C) - 1 \Rightarrow C \\
&P_3: (AQ_i) \Rightarrow AQ_{i+1} \qquad \text{for } i = 0, \dots, 10 \\
&\quad 0 \Rightarrow A_0 \\
&P_4: (R_1) \oplus (Q_1) \Rightarrow A_1 \qquad 1 \Rightarrow A_6 \\
&P_5: \text{Multiplication completed}
\end{aligned}
\tag{12-2}
$$

Division. A binary division configuration is shown in Fig. 12-6 for numbers in signed-2's-complement representation. There are three registers R, A, and Q.

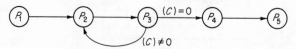

FIG. 12-5   State diagram of binary multiplication.

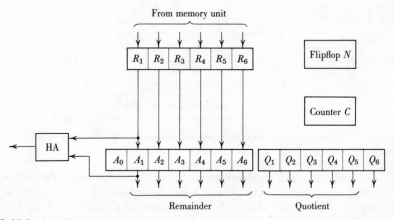

FIG. 12-6   A parallel arithmetic unit in division configuration with numbers in signed-2's-complement representation.

Register A is an accumulator. Registers A and Q are also combined into one shift register capable of shifting the combined contents to the left. Flipflop A_0 stores the sign of the dividend for checking the divide-stop condition. The half adder compares the sign bits of the divisor and the partial remainder. Counter C tallies the number of additions or subtractions required for the division. Flipflop N indicates an alarm condition when a divide-stop condition occurs. The chosen algorithm is the nonrestoring method given in Table 1-23.

Initially, the dividend has been stored in register A. The divisor is taken from memory and stored in register R, register Q is set to zero, and counter C is set at the number 5 (for 5 number bits). The first task is to test whether or not a divide-stop condition exists. This is achieved first by adding the number in register R to, or subtracting it from, the number in register A, depending on whether the signs of the divisor and the dividend are different or the same, respectively. A test is then made to determine the divide-stop condition. The algorithm for this test is derived from the condition that the absolute magnitude of the dividend should be smaller than that of the divisor. (The derivation is left as a problem.) If such a condition occurs, flipflop N is turned on and the computer is stopped.

If the divide-stop condition does not occur, the division begins by restoring the contents of register A. The first quotient bit, which is 1 or 0 according to the sign bits of the divisor and the partial remainder being the same or different, respectively, is then determined. This bit is inserted into Q_6. The number in counter C is then reduced by 1. The contents of the combined register are then shifted 1 bit to the left; the shifting follows the algorithm in Table 1-9. If the quotient bit is 1, the contents of register R are subtracted from the contents of register A; if not, the contents of register R are added to those of register A. Sign bits R_1 and A_1 are again compared and the comparison in turn determines the second quotient bit. This process continues until quotient bits Q_1 to Q_5, but not Q_6, are filled. At this time, the counter shows a number of 0. A correction is then applied to the pseudo-quotient bits in Q_1 to Q_5. The correction consists in adding 1 to Q_1 (or complementing the content of Q_1) and to Q_6 (or inserting 1 into Q_6). A correct sign is produced in Q_1. The remainder is in the accumulator.

The above division will now be expressed in symbolic statements. This calls for the division of the contents in register A (dividend) by the contents in a memory register (divisor). Symbol AQ denotes the combined register, consisting of all bits in registers A and Q. AQ_1 to AQ_6 denote A_1 to A_6, and AQ_7 to AQ_{12} denote Q_1 to Q_6. (M) denotes the contents of the memory. P_i indicates the counter states or control signals. The state diagram is shown in Fig. 12-7; the symbolic statements are as follows:

$$P_1: (M) \Rightarrow R \qquad 0 \Rightarrow Q \qquad 5 \Rightarrow C \qquad (A_1) \Rightarrow A_0$$
$$P_2, P_5, P_9: (A) - (R) \Rightarrow A$$
$$P_3, P_6, P_{10}: (A) + (R) \Rightarrow A$$
$$P_4: 1 \Rightarrow N \qquad \text{if } \left\{ (A_0 \odot A_1) + \prod_{i=1}^{6} \bar{A}_i \right\} = 1$$

No operation otherwise $\qquad\qquad$ (12-3)

$$P_7: 1 \Rightarrow Q_6 \qquad \text{if } R_1 \oplus A_1 = 0$$
$$ 0 \Rightarrow Q_6 \qquad \text{if } R_1 \oplus A_1 = 1$$
$$ (C) - 1 \Rightarrow C$$
$$P_8: 0 \Rightarrow Q_6 \qquad (AQ_i) \Rightarrow AQ_{i-1} \qquad \text{for } i = 1, \ldots, 12$$
$$P_{11}: 1 \Rightarrow Q_6 \qquad (Q_1) \Rightarrow Q_1 \qquad \text{Division completed}$$

Square Root. Extraction of a binary square root of a positive number is quite similar to binary division. The configuration is shown in Fig. 12-8. There are three registers R, A, and Q, and register A is an accumulator. Registers A and Q (except bit Q_1) are again combined into one shift register capable of shifting the combined contents to the left. Counter C tallies the number of additions or subtractions required for the square root. Flipflop N indicates an alarm condition when the radicand is a negative number. The chosen algorithm is the nonrestoring method given in Table 1-25.

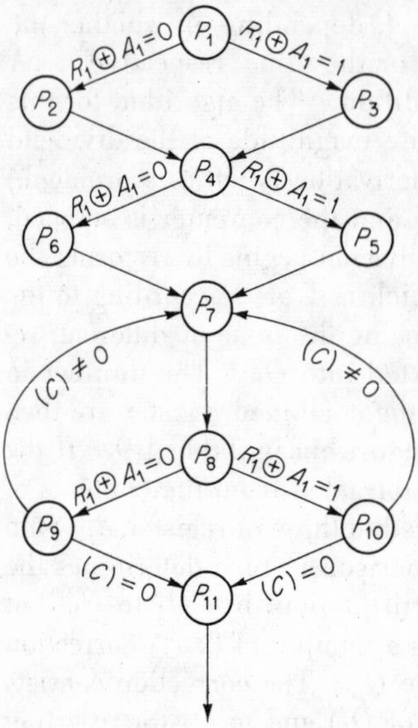

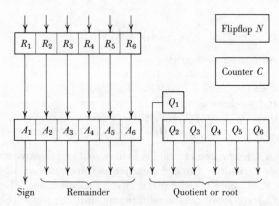

FIG. 12-7   State diagram of binary division.

The sequential operations of the three registers for extraction of a square root are shown in Fig. 1-5. Initially, the radicand is taken from the memory, stored in register R, and then transferred to register A. Register Q is set to 0, and counter C is set at number 5 (for 5 number bits). A test is then made at bit R_1 to determine whether or not the radicand is a negative number. If it is a negative number, flipflop N is turned on and the machine halts.

If it is not a negative number, the first root extractor is formed in register R by inserting the constant 001000 into the register. The root extractor is equivalent to the divisor in division, but it changes after each quotient digit is found. The number in register R is next subtracted from the radicand in the accumulator, and the difference (the first partial remainder) is stored in the accumulator. Whether the sign bit A_1 of the partial remainder is 0 or 1 determines whether the quotient bit is 1 or 0 and whether the subsequent operation is a subtraction or an addition. If bit A_1 is 0, the quotient bit 1 is inserted into bit Q_6 and constant 101 is inserted into $R_2R_3R_4$. The number in register R now is the second root extractor. The combined shift register then shifts the contents 1 bit to the left; this is followed by a subtraction of the number in register R from the partial remainder in the accumulator. The number in the accumulator now is the second partial remainder. If bit A_1 is 1, quotient bit 0 is inserted into bit Q_6 and constant 011 is inserted into $R_2R_3R_4$. The combined shift register again shifts, but

FIG. 12-8   A parallel arithmetic unit in square-root configuration.

this is followed by an addition of the number in register R to the number in the accumulator. In either case, the number in the counter is reduced by 1.

The second quotient bit is now determined by bit A_1 of the second partial remainder in the accumulator. If bit A_1 is 1, quotient bit 1 is inserted into bit Q_6 and constant 101 is inserted into $R_3R_4R_5$. The combined register again shifts, and this is followed by a subtraction of the number in register R from the partial remainder in the accumulator. If bit A_1 is 0, quotient bit 0 is inserted into bit Q_6 and constant 011 is inserted into $R_3R_4R_5$. The combined register again shifts, and this is followed by an addition. Again the number in the counter is reduced by 1.

This process continues until the number in the counter is 0. At this time, the quotient appears in both registers Q and R and the remainder in the accumulator.

The above square-root process using the nonrestoring method will now be expressed in symbolic statements. This calls for the square root of a radicand in the memory. Symbol AQ signifies the combined register consisting of A_1 to A_6 and Q_2 to Q_6; they are denoted by AQ_0 to AQ_{10}. (M) denotes the contents of the memory. P_i indicates the counter states or control signals. The state diagram is shown in Fig. 12-9; the symbolic statements are as follows:

$$
\begin{aligned}
&P_1: (M) \Rightarrow R \\
&P_2: (R) \Rightarrow A \qquad 0 \Rightarrow Q \qquad 5 \Rightarrow C \\
&P_3: 1 \Rightarrow N \qquad \text{Machine halts} \\
&P_4: 001000 \Rightarrow R \\
&P_5, P_{12}: (A) - (R) \Rightarrow A \qquad (C) - 1 \Rightarrow C \\
&\quad P_6: \text{If } A_1 = 0 \quad 1 \Rightarrow Q_6 \quad \text{and} \quad 101 \Rightarrow R_2R_3R_4 \\
&\qquad\quad \text{If } A_1 = 1 \quad 0 \Rightarrow Q_6 \quad \text{and} \quad 011 \Rightarrow R_2R_3R_4 \\
&\quad P_7: \text{If } A_1 = 0 \quad 1 \Rightarrow Q_6 \quad \text{and} \quad 101 \Rightarrow R_3R_4R_5 \\
&\qquad\quad \text{If } A_1 = 1 \quad 0 \Rightarrow Q_6 \quad \text{and} \quad 011 \Rightarrow R_3R_4R_5 \\
&\quad P_8: \text{If } A_1 = 0 \quad 1 \Rightarrow Q_6 \quad \text{and} \quad 101 \Rightarrow R_4R_5R_6 \\
&\qquad\quad \text{If } A_1 = 1 \quad 0 \Rightarrow Q_6 \quad \text{and} \quad 011 \Rightarrow R_4R_5R_6 \\
&\quad P_9: \text{If } A_1 = 0 \quad 1 \Rightarrow Q_6 \quad \text{and} \quad 01 \Rightarrow R_5R_6 \\
&\qquad\quad \text{If } A_1 = 1 \quad 0 \Rightarrow Q_6 \quad \text{and} \quad 10 \Rightarrow R_5R_6 \\
&\quad P_{10}: \text{If } A_1 = 0 \quad 0 \Rightarrow Q_6 \quad \text{and} \quad 0 \Rightarrow R_6 \\
&\qquad\quad \text{If } A_1 = 1 \quad 1 \Rightarrow Q_6 \quad \text{and} \quad 1 \Rightarrow R_6 \\
&\quad P_{11}: (AQ_i) \Rightarrow AQ_{i-1} \qquad \text{for } i = 1, \ldots, 10 \\
&\qquad\quad 0 \Rightarrow AQ_{10} \\
&\quad P_{13}: (A) + (R) \Rightarrow R \qquad (C) - 1 \Rightarrow C \\
&P_{14}, P_{15}: \text{No operation} \\
&\quad P_{16}: \text{Square root completed}
\end{aligned}
$$

$$(12\text{-}4)$$

12-2 *A Serial Binary Arithmetic Unit*

A serial arthmetic unit capable of performing addition, subtraction, multiplication, and division is essentially a serial binary accumulator with two additional registers. The algorithms developed in Chap. 1 are also applied to the serial unit. Because the serial word arrives one bit at a time, implementation of the algorithms requires the consideration of time sequence of the serial word. For this reason, the time sequence of a serial word is established and shown in Fig. 12-10. In this figure, each pulse indicates the location of 1 bit of the serial word. These timing pulses are divided by means of a counter into *word times*, or *word periods*. Each word time is subdivided into a number of *bit times*, or *bit periods*. Assume that there are 6 bits in each word, including the sign bit. Each word time in Fig. 12-10 consists of seven bit times; the extra bit, called the *space bit*, is often provided. The seven bit times are designated as D_0 to D_6 and the word times as W_0, W_1, etc. For example, $W_0 D_3$ signifies the time at which bit time D_3 occurs during word time W_0. In the subsequent description of the serial arithmetic unit, addition or subtraction requires at least one word time, while multiplication or

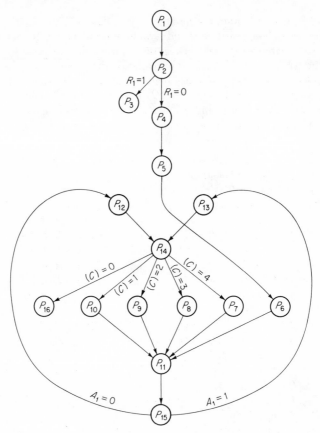

FIG. 12-9   State diagram of binary square root.

division requires approximately as many word times as the number of bits in the serial word.

A serial arithmetic unit consists also of three registers A, R, and Q; they are essentially the same as those shown in Table 12-1. The three registers in the serial arithmetic unit are all shift and circulating registers, and the same letters and subscripts mentioned in regard to the parallel unit are again used to denote their flipflops. However, the contents of the flipflops represented by these symbols in a serial unit change at each bit time.

Since registers A, R, and Q are all shift and circulating registers, one may consider the use of one word location in a track of a magnetic drum (or a magnetic disk) as such a register. This has the advantage of being much less expensive. Thus, the magnetic drum (or the magnetic disk) is not only a memory unit but can also be made a part of a serial arithmetic unit.

In a serial arithmetic unit, the time sequence of the bits of a serial word may be arranged in two ways. One way is to have the least significant bit lead the word, followed by the more significant bits, with the sign bit trailing at the end. A word sequence with an ascending weight in the number bits as time goes on is a practical necessity, because in a serial operation this results in a simple handling of the carry or borrow. The other way is to have the sign bit lead the word and the most significant bit stay at the end. The latter way is invariably used in serial operation for numbers in signed-magnitude representation.

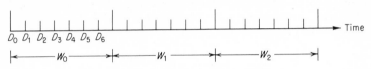

FIG. 12-10   Timing pulses for word times and bit times.

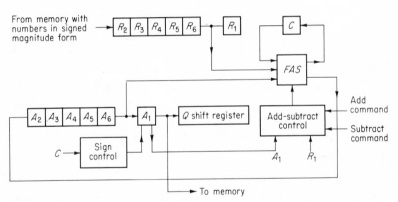

FIG. 12-11   A serial binary arithmetic unit in addition and subtraction configuration with numbers in signed-magnitude representation.

Addition and Subtraction for Signed-magnitude Numbers.

The configuration of a serial arithmetic unit varies to a certain extent with the chosen number representation. A configuration for numbers in the arithmetic and memory units represented by signed magnitude is shown in Fig. 12-11. The addend and augend are stored in shift registers R and A, respectively, the sign bit leading the word. Register Q is not used. One full adder–subtractor (FAS) and one carry flipflop C are the circuits where the addition and subtraction are actually performed. The addition or subtraction performed by the FAS is controlled by the add-subtract control block, which in turn is determined by the add command, the subtract command, and the two signs in R_1 and A_1 according to the algorithms in Table 1-11. The carry flipflop should be cleared before an addition or a subtraction begins. Later, there is a need to complement the contents in the A register; for this reason, the minuend and the subtrahend are stored, respectively, in the R and A registers.

An addition or a subtraction operation in the configuration of Fig. 12-11 may require three word times after the subtrahend (or addend) has been transferred into the A register. During the first word, the minuend (or augend) is shifted into the R register. During the second word time, the number bits of the minuend (or augend) and subtrahend (or addend) are both shifted out of R and A registers, one bit at a time, and into the FAS for subtraction (or addition). Sign bits R_1 and A_1 are not shifted but remain in R_1 and A_1. The difference (or sum) from the FAS is fed back and stored one bit at a time in the A register. If there is a borrow coming from the most significant bit in the case of the FAS performing a subtraction, the difference is negative and a negative sign is inserted into A_1. When the difference is negative, the number bits in the A register are in 2's-complement form. This cannot be converted into the sign and magnitude form until the subtraction is completed because the appearance of the borrow will not be known until then. This conversion is performed in

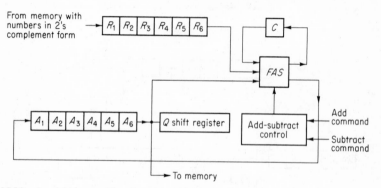

FIG. 12-12 A serial binary arithmetic unit in addition and subtraction configuration with numbers in signed-2's-complement representation.

the third word time. During the third word time, the R register is first cleared, and the number in register A is subtracted from the zeros in register R. The number bits from the FAS again stored in the A register are of the required magnitude.

The three word times for an addition or a subtraction can be reduced. The first word time can be eliminated by feeding the serial word from the memory directly to the FAS. The third word time may utilize the word time in transferring the word from register A to the memory.

Addition and Subtraction for Signed-complement Numbers. A configuration for numbers in signed-2's-complement representation is shown in Fig. 12-12. The sign bit trails at the end of the serial word, as the sign bit is treated as a number bit. An addition or a subtraction may require two word times after the augend or the minuend has been transferred to the A register. During the first word time, the addend or the subtrahend is transferred to the R register. The addition or subtraction is performed during the second word time. The addition or subtraction in the FAS is controlled directly by a command from the computer control unit. The sum or difference can be either stored in the A register or sent to the memory. The first word time can be eliminated if the word from the memory is sent directly to the FAS; if this is done, only one word time is required for an addition or a subtraction.

A configuration for numbers in signed-magnitude representation in the memory but in signed-2's-complement form in the arithmetic unit is shown in Fig. 12-13. Two serial complementers are employed. However, either a full adder (FA) or a full subtractor (FS) is sufficient because subtraction by addition of the 2's-complement method or addition by subtraction of the 2's-complement method can be used. The serial complementer 1 is actuated by the add and subtract commands and the 2 sign bits; thus, the sign bit should lead the serial word. On the other hand, the arithmetic operation requires the sign bit to trail at the end of the serial word. Therefore, the complementer should not only complement the number but also reverse the location of the sign bit. The operation in the serial arithmetic unit is better described by a timing chart, as shown in Fig. 12-14. In this figure, the small letters l, m, and s denote, respectively, the least significant bit,

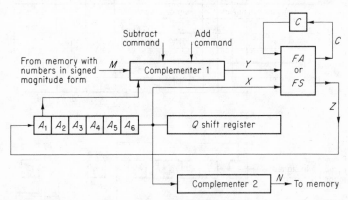

FIG. 12-13 A serial binary arithmetic unit in addition and subtraction configuration with two number representations.

the most significant bit, and the sign bit. During W_0, the serial word from the memory arrives at complementer 1 with a leading sign bit. The complementer complements the number bits if the number is negative and rearranges the word with a trailing sign bit. This rearranged word then passes through the FA (or FS) with no arithmetic operation and is stored in the A register. This is shown in the W_0 word time of Fig. 12-14. The addition or subtraction is carried out during W_1. The sum or difference is transferred to the memory in W_2, during which the serial word is restored with a leading sign bit and with the number bits complemented if necessary by serial complementer 2. Addition or subtraction in the configuration of Fig. 12-13 requires only one word time.

The two complementers in Fig. 12-13 can be avoided if the FA (or FS) is used to perform the 2's complement of the number bits of the number to or from the memory. This is, however, at the expense of one additional register to store an operand and of two additional word times.

The representation of numbers in signed-1's-complement form is not especially desirable in a serial arithmetic unit, because the operation for end-around carry or end-around borrow requires an additional word time. Otherwise, the configurations for addition and subtraction are similar to those of Figs. 12-12 and 12-13.

Multiplication. A multiplication configuration is shown in Fig. 12-15 for numbers in signed-magnitude representation. There are three shift registers R,

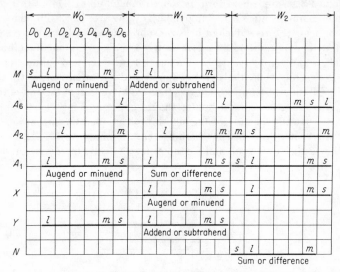

FIG. 12-14 Timing chart for addition and subtraction.

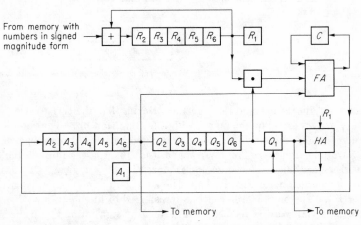

FIG. 12-15 A serial binary arithmetic unit in multiplication configuration with numbers in signed-magnitude representation.

A, and Q, a serial adder, and a half adder. The sign bit leads the serial word as indicated by the subscripts of the letters R, A, and Q in the figure. All bits (except bit Q_1) of registers A and Q form a combined shift register. Register R is also a circulating register.

Initially, the multiplier is stored in register Q with the sign bit in Q_1. During word time W_0 the multiplicand is serially transferred to register R with the sign bit in R_1.   Sign bits R_1 and Q_1 do not move during the succeeding shifting of the contents of registers.

During word time W_1 the value of 1 or 0 of the least significant bit of the multiplier in Q_6 determines whether or not the number bits of the multiplicand are to be added; and the addition, if there is one, is carried out.   Also, during W_1, the circulating register R restores its original contents, and the partial product is serially inserted into register A, occupying bits A_2 to A_6.   The combined register is then shifted 1 bit to the right during the space-bit time; during this shift, any carry bit left in flipflop C is shifted into A_2, and the least significant bit is now at Q_2.   The next addition begins at bit A_6 but not at bit Q_2.

After the right shift, the least significant bit of the multiplier in Q_6 is lost, as Q_1 is not a part of the combined register. Q_6 now contains the second least significant bit of the multiplier, which initiates another possible addition during W_2.

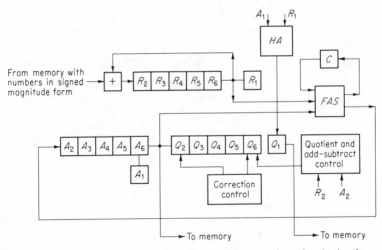

FIG. 12-16   A serial binary arithmetic unit in division configuration with numbers in signed-magnitude representation.

This process of addition and right shifting continues until all multiplier number bits are shifted out of the combined register.   By then, the product is available in the combined register, the most and the least significant halves of the product being stored, respectively, in the A and Q registers.   With no round-off, the sign bit is inserted into Q_1.   With round-off, 1 is inserted into bit A_6, and the sign of the product (determined by the HA) is inserted into bit A_1; the number in register A is now in the desired order.   Since one word time is required for one addition, multiplication using the configuration of Fig. 12-15 requires approximately as many word times as the number of bits in the word.

Division.   A division configuration for numbers in signed-magnitude representation with a leading sign bit is shown in Fig. 12-16.   Bits A_2 to A_6 and Q_2 to Q_6 form a combined shift register.   Initially, the dividend is stored in shift register A, and register Q is cleared.   During word time W_0 the divisor is transferred to register R.   The sign bits of the divisor and dividend are now stored in R_1 and A_1, respectively; they remain there during the division. At this time, a test of the divide-stop condition is made during word time W_1 by subtracting the number bits in register R from those in register A. If a borrow appears at flipflop C at the end of the subtraction, the divide-stop condition does not occur. The number bits in register R are restored during W_1 by the circulating nature of register R. The number bits in register A are then restored during W_2 by adding those in register R.

The division begins during word time W_3. Here, the algorithm of the non-restoring method given in Table 1-23 is chosen. Briefly, during W_3 whether the first quotient bit is 1 or 0 is determined by whether the values in R_2 and A_2 are the same or different, and the first quotient bit is inserted into Q_6. When the quotient bit is 1, the contents of the combined register are shifted 1 bit to the left and the number in register R is subtracted from the number in register A. When the quotient bit is 0, similar shifting occurs but an addition instead of a subtraction is performed. After this addition or subtraction, whether the second quotient bit is 1 or 0 is again determined during W_4 by whether the values of R_2 and A_2 are the same or different. The value 1 or 0 of the second quotient bit determines whether the next operation is left-shifting-and-subtraction or left-shifting-and-addition, respectively. This process continues in the subsequent word times until quotient

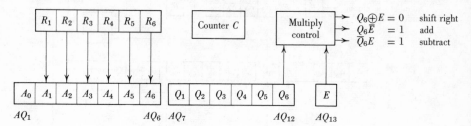

FIG. 12-17 A multiplier using Booth's algorithm.

bits Q_2 to Q_5 are filled. During the last word time W_7, the contents of Q_2 is complemented, and 1 is inserted into Q_6; the sign of the quotient is inserted into Q_1 from the HA. After completion of the division process, the quotient and remainder are stored in the Q and A registers, respectively. The division requires at least as many word times as the number of bits in the word.

12-3 Binary Multipliers

There are three general methods for designing a binary multiplier. These are the repeated-addition method, the paired-digit- (or multiple-digit-) multiplication method, and the simultaneous-multiplication method, in addition to their possible variations and combinations. The particular choice is usually a compromise between multiplication time and the amount of circuitry. Four multipliers using these methods are now described.

A Multiplier Using Repeated-addition Method. The repeated-addition method has already been described in regard to the serial and the parallel arithmetic unit. The method takes about as many addition times in the parallel unit and as many word times in the serial unit as the number of bits in the multiplier, but it is comparatively simple. Figure 12-17 shows a parallel binary multiplier using the repeated method by means of Booth's algorithm for numbers in signed-2's-complement form. There are three registers R, A, and Q, a reference flipflop E, and a counter C. Registers A and Q and flipflop E form a combined shift register. Bit A_0 is for temporary storing of the carry during multiplication. Initially, the multiplier is stored in register Q. The multiplication begins by first taking the multiplicand from the memory and storing it in register R; in the meantime, register A and flipflop E are cleared, and the number 6 is placed into counter C. Multiplication then proceeds by examining the contents of Q_6 and E. If the contents are 00 or 11, the combined register is shifted 1 bit to the right. If they are 01 or 10, the contents of the R register are respectively added to or subtracted from those of the A register and the combined register is then shifted 1 bit to the right. When the contents of Q_6 and E are first examined, they can only be 00 or 10. This process continues until the contents of Q_1 are shifted into Q_6. Now comes the final examination of Q_6 and E. If they are 00 or 11, nothing is to be done. If they are 01 or 10, the contents of the R register are respectively added to or subtracted from those of the A register. No shifting operation is performed during this last round. Afterward, Q_6 and E are cleared. The most significant half of the product is stored in A_1 to A_6 and the least significant half in Q_1 to Q_5 with the sign in A_1. The above shift-right operation observes the shifting algorithm for signed binary numbers.

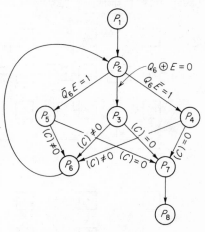

FIG. 12-18   State diagram of binary multiplication.

The foregoing multiplying process will now be expressed in symbolic statements. This calls for the multiplication of a number in the memory by the number in the Q register. The state diagram is shown in Fig. 12-18; the symbolic statements are as follows:

$$P_1: (M) \Rightarrow R, \qquad 0 \Rightarrow A, \qquad 0 \Rightarrow E, \qquad 6 \Rightarrow C,$$
$$P_2: (C) - 1 \Rightarrow C,$$
$$P_3: \text{No operation}$$
$$P_4: (A) + (R) \Rightarrow A$$
$$P_5: (A) - (R) \Rightarrow A$$
$$P_6: (AQ_i) \Rightarrow AQ_{i+1} \qquad \text{for } i = 1, \ldots, 12$$
$$(AQ_1) \Rightarrow AQ_1$$
$$P_7: 0 \Rightarrow Q_6 \qquad 0 \Rightarrow E$$
$$P_8: \text{Multiplication completed.}$$

(12-5)

A Serial-Parallel Multiplier. To reduce the multiplication time in a serial arithmetic unit, the serial-parallel multiplier should be considered. A configuration of this type for numbers in signed-magnitude representation is shown in Fig.

12-19.   There are three registers, X, Z, and W.   For a 6-bit number including a leading sign bit, six full adders are required.   The multiplicand is first transferred serially into the X register; this takes one word time.   The sign bit is stored in X_1.   As the first sign bit of the multiplier arrives from the memory, the sign bit is added to the contents of X_1 and the resulting sum bit is now in X_1.   This modulo-2 sum bit is the correct sign of the product and is next inserted into the sum flipflop Z_1.   As the succeeding serial-multiplier bits arrive, each bit causes either an add (for the multiplier bit being 1) or a shift (for the multiplier bit being 0).   If it is an add, the configuration is that of Fig. 12-19a; if it is a shift, the configuration is that of Fig. 12-19b.   In the addition configuration, the flipflops in the W register function as carry flipflops for each full adder, and the manner

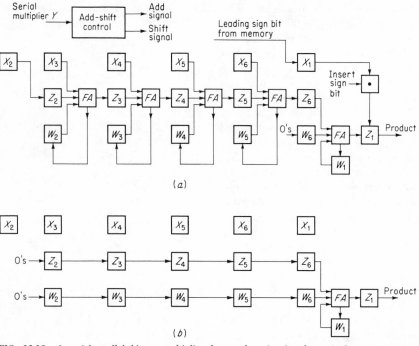

(a)

(b)

FIG. 12-19   A serial-parallel binary multiplier for numbers in signed-magnitude representation. (a) Addition configuration when the multiplier bit is 1; (b) shift configuration when the multiplier bit is 0.

of connecting these flipflops performs the shift-right operation automatically after each addition.   In the shift configuration, the Z and W registers function as shift registers.   As the addition or shift is being performed, the product bits become available at the output of Z_1, one bit at each bit time.   The multiplication is completed in one word time, during which the least significant half of the product is delivered at the output of Z_1.   The most significant half is now stored in the Z register.   It takes another word time to shift its contents out of the multiplier. The muliplication takes a total of three word times.

This multiplier actually employs repeated addition.   It makes possible the reduction of multiplication time in a serial unit to only three word times, at the expense, however, of a large number of adders.

A Multiplier Using the Paired-digit-multiplication Method. Paired-digit multiplication, which was described in Chap. 1, requires the generation of $2X$ and $3X$, where X is the multiplicand. A serial-parallel binary multiplier using this multiplication method is shown in Fig. 12-20. In Fig. 12-19 the multiplicand is stored in a register, while the multiplier arrives serially from the memory. In Fig. 12-20, the *multiplier* is stored (not shown, but indicated by the symbol Y_i); as the serial multiplicand X_i appears, $2X_i$ and $3X_i$ are being generated by using delays and a full adder. A pair of adjacent multiplier bits make a choice among four quantities, 0, X_i, $2X_i$, and $3X_i$. The sign bit is inserted into flipflop Z at an appropriate time. The multiplication time is two word times, the word time for storing the multiplier being excluded. The above can be readily extended to configurations using multiple-digit multiplication.

A Simultaneous Multiplier. Binary multiplication is merely many additions of a shifted multiplicand. An ordinary parallel binary adder can add only two numbers at a time, and the time of carry propagation limits the speed. An

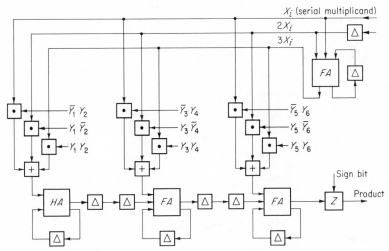

FIG. 12-20　A serial-parallel binary multiplier using paired digit multiplication.

extremely fast multiplier needs a parallel binary adder which can simultaneously sum as many numbers as the multiplier bits. Such a multiplier is called a *simultaneous multiplier.*

A simultaneous multiplier for multiplying two 3-bit numbers is shown in Fig. 12-21. The parallelogram matrix simultaneously generates three shifted multiplicands. The *and*-gate outputs on the same column (of the matrix) are connected to a half adder, a full adder, or a multiple-input adder (MA). The MA in Fig. 12-21 has four inputs, including a carry input; it can be built from half and full adders or from a matrix.

The simultaneous multiplier is very rapid, as it requires only a single addition time, carry propagation time being included. It is feasible but rather impractical because an enormous number of components are required when the number of bits in a word lie in the practical range of 20 to 64 bits.

It is noted that the squaring matrix described in Chap. 9 is a special case of the simultaneous multiplier.

12-4   *A Serial Binary Floating-point Arithmetic Unit*

In the following, the adding, subtracting, multiplying, and dividing operations of a serial binary floating-point arithmetic unit are described.   The description is rather brief and is limited to those operations which add to the operations in a fixed-point arithmetic unit.

Number Representation.   Floating-point arithmetic was discussed in Chap. 2.   Let the floating-point binary number be represented by $f2^e$, where f is a 6-bit

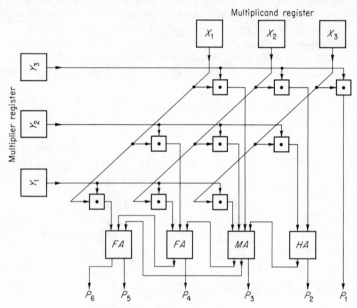

FIG. 12-21   A simultaneous multiplier.

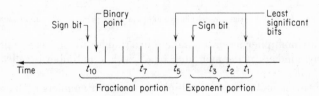

FIG. 12-22   Time sequence of a floating-point binary number.

fractional number and e a 4-bit exponent number.   The time sequence of this number is shown in Fig. 12-22; the exponent portion leads the fractional portion.   The binary number f adopts the conventional fractional form; its most significant bit is the sign, and the other bits are fractional.   It has a fixed binary point, and its negative number is in 2's-complement form.   The 4-bit exponent portion e is an integer, its most significant bit representing the sign.   When it is negative, it is in 2's-complement form.   Thus, the range of the exponent number is

$$+8 > e \geq -8$$

Numbers are stored in the memory in the normalized form. The range of the normalized fractional number is

$$1 > f \geq \tfrac{1}{2} \qquad \text{for positive binary number}$$
$$-\tfrac{1}{2} > f \geq -1 \qquad \text{for negative binary number} \qquad (12\text{-}6)$$

Several examples are given below. Notice that the fractional numbers a and c are in normalized form, while examples b and d are not. The normalized form has been chosen so that there is a *change-over* in values between the sign bit and the most significant bit.

(a)	$0.10000 = +\tfrac{1}{2}$
(b)	$0.01000 = +\tfrac{1}{4}$
(c)	$1.00000 = -1$
(d)	$1.10000 = -\tfrac{1}{2}$

Example a illustrates the change-over of 01 for a positive number, and example c shows that of 10 for a negative number. This change-over serves as a means for sensing the number of bit shifts to normalize a number. Since the fractional number arrives serially with the sign bit trailing, it is the last change-over that is important for the later description of the normalizing process.

Configuration. A serial floating-point binary arithmetic unit is shown in Fig. 12-23. There are three registers: A, R, and Q. The A and R registers consist of two portions, an exponent portion and a fractional portion. They are denoted subscripts e and f, respectively. The A_f, R_f, and Q registers form a serial accumulator for arithmetic operations on the fractional portion, while the A_e and R_e registers form another accumulator for adding and subtracting operations on the exponent portion. Because of possible overflow during addition, overflow bits A_{fo} and A_{eo} are provided, respectively, in the A_f and A_e registers. With them, the range of the number in the A register becomes $2 > f \geq -2$, and that in the A_e register $16 > e \geq -16$.

In the floating-point arithmetic unit there are two additional operations, the shift of the fractional number by a specified number of bits, and the normalization of the number after an arithmetic operation. The former operation is achieved under the shift control block and the latter by using the Z counter, as indicated in Fig. 12-23.

Addition and Subtraction. Addition or subtraction in the floating-point arithmetic unit follows Eqs. (2-26) to (2-28). It takes four word times, the time to take two numbers from the memory to registers A and R being excluded. Each word time in the floating-point unit is shorter that that in the fixed-point unit for the same word length, because the actual number bits are fewer in the floating-point unit. Assume that two numbers have been transferred into registers A and R. The operation is described below:

1. During the first word time, the contents in register R_e are subtracted from those in register A_e. The difference, denoted by d, is stored in register A_e.

2. During the second word time, the contents of register A_f or R_f are shifted, depending on the difference d. If d is positive (i.e., flipflop W_e shows a 0), the contents in register A_e remain unchanged but those in register R_f are shifted d bits to the right. If d is negative (W_e shows a 1), the contents in register A_e are replaced by those in register R_e in a parallel transfer and those in register A_f are shifted d bits to the right.

3. During the third word time, the contents in register R_f are added to or subtracted from (depending on the command signal) the contents in register A_f. Also, during this word time, counter Z establishes the number of bits to be shifted and the shift direction for normalization.

4. During the fourth word time, normalization of the sum or difference in register A_f occurs. The number in register A_f is shifted to the right or left a number of bits specified by counter Z. And the number of shifts is added to or subtracted from the number in register A_e. The most significant number bit in register A_f is now adjacent to the sign bit (i.e., the last change-over appears at the sign bit) and the number in register A_f is normalized.

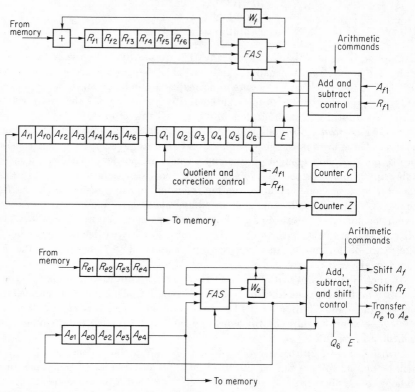

FIG. 12-23   A serial binary floating-point arithmetic unit with numbers in signed-2's-complement representation.

Counter Z is a binary counter, counting a sequence of seven timing pulses during the third word time when the sum or difference bit appears at the output of the full adder–subtractor. Counter Z is initially reset to 0 and is reset to 0 during counting every time a change-over signal appears. The change-over signal is obtained by sending the output from full adder–subtractor to one input of a half adder and sending the same output first through a 1-bit time delay and then to the other input of the half adder. The change-over signal occurs at the second bit of a pair of change-over bits. When the last change-over signal occurs, the count in counter Z indicates the amount of shift. The required maximum shift to the right is 1, and that to the left is 5. The interpretation of the counts in counter Z is as follows: A count of 1 means a 1-bit shift to the right. A count of 2 means no shift. A count of 3 to 7 means a shift to the left 1 bit to 5 bits, respectively. When the count in counter Z is 7 (the maximum count), the contents of register A_e is 0. The number zero ($000000 \cdot 2^0$) in the normalized form is $010000 \cdot 2^{-8}$. Because of the available bits for overflow, the contents of registers A_f and A_e should be $0(0)10000$ and $1(0)000$, where the bit in the parentheses is the overflow bit.

Because of the need for separate operations on exponent and fractional portions, as well as the need for normalization, floating-point addition or subtraction takes more time than fixed-point addition or subtraction, particularly in a serial arithmetic unit.

Multiplication and Division. In multiplication, no alignment of the binary point of the two floating-point numbers is needed. Figure 12-23 shows the use of Booth's algorithm, as indicated by flipflop E. The fractional and exponent portions of the multiplicand are stored in registers R_f and R_e, respectively, while those of the multiplier are stored in registers Q and A_e, respectively.

During the first word time, multiplication of the least multiplier bit is performed. In the meantime the contents in the R_e register is added to that in the A_e register. The multiplication process in the subsequent word times is similar to that described previously and shown in Fig. 12-17. After completion of multiplication, the normalization process takes place. Since both the multiplicand and the multiplier are in the normalized form, the maximum shift required in the product during normalization would be one left shift. However, because of the overflow bit A_{fo}, the maximum shift can be two left shifts. The round-off, if called for, may be applied afterward.

In division, the dividend and the divisor are also in the normalized form. First, the divide-stop condition should be tested for. If it occurs, the dividend may be made smaller by a 1-bit right shift and the division process proceeds. The contents in the R_e register are subtracted from those in the A_e register. The quotient in the Q register (after the division) is transferred to the A_f register so that normalization of the quotient can take place there. Afterward, the round-off process may be applied.

The time for floating-point multiplication (or division) is shorter than that for fixed-point multiplication (or division) because the word time in the floating-point process is shorter, despite the possible need for normalization afterward.

Although the floating-point arithmetic unit helps greatly in the programmer's scaling problem, yet it gives less accuracy for a given word length because the number bits for arithmetic operations are reduced.

12-5   *Instruction Formats and Repertoire*

Previous sections of this chapter have described the organization and operation of arithmetic units; the remaining sections discuss the organization and operation of control units.

A stored-program digital computer has at least two types of word format—number and instruction. The number format specifies a fixed or variable word length, the number of digits in the word (in case of a fixed word length), the location of the radix point, the sign digit, and the number digits. In a parallel binary computer the sign digit is usually the most significant bit; in a serial binary computer the sign bit may be either a leading or a trailing bit. The word length for a commercial binary computer ranges from 20 to 64 bits.

The instruction format is the structure of orders that a computer understands and follows. The design of a program control unit is affected by the choice of the instruction format or formats. Early computers usually have one instruction format; a modern machine may have several formats to accommodate a large instruction repertoire.

Early Instruction Formats. Early instruction formats are classified according to the number of memory addresses in the instruction—single-address format, two-address format, three-address format, and four-address format; these formats are shown in Fig. 12-24.

A number of bits of an instruction word allocated for a special purpose is called

Operation code	Operand address

(a)

Operation code	Operand address	Operand address

(b)

Operation code	Operand address	Operand address	Result or instruction address

(c)

Operation code	Operand address	Operand address	Result address	Instruction address

(d)

FIG. 12-24 Single- and multiple-address instruction formats. (*a*) Single-address format; (*b*) two-address format; (*c*) three-address format; (*d*) four-address format.

a *field*. The single-address format consists of two fields: operation code and address. The operation code specifies the operation to be performed on the operand in the memory located at the address specified by the address field. An addition of two operands thus needs at least two single-address instructions. The next-instruction address does not appear in the format; it is normally the address following the instruction address. Examples of early machines using this simple format include the MIT Whirlwind, IBM 701, and Datatron Computers. The single-address format has the distinct advantage of simplicity.

The two-address format is the same as the single-address format, with the addition of a third field showing a second address for another operand. The operation code specifies the operation to be performed on the two operands. An addition of two operands now requires only one instruction. The next-instruction address is normally again the memory address following the current-instruction address. The Univac Scientific 1103 Computer exemplifies the use of a two-address format. In certain computers such as the IBM 650, the second address field is the next-instruction address; in this case, it is called the *one-plus-one-address format.*

The three-address format has four fields: one for the operation code, one each for two operand addresses, and the remaining one for the memory address at which the result from the operation on the two operands is stored. The SEAC Computer (National Bureau of Standards) exemplifies the use of this format. Alternatively, the third address can be made the next-instruction address.

The four-address format has five fields: one for the operation code, one each for two operand addresses, one for the address at which the result is stored, and the remaining one for the next-instruction address. This format contains addresses for a complete arithmetic operation. The SWAC Computer (National Bureau of Standards) uses this format.

The multiple-address format has some advantage in speed for instructions with multiple operands, and it is more logical for specifying a complete arithmetic

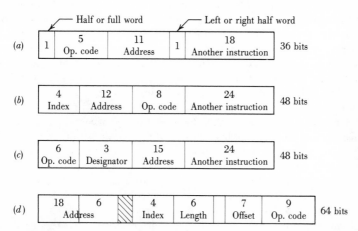

FIG. 12-25 Examples of instruction formats. (*a*) IBM 701 computer instruction format; (*b*) Philco S-2000 computer instruction format; (*c*) CDC 1604 computer instruction format; (*d*) IBM Stretch computer instruction format.

operation. However, it tends to waste memory space for instructions where there is no operand or only one operand. Often the fitting of the instruction word to a desired data-word length is a strong factor to be considered in selecting an instruction format. Two cases can be cited. There are computers where two single-address instructions form an instruction format; in this way, the selected word length can be more efficiently used. An example of the computer using this two-single-address format is the IBM 701; its format is shown in Fig. 12-25a. There are computers where the next-instruction address is the operand address plus another, shorter address field which represents the amount of change. In this way, an increment of address is squeezed into a given data-word length. This increment is sometimes referred to as a *half address.* An ideal format would be one in which the number of addresses varies with the number of operands associated with the operation. One possible approach is to use several instruction formats to suit various types of instructions.

Address Modification and Index Field. It is possible in a stored-program computer to modify an instruction of a program by the program itself. In practice, the modification is usually in the address or addresses of the instruction. The provision of address modification in the instruction makes the instruction more powerful.

Address modification can be effectively achieved by using one or more index registers (sometimes called *B registers*), an index adder, and associated control circuits. The amount of change of an address, called the *index value*, is stored in an index register. This idea was first introduced in the 1949 model of the Manchester Computer in England. Figure 12-25*b* shows a two-single-address format with an *index field;* it is an instruction format of the Philco S-2000 Computer. The number in the index field designates the index register selected. The index register has as many bits as a memory address. For an instruction with an index field, the operand is located at an address whose number is the sum (or difference if so designed) of the address in the address field of the instruction and the index value in the designated index register. This new address is called the *effective address*. The address modification could otherwise be accomplished in the arithmetic unit; however, this involves many "red-tape" instructions and may make the program quite long, as many address modifications may be required in a program. By using the index register, the effective address of an instruction is not fixed but rather is changeable by merely changing the index value. The index register may also be designed for use as a counter and as a temporary register in storing a return address. It thus provides an extremely convenient means for programming loops and for incorporating subroutines.

Since the advent of the index register, the programmer has demanded more index registers in a computer. Instead of increasing the number of these registers, one approach is to use a part of the high-speed random-access memory as index registers. The index field thus becomes a memory address; its contents are used to modify the address of the instruction to be indexed.

Fig. 12-25*c* shows an instruction format for Control Data Corporation's Model 1604 Computer. It is again a two-single-address format. There are three fields: operation code, designator, and address. The designator is the index field for most operation codes. For the conditional-transfer operation code, the designator field specifies the transfer condition in code, and this field is not used for certain operation codes. Another variation of this format is that for certain operation codes the address field is the operand itself, without further reference to the memory.

Multiple Indexing. The above indexing approach to address modification can be extended to multiple indexing. In this case, there are several index values: one of these values is used to modify the index value in another index register; or the index values are used successively. The index register for storing the index values can be a part of the high-speed memory.

Instead of using several index values, other values may be used. One method makes use of the logical sum (or logical product) of the corresponding bits of the index values of two selected index registers; this method is used in the IBM 704 and 709 Computers.

Indirect Addressing. If the address in an instruction is not the address of an operand but the address of the address of the operand, this is called *indirect* *addressing.* In other words, the memory word of the first address is the address of a second memory word. The second memory word can be the address of a third memory word; thus, the indirect addressing can continue in many steps.

Indirect addressing may also be applied to the index-register address. As an example, consider the above case of multiple indexing in which index registers are a part of the memory. The index field is an address. The memory word at this address contains several other addresses. The memory word at each of these addresses is used as an index register for storing the index value.

Increment (or Decrement) Field. Besides its use in address modification, the index register may also have its value modified by an *increment field* (or a decrement field) provided in the instruction format. The index value is modified by adding an increment to (or subtracting a decrement from) the index value in the index register during the execution of the instruction. An example of a decrement field is the instruction format of an IBM 704 Computer.

Variable-word-length Format. A word in a computer means a normal unit of bits in which information can be stored, transmitted, or operated upon within the computer. Most digital computers have a fixed word length. For scientific computing, the word length is determined by the required degree of accuracy. For business data processing, on the other hand, the machine does not handle numerical data alone but also handles nonnumerical items such as alphabetic letters, marks, and special symbols. There is little consistency between the degree of accuracy and the word length required for the business processing of numerical data. The variable-word-length format is often a practical choice for a business data processor. In some computers such as the IBM 1620 Computer, the instruction word has a fixed word length of 12 digits, while the data word length can vary.

The variable-word-length format calls for a random-access memory which is capable of being addressed at variable lengths. One way is to use a short memory word of several bits which represent one character; in this way, machine words of variable lengths are formed by using a number of such characters. For example, a memory word may be only 6 bits, and each 6-bit unit is a coded alphanumeric character. A machine word now consists of a varying number of these characters for data processing, and each character is addressable.

Another way is to make each bit of the memory addressable; in this case, a memory word may be formed by specifying the address of the leading bit and the number of bits in the memory word. This method has been used in IBM Stretch Computer; such a format is shown in Fig. 12-25d. In this format, the operation-code field and the index field are conventional. The word address field consists of 24 bits which can address 2^{24} bits of the memory. The first 18 bits specify memory words of 64 bits in length for use in fixed-word-length operations, while the remaining 6 bits can select a single bit of the 64 bits. The 24-bit address designates the first bit of a memory word, and a length field specifies the word length. The offset field specifies a shift operation of the data without the need of a separate instruction.

Other Instruction Formats. There are many other instruction formats, including those for handling information transfer by means of input-output devices, those for performing special operations such as table look-up, data block transfer, priority control, etc., and those for convenience in setting up a programming loop.

Instruction Repertoire. The instruction repertoire of a digital computer is a set of machine instructions which describe the operation capability of the computer. The selection of the instruction repertoire during design often becomes a compromise between computer cost and operation capability. For economy, one tends to choose a simple set of instructions, limited in number. For writing a more efficient program, the programmer would like to have more and powerful instructions. A good compromise perhaps would be to achieve a high ratio of operation capability to cost with due consideration to factors such as price range, reliability, speed, size, weight, and serviceability.

Machine instructions may generally be classified according to the following types:

1. Arithmetic instructions
2. Loading and storing instructions
3. Transfer-of-control instructions
4. Indexing instructions
5. Logic instructions
6. Editing instructions
7. Input-output instructions
8. Special instructions

Arithmetic instructions are those requiring the computer to perform arithmetic operations such as fixed-point or floating-point addition, subtraction, multiplication, etc. Loading instructions transfer a computer word from the memory to various registers; storing instructions transfer a computer word from various registers to the memory for storage. Transfer-of-control instructions call for conditional or unconditional change from the normal sequence of computer operation. Transfer can be designed to be conditional for the sign bit or overflow bit in the accumulator, the sign bit of the multiplier-quotient register, the error bit in a parity-check circuit, the condition of an indicator, or the console switch position. These instructions together with others enable the computer to make a test or a decision operation. Indexing instructions concern operations on indexing such as loading an index register from the memory or from the accumulator, modifying the contents of an index register, or performing index arithmetic. Logic instructions refer to logical-*and*, logical-*or*, or other logic operations of the corresponding bits of two binary numbers. Repeat, comparison, and stop instructions may also be regarded as logic operations. Editing instructions perform operations such as shifting and rearranging the data, inserting commas and decimal points, or combining two small numbers into one number. Input-output instructions deal with communication operations between the memory and input-output devices. Special instructions prescribe special operational capabilities of the computer such as block transfer, table look-up, skip, and others.

12-6   *Control Unit*

The digital computer is a machine automatically sequenced to carry out a program initially placed in the memory. The sequential control of the program is the function of the control unit. The configuration of the control unit depends on the number of addresses in the instruction format and on whether the operation is in serial or in parallel. Several configurations are described in subsequent paragraphs.

Configurations for Parallel Operation. A control unit for a parallel computer using the single-address format is shown in Fig. 12-26a. It consists of the following elements:

1. Instruction register
2. Decoder
3. Control circuit
4. Memory-address register
5. Next-instruction counter
6. Index registers, index adder, and selection matrix.

The operation of the control unit follows a time reference, the *machine cycle*, which is usually established with reference to the memory. In the case of the

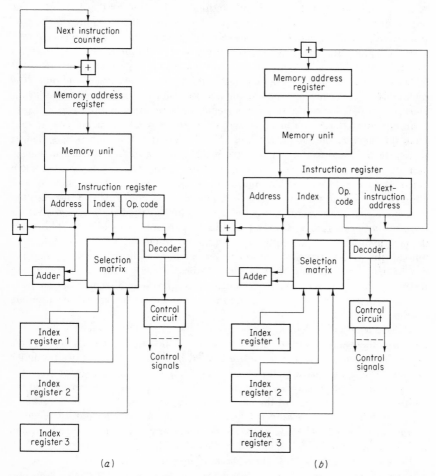

(a)   (b)

FIG. 12-26   A program control unit for a parallel digital computer. (*a*) For a single-address format; (*b*) for a two-address format.

magnetic-core memory, the machine cycle makes use of the read-write cycle. Each single-address instruction is carried out first in an instruction cycle (during which an instruction is taken from the memory) and then in an execution cycle (during which the operand is taken from the memory and the required execution is performed). The instruction cycle lasts one machine cycle, while the execution cycle lasts one or more machine cycles, depending on the instruction.

When the computer first starts, the registers and counters (except the memory) are initially set to a certain state, sometimes 0. In this case, the first memory address is the number 0, and thus the contents in that memory location are the first instruction ready to be read out. The computer begins with an instruction cycle during which a sequence of elementary operations are performed. Those elementary operations which can be executed in one pulse time are called *micro-operations*. The first micro-operation is to take the instruction word at the first address from the memory and store it in the instruction register. The contents of the operaion-code field in the instruction are decoded by the decoder. The output of the decoder is a signal on one of a number of lines going to the control circuit. This signal actuates the control circuit to generate the control signals for a subsequence of micro-operations to execute the operation called for by the instruction. Another micro-operation is to transfer the contents of the address register so that the operand in the memory is ready to be read out. The instruction cycle is now completed, and a control signal starts the execution cycle. During the execution cycle, another subsequence of micro-operations is performed. If an operation requires a memory reference, the first micro-operation is to take from the memory the operand, which is now located at the address specified by the instruction, and to transfer it to the designated register. If an instruction requires no memory reference (a shift instruction is an example), no word is taken out of the memory. Then the operation is carried out in one or more micro-operations. In the meantime, a micro-operation is performed to increase the contents of the next instruction counter (sometimes called the *program counter*) from its initial content of 0 to 1 (the add-1 operation), which is the address of the next instruction. This is followed by the micro-operation to transfer the contents of the next-instruction counter to the memory-address register so that the next instruction in the memory is ready to be read out. The execution of one instruction is now completed. A control signal starts another instruction cycle and then another execution cycle; the instruction and execution cycles alternate continuously.

If there is an index field in the single-address format, one or more index registers, an adder, and an index-selection circuit are provided. The contents of the index register to be selected should be loaded beforehand with the desired index value. During the instruction cycle, the contents of the index register (selected by the contents of the index field in the instruction) and the contents of the address field are added, and the sum is transferred to the memory-address register. In this way the operand is taken from the memory at the address modified by the index value. The address addition is performed by the index adder, and the selection of the index registers is achieved by the index-selection matrix.

Because the contents of the next-instruction counter is increased by 1 during the execution of each instruction, the program is carried out automatically in a sequential manner. If the program control sequence is to be changed, this is done by a transfer instruction. During the execution cycle, the contents of the next-instruction counter is not transferred to the memory-address register; consequently, the address in the memory-address register is not the address in the normal sequence but the address called for by the transfer instruction. If the change of the program control sequence is conditional (for example, conditional on the sign digit in the accumulator or on the presence of an overflow digit), the above transfer of the contents of the next-instruction counter to the memory address register is not carried out when the condition is fulfilled. If not fulfilled, the above transfer is performed and the normal program control sequence porceeds.

A control unit for a parallel computer using a two-address format is shown in Fig. 12-26b. One of the two-address fields in the instruction format is for an operand and the other for the next instruction. The required circuits are similar to those for the single-address format except that the next-instruction counter is

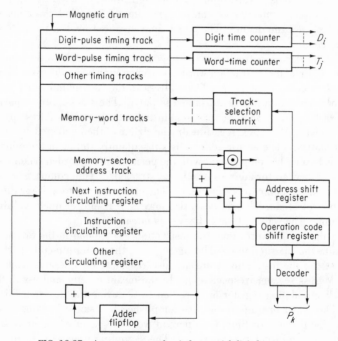

FIG. 12-27   A program control unit for a serial digital computer.

a register and becomes a part of the instruction register. The operation is similar, but the control subsequence for the micro-operations generated by the control circuit will differ somewhat. The sequence of the program is written by the programmer but is carried out automatically by the computer.

A Configuration for Serial Operation.   A serial digital computer offers the advantage of using fewer components and circuits, particularly if a sequential memory such as the magnetic-drum memory is used. In this case, inexpensive circulating registers on the drum can be used as shift registers. The following description assumes the use of a magnetic-drum memory.

A control unit for a serial computer using the single-address format is shown in Fig. 12-27. It consists mainly of the following elements:

1. Digit-time counter
2. Word-time counter
3. Next-instruction circulating register
4. Memory track-address shift register
5. Track-selection matrix
6. Address register
7. Instruction circulating register
8. Operation-code shift register
9. Decoder

The machine cycle for the serial operation is the *word time;* each word time consists of a sequence of *digit times.* If there are 32 bits in a word, 32 digit times may be used as a word time. These digit times, denoted by D_i, are established by a digit counter which counts permanently recorded clock pulses from a timing track on the drum. The word time, denoted by W_i, is established by word-time counter.

Each single-address instruction is carried out in four or more word times. During the first word time, the instruction word is searched for whose address is in the next-instruction circulating register. The address in the instruction word consists of a track-address part and a sector-address part. The track-address part is first read out of the circulating register and shifted into the track-address part of the address register; the track location on the drum is then selected by the track-selection matrix. The sector address is subsequently stored in the address register and is located by comparing it with the permanently recorded sector addresses on the memory sector-address track (or tracks). The comparison may be achieved by using coincidence circuits. The computer has to wait for the desired word in the selected track to appear; this may take as long as one revolution time of the drum. The waiting time is known as *latency.*

During the second word time, the instruction word found in the first word time is read into the instruction circulating register; the operation-code part and the address part of the instruction word are also read into the operation-code register and the address register, respectively. In the meantime, the address in the next-instruction circulating register is increased by 1 during the insertion for recirculation. This add-1 operation can be accomplished by using a flipflop.

During the third word time, the operand word is sought whose address is now in the instruction circulating register. The searching process is similar to that during the first word time. The waiting time, or latency, can be minimized if the operand is located at an optimum address by the programmer. This technique is known as *minimum-access programming.*

During the fourth word time, the operation called for in the instruction word is executed; a few instructions require more than one word time. When this word time is completed, the counter restarts from the first word time.

The processing of one instruction takes many machine cycles; during each machine cycle, a micro-operation is performed. The control signals are derived from the decoder. The decoder decodes the contents in the operation-code register and gives an output which is a signal on one of a number of lines; these outputs are denoted by P_k. The control signal for each micro-operation can be established by a logical-*and* combination of the digit time D_i, the word time W_j, and the operation P_k.   The control signals can also be obtained by providing other permanently recorded timing tracks on the drum and then processing these timing pulses.   Local control flipflops are also needed, such as the flipflop to store the halt condition or the flipflop to store a multiplier digit; they may be time-shared. For instance, during a prolonged operation such as multiplication or division, the instruction circulating register may be used to store the multiplicand or the divisor, and the address register may be used to perform local control and storing functions required during a multiplication or a division.

To change the program control sequence, the transfer instructions are used.   In these cases, the contents of the instruction circulating register are transferred to the next-instruction circulating register during the fourth word time.   The halt state of the computer can be achieved by making the advance of the first to the second word time contingent upon the 1 state of the halt flipflop.   When the halt state is called for, the halt flipflop is reset to 0 and thus the first word time repeats itself indefinitely.   The halt state is triggered when a halt instruction is being executed, in the presence of an overflow, at the occurrence of a divide-stop condition, or by a manual control button.

12-7   *Microprogrammed Control Unit*

In the control unit of Fig. 12-26, a sequence of control signals is generated for each decoded operation code.   If operations called for by instructions change, different sequences of control signals have to be generated.

The microprogrammed control unit, first reported by Wilkes and Stringer [3] of England, takes a different approach and gives a more flexible control logic.   In the following description, the computer is considered to be in parallel operation and to employ a single-address format.   This method can be extended to a serial computer and to a multiple-address format.

Concept of Microprogramming.   The program for a digital computer can be broken down into a set of machine operations, such as addition, multiplication, and the like, which are at the programmer's disposal.   Inside the machine, these machine operations can be broken down into a set of micro-operations, such as shifting, counting, word transfer, and the like, which are at the designer's disposal. The design of a control unit can take an approach similar to the programmer's preparation of a program.   In other words, the designer formulates a *microprogram* of micro-instructions which is capable of executing the required set of machine operations; the control unit merely implements this microprogram by issuing a sequence of micro-instructions.   A micro-instruction is an operation code for one or more micro-operations.   The microprogram is stored in a control memory which can be a diode matrix, a magnetic-core matrix, or any other rapid-access memory.   As an example, the nine machine operations in Table 11-11 for the simple digital computer of Chap. 11 are broken down into micro-operations in Table 11-3 and also in Fig. 11-3.   The state diagram in Fig. 11-6 is essentially the microprogram, while the matrix in Fig. 11-7 is the control memory.

A control unit using the concept of microprogramming has the advantage of flexibility in modifying or changing machine operations.   In this case the microprogram is changed for a new machine instruction or instructions; the micro-operations may remain unchanged.   If the control memory is changeable by use of pluggable components, the new microprogram can be readily provided. If the control memory is randomly accessible, the new microprogram can then be written into without changing the hardware of the machine.

Subroutines are normally employed in a computer program to eliminate the difficulty of completely detailed programming. If the concept of subroutine is extended to microprogramming, the microprogram may (in turn) utilize *microsubroutines*. In this case, each microsubroutine is a special sequence of micro-instructions. These microsubroutines may be regarded as additional microinstructions and are also stored in the control memory. By using the microsubroutine, the number of micro-instructions in a microprogram can be reduced.

Another approach to the concept of microprogramming is to permit certain logic gates, flipflops, counters, and the like, to be controlled directly from bit positions in an instruction word. That is, the control of the micro-operations is also at the programmer's disposal. The functions of the programmer and the logic designer of the control unit are combined into one. It is a question whether the programmer is given more flexibility or more work. This, of course, is a novel approach; no computer is known to have been built in this manner.

Symbolic Design of a Microprogrammed Control Unit. A microprogrammed control unit is shown in Fig. 12-28. The left portion of the unit is almost the same as that shown in Fig. 12-26a, while the right portion replaces the decoder and the control circuit of Fig. 12-26a. The right portion of the microprogrammed control unit consists of control memory N, control-memory-address register H, and operation register F, in addition to the counter T and the overflow flipflop V. Operation register F stores the selected control word taken from the control memory. It consists of two parts, the address part $Ad[F]$ and the micro-instruction part $I[F]$. The address part $Ad[F]$, which has the same number of bits as that of control-memory-address register H, normally specifies the address of the control word in the control memory for the succeeding memory cycle. Either the operation-code part of instruction register $Op[R]$ or the address part of operation register $Ad[F]$ is transferrable to register H.

The machine states may be established as follows: Let f_i denote the micro-instruction specified by the micro-instruction part of the operation register $I[F]$. Furthermore, let a and $\bar{a}$ represent, respectively, the instruction cycle and the execution cycle, where a and $\bar{a}$ are specified in the following manner:

$$a = 1 \qquad \text{when } Ad[F] = 0$$
$$\bar{a} = 1 \qquad \text{when } Ad[F] \neq 0$$

The above state that, when the contents of the address part of register F are zero, the machine is in the instruction cycle; otherwise, it is in the execution cycle. Assume that the memory cycle is the same for both the main and control memories, that the machine cycle is the same as the memory cycle, and that each memory cycle can be broken into three phases P_1, P_2, and P_3 in time sequence. The machine state may now be specified by a logical-*and* combination of a (or $\bar{a}$), f_i, and P_j. For example, if f_0 represents a micro-instruction under which one or more micro-operations are performed during the instruction cycle, the three sequential machine states during the instruction cycle are af_0P_1. af_0P_2, and af_0P_3. This formulation shows clearly whether a given machine state is in the instruction or in the execution cycle.

The design of the control unit now becomes a matter of specifying the micro-operations to be accomplished under each machine state for the selected set of machine instructions. The micro-operations during the instruction cycle are the same, while those during the execution cycle are different and are selected according to each machine instruction. The instruction cycle usually lasts one memory cycle; the execution cycle lasts one or more cycles.

Assume that the micro-operations to be performed during the instruction cycle

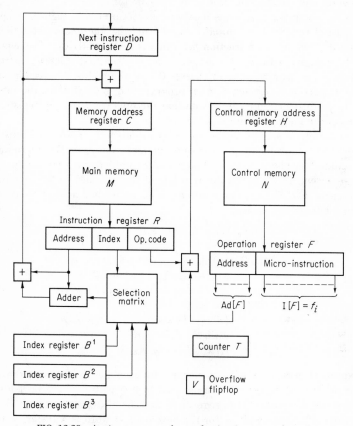

FIG. 12-28 A microprogrammed control unit using a control memory.

are under micro-instruction f_0. These micro-operations, as an example, are specified by the following symbolic statements:

$$af_0P_1: (M < C >) \Rightarrow R$$
$$af_0P_2: \text{Ad}[R] + (B < \text{In}[R] >) \Rightarrow C$$
$$(D) + 1 \Rightarrow D \tag{12-7}$$
$$(\text{Op}[R]) \Rightarrow H$$
$$af_0P_3: (N < H >) \Rightarrow F$$

As stated above, during state af_0P_1 the micro-operation is to transfer to register R the memory word in the main memory addressed by the contents in register

C. During state af_0P_2, three micro-operations are performed: the transfer of the address, which is the arithmetic sum of the address part of register R and the contents of the index register as selected by the index part of register R, to register C; the add-1 operation in register D; and the transfer of the operation-code part of the R register to the H register. During state af_0P_3, the micro-operation is to transfer to register F the control word in the control memory addressed by the contents in register H. At the end of this state, the address part of register F is not zero, and the machine begins its execution cycle.

When the computer first starts its operation, assume that register C and the address part of register F are initially cleared and that the micro-instruction part of register F is the micro-instruction f_0 (which is numerically 0). Consequently, the machine begins with the instruction cycle, and the first machine instruction is taken from the main memory at address 0. At the end of an execution cycle, the address part of F register is microprogrammed to be 0; thus, the machine returns to the instruction cycle. Note that the operation code in register R is merely a control memory address.

As an example of specifying the micro-operations to be performed during the execution cycle, consider the addition instruction. Let f_1 be the micro-instruction. Assume that the number is in signed-2's-complement representation. A_0 and R_0 represent, respectively, the sign bits of the numbers in the accumulator A and register R. The micro-operations to be performed are expressed in the following symbolic statements:

$$\overline{a}f_1P_1: (M < C >) \Rightarrow R$$
$$0 \Rightarrow T$$
$$\overline{a}f_1P_2: b(\mathrm{Ad}[F]) + \overline{b}(H) \Rightarrow H$$
$$\text{where } b = 1 \quad \text{when } (T) = 0$$
$$\overline{b} = 1 \quad \text{when } (T) \neq 0 \qquad (12\text{-}8)$$
$$\overline{a}f_1P_3: (D) \Rightarrow C$$
$$(A) + (R) \Rightarrow A$$
$$w_0\overline{A}_0\overline{R}_0 + \overline{w}_0A_0R_0 \Rightarrow V$$
$$(N < H >) \Rightarrow F$$

As expressed in the symbolic statements, during state $\overline{a}f_1P_1$, two micro-operations are performed: transfer of the operand in the main memory (as addressed by the contents of register C) to register R, and the clearing of register T. During the state $\overline{a}f_1P_2$, the address for the next control word is transferred to register H. If the contents of register T are 0, the address part in register F is transferred to register H; otherwise, the micro-instruction is repeated. In this example, the micro-instruction f_1 is not repeated, because the contents of register T were cleared during state $\overline{a}f_1P_1$. The address for the next control word is the address part of register F, which should be microprogrammed 0 so that the machine returns to the instruction cycle when the next memory cycle begins. During state $\overline{a}f_1P_3$, there are four micro-operations: the transfer of the contents of register D to register C, the addition of the contents of register R to those of register A (with the sum appearing in register A), the transfer of the overflow bit (if it occurs) to overflow flipflop V, and the transfer of the control memory addressed by register H (0 as mentioned above) to register F. The overflow expression states that, if both (A) and (R) are initially positive (indicated by $\overline{A}_0$ and $\overline{R}_0$), then a carry into the sign bit specifies an overflow or that, if both (A) and (R) are initially negative, then the absence of a carry into the sign bit specifies an overflow. The above statements for the micro-operations are not necessarily the simplest, but these micro-operations are formulated so that they can be readily used for other micro-instructions.

As another example, consider the conditional-transfer instructions. Let f_2 be the transfer micro-instruction conditional on the sign bit in the register A. The symbolic statements express the micro-operations as follows:

$$\overline{a}f_2P_1:\ 0 \Rightarrow T$$
$$\overline{a}f_2P_2:\ b(\mathrm{Ad}[F]) + \overline{b}(\mathrm{H}) \Rightarrow H$$
$$\overline{a}f_3P_3:\ A_0\{\mathrm{Ad}[R] \Rightarrow \mathrm{C}\} + \overline{A}_0\{(D) \Rightarrow \mathrm{C}\}$$
$$(N < H >) \Rightarrow F \qquad (12\text{-}9)$$

The micro-operations during states $\overline{a}f_2P_1$ and $\overline{a}f_2P_2$ are two that have been previously described. There are two micro-operations during state $\overline{a}f_2P_3$. The first one transfers the address part of register R to register C if sign bit A_0 is negative $(A_0 = 1)$ or transfers the contents of register D to register C if sign bit A_0 is positive $(A_0 = 0)$. The second operation transfers the control word in the control memory as addressed by register H; the address part of the control word should be microprogrammed 0 so that the machine returns to the instruction cycle.

For the other machine instructions, the micro-operations are similarly specified; in certain prolonged instructions such as multiplication and division more than one micro-instruction is needed. After the micro-operations for all machine instructions are specified, the code for the micro-instructions is established. The microprogram is then prepared by sequencing the micro-operations. A state diagram can be drawn from the microprogram. Conversely, one may first construct a state diagram to facilitate preparation of the microprogram.

The concept of microprogramming can also be applied to a serial computer. In this case, operation of the control memory and its associated registers can be either in series or in parallel. In either case, the output of the micro-instruction part of the operation register is used in conjunction with other timing signals to establish the control signal.

12-8 Other Microprogrammed Control Units

The microprogrammed control unit of Fig. 12-28 is but one of several possible configurations. Descriptions follow of other configurations using the same concept.

A Microprogrammed Unit Using an Operation Counter. A microprogrammed control unit using an operation counter is shown in Fig. 12-29. Operation counter F controls a decoder, which routes an input pulse to a particular output line that corresponds to the number in the counter. There are three other matrices: the conditional matrix, the next-step coder, and the micro-instruction coder. The conditional matrix makes it possible to deal with conditional operations. The input lines of the conditional matrix are controlled by certain flipflops in other units of the computer. The output of the next-step coder controls the setting of the operation counter F; thus, an automatic counting sequence of the operation counter can be built in by properly designing the next-step coder. Since the outputs of the conditional matrix can branch the outputs of the next-step coder, the counting sequence of the operation counter can be branched by the contents of certain flipflops. The outputs of the next-step coder are connected through delays (not needed if sufficient delay exists in each stage of the counter) to the operation counter. The outputs of the micro-instruction coder are connected to the various transfer gates in other units of the computer.

Once the sequence of operations for the execution of a machine instruction has been initiated, the sequential operations follow each other according to the configuration of the matrices which constitute the control memory. The desired sequence of a given machine instruction is initiated by transferring the operation-code part of instruction register R to operation counter F. This transfer is made under the control of the outputs of the micro-instruction coder.

The control unit (Fig. 11-7) of the simple digital computer of Chap. 11 is of the configuration shown in Fig. 12-29. In this latter illustration, the decoder, the conditional matrix, and the next-step coder appear in one matrix. The micro-instruction coder has not been used here, because the computer is extremely

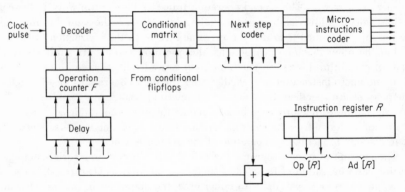

FIG. 12-29 A microprogrammed control unit using an operation counter.

simple. Neither the connections nor the delays have been shown for the transfer from instruction register R to operation counter F, because each flipflop has been assumed to have a sufficient delay.

A Microprogrammed Unit Using an Operation Register. A control unit using an operation register instead of an operation counter is shown in Fig. 12-30. This illustration differs from Fig. 12-28 in that a conditional matrix is employed in Fig. 12-30. Instead of an operation counter, a control-memory-address register H and an operation register F are used; the next-step coder is now called the *next-address coder*. The outputs of the next-address coder and the micro-instruction coder are connected to operation register F, and the address part of the number stored therein is transferable to register H. The address part of the operation register is a buffer storage to replace the delay in Fig. 12-29; the providing of a separate buffer storage can speed up the operation of the control unit.

The connections of the micro-instruction coder are such that each horizontal line corresponds to one micro-instruction. Each vertical line corresponds to one micro-operation or a group of simultaneously operated micro-operations. The vertical lines are connected through the flipflops of the instruction part of register F to the control gates of various registers. In operation the micro-instruction coder transfers a pulse from the horizontal line to one or more vertical lines for the execution of one or more micro-operations that make up the micro-instruction. The next-address coder continues to control the operating sequence.

For illustration, the microprogrammed control unit of Fig. 12-30 is drawn for the simple digital computer of Chap. 11. The design of this microprogrammed unit may begin, as mentioned previously, by preparing a microprogram; in this computer, the microprogram is prepared by using the state-operation diagram of Fig. 11-6 and is shown in Table 12-2. This table contains 14 control memory addresses, the addresses 0110 and 0111 not being used (see Table 11-4). The numbers in the last column represent the micro-instruction codes, which are the same as those of Fig. 11-6. The numbers in the first column are the control

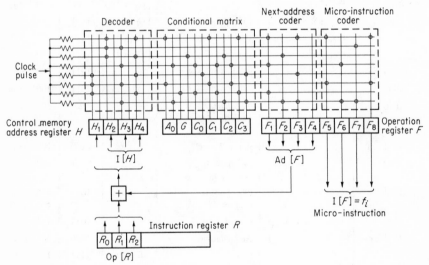

FIG. 12-30   A microprogrammed control unit using an operation register. *Note:* The circles in the matrices are diodes; they are drawn for illustration.

memory addresses and are chosen to be the same as those in the last column. The numbers in the $\mathrm{Ad}[F]$ column are the next control memory addresses. The numbers in the last two columns are thus the control words. With these numbers, the beginning address is not 0 but 0100 for the micro-instructions to be performed during the instruction cycle. Consequently, when the computer is first switched for computation, the address part of register F is set to 0100. There are several minor changes from the state-operation diagram of Fig. 11-6 to the microprogram in Table 12-2. The following micro-operation,

$$f_{10}\{(\mathrm{Op}[R]) \Rightarrow \mathrm{I}[H]\} + \bar{f}_{10}\{(\mathrm{Ad}[F]) \Rightarrow H\}$$

replaces the original micro-operation,

$$(\mathrm{Op}[R]) \Rightarrow \mathrm{I}[F]$$

Table 12-2   Microprogram for Simple Digital Computer†

Control memory address (H)	Instruction code	Micro-operation	Condition, if any	Control word	
				Ad[F]	I[F] = f_i
0000	Add	$(M<C>) \Rightarrow R$ $(\text{Ad}[R]) \Rightarrow C$	$\cdots$	1000	$0000 = f_0$
0001	Subtract	$(M<C>) \Rightarrow R$ $(\text{Ad}[R]) \Rightarrow C$	$\cdots$	1001	$0001 = f_1$
0010	Conditional transfer	No operation	$A_0 = 1$	0100	$0010 = f_2$
		$(\text{Ad}[R]) \Rightarrow C$	$A_0 = 0$	1011	0010
0011	Store	$(A) \Rightarrow M<C>$ $(\text{Ad}[R]) \Rightarrow C$	$\cdots$	1011	$0011 = f_3$
0100	Transfer	$(M<C>) \Rightarrow R$	$G = 1$	1010	$0100 = f_4$
			$G = 0$	1111	0100
0101	Shift right		$C_0 = 1$	1100	$0101 = f_5$
	Shift left	$(\text{Ad}[R]) \Rightarrow C$	$C_1 = 1$	1101	0101
	Clear accumulator	$0 \Rightarrow G$ if $C_3 = 1$	$C_2 = 1$	1110	0101
	Stop		$C_3 = 1$	1111	0101
1000	$\cdots$	$(R) + (A) \Rightarrow A$	$\cdots$	1011	$1000 = f_8$
1001	$\cdots$	$(A) - (R) \Rightarrow A$	$\cdots$	1011	$1001 = f_9$
1010	$\cdots$	$0 \Rightarrow H_1$ $(\text{Ad}[R]) \Rightarrow C$ $(C) \Rightarrow \text{Ad}[R]$	$\cdots$	‡	$1010 = f_{10}$
1011	$\cdots$	$(C) + 1 \Rightarrow C$	$\cdots$	0100	$1011 = f_{11}$
1100	$\cdots$	$(A_{i-1}) \Rightarrow A_i$ $(A_0) = A_0$	$\cdots$	1011	$1100 = f_{12}$
1101	$\cdots$	$(A_{i+1}) \Rightarrow A_i$ $(A_0) \Rightarrow A_8$	$\cdots$	1011	$1101 = f_{13}$
1110	$\cdots$	$0 \Rightarrow A$	$\cdots$	1011	$1110 = f_{14}$
1111	$\cdots$	No operation	$G = 1$	0100	$1111 = f_{15}$
		$0 \Rightarrow C$	$G = 0$	1111	1111

† The following micro-operation is performed at every clock pulse:
$$f_{10}\{(\text{Op}[R]) \Rightarrow I[H]\} + \bar{f}_{10}\{(\text{Ad}[F]) \Rightarrow H\}$$
‡ Op[R] is transferred to the control-memory-address register H, and so the Ad[F] of this control word has no use.

and is performed at every clock pulse. Another micro-operation,

$$0 \Rightarrow H_1$$

is added when the micro-instruction is f_{10}. The original micro-operation,

$$1 \Rightarrow F$$

is not needed and therefore is omitted. It is apparent that for the simple digital computer the configuration of Fig. 12-29 is the simpler one.

A Microprogrammed Unit Using Two Decoders. A microprogrammed control unit using two decoders is shown in Fig. 12-31. It is capable of high-speed operation. In this figure the decoder is divided into two units 1 and 2, each unit providing half the original number of output lines. Decoders 1 and 2 are controlled, respectively, by registers H_1 and H_2. There are two separate next-address coders; the outputs of coders 1 and 2 are transferred, respectively. to registers H_2 and H_1 without using a buffer storage. There is only one micro-instruction coder, jointly controlled by the two decoders. There may be either one or two conditional matrices; only one is shown in Fig. 12-31. The operation-code part of the instruction register can be transferred to register H_1. In operation, pulses are applied alternately to the inputs of the two decoders. The advantage of the rapid operation possible with this configuration is partially offset by the loss of flexibility resulting from the fact that the steps to execute an instruction alternate between the two halves of the unit.

The Use of Magnetic-core Matrices [22]. Diode matrices are widely used for the control unit of a computer. When the computer requires an elaborate

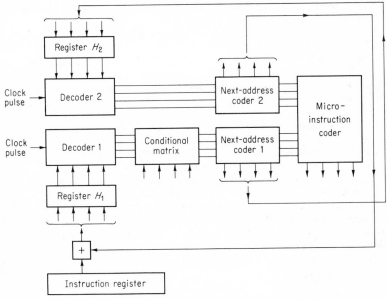

FIG. 12-31 A microprogrammed control unit using two decoders.

set of machine instructions, it may be preferable to use coincident-current magnetic-core matrices similar to the matrix shown in Fig. 9-27 (with the addition of a bias winding on each core). There are several advantages in using such magnetic-core matrices. First, two independent sets of output windings can be threaded through the same matrix of cores according to the set of machine instructions. One of the two sets of output windings corresponds to the next-address coder of Fig. 12-30, and the other corresponds to the micro-instruction coder. This possesses the advantage that the decoder and the two coders utilize only one matrix of cores. Second, the output from the selected core is a positive pulse followed by a negative pulse because of the use of a bias winding. The positive pulse may be clipped and not used. The use of the negative pulse gives the advantage that the delay in the negative pulse provides the buffer storage for the number to be set into the memory-address register. Third, the conditional function performed by the conditional matrix of Fig. 12-30 can be achieved by locating two cores, instead of one, at some of the intersections of the matrix. Each of these cores has an extra winding. The current flowing through the extra winding on one of the cores, in conjunction with the current flowing through the normal bias winding, is sufficient to prevent the core from being switched even when the intersection containing the core is selected. The conditional function is achieved by applying or not applying current to the extra winding at the selected intersection. It is possible to locate more than two cores at an intersection, a multiple-condition function being thus obtained.

Problems

1. Find logic equations from symbolic statements (12-1) for addition and subtraction of two binary numbers in signed-magnitude representation.

2. Express in symbolic statements the addition and subtraction of two binary numbers in signed-2's-complement representation in the parallel binary arithmetic unit.

3. Find logic equations from symbolic statements (12-2) for multiplication of two binary numbers in signed-magnitude representation.

4. Express in symbolic statements the binary multiplication of two numbers in signed-2's-complement representation in the parallel binary arithmetic unit, assuming that Robertson's first method is used.

5. Establish the algorithm for the divide-stop condition shown in symbolic statements (12-3).

6. Find logic equations from symbolic statements (12-3) for nonrestoring binary division of two binary numbers in signed-2's-complement representation.

7. Find logic equations from symbolic statements (12-4) for the nonrestoring method of extraction of the binary square root of a positive binary number.

8. Express the symbolic statements for the operation of the serial binary addition and subtraction configuration shown in Fig. 12-13. The numbers stored in the memory are in signed-magnitude representation, while the numbers in the arithmetic unit are in signed-2's-complement representation. The timing chart is shown in Fig. 12-14.

9. Express in symbolic statements the binary addition and subtraction in the serial binary floating-point arithmetic unit.

References

1. Staff of Harvard Computation Laboratory: "Synthesis of Electronic Computing and Control Circuits," vol. 27, Harvard University Press, Cambridge, Mass., 1951.

2. Auerbach, A. A., J. P. Eckert, R. F. Shaw, J. R. Weiner, and L. D. Wilson: The Binac, *Proc. IRE*, January, 1952, pp. 12–29.

3. Wilkes, M. V., and J. B. Stringer: Micro-programming and the Design of the Control Circuits in an Electronic Digital Computer, *Proc. Cambridge Phil. Soc.*, vol. 49, pt. 2, pp. 230–38, April, 1953.

4. Aldrich, J. C.: Engineering Description of the Electro-data Digital Computer, *IRE Trans. on Electronic Computers*, March, 1955, p. 110.

5. Woods-Hill, W.: An Outline of an Electronic Arithmetic Unit, *Electronic Eng.*, May, 1955, pp. 212–217.

6. Richards, R. K.: "Arithmetic Operations in Digital Computers," D. Van Nostrand Company, Inc., Princeton, N. J., 1955.

7. Allen, M. W.: A Decimal Addition-Subtraction Unit, *Proc. IRE*, vol. 103, pt. B, suppl. pp. 138–144, April, 1956.

8. Lonsdale, K., and E. T. Warburton: Mercury: A High-speed Digital Computer, *Proc. IEE (London)*, pt. B, suppl., pp. 174–183, April, 1956.

9. Bird, R.: The HEC Computer, *Proc. IEE (London)*, pt. B, suppl., pp. 247–268, April, 1956.

10. Kilburn, T., D. B. G. Edwards, and G. E. Thomas: The Manchester University Mark II Digital-computing Machine, *Proc. IEE (London)*, vol. 103, part B, suppl., pp. 247–268, April, 1956.

11. Blankenbaker, J.: How Computers Do Arithmetic, *Control Eng.*, April, 1956, pp. 93–99.

12. Freeman, H.: System Design of the Sperry Digital Computer, *Proc. Natl. Electronic Conf.*, 1956, pp. 644–645.

13. Glantz, H. T.: A Note on Microprogramming, *J. ACM*, vol. 3, pp. 78–84, April, 1956.

14. Frankel, S. F.: The Logical Design of a Simple General-purpose Computer, *IRE Trans. on Electronic Computers*, March, 1957, pp. 5–14.

15. Mercer, R. J.: Micro-programming, *J. ACM*, vol. 4, pp. 157–71, April, 1957.

16. Astraham, M. M., B. Housman, J. F. Jacobs, R. P. Mayer, and W. H. Thomas: Logical Design of the Digital Computer for the Sage System, *IBM J. Research Develop.*, January, 1957, pp. 76–83.

17. Dinneen, G. P., I. L. Lebow, and I. S. Reed: The Logical Design of CG24, *Proc. Eastern Joint Computer Conf.*, 1958, pp. 91–94.

18. Blaauw, G. A.: Data Handling by Control Word Techniques, *Proc. Eastern Joint Computer Conf.*, 1958, pp. 75–79.

19. Richards, R. K.: New Logical and Systems Concepts, *Proc. Eastern Joint Computer Conf.*, 1958, pp. 128–130.

20. Bauer, W. F.: Computer Design from the Programmer's Viewpoint, *Proc. Eastern Joint Computer Conf.*, 1958, pp. 46–51.

21. Buchholz, W.: The Selection of an Instruction Language, *Proc. Western Joint Computer Conf.*, 1958, pp. 128–130.

22. Wilkes, M. V., W. Renwick, and D. J. Wheeler: The Design of the Control Unit of an Electronic Digital Computer, *Proc. IEE (London)*, vol. 105, pt. B, pp. 121–28, June, 1959.

23. Wilkes W. V.: Microprogramming, *Proc. Eastern Joint Computer Conf.*, 1958, pp. 18–19.

25. Estrin, G.: The Shiftrix-machine Organization for High-speed Digital Computation, *Proc. Western Joint Computer Conf.*, 1958, pp. 207–210.

25. Brooks, F. P., Jr., G. A. Blaauw, and W. Buchholz: Processing Data in Bits and Pieces, *IRE Trans. on Electronic Computers*, June, 1959, pp. 118–124.

26. Green, A., Taller, and Cooper: Binary Multiplication in Digital Computers, *Proc. IRE.*, June, 1959, pp. 1159–1160.

Index

A-c coupled circuit, 161
Absorption theorems, 94
Accumulator, 26, 37, 382, 400, 416, 430–444
Add-1 operation, 407
Addend, 10, 16–24, 363, 431
Adders, 363, 364
  full, 202, 226, 246, 309, 323, 345, 363, 381
  half, 166, 363
  parallel and serial, 364
Addition, 15–24, 57–61, 401, 431, 439–440, 449
Address decoder, 400, 406, 420
Address modification, 454
Address-return operation, 407
Algorithm, for addition and subtraction of binary numbers, in signed-magnitude representation, 17
    signed-1's-complement representation, 23
    in signed-2's-complement representation, 21
  for binary-decimal conversion, 7–8
  for binary division, methods, comparison, 37
    nonrestoring, 41
    restoring, 37
  for binary multiplication, methods, Booth's, 33, 444
    Burks–Goldstine–von Neumann, 28
    direct multiplication, 26

Algorithm, for binary multiplication, methods, Robertson's first, 30
    Robertson's second, 31
  for binary square root, methods, comparison, 45
    nonrestoring, 48
    restoring, 45
  for comparing signed numbers, 14, 57
  for decimal-binary conversion, 6
  for decimal-digit addition and subtraction, in excess-3 code, 60
    in 2-4-2-1 code, 61
    in 8-4-2-1 code, 60
  definition of, 1
  for 9's complement of a number, 4
  for shifting of signed binary number, 13, 57
  for 10's complement of a number, 4
Alpha-number theorems, 116
Alphanumeric characters, 2
And operation, 93, 109, 113, 160
And-or logic, 101
Andnot operation, 109, 112–114, 160
Andrews, L. J., 283, 286, 299, 346
Anticoincident-current matrix, 338
Arithmetic unit, 398, 430–451
  parallel, 430
  serial, 437
Associative theorems, 94, 96
Asynchronous operation, 163
Augend, 10, 16–24, 363, 431
Average-length carry, 387

B register, 454
Backward tunnel diode, 234, 237
Bartee, T. C., 156
Base, 2, 73
Basic logic circuits, 160
Biased core, 338
Biax core, 298
Bilateral counter, 371
Binary addition by subtraction, of 1's
    complement, 22, 24
    of 2's complement, 19, 21
Binary-coded decimal number, 53
Binary counter, 371
Binary-decimal conversion, 7
Binary fractional computer, 398
Binary multiplication by repeated addi-
    tion, methods, Booth's, 25, 32,
    445
    Burks–Goldstine–von Neumann, 25,
    27
    direct multiplication, 25
    Robertson's first, 25, 29
    Robertson's second, 25, 31
    short-cut, 34
Binary-octal conversion, 5
Binary point, location of, 14
Binary sequence, 123
Binary sequence filter, 125, 328
Binary sequence generator, 124, 211,
    268, 328
Binary subtraction by addition, of 1's
    complement, 22, 24
    of 2's complement, 19, 22
Bit, 2
    space, 438
Bit time, 123, 438
    (*See also* Digit time)
Bloch wall, 253
Block representation of logic opera-
    tions, 93, 112, 122, 128, 131
Boole, G., 89
Boolean function, 99
    minimization of, 136–157
    simplification of, 110, 333
Boolean matrix, 310
Boolean matrix function, 309
    in canonical form, 309–313
    in elementary form, 324

Boolean matrix function, in nonele-
    mentary form, 327
    simplification of, 333
Booth, A. D., 32
Booth, K. H. V., 32
Borrow, 10, 16–24, 50, 363, 386
Borrow propagation, 386
Buck, D. A., 219
Burks, A. W., 27, 40

Canonical form, 103, 136
Canonical symmetric function, 118
Canonical term, 101
Carry, 10, 16, 23, 50, 363, 386, 416
Carry propagation, 386
CDC computer, 454
Change-over, 449
Character generator, 331
Characteristic number, 105
Check number, 84
Circulating register, 123, 211, 268,
    369, 459
Clock pulse, 161, 204, 209, 237, 368,
    393
Clocking, 204, 209
Code, biquinary, 56
    8-4-2-1, 53
    8-4-$\overline{2}$-$\overline{1}$, 53
    8-6-4-2-1, 55
    error-checking, 78
    error-correcting, 84
    excess-3, 54
    5-0-4-3-2-1-0, 56
    5-1-1-1-1, 55
    5-4-3-2-1-0, 55
    four-bit, 53
    more-than-4-bit, 55
    self-complementing, 55
    2-4-2-1, 53
    2-out-of-5, 56
    unweighted, 54
    weighted, 54
        biased, 55
        negatively, 54
        positively, 54
Code number, 54
Coercive force, 251

Coincidence operation, 109, 112, 160
Coincident-current matrix, 337
Collins, S. C., 218
Command signals, 408
  (*See also* Control signals)
Commutative theorems, 94, 96
Commutator, 317
Comparator matrix, 326
Comparison method, for binary division, 35–39
  for binary square root, 43–45
Complement, of a digit, 2
  logical, 90, 109
  of a number, 5
  radix, 5n.
  of a residue number, 75
Complementary circuits, 163
Complementation theorems, 93
Complementers, 365, 441
Computer characteristics, 428
  (*See also* specific types of computers)
Conditional matrix, 466–469
Conditional transfer, 401
Congruence, 3, 73
Constant-pi generator, 329
Constantine, G., 342
Control coil of a cryotron, 220
Control matrix, 392
Control memory, 461
Control signals, 392
  (*See also* Command signals)
Control unit, 399, 456–470
Critical magnetic field, 219
Cryotron, 219
  thin-film, 230
Cryotron control characteristic, 222
Cryotron logic circuits, 223–229
Cryotron matrix, 355
Cryotron switching characteristic, 221
Curie temperature, 255
Current, persistent, 218
Current gain, 175, 222, 235
Current-steered matrix, 348

D-c coupled circuit, 161
Decimal addition by subtraction, of 9's complement, 58

Decimal addition by subtraction, of 10's complement, 57
Decimal-binary conversion, 5
Decimal-digit counter, 371, 376
Decimal division, methods, Gilman's, 65, 69
  halving-the-divisor, 65, 68
  nine-multiples-of-divisor, 65, 67
  nonrestoring, 65
  restoring, 65
Decimal multiplication, methods, binary multiplication, 61
  doubling-and-halving, 61, 63
  nine-multiples-of-multiplicand, 61
  repeated addition, 61
  right-and-left components, 61, 64
Decimal subtraction by addition, of 9's complement, 58
  of 10's complement, 57
Decrement field, 455
Delay, 122, 160, 209, 258, 369, 397
De Morgan's theorems, 94, 97
Difference, 10, 16, 363, 431
Digit, 1
Digit parity check, 81
Digit time, 123, 460
  (*See also* Bit time)
Digit time counter, 459
Digital arithmetic, 1
Digital transfer function, 125
Digital tubes, 213
Diminished radix complement, 5n.
Diode logic circuit, 168–174
Diode matrix, 318–332
Diode-transformer matrix, 353
Diodeless transfer loop, 271
Direct addition method, in signed-magnitude representation, 16, 57
  in signed-1's-complement representation, 22
  in signed-2's-complement representation, 19
  in signed-9's-complement representation, 58
  in signed-10's-complement representation, 57
Direct-coupled transistor logic circuits, 198–205, 247

Direct-coupled transistor matrix, 352
Direct subtraction method, in signed-magnitude representation, 18
  in signed-1's-complement representation, 23
  in signed-2's-complement representation, 21
  in signed-9's-complement representation, 58
  in signed-10's-complement representation, 57
Disjoint, 91
Distributive theorems, 94, 96
Distributor, 317
Divide stop, 36, 50, 435, 444, 451
Dividend, 36–43, 431
Division, 35, 65, 434, 443, 451
Divisor, 36, 431
Divisor register, 37, 430, 434, 443
Domain theory, 252
Don't care term, 145
Dual-tree matrix, 311, 318
Duality, 95

Easy magnetization, direction of, 252
Effective address, 454
Electroluminescence, 244
Electroluminescent-photoconductor logic circuits, 245–248
Electroluminescent-photoconductor matrix, 358
Elementary area, 139
Elementary form, 111, 142
Elementary terms, 110, 138, 148
Emitter-follower logic circuits, 182
Encoder, 317
End-around borrow, 24
End-around carry, 23
Equality, 90
Esaki, L., 232
Essential elementary term, 144, 149
Even parity check, 80
Exclusive-*or* operation, 109, 112–115, 160
Execution cycle, 404–406

Fan-in, 157, 161, 198, 201
Fan-out, 157, 161, 198, 201
Ferractor, 275
Ferrite core, 253
Fetch instruction operation, 405
Fetch operand operation, 407
Fixed-point computer, 398
Flipflop, 127, 167, 185, 199, 202, 227, 238, 247
Flipflop input equation, 369–370, 373, 375–376, 380, 415–425
Flipflop state equation, 130, 369, 373, 376
Floating-point computer, 398
Floating-point numbers, 71, 448
Flux summation core, 293
Forbidden-combination check, 79
Forced phase locking, 241
Forward counter, 371
Four-address format, 452
Full adder, 202, 226, 246, 309, 323, 345, 363, 381
Full subtractor, 266, 363

Garner, H. L., 81
Gate, 160, 220
Gate efficiency, 222
Gated carry, 387
Gated-diode transfer loop, 270
Gated pulse amplifier, 212
Gilchrist, B. J., 388
Glow-lamp matrix, 357
Goldstine, N. N., 25, 27, 40
Goto, E. K., 286
Goto pair, 235
Ground plane, 231
Guided phase locking, 241

Half adder, 166, 363
Half-address format, 453
Half-select current, 337
Half subtractor, 266, 363
Hamming, R. W., 84
Harvard chart, 147–152

Huffman, D. A., 125
Huntington, E. V., 89
Hysteresis loop, 251

IBM computers, 452–455
Idempotency theorems, 94
Inclusive-*or* operation, 109, 112, 160
Increment field, 455
Index field, 454
Index registers, 454, 457, 463
Indirect addressing, 454
Information transfer, 378
Inhibit transfer loop, 270
Inhibit wound core, 283, 286, 299, 346
Inhibitor, 160
Insert-1 operation, 407
Instruction, 399, 456
Instruction address, 405
Instruction cycle, 404–406
Instruction format, 398, 451–453
Instruction register, 309, 420, 462
Intersection, 91, 94
Inverter, 166, 179
Inverter logic circuits, 182
Involution theorems, 93

Jeffrey, R. C., 429
JK flipflop, 128
Junction temperature, 179

Karnaugh, M., 280, 345

Laddic core, 296
Latency, 460
Linear sequential feedback filter, 126
Linear sequential filter, 125, 328
Lockhart, N. F., 307
Lockhart, R. K., 239
Logic design, 396
Logic diagram method, 382

Logic equation method, 382
Logic operation, 92, 109, 112, 122, 130
    symbolic representation of, 93, 112, 122, 128, 131

m-out-of-*n* circuits, 116
McCluskey, E. J., 153
Machine cycle, 457
Machine word, 2, 397
MAD core, 303
Magnetic-amplifier logic circuits, 275–277
Magnetic-core logic operation, 258–260
Magnetic-core matrix, 340–347, 469
Magnetic-core memory, 337, 458
Magnetic-core–transistor logic circuit, 273
Magnetic-drum memory, 325, 459
Magnetic-rod logic circuits, 285
Majority operation, 130, 289
Many-one matrix, 317
Matrix, anticoincident-current, 338
    Boolean, 310
    coincident-current, 337
    comparator, 326
    conditional, 466–469
    cryotron, 355
    current-steered, 348
    diode, 318–332
    diode-transformer, 353
    direct-coupled transistor, 352
    dual-tree, 311, 318
    electroluminescent-photoconductor, 358
    glow-lamp, 357
    magnetic-core, 340–347, 469
    many-one, 317
    multiple-level, 313, 327, 329, 336
    one-many, 317
    output, 310
    product-term, 310
    pyramid, 313
    rectangle, 312, 318, 417
    selection, 317, 320

Matrix, squaring, 327
  sum-term, 310
  transfluxor, 343
  transistor, 350
  transistor-resistor, 351
  transistor-transformer, 354
  tree, 313, 318
  triangle, 340
Matrix multiplication, 309–310
Maxterm, 136
Meissner effect, 299
Memory-address register, 400, 419, 457, 462
Memory cycle, 338, 462
Memory unit, 398, 400, 424
Metal-ribbon core, 253
Micro-instruction, 461, 468
Micro-operation, 392, 458
Micro-subroutine, 462
Microprogram, 461, 468
Microprogrammed control unit, 461–470
Microwave logic circuits, 242–244
Minimization, 143–156
Minimum-access programming, 460
Minority logic operation, 131
Minterm, 136
Minuend, 10, 16–24, 363, 431
Mirror symbol, 277
MIT Whirlwind computer, 452
Mixed logic designation, 277
Modulo, 3, 73
Modulo sum, 3, 16, 25, 76
Moll, J. L., 176
MQ register, 430
Multiple-address format, 452
Multiple-digit multiplication, 24, 34
Multiple indexing, 454
Multiple-level circuit, 111, 157, 171
Multiple-level matrix, 313, 327, 329, 336
Multiple-output circuits, 157, 309
Multiple-path sequence, 408
Multiplicand, 10, 25–35, 431
Multiplicand register, 26, 431
Multiplication, 24–35, 61–64, 432, 442, 451
  simultaneous, 24, 35

Multiplier, 10, 25–35, 431
  paired-digit, 35, 447
  serial-parallel, 445
  simultaneous, 447
Multiplier-quotient register, 26, 37, 430
Multipurpose logic circuits, 295

Nand operation, 109, 112, 160
NBS computers, 453
Negative logic, 162
Negative numbers, 3
Neutral function, 105
9's complement, 3, 5
Nonelementary form, 111
Nonrestoring method, for binary division, 35, 39–43
  for binary square root, 45–48
  for decimal division, 65
Nor operation, 109, 112–114, 160
Normalization, 72, 449–450
Not operation, 92, 109, 160
Null sequence, 126
Number format, 398
Number parity check, 81
Number representation, for floating-point number, 71
  for residue-coded decimal number, 77
  for residue number, 73
  for signed binary number, 10
  for signed decimal number, 56
  for unsigned number, 1
Number system, 3

Octal-decimal conversion, 9
Odd parity check, 79
Olsen, K. H., 340, 346
One-many matrix, 317
One-plus-one-address format, 453
1's complement, 4
1's complementers, 366
Onnes, H. K., 218
Operand, 398
Operand address, 405
Operation code, 398, 401

Operation counter, 400, 415, 465
Operation decoder, 400, 417
Operation register, 462
Or operation, 92, 109, 113, 160
Or-and logic, 101
Ornot operation, 109, 112, 160
Output matrix, 310
Overflow, 15, 50, 433

Paired-digit multiplier, 35, 447
Parallel accumulator, 27, 38, 383, 417, 430
Parallel adder, 364
Parallel arithmetic unit, 430
Parallel information transfer, 381
Parallel subtractor, 364
Parametric oscillation frequency, 240, 286
Parametric subharmonic oscillator, 286
Parametron, 242, 287
Parity check, for arithmetic operation, 82
  for binary coded number, 79
  for binary number, 79
  bit change of, 79
  for decimal number, 81
Partial product, 25–35
Partial remainder, 36–48
Perfect induction, method of, 95
Persistent current, 218
Philco computer, 454
Photoconductor, 244
PLO logic circuits, 240–242
Pomerene, J. H., 388
Positive logic, 162
Prime implicant, 153
Priority control, 455
Product, 10, 26, 28, 30, 431
  partial, 25–35
Product term, 101
Product-term matrix, 310
Program control unit, 399, 456–470
Program counter, 458
Programming, 396
Programming loop, 454
Propagation time, 160
Pulse generator, 211, 400

Pump frequency, 240, 286
Pyramid matrix, 313

Quenching characteristic, 220n.
Quine, W. V., 153
Quine-McCluskey method, 153–156
Quotient, 36–48, 431

Radicand, 43–48, 431
Radix, 2, 371
Radix complement, 5n.
Radix converter, 317
Rajchman, J. A., 341
Read-write cycle, 458
Rectangle matrix, 312, 318, 417
Reed, I. S., 87, 396
Register, 17, 26, 37, 400, 431
  B, 454
  circulating, 123, 211, 268, 369, 459
  divisor, 37, 430, 434, 443
  index, 454, 457, 463
  instruction, 309, 420, 462
  memory-address, 400, 419, 457, 462
  MQ, 430
  multiplicand, 26, 431
  multiplier-quotient, 26, 37, 430
  operation, 462
  shift, 123, 162, 306, 369, 439
Relay-circuit analyzer, 158
Relay logic circuits, 163–165
Remainder, 36–48, 65, 431
Remanence, 251
Reset winding, 257
Residue, 73
Residue number, 74
Resistor-coupled–transistor logic circuits, 179–185
Restoring method, for binary division, 35, 39
  for binary square root, 45
  for decimal division, 65
Reverse counter, 371
Reversible counter, 371
Ring counter, 371, 376
Root extractor, 43–48, 431

Rosenfeld, J. L., 282
Round-off, 36, 48
RS flipflop, 128, 369, 372, 377, 381
RST flipflop, 129
Russell, L. A., 271

Saturation voltage drop, 175
Selection matrix, 317, 320
Self-field, 221
Self-organizing network, 359
Sequential function, 122
Serial accumulator, 383
Serial adder, 364
Serial arithmetic unit, 437
Serial information transfer, 381
Serial-parallel multiplier, 445
Serial subtractor, 364
Set winding, 257
Shannon, C. E., 98, 116
Sheffer's stroke function, 112
Shift register, 123, 262, 306, 369, 439
Signal representation, 161
Signed-magnitude representation, 11, 56, 431, 439, 442
Signed-1's-magnitude representation, 11
Signed-2's-complement representation, 11, 434, 440
Signed-9's-complement representation, 56
Signed-10's-complement representation, 56
Silsbee hypothesis, 221
Simple symmetric function, 120
Simplification of Boolean matrix function, 333
Simultaneous carry, 390
Simultaneous multiplication, 24, 35
Simultaneous multiplier, 447
Single-address format, 398, 452, 457
Single-diode transfer loop, 261
Single-input flipflop (trigger flipflop), 127, 371, 380, 397
Single-shift-line transfer loop, 263
Smith, J. L., 391
Space bit, 438
Split-winding transfer loop, 269

Square root, 43–48, 435
Squareness ratio, 252
Squaring matrix, 327
State diagram, 375, 408, 432, 434, 436, 438, 445
State-operation diagram, 411
Stored carry, 387
Stored program computer, 397, 428
Stringer, J. B., 461
Subroutine, 454
Subtraction, 15–24, 57–61, 401, 431, 439, 440, 449
Subtractors, 363
    full, 266, 363
    half, 266, 363
    parallel, 364
    serial, 364
Subtrahend, 10, 16–24, 363
Sum, 10, 16, 363, 431
Sum term, 101
Sum-term matrix, 310
Superconductive thin film, 229
Superconductivity, 218
Switching coefficient, 253
Switching time, 176, 223, 232, 253
Symbolic design, 396, 402
Symbolic method, 378
Symbolic representation of logic operations, 93, 112, 122, 128, 131
Symbolic statements, 378–381, 384–385, 403, 432–437, 445, 463–468
Symbols, 378, 402
Symmetric Boolean function, 116, 131, 295
Symmetry variables, 116
Synchronous computer, 161, 163
Synchronous operation, 163, 397, 428

T flipflop (trigger flipflop), 127, 371, 380, 397
Table look-up, 455
Tabular study, 410–415
10's complement, 3, 5
Thin-film cryotron, 230
Three-address format, 452
Timing chart, 442

Timing levels, 393
Timing pulse, 439
Transfluxor core, 300
Transfluxor matrix, 343
Transistor breakdown voltage, 178
Transistor current-switch logic circuits, 205–208
Transistor cutoff frequency, 178
Transistor-diode logic circuits, 194–196
Transistor fall time, 178
Transistor matrix, 350
Transistor-resistor logic circuits, 196–198
Transistor-resistor matrix, 351
Transistor rise time, 176
Transistor-transformer matrix, 354
Transition temperature, 218
Translator, 317, 323
Tree matrix, 313, 318
Triangle matrix, 340
Trigger flipflop, 127, 371, 380, 397
Truth function evaluator, 156
Truth table, 92, 99
Tunnel-diode logic circuits, 232–240
Two-address format, 452, 457
Two-level logic, 101, 111, 156, 169
Two-line representation, 161

2's complement, 4
2's complementer, 366

Unconditional transfer, 401
Underflow, 15
Union, 90, 94
Uniqueness theorems, 93
Univac computer, 452
Universal logic network, 359

Vacuum-tube logic circuits, 165–168
Variable word length, 455
Veitch diagram, 103, 136–146
Venn diagram, 90, 103
von Neumann, John, 25, 27, 40, 287

Weinberger, A., 391
Wilkes, M. V., 461
Wong, S. Y., 388
Word format, 397
Word time, 439, 460
Word time counter, 459

Z counter, 450